S0-AIO-429

NO LONGER
PROPERTY OF
OLIN LIBRARY
WASHINGTON UNIVERSITY

STATISTICAL MECHANICS

FOUNDATIONS AND APPLICATIONS

Proceedings of the I.U.P.A.P. Meeting, Copenhagen, 1966

Thor A. Bak, Editor

W. A. BENJAMIN, INC.

New York Amsterdam 1967

STATISTICAL MECHANICS: FOUNDATIONS AND APPLICATIONS

Copyright © 1967 by W. A. Benjamin, Inc.
All rights reserved

Library of Congress Catalog Card Number 67-28999
Manufactured in the United States of America

W. A. BENJAMIN, INC.
New York, New York 10016

PREFACE

This volume contains almost all of the lectures delivered at the I. U. P. A. P. conference on Statistical Mechanics and Thermodynamics which was held in Copenhagen July 11 to July 15, 1966. In addition it contains a fairly complete record of the discussion which followed the presentation of the papers, and one paper (that of Dr. Sinai) which was not presented at the conference.

The Organizing Committee for the meeting consisted of Professor O. Klein (Chairman) Professor L. Rosenfeld, Professor H. Wergeland, Professor M. Pihl and Professor Thor A. Bak (Secretary). It would not have been possible to arrange the conference, however, without the enthusiastic support of Miss Emmy Christiansen, Dr. E. Fisher, Mr. F. Hynne, Dr. Svend Erik Nielsen, Dr. Eigil Præstgaard, Mr. J. Rassing and Mr. P. Graae Sørensen.

The conference is indebted to I. U. P. A. P., to the Rask-Ørsted Foundation and to Nordita for economic support. The economic guarantee which we received from the Danish Ministry of Education is also gratefully acknowledged.

Most of the papers in this volume were received at or shortly after the conference and first proof were normally read by the authors whereas second proofs were read by my collaborators or by myself. I am especially indebted to Dr. Svend Erik Nielsen who did a very large part of this work. The papers were typed by Mrs. Aase Eldov and the discussions were typed by Mrs. Birthe Brask and we gratefully acknowledge their expert help.

The conference benefited very much from the facilities at the H. C. Ørsted Institute put at our disposal by the University of Copenhagen and I am happy to take this opportunity to express the gratitude of the Organizing Committee.

Thor A. Bak.

University of Copenhagen
June 1967.

CONTENTS

ERGODIC THEORY IN CLASSICAL STATISTICAL MECHANICS

I. E. FARQUHAR
Queen Mary College
University of London.

ABSTRACT

One can attempt to justify the methods of statistical mechanics, whether in classical or in quantal theory, by establishing the equality of time averages and ensemble averages; the former represent the results of measurements made on a physical system, the latter are the quantities calculated in statistical mechanics.

Here may be seen a prime example of the interplay between mathematics and physics, for, arising from this 'ergodic problem' of physics, there has developed a considerable body of abstract mathematical theory designated 'ergodic theory' by mathematicians. How far results of this theory are relevant to the physical problem in classical statistical mechanics is to be discussed here; it is held that the present mathematical theory is in itself insufficient for the solution of the physical problem.

Further attempts on this problem have generally proceeded by narrowing the range of physical systems for which it is hoped to establish ergodicity. Although some interesting results have been obtained in this way, no adequate solution of the ergodic problem has yet been attained.

1. It is now thirty-five years since the classical ergodic problem was solved - and we are still without a solution of the classical ergodic problem!

There is no paradox here but merely a confusion of terminology between mathematical and physical solutions. The ergodic problem in statistical mechanics, whether classical or quantal, is that of establishing the equality of time averages and ensemble averages. Whereas the time averages represent the results of measurements made on a physical system, it is ensemble averages that are calculated in statistical mechanics. Thus by showing that these averages are equal one may hope to justify the methods of statistical mechanics by relating them to the methods of 'exact' mechanics, whether classical or quantal.

As is well known, this ergodic problem was taken up by mathematicians, who have now erected an edifice of 'ergodic theory' as a branch of the abstract theories of measure and of integration. In its scope this theory goes, of course, far beyond the original problem of statistical mechanics, and our task in reviewing the situation as regards classical statistical mechanics is to determine how far any of the results of this general mathematical theory are relevant to the original problem.

It is sufficiently general for our purposes to consider that we have:

(i) a classical system of n degrees of freedom,

(ii) the phase space Γ described by the generalised coordinates and momenta of the system as cartesian coordinates of Γ,

(iii) Hamiltonian equations of motion generating a transformation U of Γ such that

$$P_t = U^t P_0 ,$$

where P_t is the phase point of the system at time t and the Hamiltonian is usually supposed not to contain time explicitly,

(iv) the set of phase trajectories each of which is specified by its initial phase P_0.

For this structure there holds Liouville's theorem, that the measure (or volume) of any set of points in Γ is invariant under the transformation U.

The problem is to relate the time average of a phasefunction f(P),

$$<f>_{\mathfrak{J}} \equiv \lim_{T \to \infty} \frac{1}{T} \int_0^T f(P_t)\, dt ,$$

to the phase average of the phasefunction. The latter cannot be taken over Γ, since Γ has infinite measure. Hence let us consider an invariant subset V of Γ (for instance, an energy shell) of finite measure $\mu(V)$. Then the phase average may be taken as

$$<f>_V \equiv \frac{1}{\mu(V)} \int_V f(P)\, d\mu .$$

Now Birkhoff's theorem[1] asserts:

(i) $<f>_{\mathfrak{J}}$ exists a. e. in V, *

(This is the difficult part of the proof of Birkhoff's theorem - unlike the situation in quantal theory where the existence of the time average is an immediate consequence of the almost periodicity of the wavefunction),

(ii) $\langle <f>_{\mathfrak{J}} \rangle_V = \langle f \rangle_V$,

(iii) a necessary and sufficient condition for $<f>$ to be constant a. e. in V (and so by (ii) for $<f>_{\mathfrak{J}} = <f>_V$ a. e. in V) is that V should be metrically indecomposable, that is, that V should not be capable of being subdivided into two invariant parts each of positive measure.

It is notorious, however, that this approach has been entirely inconclusive as regards statistical mechanics, since it is not known whether an arbitrary physical system satisfies the condition of metrical indecomposability. Thus the problem of ergodicity is merely exchanged for the problem of metrical indecomposability.

The existence of any integral of motion that defines a (2n - 1) -

---

*) 'A. e. in V' stands for 'almost everywhere in V', that is, 'at all points of V except, at most, on a set of measure zero'.

dimensional surface in Γ enables the region V to be decomposed metrically. If there exist m such global integrals of motion, Lewis's theorem[2] asserts that

$$\langle f\rangle_{\mathcal{J}} = \langle f\rangle_{M} \qquad \text{a.e. in } M,$$

where M is the invariant manifold defined by <u>all</u> these global integrals of motion of the system. (In defining $\langle f\rangle_M$ it is not sufficient to use the ordinary (2n-m)-dimensional measure, since Liouville's theorem holds for V not for M; an appropriate modification in the measure function must thus be made). Once the significance for Birkhoff's theorem of the existence of global integrals of motion had been established, most physicists assumed intuitively the result subsequently given rigorous proof by Lewis.

Since the energy of the system is usually taken to be an integral of the motion, V is usually to be reduced to an energy surface S unless the energy is regarded as coarse-grained.

In this approach, however, the problem of metrical indecomposability is merely exchanged in turn for that of determining the number of global integrals of motion of an arbitrary system - and although this exchange may yield a gain in conceptual clarity the latter problem is equally unsolved. For this reason the theorems of Birkhoff and of Lewis, whilst solving the mathematical problem, are in themselves insufficient for the solution of the ergodic problem in statistical mechanics.

Here we may call attention to the qualification appearing in these theorems, namely, that equality of the averages is established not everywhere in V or in M but only almost everywhere in V or in M. This may seem a small point, but our contention, indeed the main theme of this talk, is that this qualification is related so closely to the questions of metrical indecomposability or of knowing all the integrals of motion as to vitiate almost all other attempts on the ergodic problem in statistical mechanics, not only in classical theory but in quantal theory also.

The point here is that we need to make some assumption about how likely the set of measure zero is to occur in practice; and it would clearly be desirable if this exceptional set of measure zero were assumed to have zero probability of containing the initial phase of the system. Now suppose for the moment that not all the global integrals of motion had been used in defining the invariant manifold M, and let us make the assumption that the exceptional set of measure zero on M has zero probability of containing the initial phase. Since there exists an integral of motion additional to those considered in defining M, all possible phase trajectories are confined to the intersection of M and the surface defined by the additional integral. And this entire intersection has measure zero with respect to the measure on M. Here then, whatever the initial phase of the system, this phase necessarily lies in a set of measure zero - and this set has been postulated to have no chance of containing the initial phase!

Of course, this situation does not in fact arise here, since integrals of motion are used to define M. The argument will recur shortly, however. In the present instance, there being no apparent reason for restricting the phase point to a set of measure zero in M, the assumption that sets of zero measure have zero probability of containing the initial phase may appear perfectly natural. Nevertheless, it should be noted that, weak and unobjectionable as it may be, a definite assumption is required here in order that the theorems may be applied.

An alternative but essentially similar method of ensuring that the exceptional set plays no physical role is to require the ergodic theorem to hold only for coarse-grained phasefunctions, obtained experimentally by macroscopic measurement and theoretically by averaging the fine-grained phasefunctions over macroscopically small phase cells in phase space. To eliminate any effect of the exceptional phases the distribution function for the averaging over phase cells has to assign zero weight to these exceptional phases; again this may appear not unreasonable but it is an assumption.

2. To circumvent the difficulties associated with metrical indecomposability and with the existence of global integrals of the motion we may weaken the requirements for ergodicity. Here let us work explicitly with an energy surface S rather than with a 2n-dimensional region V.

Thus instead of demanding, as before, that the equality

$$|\langle f\rangle_{\mathfrak{I}} - \langle f\rangle_S| = 0$$

should hold except at most on a set of measure zero on the energy surface S, we may accept as sufficient for physical purposes the approximate ergodicity expressed by the inequality

$$|\langle f\rangle_{\mathfrak{I}} - \langle f\rangle_S| < \epsilon, \quad \epsilon \text{ small},$$

holding except at most on a set of measure zero, or, less stringently, except at most on a set of small measure on S.

A simple general result along these lines may be obtained as follows:

For any (integrable) phasefunction f we have

$$\langle (f - \langle f\rangle_{\mathfrak{I}})^2\rangle_{\mathfrak{I}} \geqq 0$$

and so

$$\langle \langle f\rangle_{\mathfrak{I}}^{\;2}\rangle_S \leqq \langle \langle f^2\rangle_{\mathfrak{I}}\rangle_S .$$

But by Birkhoff's theorem* applied to f^2 we have

$$\langle \langle f^2\rangle_{\mathfrak{I}}\rangle_S = \langle f^2\rangle_S .$$

Hence we obtain the inequality

$$\langle \langle f\rangle_{\mathfrak{I}}^2\rangle_S \leqq \langle f^2\rangle_S ,$$

and, if f be replaced by $(f - \langle f\rangle_S)$, it follows that

$$\langle (\langle f\rangle_{\mathfrak{I}} - \langle f\rangle_S)^2\rangle_S \leqq \langle (f - \langle f\rangle_S)^2\rangle_S . \tag{1}$$

---

*) Strictly this theorem refers to V not to S but the necessary modification can be made easily.

Now let us apply Tschebyshev's inequality to $\langle f \rangle_{\mathfrak{J}} / \langle f \rangle_S$. Then for arbitrary $\alpha > 0$ there holds the inequality

$$\mathcal{P}\left[P: \left| \frac{\langle f \rangle - \langle f \rangle_S}{\langle f \rangle_S} \right| \geqq \alpha \right] \leqq \frac{1}{\alpha^2} \frac{\langle (\langle f \rangle_{\mathfrak{J}} - \langle f \rangle_S)^2 \rangle_S}{\langle f \rangle_S^2}$$

$$\leqq \frac{1}{\alpha^2} \frac{\langle (f - \langle f \rangle_S)^2 \rangle_S}{\langle f \rangle_S^2} \qquad \text{by (1)}$$

$$\equiv \frac{1}{\alpha^2} \sigma_R^2$$

where σ_R is the relative standard deviation of f on S and $\mathcal{P}[P:\phi]$ is the probability of the set of points P that satisfy the condition ϕ. Now for α let us choose $k\sigma_R^{1/2}$, where k is an arbitrary positive number. Then we have the final inequality

$$\mathcal{P}\left[P: \left| \frac{\langle f \rangle_{\mathfrak{J}} - \langle f \rangle_S}{\langle f \rangle_S} \right| \geqq k\sigma_R^{1/2} \right] \leqq \frac{\sigma_R}{k^2} .$$

This result is due to Kurth[3]; earlier Khinchin[4] had given a similar result, although by a less simple proof.

This concludes the dynamical features of the argument. The problem now is the geometrical one of determining phasefunctions that have small dispersion on S; for these phasefunctions ergodicity is obtained in the approximation given by (2). There is here, of course, a restriction on the original form of the ergodic theorem not only because of the approximation in the form of the theorem but also because the result is valid only for a certain class of phasefunctions and not for all phasefunctions.

Now which phasefunctions of an arbitrary physical system have small microcanonical dispersion? Again there is no answer.

So to progress farther we again restrict the structure of interest - and here the restriction is very significant. All the foregoing discussion has referred to general dynamical systems, for which the number of degrees of freedom may be as small as desired. For the purposes of statistical mechanics it is only macroscopic systems that are required to exhibit ergodicity, and by dealing explicitly with macroscopic systems Khinchin[4] has obtained the result that phasefunctions have small dispersion.

Nevertheless there is here yet a further restriction. Even for macroscopic systems it is only a certain type of phasefunction that has been shown to have small dispersion and this moreover only for a certain type of macroscopic system.

We may summarise the conditions that have been used in obtaining phasefunctions of small dispersion:

(i) the system has separable Hamiltonian, that is,

$$H(P) = \sum_{i=1}^{N} H_i(P_i),$$

where the system contains N particles,

(ii) only those phasefunctions that are sum functions

$$f(P) = \sum_{i=1}^{N} f_i(P_i)$$

are considered (these in any event are of particular interest in statistical mechanics),

(iii) N must be large, since the result is obtained in the asymptotic form

$$\sigma_R = O(N^{-1/2}).$$

This is Khinchin's result - that sum functions of a macroscopic system with separable Hamiltonian have small microcanonical dispersion. The undesirable restriction that the Hamiltonian should be separable has since been removed by Mazur and van der Linden[5], who considered the asymptotic behaviour as $N \to \infty$ of sum functions of a system of particles interacting through a short range hard core interaction. Their argument requires an assumption that the zeros of a certain polynomial related to the configurational integral of the system are not dense in intervals of the real axis, but this assumption seems not unreasonable in the context.

Here is then, in general, an approximate ergodic theorem valid for any phasefunction of small dispersion and, in particular, an asymptotic ergodic theorem valid for sum functions of a macroscopic system. The set of phase points for which ergodicity is not obtained is not of measure zero but is yet of small measure; and there is no apparent requirement of metrical indecomposability or of knowing all the integrals of motion of the system.

But to apply this theorem we need the set of small measure for which time averages are not equal to phase averages to have little chance of containing the initial phase point of the system, and this suggests that we should assume that sets of small measure on S have small probability of containing the initial phase. The situation here, however, is much worse than previously. For suppose there exist global integrals of the motion additional to the energy, each defining a hyper-surface in the phase space; then the phase trajectory is confined to a manifold M which has measure zero with respect to the measure on S. The system being taken to be macroscopic and to have suitable Hamiltonian, the microcanonical dispersion on S of any sum function remains small. The result that the time average of any sum function differs from the phase average only on a set of small measure remains formally valid; it has no dynamical significance, however, since the phase trajectory is confined to the manifold of measure zero, and so it is precisely the exceptional set that is of dynamical significance. Thus to assume that sets of small measure on S have small probability of containing the initial phase would be to assign zero probability of occurrence to the only set of phases that can actually occur whenever there exist additional integrals of motion.

This contradiction illustrates the incompatibility of the assumption referred to and the existence of additional global integrals of the motion.

The difficulty is not resolved by the introduction of coarse-graining, although it is alleviated somewhat. With coarse-grained integrals of motion, including coarse-grained energy, the reduced manifold is still of 2n dimensions. And, provided all the global integrals of motion were sum functions, Khinchin's argument would show that the reduced manifold has measure negligibly different from that of the energy shell V. The trouble is, of course, that it is not known that all integrals of motion are sum functions.

Hence, although a knowledge of the integrals of motion of a system is indeed not required for the validity of Khinchin's theorem, it is yet needed for the applicability of the theorem.

To link this general approach with those of quantal ergodic theory it is convenient to reformulate the argument by expressing the result in terms of an average over the microcanonical distribution rather than, as with Tschebyshev's inequality, in terms of the distribution itself. For this purpose let us start with the purely geometrical property that the coefficient of variation $\sigma/\langle f\rangle_S$ of a (positive) sum function with respect to the microcanonical distribution satisfies the relation

$$\frac{\langle (f - \langle f\rangle_S)^2\rangle_S}{\langle f\rangle_S^2} = O(\tfrac{1}{N}) ,$$

and let us average this over time to obtain

$$\frac{\langle \langle (f - \langle f\rangle_S)^2\rangle_S\rangle_{\mathfrak{J}}}{\langle f\rangle_S^2} = O(\tfrac{1}{N}) .$$

Interchanging the two averaging processes* yields

$$\frac{\langle \langle (f - \langle f\rangle_S)^2\rangle_{\mathfrak{J}}\rangle_S}{\langle f\rangle_S^2} = O(\tfrac{1}{N}) ,$$

*) This is permissible since

$$\langle \langle f\rangle_{\mathfrak{J}}\rangle_S = \langle f\rangle_S$$

by Birkhoff's theorem and since

$$\langle \langle f\rangle_S\rangle_{\mathfrak{J}} = \langle f\rangle_S$$

because the microcanonical is a stationary distribution in virtue of Liouville's theorem.

and finally Schwarz's inequality gives

$$\frac{\langle (\langle f \rangle_{\mathcal{T}} - \langle f \rangle_S)^2 \rangle_S}{\langle f \rangle_S^{\,2}} = O\left(\frac{1}{N}\right) .$$

This constitutes an ergodic theorem. It indicates that, under the appropriate conditions on the Hamiltonian of the system, the time average of a sum function of a macroscopic system is likely to differ significantly from the microcanonical average of the sum function for only a very small proportion of initial phases - provided, however, that the microcanonical distribution may be taken to be an appropriate representation of the distribution that specifies the actual frequency of occurrence of initial phases. And it is this last point that is violated whenever the system possesses an additional integral that defines a surface in phase space.

Whilst we must not trespass on the grounds of the review of quantal ergodic theory to be given after this[6], it should be noted that the original quantal ergodic theorem of von Neumann[7] and the less objectionable theorems of the Italian school[8] all involve averagings of just this kind - indeed the foregoing in its structure is essentially a classical formulation of Bocchieri and Loinger's quantal theorem[8] (although the latter is not restricted to sum functions). And all these theorems seem subject to the same criticism, that although the validity of the theorems does not depend on any ergodicity criterion such as metrical indecomposability - and indeed this is usually stressed as being an advantage of these theorems - the application of the theorems to physical systems depends on there existing no additional integral of motion defining a surface.

To put the matter provocatively: the indiscriminate application of the theorems would suggest that all systems are ergodic - even those that are non-ergodic. Or otherwise: the theorems may be applied, to yield the result that a system is ergodic, provided the system is not non-ergodic - and the theorems themselves give no help at all in determining whether the latter condition is satisfied.

3. We have noted how various restrictions have been introduced progressively into the original ergodic theory.

One positive result, indeed it seems the only positive result of ergodic theory for statistical mechanics, has been obtained recently by restricting attention even more - to a particular system, in fact. However, this result is a by-product as it were of a different programme, having arisen from the considerable developments in general dynamics, not restricted to macroscopic systems, that have been initiated by the introduction into the theory of the concept of entropy. Actually, the concept is somewhat different from that of entropy in statistical mechanics and in information theory; its introduction and the determination of its properties are due to Kolmogorov[9] and to Sinai[10]. Although this has stimulated much activity among mathematicians, it appears that so far its only consequence for the ergodic problem in statistical mechanics, albeit an important consequence, is Sinai's proof[11] of the ergodicity of a hard sphere gas.

Closely related to the concept of entropy in general dynamics is that of a K-system; the properties of K-systems have been studied extensively by the Russian school[12] and all K-systems have been shown to be ergodic. These ideas of entropy and of K-systems have been used to study geodesic flows in spaces of negative curvature, and, subsequent to Krylov's[12] pointing out the mathematical similarity between such flows and the hard sphere gas with elastic collisions, Sinai has shown that the hard sphere system is ergodic and furthermore is a K-system. It should be realised that this is a completely general result, being restricted neither to macroscopic systems nor to special types of phase-functions, although it is indeed a macroscopic system of hard spheres that is of specific interest in statistical mechanics. Again the equality of time and phase averages is obtained only almost everywhere in S. It is, of course, possible to conceive of initial phases for which the hard sphere gas is non-ergodic - for instance, if each particle moves in a different straight line normal to a pair of opposite faces of the cuboid container of the gas - but again also it is desirable that the set of such exceptional phases be accorded zero probability of occurring in practice.

We may hope that the property of ergodicity may yet be established for other types of many-body system, but at the moment the one clear cut result of ergodic theory for statistical mechanics is this for the hard sphere gas. As for the rest - the verdict may seem unduly harsh, but we are here so close to Elsinore that we may well echo Hamlet. And so, as for the rest, "the rest is silence".[13]

REFERENCES

1. G. D. Birkhoff, Proc. Natl. Acad. Sci. U.S. 17, 656 (1931).

2. R. M. Lewis, Arch. Rational Mech. Anal. 5, 355 (1960).

3. R. Kurth, Z. angew. Math. Phys. 3, 232 (1952), R. Kurth, Z. Naturforsch. 13a, 110 (1958).

4. A. I. Khinchin, Mathematical Foundations of Statistical Mechanics, Dover Publications Inc., New York, 1949.

5. P. Mazur and J. van der Linden, J. Mathematical Phys. 4, 271 (1963).

6. G. M. Prosperi and P. Bocchieri, these Proceedings.

7. J. von Neumann, Z. Physik 57, 30 (1929).

8. P. Bocchieri and A. Loinger, Phys. Rev. 114, 948 (1959). G. M. Prosperi and A. Scotti, Nuovo Cimento 13, 1007 (1959) and 17, 267 (1960), G. M. Prosperi and A. Scotti, J. Mathematical Phys. 1, 218 (1960).

9. A. N. Kolmogorov, Dokl. Akad. Nauk. U.S.S.R. 119, 861 (1958).

10. Ja. G. Sinai, Dokl. Akad. Nauk. U.S.S.R. 124, 768 (1959).

11. Ja. G. Sinai, Dokl. Akad. Nauk. U.S.S.R. 153, 1261 (1963), (English translation Soviet Math. Dokl. 4, 1818 (1963)), Ja. G. Sinai, these Proceedings.

12. See the references at the end of the paper by Ja. G. Sinai in these Proceedings.

13. W. Shakespeare, The Tragedy of Hamlet, Prince of Denmark, V, (ii) (c. 1603).

DISCUSSION

Frölich: I am worried about the time average in the infinite time limit.

Farquhar: The mathematics requires $t \to \infty$, which is all right physically as long as t is large compared with the macroscopic relaxation time of the system. The ergodic theorem is purely an existence theorem. It cannot tell us, a priori, whether an arbitrary system can tend towards equilibrium.

Temperley: Is there a restriction on the density?

Farquhar: No, there is no restriction.

Uhlenbeck: I certainly have not digested the work of Sinai, but perhaps it is helpful to mention the following points. I believe that Sinai's work can be considered as an enormous generalization of the earlier work of Hopf and Hedlund who showed that the geodesic flow on a surface of constant negative curvature is metrically transitive. If this theorem can be generalized to surfaces of variable negative curvature and of an arbitrary number of dimensions, then, since the mechanical motion can always be described as a geodesic on an appropriate surface, the proof of the metrical transitivity of the motion is reduced to the proof that this surface has the required negative curvature. Apparently, Sinai was able to show this for the motion of three or more hard spheres.

I would also like to mention the result of Kac, that for a metrically transitive system not only the average time the phase point spends in a region is proportional to its area but also the average recurrence time to come back to a region is inversely proportional to its area, just as one would expect.

Van Kampen: If you have three hard spheres in a narrow tube such that they cannot pass each other, the energy surface is metrically decomposable.

Uhlenbeck: I believe that Sinai always used periodic boundary conditions which might help to avoid such locked situations. But it also may be that one should not be too close to the closed packed configurations. I just do not know.

Lebowitz: There must be parts in phase space where the particles have no collisions.

Uhlenbeck: I suppose there will always be such zero measure motions. Also the space in which the spheres move cannot be one-dimensional.

Scotti: But the question of additional constants of the motion remains.

Farquhar: No, Sinai shows, effectively, that the energy is the only constant of the motion for a hard sphere system.

Mayer: It is good to find that the ergodic theorem cannot be proved for general systems since it can only be correct for a few systems. The time required to reach equilibrium is strongly dependent on the specific system, and on the variable which is displaced from equilibrium. In practice an observer making observations with a short time scale might say the real system is non-ergodic when a model is used which gives the "correct" result for a slower observer.

Sinai: I considered the case of spheres contained in a box (not periodic boundary conditions). If the density is too large and the spheres cannot exchange their places by a continuous displacement then it corresponds to the fact that phase space becomes unconnected. Then the theorem asserts that the system is ergodic on every connected component. The case which was mentioned by Prof. van Kampen permits us to reduce the system to a system of one-dimensional particles if the diameter of the tube is equal to the diameter of the spheres. If the first is larger then the system is ergodic with the order of particles being fixed.

RECENT DEVELOPMENTS IN QUANTUM ERGODIC THEORY

P. BOCCHIERI
Istituto de Fisica della Universita di Pavia - I. N. F. N., Gruppo di Pavia
and
G. M. PROSPERI
Istituto di Fisica della Universita di Bari - I. N. F. N., Sottosezione di Bari.

In this brief review we will deal shortly with the development of the ergodic theory in quantum mechanics. We will not aim at completeness, many interesting papers will not be mentioned at all. We will rather expose the point of view of the authors on the whole problem, without making any reference to the original contributions.

The ergodic problem has rather formally different aspect in classical and in quantum mechanics even if the aim is essentially the same in the two theories, i. e. to explain on the basis of the dynamics the results of statistical mechanics in its domain of applicability, chiefly insofar as the equilibrium state and the fluctuations are concerned.

There are essentially two cases, closely connected, that one describes by means of the ensemble theory of statistical mechanics:

1) The case of an isolated system with a great number of degrees of freedom. This case describes a physical system in which interactions with the rest of the world can be disregarded.

2) The case of a system with any number of degrees of freedom (small or large) in interaction with a much larger system (thermostate.)

We will keep, for reason of exposition, the two cases essentially distinct. The first case is described in statistical mechanics by means of a microcanonical ensemble, while the second one is described by the canonical ensemble in which appears, as the only parameter of the thermostate, its temperature.

First we will discuss in detail the case 1) that seems to us to be more interesting from the point of view of the principles. From this discussion we will abstract the fundamental ideas for dealing with the second case and for understanding its connection with the first.

Let us consider an isolated dynamical system whose hamiltonian is H. Let $\Psi(t)$ be its state vector in the Schroedinger picture. Let us suppose that informations of macroscopical nature allow us to establish that the energy of the system belongs to a certain interval. The development of $\Psi(t)$ in series of eigenvectors of H will contain then only a finite number S of components, i.e. $\Psi(t)$ will belong to an unitary space with a finite number S of dimensions. We will call this space (for reasons of classical analogy) the energy shell, or microcanonical ensemble.

Let then the energy of the system belong to the interval E, E + dE.

If the system has many degrees of freedom the number of eigenfunctions of H whose eigenvalues belongs to this interval will be extremely great. If we denote these eigenfunctions with φ_k, (k = 1, 2, . . . , S) we can write:

$$\Psi(t) = \sum_1^S a_k \varphi_k e^{-i E_k t/\hbar}$$

If one requires, analogously to the classical case, that the microcanonical average of any observable coincide with the time average of its expectation value one has to impose the equality between the expression (the bar denotes time averaging)

$$\overline{(\Psi(t), A\Psi(t))} = \sum_{kl} a^*_k a_l (\varphi^*_k A \varphi_l) \overline{\exp\left[-i(E_l - E_k)\frac{t}{\hbar}\right]} \tag{1}$$

and the average

$$<A>_{micr.} = \frac{1}{S} \sum_k A_{kk} \tag{2}$$

over the quantum microcanonical ensemble.

Let us consider for instance the case of absence of degeneracies in the spectrum of the hamiltonian. The equality is then possible for all the observables only if the modulus of the a_k $(k = 1, 2, \ldots, S)$ is independent of k and such that

$$|a_k| = \frac{1}{\sqrt{S}} \tag{3}$$

An ergodic theorem similar to the classical one is therefore possible in quantum theory for well specific initial states only. But these states are particular ones and constitute a very small ensemble in the totality of the possible states. We are so in a situation which is not at all satisfactory. This difficulty can be avoided by introducing the macro-observables.

One remarks that the observables having a physical interest for a system with many degrees of freedom are not observables which refers to one molecule or few molecules, but they are observables that involve first of all many molecules and in general the whole system, such as e.g. the density, the hydrodynamical velocity, the energy, the magnetic moment.

The distribution functions of particles in space or in the momentum space are examples of macro-observables. Furthermore the accuracy required in measurements of such observables is much smaller than the one is needed for having a significant determination of the atomic observables.

To justify the point 1) it is therefore sufficient, from a physical point of view, to consider the macro-observables only and to prove that the time average of the expectation value of a macro-observable coincide with its micro-canonical average.

To solve the problem completely a precise mathematical characterization of a macro-observable would be necessary. The problem of such characterization cannot be considered as completely solved, in the sense that one does not know a way which is sufficiently general simple and unambigous for constructing the operator which corresponds to a macro-observable.

However one can draw conclusions concerning the ergodic problem only by knowing some general properties of the macro-observables.

From the papers of von Neuman and of other authors it results evident that any macro-observable O is an observable which presents many degeneracies. Consequently within every energy shell it can be mathematically characterized by an expression of the type:

$$O = \sum_{\nu=1}^{N} O_\nu P_\nu \tag{4}$$

where the P_ν are projector on suitable varieties V_ν which will be named phase-cells. If s_ν is the dimension of such a variety it is reasonable to suppose that this number is very great and that satisfies the inequality:

$$\frac{S}{s_\nu} \ll s_\nu \tag{5}$$

Furthermore we will denote with $\{\omega_{\nu,\gamma}\}$, $(\nu = 1, 2, \ldots, N)$, $(\gamma = 1, 2, 3\ldots, s\ )$ a set of eigenvectors of the macro-observables. Since the microcanonical average of a macro-observable is expressed by:

$$<O>_{micr.} = \sum_{\nu=1}^{N} O_\nu \frac{s_\nu}{S} \tag{6}$$

and since the expectation value of O at the instant t is given by

$$<O> = \sum_{\nu=1}^{N} O_\nu U_\nu(t) \tag{7}$$

(U_ν (t) being the probability of finding the system in the phase-cell V_ν), in order to justify, from a dynamical point of view the statistical mechanics of an isolated system it will be sufficient to prove that $\overline{<O>}$ coincide with $<O>_{micr.}$. This will happen when

$$U_\nu(t) \approx \frac{s_\nu}{S} \qquad (\nu = 1, 2, \dots, N) \tag{8}$$

Evidently this condition will be realized if the deviation of $U_\nu(t)$ from $\frac{s_\nu}{S}$ will be sufficiently infrequent in time for all the initial states of the system and for all the macro-observables.

The consideration we have made until now refer more specifically to the point of view 1).

Before going on and discussing the conditions of validity of eqs. (8) let us speak briefly of the point of view 2).

In statistical mechanics the system we consider in 2) can be small or large provided that it is in interaction with a much larger system which we have called the thermostate.

Let us consider any observable, even a microscopic one, in the small system. To the precise determination of an observable of the small system (one can think e.g. of a molecule and of its energy) will correspond many eigenfunctions of the total system. To be more specific let us suppose that, for instance, the small system has an unperturbed energy ϵ_ν. These eigenfunctions will constitute a phase cell in the energy shell.

When the state vector of the total system is in this phase cell the small system has energy ϵ_ν. The determination of an observable in the small system will therefore induce in the microcanonical ensemble of the total system a subdivision in cells of the type of that induced by a macro-observable.

If the small system has many degrees of freedom we will determine in it macro-observables and the measurement of a set of macro-observables will evidently induce again in the total energy shell a subdivision in phase cells.

The validity of the relations (8) for the total system justifies (this can be done with the usual procedure by means of which one deduce the canonical ensemble form the microcanonical one) on a dynamical basis the use of the canonical ensemble. The whole ergodic problem is then reduced to the problem of understanding the relations (8).

The first result that one can establish in a very simple way is the following: for a system with a very great number of degrees of freedom the inequality

$$\mathcal{A}\,(U_\nu(t) - \frac{s_\nu}{S})^2 < \frac{1}{S} \tag{9}$$

is valid without any specific assumption on the Hamiltonian of the system.

In this inequality $\mathcal{A}$ is the averaging over the initial states $\Psi(0)$ of the system performed in such a way that no initial state is favoured with respect to the others. This can be obtained if in this averaging the initial vectors $\Psi(0)$ run with an uniform distribution through the complex sphere of S dimensions which constitutes the energy shell.

From the inequality (9) it follows that

$$(U_\nu\,(t) - \frac{s_\nu}{S})^2 \approx 0 \tag{10}$$

and in particular relations (8), for the greatest majority of initial states. In other words $U_\nu(t)$ is equal to its microcanonical value s_ν/S for the greatest part of the time for the greatest majority of initial states.

The result is a consequence of the geometrical nature of the energy shell and of the unitarity of the evolution operator.

Unfortunately by means of the averaging over initial states one cannot know for which of the initial states the ergodic theorem holds. In particular from the inequality (9) one cannot understand if (8) holds for the microscopic states which correspond to a given macroscopic situation, because these states have a weight zero in the energy shell. This fact in particular would be desirable for understanding if a given macrostate evolve towards equilibrium.

Looking for a stronger result then eq. (9) one can take first a radical attitude and ask that eqs. (8) are verified for any initial state belonging to the energy shell without exceptions.

If one writes

$$H = \sum_{\rho} \epsilon_{\rho} E_{\rho} \tag{11}$$

where E_{ρ} is the projector on the eigenspace corresponding to the eigenvalue ϵ_{ρ}, one can check easily that eqs. (8) can hold if and only if the following relations

$$\sum_{i} \sum_{\rho} (\omega_{\nu i} E_{\rho} \omega_{\mu j})^{*} (\omega_{\nu i} E_{\rho} \omega_{\mu' j'}) = \frac{s_{\nu}}{S} \delta_{jj'} \delta_{\mu\mu'}$$

$$(\nu = 1, 2, \ldots, N) \tag{12}$$

are satisfied, or, in the assumption of no degeneracy in the spectrum of the hamiltonian

$$\sum_{i} | U_{\rho, \nu i} |^{2} = \frac{s_{\nu}}{S} \qquad (\nu = 1, 2, \ldots, N) \tag{13}$$

where $U_{\rho, \nu j}$ is the unitary matrix which connects the basis $\{\omega_{\nu j}\}$ with the basis of the eigenvectors of the energy. In the following we shall refer to eqs. (12) or eqs. (13) as "strong ergodicity conditions".

Adopting a less radical attitude, weaker ergodicity conditions can be obtained on the basis of the following considerations.

If we perform on the system a macro-observation at the time $t = 0$ finding for O the eigenvalue O_{μ} we assign as a consequence the initial state vector to the corresponding eigen-manifold.

The initial states as determined by macro-observations are therefore all those belonging completely to the manifolds V_u ($\mu = 1, 2, \ldots, N$). One is interested in showing that the relations (8) are satisfied for such macroscopically significant states or at least for the greater majority of them.

Noting that one cannot distinguish among the different possible states belonging to the same phase cell, one substitutes in (8) $U_{\nu}(t)$ with B $U_{\nu}(t)$. B is an averaging procedure similar to $\mathcal{A}$ but performed in the interior of a given cell which corresponds to the result of the initial observation.

Let

$$\sum_{ij} \sum_{\rho} |(\omega_{\lambda i} E_{\rho} \omega_{\lambda j})|^2 = \frac{s_\nu}{S} (1 + \eta_\lambda)$$

the condition under which the equation

$$B_\mu \overline{U_\nu(t)} \approx \frac{s_\nu}{S} \tag{14}$$

hold for every μ and ν can be shown to be

$$\eta_\lambda \ll 1 \tag{15}$$

In the language of statistical operators eq. (14) is equivalent to say that eq. (8) is verified for the expression $U_\nu(t) = T_r(P_\nu W(r))$ for the initial condition $W(0) = \frac{1}{s_\mu} P_\mu$.

It may be worthwhile to recall that the eq. $\eta_\lambda = 0$ is completely equivalent to eq. (12), and eq. (8) can be deduced for any initial state under such conditions.

If only relation (15) is assumed, the following remarkable result

$$\frac{B_\mu (\overline{U_\nu(t)} - \frac{s_\nu}{S})^2}{s_\nu^2/S^2} \approx \eta_\lambda \tag{16}$$

can be deduced.

Eq. (15) and (16) shows that eq. (8) is not only satisfied in the average (see eq. (14)) but it holds also for the greatest majority, as specified by the averaging B, of the initial macrostates belonging to a given macrostate.

According to some people the inequalities (16) have not a great physical meaning eq. (14) alone being sufficient. The reason is that in quantum mechanics there is not a substantial difference between pure states and mixtures, both corresponding to a statistical ensemble. In our opinion however eq. (14) alone says too little. In fact if one thinks to perform many measurements one after the other, one imposes on the state vector the system after the last observation, restrictions stronger that the one of belonging to one phase cell.

Let us for instance perform a macro-measurement at $t = 0$ and find the system in the macro state λ, and another measurement at the instant t_1 and find the system in the macrostate μ.

The state of the system after t_1 will be of the form Ψ_1 = const. $P_\mu e^{-iHt_1/k} \Psi(0)$ and this state does not describe in general the manifold V_μ when $\Psi(0)$ varies in V_λ. In this sense it seems to us that eq. 16) has at least a qualitative value.

Let us now go back to the ergodicity conditions (12), (13) and (15).

A great part of the preceding discussion remains rather formal if one does not succeed to prove that the ergodicity conditions are verified for physically significant systems.

Let us consider e.g. the eq. (13) under which an ergodic theorem holds for all initial states in the case of absence of degeneracy of the Hamiltonian.

The arguments we are giving here are valid also when the degree of degeneracy of the Hamiltonian is not too great.

The matrix $U_{\rho,\nu J}$ gives the position of the basis of the Hamiltonian of the system with respect to the basis of the macro-observable.

If M denotes an average over the relative position of the two bases, which is essentially the same as von Neumann average over the macro-observers one can prove that

$$M \left[\Sigma_J \left| U_{\rho,\nu J} \right|^2 - \frac{s_\nu}{S} \right]^2 < \frac{1}{S}$$

so concluding that the ergodicity condition (13) is satisfied for practically all the possible Hamiltonians of the system, or that, in other words, it should be violated for particular types of Hamiltonians only.

From the point of view 2) the matrix $U_{\rho,\nu J}$ is essentially determined by the interaction among the small system and the thermostate since the basis of the macro-observable is the basis of the unperturbed energy.

It can therefore be said that the eqs. (13) hold for practically all the possible interactions among the system and the thermostate.

It is impossible, however, to say anything definite about a specific interaction.

One justifies in this way the use of the canonical ensemble, and, in the case of a small system with many degrees of freedom, the use of the micro-canonical ensemble.

We made these consideration explicitly because it seems to us that the justification of the canonical or micro-canonical ensemble can be made, contrary to what someone said, only on the basis of mechanics without the introduction of "random" interactions.

There are of course interactions for which the eqs. (13) are violated (e.g. the case of no interaction or cases in which the interaction has particular simmetries), but we can say that in the other cases one should expect they hold true. However no specific example has been given for which the ergodicity conditions (12) or (13) have been actually proved.

The situation is somewhat better insofar as eqs. (15) are concerned. Eqs. (15) can be established for the class of Hamiltonians which have been considered by Van Hove in his theory of the master equation. Due to the interest of such result it may be worth recalling briefly the assumptions on which this theory is based.

Let us consider a system with N components (Molecules in gases, phonons, or Bloch electrons in solids) and assume that such a system is contained in a volume Ω. Let us write the Hamiltonian as

$$H = H_o + V$$

(where H_o represents the non interacting components and V the interaction) and denote with $|\alpha>$ and $c = \frac{N}{\Omega}$ the eigenstates of H_o and the average density of the system respectively.

Then one assume that:

1) Expressions like $<\alpha \mid VAV...VAV \mid \alpha'>$ (A being an operator diagonal in the $|\alpha>$ representation) tend to

$$W_A(\alpha)\, \delta(\alpha - \alpha') + Y_A(\alpha, \alpha')$$

for $N \to \infty$ with $c = \text{const.}$

2) The macroscopic observables are given by a convergent series, each term of which is a product of creation and destruction operators whose number is very small compared with N.

3) Some further conditions which are in the last analysis equivalent to the non existence of macroscopic integrals of the motion.

Such class of system contains, as it is well known, a large number of examples having an actual physical interest and therefore in conclusion eqs. (14) and (15) are certainly valid for a significant class of systems.

In our opinion this is the situation in the quantum ergodic theory intending with such term the discussed equivalence of time averages and ensemble averages. This seems to us to be the point of view closest to the classic formulation of the ergodic problem in classical mechanics.

Other method have been developed in dealing with the problem of the tendency towards equilibrium. Such methods consist in general in proving that $U_\nu(t)$ tends towards its microcanonical value $\frac{s_\nu}{S}$ for an isolated system or to its canonical value for a small subsystem of a large isolated system.

A number of very interesting results have been obtained in this order of ideas.

In particular we note that the relation

$$U_\nu(t) \underset{t \to \infty}{\longrightarrow} \frac{s_\nu}{S} \tag{17}$$

has been proved in the theory of the master equation under the hypothesis we have said above in relation with eq. (15). Of course the eqs. (17) hold when t is small in comparison with the Poincaré times. This is due essentially to the fact that in expressions of the kind

$$U_\nu(t) = \sum_{i\rho\rho'} (\omega_{\nu i} E_\rho \omega_{\mu J})^* (\omega_{\nu i} E_{\rho'} \omega_{\mu' J'}) \, e^{+\frac{i}{\hbar}(\epsilon_\rho - \epsilon_{\rho'})t} \, c_{\mu' J'} c^*_{\mu J}$$

one replaces the Fourier series by an integral i.e. one treats the energy spectrum as continuous. The limit $t \rightarrow \infty$ must therefore be understood accordingly since t has to be large compared with the significant macroscopic relaxation times, but small compared to the recurrence times.

In eq. (8) instead the average is over the whole history of the system.

The two points of view are in some sense complementary. They give the same results insofar as the equilibrium state is concerned. The ergodic approach however has a greater interest for the theory of the fluctuations, while on the other side the theory of the master equation does not only prove the existence of an equilibrium state but aims also to describe the details of the processes by which the equilibrium is attained.

REFERENCES

1. J. Von Neumann, Z. Physik 57, 30 (1929).

2. W. Pauli and M. Fierz, Z. Physik 106, 572 (1937).

3. N. G. von Kampen, Physica 20, 603 (1954).

4. M. Fierz, Helv. Phys. Acta, 28, 705 (1955).

5. I. E. Farquhar and P. T. Landsberg, Proc. Roy. Soc. of London, A. 239, 154 (1957).

6. P. Bocchieri and A. Loinger, Phys. Rev. 111, 668 (1958).

7. P. Bocchieri and A. Loinger, Phys. Rev. 114, 948 (1959).

8. R. Jancel, Compt. Rend. Acad. Sci. (Paris) 250, 67 (1960).

9. G. M. Prosperi and A. Scotti, Nuovo Cimento 13, 1007 (1959); 17, 267 (1960).

10. G. M. Prosperi and A. Scotti, J. Math. Phys. 1, 218 (1960).

11. G. M. Prosperi, J. Math. Phys. 3, 329 (1962).

12. P. T. Landsberg, Proc. Roy. Soc. of London A 262, 100 (1961).

13. G. Ludwig, Z. Physik 150, 346 (1958); 152, 98 (1958).

14. S. Grossmann, Nuovo Cimento 24, 201 (1962).

15. M. Delbrück and G. Moliere, Abbandl. preuss. Akad. Wiss. Kl. Physik Math. No. 1 (1936).

16. M. J. Klein, Phys. Rev. 87, III (1952).

17. H. Ekstein, Phys. Rev. 107, 333 (1957).

18. P. G. Bergmann and J. L. Lebowitz, Phys. Rev. 99, 578 (1955).

19. J. M. Blatt, Progr. Theoret. Phys. (Kyoto) 22, 745 (1959).

20. G. V. Chester, Rept. Progr. Phys. 26, 411 (1963).

21. J. E. Mayer, J. Chem. Phys. 34, 1207 (1961).

22. J. Emch, Preprints of the University of Maryland (1965).

23. L. van Hove, Physica 21, 517 (1955); 23, 441 (1957); 25 268 (1959).

24. A. Janner, Helv. Phys. Acta, 35, 34 (1965), 36, 155, (1963).

25. I. E. Farquhar, Ergodic Theory in Statistical Mechanics Interscience London (1964).

DISCUSSION

Fröhlich: Are there not considerable difficulties in defining a heat bath for quantum systems?

Bocchieri: There are no special difficulties, however a system having many degrees of freedom is needed.

Fröhlich: What about particle exchange?

Bocchieri: I am thinking of divided systems.

Fröhlich: They do not exist in reality.

Bocchieri: I quite agree that you cannot exactly divide systems in reality, but this is an idealization which is commonly used.

CONSIDERATIONS ON THE PROBLEM OF DERIVING THE MASTER EQUATION AND CHARACTERIZING MACROSCOPIC OBSERVABLES

L. LANZ
and
G. RAMELLA LANZ
Istituto di Fisica dell'Universita - Milan (Italy)
and
A. SCOTTI
Euratom C. C. R. Ispra-Varese
Italy

ABSTRACT

The generalized Master Equation is derived in a simpler way than hitherto followed, for instance by G. Ludwig and G. Emch. The only properties used in this derivation are the fact that for an isolated system one can always assume the Hilbert space to be finite dimensional and the hermiticity of the operator $(1-\mathcal{P})\mathcal{H}(1-\mathcal{P})$ ($\mathcal{H}= [H, \cdot]$, $\mathcal{P}$ coarse graining operator).

The result is valid independently of the choice of a set of orthogonal cells in Hilbert space, if only the statistical operator is initially uniform in each cell.

Next one tries to characterize the subdivision in cells in such a way that the generalized Master Equation reduces to a good approximation to the Master Equation proper. One can prove in a completely rigorous manner that this can be accomplished if the time evolution of the system is such that there are two well separated characteristic times: a macroscopic relaxation time connected with the fact that the hamiltonian H is nearly diagonal on the basis states spanning the cells; a microscopic relaxation time $\hbar/\delta q$, where δq characterizes the rate of change of the following quantity:

$$F(q) = \mathrm{Tr}\,\{P_\lambda \mathcal{H}[\frac{1}{(1-\mathcal{P})\mathcal{H}(1-\mathcal{P}) - q - i\epsilon} - \frac{1}{(1-\mathcal{P})\mathcal{H}(1-\mathcal{P}) - q + i\epsilon}]\mathcal{H} P_{\lambda'}\}$$

where P_λ and P_λ are projection operators on the cell λ and λ'. By means of a perturbative technique one studies then under under what conditions $F(q)$, in the case of pure scattering, can be approximated by a continuous function which is slowly varying in an interval δq.

Stringent conditions are found in this way on the structure of the cells' subdivision of the Hilbert space, more precisely one finds that the deviation of the matrix elements of H, in any given cell, from the average value should be small in comparison with the average value itself.

Finally one studies the contributions to the Master Equation proper of the pure scattering terms.

The possible applications to the interpretation of neutron time dependent thermalization in cold crystalline samples is also discussed.

Starting from the Generalized Master Equation (G. M. E.) for a macroscopic system we consider the problem of characterizing the class of (Macroscopic)Observables (M. O.) whose time evolution is, to a very good approximation, stochastic.

To this end we develop an iterative scheme such that the zeroth order term is a solution of the G. M. E.

What we try to prove is that the successive terms are negligible, in a suitable time interval, if one makes an appropriate choice of the M. O.

Let $\{\mathcal{S}\}$ be the Hilbert space of the system, and P_λ ($\lambda = 1, \ldots, N$) the projection operators on a set of orthogonal subspaces which represent a subdivision of $\{\mathcal{S}\}$, and will be called "cells".

Introduce the following definition:

$$\mathcal{P} W(t) = \Phi(t)$$

where

$$\mathcal{P} \cdot \equiv \sum_\lambda P_\lambda / s_\lambda \; \mathrm{Tr}(P_\lambda \cdot)$$

W(t) is the statistical operator and s_λ the dimension of the "cell" λ.

From Liouville's equation one derives then*), using the notation

$$\mathcal{H}_{10} = \mathcal{P}\mathcal{H}(1-\mathcal{P}), \mathcal{H}_{01} = (1-\mathcal{P})\mathcal{H}'\mathcal{P}, \mathcal{H}_{oo} = (1-\mathcal{P})\mathcal{H}(1-\mathcal{P})$$

---

*) See, for example, R. Zwanzig,Physica (1964), G. Ludwig Z. Physik 173, 232, (1963), G. Emch, Helv. Phys. Acta 37 (1964). Eq. (1) can be derived in an elementary way using the hermiticity of the operator $\mathcal{H}_{oo}$ for the case in which the Hilbert space is finite-dimensional. This is actually the case for a system which is confined to a finite region in space and has a finite energy. Naturally, from this point of view, the G. M. E. can only be approximated by the stochastic M. E., and only in an interval of time small compared to the Poincare recurrence time.

$$\frac{d\Phi(r)}{dt} = -1/\hbar^2 \int_0^t \mathcal{H}_{10}\, e^{-\frac{i}{\hbar}\mathcal{H}_{oo}(t-t')} \mathcal{H}_{o1}\, \Phi(t')\, dt' \qquad (1)$$

where $\mathcal{H}\cdot = [H, \cdot]$, and the initial condition has been taken to be

$$(1 - \mathcal{P})W(0) = 0 \qquad (2)$$

corresponding to the assumption of equal "a priori" probability and random phases.

Now we can rewrite equation (1) in the following way

$$\frac{d\Phi}{dt} = -1/\hbar^2 \int_0^{+\infty} \mathcal{H}_{10}\, e^{-\frac{i}{\hbar}\mathcal{H}_{oo}t'} \mathcal{H}_{01}\, dt'\, \Phi(t) +$$

$$+ \gamma\{-\frac{1}{\hbar^2} \int_0^t \mathcal{H}_{10}\, e^{-\frac{i}{\hbar}\mathcal{H}_{oo}t'} \mathcal{H}_{01}\, \Phi(t-t')dt' +$$

$$+ \frac{1}{\hbar^2} \int_0^{+\infty} \mathcal{H}_{10}\, e^{-\frac{i}{\hbar}\mathcal{H}_{oo}t'} \mathcal{H}_{01}\, dt'\, \Phi(t)\}$$

where γ is the expansion parameter, which eventually will be put equal to one.

If we now put $\Phi(t) = \Phi^{(0)}(t) + \gamma\Phi^{(1)}(t) + \ldots$ we obtain

$$\frac{d\Phi^{(0)}}{dt} = -1/\hbar^2 \int_0^{+\infty} \mathcal{H}_{10}\, e^{-\frac{i}{\hbar}\mathcal{H}_{oo}t'} \mathcal{H}_{01}\, dt'\, \Phi^{(0)}(t)$$

$$\frac{d\Phi^{(1)}}{dt} = -1/\hbar^2 \int_0^{+\infty} \mathcal{H}_{10}\, e^{-\frac{i}{\hbar}\mathcal{H}_{oo}t'} \mathcal{H}_{01}\, dt'\, \Phi^{(1)}(t) +$$

$$+ \{-\frac{1}{\hbar^2} \int_0^t \mathcal{H}_{10}\, e^{-\frac{i}{\hbar}\mathcal{H}_{oo}t'} \mathcal{H}_{01}\, \Phi^{(0)}(t-t')\, dt' +$$

$$+ \frac{1}{\hbar^2} \int_0^{+\infty} \mathcal{H}_{10}\, e^{-\frac{i}{\hbar}\mathcal{H}_{oo}t'} \mathcal{H}_{01}\, dt'\, \Phi^{(0)}(t)\} \quad \text{etc.}$$

where the initial conditions are

$$\Phi(0) = \Phi^{(0)}(0) \; ; \quad \Phi^{(1)}(0) = \Phi^{(2)}(0) = \ldots = \Phi^{(N)}(0) = 0$$

Our analysis allows one to establish that, if there are two characteristic times for the system under consideration, which will be defined presently, that are well separated, then the dominant part of the inhomogeneous term in the equations for $\Phi^{(1)}(t)$, $\Phi^{(2)}(t), \ldots,$ $\Phi^{(N)}(t)$, is negligible and leads, in a suitable time interval, to negligible correction terms $\Phi^{(1)}(t), \ldots, \Phi^{(N)}(t)$.

Let $|\lambda i>$ be the states which span the statistical "cell" λ, consider their expansion in energy eigenstates

$$|\lambda i> = \sum_{E,j} c_{Ej}^{(\lambda i)} \, |Ej> \tag{3}$$

We want to make the assumption that it is possible to define a Δ such that for each λ, i, the following relations are satisfied

$$c_{Ej} \approx 0 \qquad \text{when} \qquad |E - E_{\lambda i}| > \Delta/2$$

The quantity Δ will be greater, the greater the off-diagonal matrix elements of the hamiltonian H turn out to be (in the basis $|\lambda i>$).

If one then considers the following function

$$\mathrm{Tr}(P_\lambda \mathcal{H} \| q >> << q \| \mathcal{H} P_{\lambda'}) = f_{\lambda\lambda'}(q) \tag{4}$$

where $<< q\|$ is an eigenstate of $\mathcal{H}_{oo}$ corresponding to the eigenvalue q, one can see that it is practically zero if $|q| > \Delta$. It follows then that the quantity

$$-1/\hbar^2 \int_T^t \mathcal{H}_{10} \, e^{-i/\hbar \mathcal{H}_{oo} t'} \, \mathcal{H}_{01} \, \Phi^{(0)}(t-t') \, dt'$$

is negligible with respect to $-1/\hbar^2 \int_0^T$ (same integrand), if the following condition is satisfied

$$\hbar/\eta T \ll 1$$

where η is defined by

$$\eta \left| \frac{d\, f_{\lambda\lambda'}(q)}{dq} \right| \sim \left| f_{\lambda\lambda'}(0) \right|$$

and besides:

$$\text{if} \quad \eta \sim \Delta \qquad \eta^2 \left| \frac{d^2 f_{\lambda\lambda'}(q)}{dq^2} \right| \sim \left| f_{\lambda\lambda'}(0) \right| ,$$

$$\text{if} \quad \eta \ll \Delta \qquad \eta^{\varkappa} \left| \frac{d^{\varkappa} f_{\lambda\lambda'}(q)}{dq^{\varkappa}} \right| \sim \left| f_{\lambda\lambda'}(0) \right|$$

all $\varkappa \leqq m$

where m is such that $(\hbar/\eta T)^{m-1} \frac{\Delta}{\eta} \ll 1$.

As for the time T it has to be such that the following relation between orders of magnitude is correct

$$T^{l} \left| \frac{d^{l}\, \mathrm{Tr}\, P_{\lambda}\, \bar{\Phi}^{(0)}(t)}{dt^{l}} \right| \sim \mathrm{Tr}(P_{\lambda}\, \bar{\Phi}^{(0)}(t)) \qquad l \leqq m$$

T is the macroscopic relaxation time and is determined by the stochastic M. E. A very rough evaluation of its order of magnitude is given by

$$T \sim \left(\frac{1}{\hbar} \sqrt{\mathrm{Tr}(\mathcal{P}_{\lambda}\mathcal{H}\mathcal{H}\mathcal{P}_{\lambda})}\ \frac{1}{s_{\lambda}} \right)_{\text{Averaged over } (\lambda)}$$

One finds that the magnitude of T is essentially determined by the "extension" of the "cells" λ and by the way in which the states $|i\rangle$ are grouped within a given "cell" λ.

In other words, for T not to be too small, states $|i\rangle$ have to be grouped in the same "cell" λ for which $|\langle i | H | i' \rangle|^2$ is sufficiently large.

We see in this way that the validity of the stochastic M. E. is intimately related to the separation of the two times $\tau_o = \hbar/\eta$ and T, i. e. the solutions of the stochastic M. E. are good approximate solutions of the G. M. E. up to terms of the order $\sim \tau_o/T$. In connection with the passage to the continuum in the variable q, we remark that the function defined in (4) can be written by means of the revolvent operator of $\mathcal{H}_{oo}$

$$1/(\mathcal{H} - z) = \mathcal{R}(z)$$

and, putting $H = H_o + V$ one can consider a perturbative expansion where the states $|\lambda i>$ are eigenstates of H_o.

If one does this the problem of the passage to the continuum becomes the problem of understanding how to do this in an expression of the type

$$\frac{1}{\Delta\lambda'} \mathrm{Tr}(P_\lambda U_{oo}\mathcal{R}^{(0)}(z) U_{oo} \ldots U_{oo} ||\xi>> <<\xi|| U_{oo} \ldots \mathcal{R}^{(0)}(z)U_{oo}P_{\lambda'})$$

where

$$\mathcal{R}_o = \frac{1}{\mathcal{H}_0 - z} ; \quad \mathcal{H}_o = [H_o, \cdot] ; \quad U\cdot = [V, \cdot] ;$$

$$U_{oo} = (1 - \mathcal{P}) U (1 - \mathcal{P}) ; \quad \mathcal{H}_o||\xi>> = \xi||\xi>>$$

and ξ is the variable which has to be made continuous.

In general among the contributions of the complete set of states $||\xi>>$ the state corresponding to the eigenvalue zero $||0>>$, for a many particle system, is much bigger than the single contributions of the other states and can be as big as the sum of all these.

We find here in a slightly different form the exceptional contribution which in a perturbative formalism of the type, for instance, developed by Van Hove, is characterized in the limit $N \to \infty$ by a delta singularity.

What we find in our case is, that it is just the presence of the operator $(1 - \mathcal{P})$ associated to the operator U_{oo} which allows one to eliminate these exceptional contributions provided the following relation between orders of magnitudes is verified

$$\left| \left[<\lambda i| V V V \ldots V |\lambda i> - \sum_{i'} \frac{1}{s_\lambda} <\lambda i'| VV \ldots V |\lambda i'> \right] \right|$$

$$\sim \; |<\lambda i| V V \ldots V |\lambda i''>|$$

That is to say the exceptional contribution due to the diagonal element is cancelled by the average of the exceptional contributions over one "cell" λ .

Clearly this condition limits the "extension" of the "cells" i.e. they have to be so small, that the dispersion of the average of the diagonal matrix elements of products of V, be of the order of magnitude of the off diagonal matrix elements. In conclusion the conditions on the structure of the "cells" are such, that they should not be too large to allow one to go over to a continous variable and they should not be too small so that T is sufficiently large: if this is the case, in the perturbative expansion, we can replace the operator U_{oo} by the operator U, the exceptional contributions being in these way eliminated. The transition to a contineous variable can then be accomplished, after having summed on the initial and final states belonging to the "cells" (λ), (λ') respectively, on the quantum numbers which characterize single particle states: for instance in the case of nearly localized particles, this is done for their momenta.

A check for the consistency of our formalism has been obtained, by applying it to the problem of justifying the Boltzmann equation, for an inhomogeneous gas, by means of a stochastic M.E. for $f(\vec{r}, \vec{p}, t)$. One finds the known results (see for instance Grossmann , Physica (1963)). The two characteristic times are found to have the obvious physical meaning: $\tau_o \sim$ collision time or average time needed to cross the extension of a nearly localized state, T $\sim$ mean time between two collisions or average time needed to cross a typical volume of macroscopic localization.

The formalism here developed seem to afford a good tool for the study of the mixed terms scattering-streaming, which could prove important when the mean free path of the particles is not of the same order of the linear dimension of the volume of macroscopic localization: this is the case for the problem of the diffusion of neutrons in a fluid or a crystal.

Work is in progress on the explicit construction of macro-observables which satisfy our general conditions.

Emch: 1) Contrary to the statement made in the lecture, there is no difference between finite and infinite Hilbert spaces in so far as the derivation of generalized master equations is concerned. Laplace transform techniques in Liouville space are also independent of whether the Hamiltonian has a discrete or a continuous spectrum.

2) As is well known, severe mathematical difficulties are bound to occur in any attempt to describe mechanical systems by means of Pauli equations. Coarse graining alone is of no help. Time smoothing should be introduced to remove internal contradictions. This does not mean that these two ingredients are sufficient by themselves to obtain a Pauli reduction of the general master equations.

3) B. Sz. Nagy's theorem on the embedding of contraction semi-groups (as generated by the Pauli equation in macroscopic Liouville space) into unitary groups (as acting in microscopic Liouville space) necessitates considering the unboundedness of the Hamiltonian.

4) Macroscopic systems exist, the evolution of which cannot be properly described, even in an approximate sense, by a Pauli equation no matter what amount of time smoothing is considered - on any time scale. An example would be the spin relaxation experiments such as those of Lowe and Norberg. The consequences of this are that supplementary conditions have to be found (and isolated in the above example) for which a Pauli reduction of the generalized master equation can be obtained.

Sewell: The major problem is to choose the macroscopic observables so that the kernel decays in a microscopic time. If this is achieved I contend that a suitable time smoothed form of the master equation will reduce to a Markoffian form to lowest order in a very small parameter whose magnitude is essentially given by a negative power of a dimensionless size parameter.

Scotti: I agree with Dr. Emch that it is clearly impossible to derive the stochastic master equation from the generalized master equation as an exact consequence. Let me repeat, however, that I have expressed the operator $\bar{\varphi}(t)$ as a series

$$\bar{\varphi}(t) = \bar{\varphi}^{(0)}(t) + \bar{\varphi}^{(1)}(t) + \cdots$$

of which only the zeroth approximation $\bar{\varphi}^{(0)}(t)$ is supposed to satisfy the stochastic master equation. What I was aiming to do was to prove that $\bar{\varphi}^{(0)}(t)$ is a good approximation, at least for a class of macroscopic observables. Naturally for a specially bounded system this is true only in an interval of time which is small compared to the Poincaré recurrence time.

Résibois: In the particular problem of the transport equation in homogeneous systems (where calculations can be performed explicitly), the approximation scheme performed by Dr. Scotti was introduced in 1961 (Résibois, Physica 27, 541, 1961; Prigogine and Résibois, Physica 27, 629, 1961) and has been used since by various authors. In this case, it was clearly shown that this scheme is only valid in the asymptotic limit, $t \to \infty$. Indeed, as was shown first by van Hove (Physica, 23, 144, 1957), - either there is a clear cut separation between the collision time and the relaxation time, as for instance in the dilute gas, and then the Boltzmann equation is sufficient (or its analog equation for the problem under consideration), - or we want to retain corrections to the Boltzmann equation (of order $a^3 \rho$) but then there is no more separation between the two times. One has then to use the complete non-Markoffian equation, except in the limit $t \to \infty$ (for proving the H theorem, for instance).

The situation is quite different when other characteristic parameters are introduced (as for instance an external electric field or a density gradient) but, for this case, it has been shown that the non-Markoffian corrections play no role (see, for instance, Balescu, Physica, 27, 693, 1961 and Résibois in E. Meixner, ed., Statistical Mechanics, North Holland Pub. 1965).

Prosperi: I agree with Dr. Emch that time smoothing can be a useful tool, however, I do not see that it is really essential. I think that it can, possibly, be replaced by appropriate assumptions on the macroscopic variables, see for example, van Kampen's considerations on the quasi-diagonality of macroscopic variables. With respect to what Résibois said, I would like to point out that the choice of the correct macroscopic observables is important. The variables which are appropriate to describe a gas in the limit of low density are not necessarily the same as those which are appropriate for finite density.

A CONTRIBUTION TO THE THEORY OF QUANTUM MECHANICAL FLUCTUATIONS FAR FROM EQUILIBRIUM

H. HAKEN
and
W. WEIDLICH
Institut für Theoretische
und Angewandte Physik
TH Stuttgart, Germany

In the case of selfsustained quantum systems like lasers and masers there arise some new phenomena which are interesting also from a fundamental point of view. In such systems we have some quantum theoretical macroscopic observables, e.g. the lasing lightmode operators, the operators for the collective level occupation numbers and dipole moments of the active atoms, behaving in a quasiclassical way, whose fluctuations exclusively stem from quantum processes like optical pumping, photon absorption and spontaneous emission. In order to describe the temporal behaviour of these variables including their fluctuations we have extended methods known e.g. from the classical theory of Brownian motion to these cases, where the system is 1.) quantum theoretical, 2.) in a stationary or nonstationary state far from thermodynamic equilibrium interacting with Markoffian reservoirs. The two equivalent methods are a) the use of quantum mechanical generally noncommuting, Langevin forces describing the fluctuation influence of the reservoirs in addition to their dissipation effect, b) the use of a Fokker-Planck equation with quantum mechanically determined dissipation and fluctuation coefficients for a distribution function over the values of the relevant macroscopic observables.

In case a) the Heisenberg equations for the operators of the Laser system, containing damping constants $\varkappa$, γ, ω and the full sets of fluctuating operator forces which stem from the influence of the surrounding reservoirs, read[1a)](see also (1b, c, d)

$$\dot{b}_\lambda^+ = (i\omega_\lambda - \varkappa_\lambda) b_\lambda^+ + i \sum_\mu g^*_{\mu\lambda} (a_2^+ a_1)_\mu + F_\lambda \tag{1}$$

$$(a_2^+ a_1)^\bullet_\mu = (i\,\epsilon_\mu - \gamma_{21})(a_2^+ a_1)_\mu - i \sum_\lambda g_{\mu\lambda} b_\lambda^+ \sigma_\mu + \Gamma_{21,\mu} \tag{2}$$

with

$$\sigma_\mu = (a_2^+ a_2 - a_1^+ a_1)_\mu$$

$$(a_k^+ a_k)^\bullet_\mu = \sum_l w_{kl} (a_l^+ a_l)_\mu - (a_k^+ a_k)_\mu \sum_l w_{kl} + (\delta_{k1} - \delta_{k2}) P_\mu + \Gamma_{kk,\mu} \tag{3}$$

with

$$P_\mu = i(a_2^+ a_1)_\mu \sum_\lambda g^*_{\mu\lambda} b_\lambda - i(a_1^+ a_2)_\mu \sum_\lambda g_{\mu\lambda} b_\lambda^+$$

and

b_λ^+ = creation operator for the λ-th light mode in the cavity.

$a_{k\mu}^+$ = creation operator for the k-th energy level of the μ-th atom.

$\Gamma_{ik,\mu}$, F_λ = fluctuating Langevin operator-forces for photons and atoms.

Correlation functions of interesting variables, like $\langle b^+(t+\tau)b(t)\rangle$, may be calculated by integration of these equations, if the correlation functions $\langle \Gamma_i(t) \cdot \Gamma_j(t') \rangle$ of the fluctuating forces are known[1)]. Generally, if the equation of motion for the operators U_j has the form

$$\dot{U}_j = f_j(U_i) + \Gamma_j \tag{4}$$

and the reservoirs are Markoffian, which results in

$$<\Gamma_j> = 0 \; ; \qquad <\Gamma_j(t) \cdot \Gamma_i(t')> = Q_{ij} \, \delta(t - t') \tag{5}$$

the fluctuation-coefficients Q_{ij} are given by

$$Q_{ij} = \lim_{\tau \to 0} \frac{1}{\tau} <(U_i(t+\tau) - U_i(t))(U_j(t+\tau) - U_j(t))> \tag{6}$$

and may be calculated by quantum theoretical perturbation theory[2,3]. In the case of the n-level atoms for instance, under the influence of reservoirs, we have the following equation of motion:

$$(a_{i_1}^+ a_{i_2})^{\bullet} = \sum_{j_1 j_2} M_{i_1 i_2; j_1 j_2} a_{j_1}^+ a_{j_2} + \Gamma_{i_1 i_2} \tag{7}$$

and we get[3,4] for $Q_{i_1 i_2; j_1 j_2}$ defined by $<\Gamma_{i_1 i_2}(t) \, \Gamma_{j_1 j_2}(t')> = Q_{i_1 i_2; j_1 j_2} \, \delta(t - t')$ the results

$$Q_{i_1 i_2; j_1 j_2} = \sum_{m,n} \{ \delta_{j_1 i_2} M_{i_1 j_2; mn} - \delta_{nj_2} M_{i_1 i_2; m j_1} - \delta_{m i_1} M_{j_1 j_2; i_2 n} \} <a_m^+ a_n> \tag{8}$$

The result (8) is also obtained by assuming (5) and that the operator relation $a_i^+ a_j a_m^+ a_n = \delta_{jm} a_i^+ a_n$, reflecting the fact, that only one level is occupied, is conserved in time in equation (7).

From the definition of Q_{ij} there also follows a general connection between Q_{ij} and the (Markoffian) master equation for the statistical operator $\tilde{\rho}$ of the system S under consideration[3]:

If the latter in interaction representation reads

$$\frac{d\tilde{\rho}}{dt} = - \frac{i}{\hbar} \left[\tilde{H}_{S1}(t) \, , \, \tilde{\rho} \right] + \left(\frac{\partial \tilde{\rho}}{\partial t} \right)_{incoh.} \tag{9}$$

where the last term stems from the influence of reservoirs, we get

$$Q_{ij}(\tilde{u}_1) = Tr_S \{ (\frac{\partial \tilde{\rho}}{\partial t})_{inc.} U_i U_j - U_i (\frac{\partial (U_j \tilde{\rho})}{\partial t})_{inc.} - (\frac{\partial (\tilde{\rho} U_i)}{\partial t})_{inc.} U_j \} \quad (10)$$

in b) we use these fluctuation coefficients and the corresponding dissipation coefficients

$$B_i(\tilde{u}_1) = \lim_{\tau \to 0} < (U_i(t+\tau) - U_i(t)) > = Tr_S \{ (\frac{d\tilde{\rho}}{dt}) U_i \} \quad (11)$$

to set up a Fokker-Planck equation for the distribution function $W(\tilde{u}_1)$ of the values $\tilde{u}_1$ of the macroscopic observables U_1 of the system S:

$$\frac{\partial W(\tilde{u}_1)}{\partial t} = - \sum_{i=1}^{n} \frac{\partial (B_i(\tilde{u}_1)W)}{\partial u_i} + \frac{1}{2} \sum_{i,j=1}^{n} \frac{\partial^2 (Q_{ij}(\tilde{u}_1)W)}{\partial \tilde{u}_i \partial \tilde{u}_j} \quad (12)$$

The stationary joint distribution function $F(\tilde{U}_1, \tilde{U}'_k; \tau)$ is then easily obtained from the solutions of this equation, and correlation functions $g_{ij}(\tau)$ and spectral densities $\tilde{g}_{ij}(\omega)$ are given by

$$g_{ij}(\tau) = \frac{1}{2\pi} \int_{-\infty}^{+\infty} \tilde{g}_{ij}(\omega) e^{i\omega\tau} d\omega = < U_i(t+\tau) U_j(t) >$$

$$= \iint \tilde{u}_i \tilde{u}'_j F(\tilde{U}_1, \tilde{U}'_k; \tau) d^n \tilde{u} d^n \tilde{u}' . \quad (13)$$

In the case of a two-level Laser model with single mode action the corresponding Fokker-Planck equation with quantum mechanically determined coefficients has been set up and solved explicitly[5, 6]. This leads to expressions for the correlation functions of the lasing lightmode, e.g.

$$g(\tau) = < b^+(t+\tau) b(t) > = n \exp \{ - \Delta\tau - h(1 - e^{-(\varkappa + \gamma_\perp)\tau}) \} \quad (14)$$

with

$$\Delta = \frac{\gamma_\perp}{4n(\varkappa + \gamma_\perp)^2} \{ \varkappa \gamma_\perp (2n_{th} + 1) + Ng^2 \}$$

$$h = \frac{1}{4n(\varkappa + \gamma_\perp)^2} \{ \varkappa^2 (\varkappa + 2\gamma_\perp)(2n_{th} + 1) - N\gamma_\perp g^2 \} \ll 1 \tag{15}$$

$n = \langle b^+(t)\, b(t) \rangle$ = photon number of the lasing lightmode.

n_{th} = thermal photon number of the lasing mode.

The linewidth Δ of Laser light as well as the expressions for intensity correlation functions agree with those obtained by method a)[1]. [Especially the expressions for the intensity-fluctuations are in good agreement with experiment.]

REFERENCES

1a. Haken, H., Z. Phys. 190, 327 (1966).

1b. Haken, H., Z. Phys. 181, 96 (1964); Z. Phys. 182, 346 (1965).

1c. Sauermann, H., Z. Phys. 188, 480 (1965); Z. Phys. 189, 312 (1966).

1d. Lax, M., Phys. Rev. 145, 110 (1966).

2. Schmid, C. and Risken, H., Z. Phys. 189, 365 (1966).

3. Risken, H., Schmid, C. and Weidlich, W., Z. Phys. 193, 37 (1966).

4. Haken, H. and Weidlich W., Z. Phys. 189, 1 (1966).

5. Risken, H., Schmid, C. and Weidlich, W., Z. Phys. 194, 337 (1966).

6. Risken, H., Schmid, C. and Weidlich, W., Phys. Letters 20, 489 (1966).

Further references may be found in these papers.

DISCUSSION

Fröhlich: What makes the ratio of the linewidth to the natural linewidth so small?

Weidlich: The collective dipole-moment of the atoms coupled coherently to the lightmodes makes an infinitely long wave track having a very sharp frequency.

Martin: Does your expression for the linewidth agree with those obtained by Lamb, Lax and others?

Weidlich: Yes, our linewidth expression agrees with that of Lax (who treats infinite wavelength) and that of Lamb (who treats the special case $\gamma \gg \kappa$). Especially it is of interest, that in all cases the linewidth decreases with increasing number of lasing photons.

Kubo: Have you considered Doppler broadening, it is very easy to take it into account.

Weidlich: Not explicitely in this lecture, but this case is considered for instance in the papers of Haken, myself and others by using the Heisenberg representation.

QUANTUM THERMODYNAMICS OF AN INFINITE SYSTEM OF HARMONIC OSCILLATORS

E. J. VERBOVEN
Institute of Theoretical Physics, University of Nijmegen, The Netherlands

ABSTRACT

An infinite system of harmonic oscillators is described by two spaces:

a) The macroscopic space E of functionals $E(\vec{x}, \vec{y})$, $(\vec{x}, \vec{y})$ being a point in classical phase space considered as a real Hilbert space. Special attention is given to the class $E_\beta(\vec{x}, \vec{y})$ corresponding to thermal equilibrium.

b) The microscopic space $H = H_F(\vec{q}) \otimes H_F(\vec{p})$. Each macroscopic state $E_\beta(\vec{x}, \vec{y})$ defines in $\mathcal{B}(H)$ a cyclic representation of the local bounded observables. For finite β the representation algebra is not of type I. For $T = 0$, $\beta = \infty$ the algebra is of type I. The infinitesimal generator of the evolution in time is given by $\mathcal{H} = (\mathcal{H}_F) \otimes 1 - 1 \otimes (H_F)$.
A generalization is proposed and briefly discussed.

It is well known that a necessary condition for a rigorous transition from statistical mechanics to thermodynamics consists in taking the so called thermodynamic limit $N \to \infty$, $V \to \infty$, N/V finite, where N represents the number of particles and V the volume of the system. Recently one has reversed the situation, consisting in studying from the start an infinite system. Such an infinite system has new symmetry properties, not present in the finite system, which must be the real root of its thermodynamic behaviour. Its energy is infinite, which means that the system does not feel the influence of a finite translation in the energy. Temperature must be related with this new symmetry property. For the same reason the system does not feel the addition of a finite number of particles. With this property must be related the existence of the chemical potential or density.

We consider a system where only the first symmetry will play a role: an infinite system of harmonic oscillators.

The behaviour of an infinite system of harmonic oscillators is governed by two spaces.

a) The macroscopic E of generating functionals $E(\vec{x}, \vec{y})$. These are the macroscopic states of the infinite system. The states $E(\vec{x}, \vec{y})$ give only information on the macroscopic behaviour of the infinite system. An important class is formed by the states $E_\beta(\vec{x}, \vec{y})$, corresponding to thermal equilibrium. They have the following form:

$$E_\beta(\vec{x}, \vec{y}) = \exp\left[\sum_{k=1}^{\infty} - \frac{1}{4\omega_k}(y_k^2 + \omega_k^2 x_k^2) \operatorname{ctnh} \frac{\beta\omega_k}{2}\right]$$

ω_k is the frequency of the k-th oscillator

y_k is the momentum of the k-th oscillator

x_k is the position of the k-th oscillator

$\vec{z} = (\vec{x}, \vec{y})$ is a vector in the infinite dimensional phase space of the harmonic oscillators considered as a real Hilbert space.

The states $E_\beta(\vec{x}, \vec{y})$ are eigenstates of the energy translation operators:

$$T_k = \frac{\delta}{\delta \frac{1}{2}(y_k^2 + \omega_k^2 x_k^2)}$$

with eigenvalues

$$- \frac{1}{2\omega_k} \operatorname{ctnh}\left(\frac{\beta\omega_k}{2}\right)$$

For an ideal Bose gas f.e. a second index is needed in order to specify the chemical potential.

b) The microscopic space $H = H_F \otimes H_F$ where H_F is Fock-Hilbert space. Each microscopic state $E_\beta(\vec{x}, \vec{y})$ defines in $\mathcal{B}(H)$ (all bounded operators on H) a cyclic representation R_β of the local bounded observables. For finite β the algebra R_β of local bounded observables is a factor of type III. T = 0 is an exception. For T = 0, R_∞ becomes identic to $B(H_F)$ and only one factor of H is needed.

Let us indicate some unbounded observables (not in R!)

$$P_k = (1+\rho_k)^{1/2}\ p_k \otimes 1 + 1 \otimes \rho_k^{1/2}\ p_k$$

$$Q_k = (1+\rho_k)^{1/2}\ q_k \otimes 1 - 1 \otimes \rho_k^{1/2}\ q_k$$

where p_k and q_k are the usual momentum and position operator and

$$\rho_k = \left[\exp(\beta\omega_k) \quad 1\right]^{-1}$$

Further the new creation and annihilation are:

$$\alpha_k^* = (1+\rho_k)^{1/2}\ a_k^* \otimes 1 - 1 \otimes \rho_k^{1/2}\ a_k$$

$$\alpha_k = (1+\rho_k)^{1/2}\ a_k \otimes 1 - 1 \otimes \rho_k^{1/2}\ a_k^*$$

P_k and Q_k as well as α_k^* and α_k fullfill the usual commutation rules for momentum and position or creation and annihilation operators.

However one can construct a second algebra R'_β of elements commuting with the elements of R_β. Some unbounded operators related to this algebra are:

$$\overline{P}_k = \rho_k^{1/2}\ p_k \otimes 1 + 1 \otimes (1+\rho_k)^{1/2}\ p_k$$

$$\overline{Q}_k = -\rho_k^{1/2}\ p_k \otimes 1 + 1 \otimes (1+\rho_k)^{1/2}\ q_k$$

and

$$\bar{a}_k^* = -\rho_k^{1/2}\, a_k \otimes 1 + 1 \otimes (1+\rho_k)^{1/2}\, a_k^*$$

$$\bar{a}_k = -\rho_k^{1/2}\, a_k^* \otimes 1 + 1 \otimes (1+\rho_k)^{1/2}\, a_k$$

It is easily verified that the new operators commute with the original unbounded observables.

Further it is seen that R_β and R'_β are very symmetric. R_β as well as R'_β may be used as algebra of local observables. The choice is limited by the dynamical behaviour. From algebraic standpoint they are isomorfic. The facts described above mean that the representation is reducible. The representation may be written as an integral of irreducible representations. These irreducible representations are:

$$E^\beta_{\vec{\bar{y}}}\,(\vec{x},\vec{\bar{y}}) = E_F(K^{-1}\,\vec{x},\; K\,\vec{\bar{y}})\, \exp(i\,\vec{\bar{y}}.\,L\vec{x})$$

with

$$(K\,\vec{x})_k = \left(\frac{\exp(\beta\omega_k)+1}{\exp(\beta\omega_k)-1}\right)^{1/2} x_k \quad , \quad (L\,\vec{x})_k = \left(\frac{4\,\exp(\beta\omega_k)}{\exp(2\beta\omega_k)-1}\right)^{1/2} x_k$$

and $\vec{\bar{y}}$ a vector in the algebraic adjoint space of $\vec{x}$.

These representations turn out to be non-stationary, i.e. they change in time. Only for $\beta = \infty$ the irreducible representation, which is the Fock representation, is stationary.

The Hamiltonian, which is the infinitesimal generator of the time-evolution operator is given by

$$\mathcal{H} = \mathcal{H}_F \otimes 1 - 1 \otimes \mathcal{H}_F$$

where $\mathcal{H}_F$ is the Fock Hamiltonian:

$$\mathcal{H}_F = \sum_k \omega_k\, a_k^*\, a_k$$

It is clear that $\mathcal{H}$ cannot belong neither to R_β nor to R'_β. In R'_β time runs in the opposite direction. The isomorfism between R_β

and R'_β is thus obtained by changing the sign of time. In equilibrium this change has no consequences. It reflects itself however on the dynamics.

For a general system one expects that the hamiltonian should be:

$$\mathcal{H} = (\mathcal{H}_o + \lambda V) \otimes 1 - 1 \otimes (\mathcal{H}_o + \lambda V)$$

where $\mathcal{H}_o$ is the "unperturbed" hamiltonian and λV is the interaction. If λV has the Van Hove diagonal singularity condition, the representations where $\mathcal{H}_o$ is diagonal and $\mathcal{H}_o + \lambda V$ is diagonal are not unitary implementable. In the derivation of the master equation one has always considered irreducible representations where $\mathcal{H}_o$ is diagonal as well as the observables. Such representations behave in an irreversible way. Stationary representations are in general of reducible type.

Only positive energy excitations are observable. Let ψ_o be the cyclic vector

$$\psi_o = \psi_{Fo} \otimes \psi_{Fo}$$

where ψ_{Fo} is the ground state of Fock Hilbert space. Then

$$\mathcal{H} a_k^* \psi_o = \omega_k a_k^* \psi_o$$

$$\mathcal{H} a_k \psi_o = -\omega_k a_k \psi_o$$

but

$$\mathcal{H} \bar{a}_k^* \psi_o = -\omega_k \bar{a}_k^* \psi_o$$

$$\mathcal{H} \bar{a}_k \psi_o = \omega_k \bar{a}_k \psi_o$$

Excitations with negative energy cannot be observed.

For a Bose gas the situation is in general the same. However in this case the states E cannot be obtained by a trace operator. This is because the particles are free. This fact suggest an essential difference between the elementary excitations in a gas, where a particle can move everywhere, and a crystal where a particle is restricted in his motion.

A list of references may be found in ref. 1.

REFERENCE

1. E. J. Verboven, Quantum thermodynamics of an infinite system of harmonic oscillators, II. To be published in "Physica".

DISCUSSION

Weidlich: Is there any connection between the function E and some expectation value in the second microscopic Hilbert space?

Verboven: For a finite number of oscillators the macrostates are constructed as trace states in Fock space. It is not possible to extend the trace to an infinite number of oscillators. However, the functional E has still a meaning for the infinite system.

Weidlich: What is the physical meaning of these representations?

Verboven: $\Psi_0 a_k^* a_k \Psi_0$ is just ρ_k , the expectation value of the number of phonons. The cyclic vector is $\Psi_0 = \Psi_{F_0} \otimes \Psi_{F_0}$, where Ψ_{F_0} is the ground state of Fock space, i.e. all the individual oscillators are in their ground states. With each temperature corresponds a different representation.

Winnink: Concerning the decomposition of the state into extremals, is this decomposition unique or does there exist another decomposition in terms of extremal invariant states.

Verboven: The states $E_{\bar{y}}^{\rho}(\bar{x},\bar{y})$ are irreducible. The decomposition can be done in terms of momentum or position.

Uhlenbeck: I would like to ask a point of information. If I

understand the model, it is an infinite number of independent oscillators. Now since I can not follow the mathematics I would only like to know what do you hope to get?

Verboven: We hope to understand the solid-fluid phase transition.

Uhlenbeck: Wouldn't one think that, so to say, the motivation of going to an infinite system would be to obtain simpler results than are obtained for a finite system?

Verboven: Not exactly, but one can use translational invariance and by this the powerful tool of group representation theory. Further one needs two spaces, a micro and a macrospace. The description of the evolution of the system in macrospace might be rather simple.

Uhlenbeck: Do you hope to be able to show that an infinite system say at zero temperature must necessarily be a crystal (in the classical theory), which means invariance with respect to a discrete lattice group?

Verboven: The macrostates must depend on the temperature and the chemical potential. We are studying this approach with two parameters. For $T = 0$, the representation is of type I and for $T \neq 0$, the representation is of type III in this simple example.

...on-equivalence of the representation ...uid phase.

... seems to me that there is little new to be expected for ...sical systems. However, in quantum mechanics there may possibly be results to be expected. Still, even then, I do not quite see that going to $N = \infty$ immediately is an advantage. Is there a feeling that it will be possible to factorize expectation values using this approach?

Verboven: As far as this model is concerned the answer is positive.

Yang: No, I am asking quite generally. What do you expect to obtain from introducing $N = \infty$ immediately?

Verboven: Things are well defined and can be studied in detail, so we do hope to be able to factorize expectation values.

Emch: One of the hopes is apparently to describe phase transitions adequately. This hope might be encouraged by the success obtained along these lines in providing a consistent frame for the BCS theory. There, the diagonalization of the Hamiltonian, in temperature dependent excitations, with different spectra, becomes exact in the thermodynamic limit, and can only be understood when one considers different, unitarily inequivalent, temperature-dependent representations of the algebra generated by the field operators. The same interpretation is to be given for the lattice-gas analog of the KUH-model for condensation.

ON THE EQUILIBRIUM STATES OF INFINITE QUANTUM SYSTEMS AT T ≠ 0.

M. WINNINK
Institute for Theoretical Physics, State University of Groningen

What I would like to talk about is some recent work which was done in collaboration with R. Haag and N. M. Hugenholtz[1].

The aim is to try and get some information about the general properties of equilibrium states of infinite quantum systems, from the point of view of c*-algebras and their representations[2]

Equilibrium states have in common their invariance under time-translations where depending upon the case one considers, there can also be invariances under other groups of transformations such as translations in one or more space-directions, translation over discrete distances, gauge-transformations etc.

We shall mainly be concerned with the invariance under time-translations, so that the results we shall come to are of a very general nature.

In order to set the stage for our discussion let me summarize those results of interest to us and already obtained by Araki and Woods[3] in their treatment of the non-relativistic infinite free Bose-gas at T ≠ 0.

They considered the von Neumann algebra $\mathcal{A}$ on Fock-space, where $\mathcal{A}$ is generated by the operators U(f) and V(g), the latter satisfying the well-known Weyl-relations:

$$U(f) \cdot V(g) = V(g).U(f)\, e^{-i(f,g)}, \quad (f,g) = \int f(x) \cdot g(x)\, d^3x$$

$$U(f) \cdot U(g) = U(f+g), \quad V(f) \cdot V(g) = V(f+g)$$

$f, g \in D$ where D is the class of all real, infinitely differentiable functions vanishing outside a finite region. By differentiating $U(\lambda f)$ and $V(\lambda g)$ with respect to λ and taking then the limit of $\lambda \longrightarrow 0$ one recovers the field and canonical conjugate momentum.

Let us denote by a, b... the elements of the algebra $\mathfrak{A}$. Consider

$$\omega_V(a) = \frac{\text{Trace}\left[a \exp\left(\beta\mu N_V - \beta H_V\right)\right]}{\text{Trace}\left[\exp\left(\beta\mu N_V - \beta H_V\right)\right]}$$

for a system in a finite box of volume V.

N_V: particle number operator

H_V: Hamiltonian

β : $(kT)^{-1}$

μ : Chemical potential

Let $V \rightarrow \infty$ and keep the particle number densities fixed. By doing so one is then provided with a positive linear functional (a) defined over the algebra $\mathfrak{A}$

$$\omega(a) = \lim_{V \rightarrow \infty} \omega_V(a) = \lim_{V \rightarrow \infty} \frac{\text{Trace}\left[a \exp\left(\beta\mu N_V - \beta H_V\right)\right]}{\text{Trace}\left[\exp\left(\beta\mu N_V - \beta H_V\right)\right]}$$

where of course the limit of numerator and denumerator separately do not exist.

One has then produced a functional describing an infinite system with a very specific particle number density in momentum space, characterized by μ and β.

Now one proceeds and constructs by the socalled Gel'fand-Segal construction a cyclic representation of the algebra $\mathfrak{A}$ associated with $\omega(a)$: $a \rightarrow R(a)$, where $R(a)$ is a bounded operator in a Hilbert space $\mathcal{H}$. Having done that one can ask the question whether such a representation is irreducible or not.

It turns out that this one is reducible i. e. the set of bounded operators which commute with all $\{R(a)\}$ is non-trivial. In fact the representation is a factor. Let us denote all the bounded operators that commute with the set $\{R(a)\}$ by $\{R(a)\}$.

2). Furthermore $\mathcal{H}_o$ has the following property:

$$a\mathcal{H}_o = 0 \rightarrow a = 0, \quad \mathcal{H}_o a = 0 \rightarrow a = 0 \text{ for } a \in B(\mathcal{H}_o).$$

As a consequence of this $\omega(a^*a) = 0 \rightarrow a = 0$ for $a \in B(\mathcal{H}_o)$. and also $\omega(aa^*) = 0 \rightarrow a = 0$ for $a \in B(\mathcal{H}_o)$.

One defines on the Hilbert-Schmidt operators a scalar product

$$(\mathcal{H}, \mathcal{H}') = \mathrm{Tr}(\mathcal{H}^* \mathcal{H}')$$

With this scalar product one can show that the Hilbert-Schmidt operators considered as a linear space form a Hilbert-space, and a Banach*-algebra. In short it is a Hilbert*-algebra.

We want to represent the algebra $\mathcal{A}$ in the space spanned by the Hilbert-Schmidt-operators in the following way:

$a \in \mathcal{A} \rightarrow U_a$: $U_a \mathcal{H} = a\mathcal{H}$ This is a*-isomorphism in terms of bounded operators $U_a \left[U_a^* = U_{a^*} \; U_{ab} = U_a U_b\right]$.

Consider the mapping:

$$a \in \mathcal{A} \rightarrow V_a: \; V_a \mathcal{H} = \mathcal{H} a.$$

This is a *-anti-isomorphism in terms of the bounded operators.

$$V_a \left[V_{ab} = V_b \cdot V_a, \; V_a^* = V_{a^*}\right]$$

One can prove

1). $U(\mathcal{A})'' = V(\mathcal{A})'$, $V(\mathcal{A})'' = U(\mathcal{A})'$

2). $\mathcal{H}_o$ is cyclic for $U(\mathcal{A})$ and for $V(\mathcal{A})$

3). $\omega(a) = (\mathcal{H}_o, U_a \mathcal{H}_o)$

4). There exist an anti-isomorphism C such that $C U_a C = V_{a^*}$ for all a in the set of Hilbert-Schmidt operators. This can be extended to all $a \in \mathcal{A}$.

The time translation automorphism $a \rightarrow a_t$ is in $\mathcal{H}_o$ given by

$$a \rightarrow a_t = u(t)\, a\, u(-t) \; \left[u(t) = e^{iHt}\right].$$

u(t) is not a compact operator so it does not belong to $\mathfrak{A}$ but to its weak closure.

$$\omega(a_t) = \omega(a) \quad \text{because} \quad [u(t), \rho] = 0.$$

Define

$U_{u(t)}$: $U_{u(t)}\mathcal{H} = u(t)\mathcal{H}$ one can show that $U_{u(t)}$ is a unitary

operator, similarly one proves that $V_{u(t)}$ is unitary. Because of the invariance of the functional we should have an operator U(t) such that $U(t)\mathcal{H}_o = \mathcal{H}_o$, and $U_{u(t)}$ does not work $[U_{u(t)}\mathcal{H}_o = u(t)\mathcal{H}_o]$.

The answer to this question is:

$$U(t) = U_{u(t)} \cdot V_{u(-t)} = U_{u(t)} \cdot V^{-1}_{u(t)} \quad ; \quad H = H_1 - H_r$$

H, H_1, H_r are the generators of U(t), $U_{u(t)}$ and $V_{u(t)}$ respectively. So we arrived at:

a) an anti-isomorphism between representation $a \to U_a$ and the representation $a \to V_a$.
b) U(t) does not belong to the representation of the algebra.
c) H is constructed from the representation and its commutant.

Changing μ, together with β, gives a set of density matrices for which the whole construction can be done, however a state with T = 0 and pure state do not have the above mentioned properties. So far for the finite system.

The states of infinite systems in equilibrium can in general not be described by means of a density matrix. On the other hand the state of an infinite system can be obtained from the state of a finite system by taking the thermodynamic limit. By this procedure $\omega(a)$ will (hopefully) retain some of the properties of a state for a finite system.

For the finite system we had $\mathcal{H}_o . \mathcal{H}_o^{-1}$ is an operator with dense domain in $\mathscr{H}_o$. Consider elements a and b ∈ $\mathfrak{A}$ such that $a_\beta = \mathcal{H}_o \, a \mathcal{H}_o^{-1}$ and $b_\beta = \mathcal{H}_o \, b \mathcal{H}_o^{-1}$ exist.

<u>This set is not empty!</u>

We then prove that $\omega(a^*_\beta\ b_\beta) = \omega(ba^*)$

This property can be defined for infinite systems and can therefore be expected to hold for the thermodynamic limit of states of infinite systems. We assume for an equilibrium state for an infinite system the following properties:

1). Time-translation invariance.
2). $\omega(a^*a) = 0$ implies $a = 0$.
3). $\omega(a_\beta{}^* b_\beta) = \omega(ba^*)$ for all a, $b \in \mathcal{A}$

$\tilde{\mathcal{A}}$ is the subalgebra of $\mathcal{A}$ for which $\hat{a}(\epsilon)$ ($a_t = \int \hat{a}(\epsilon)\, e^{-i\epsilon t}\, d\epsilon$) has compact support.

For $a \in \tilde{\mathcal{A}}$ we define $a_\beta = \int d\epsilon\, \hat{a}(\epsilon)\, e^{\frac{1}{2}\beta\epsilon}$

$a \rightarrow a_\beta$ is an automorphism of $\tilde{\mathcal{A}}$. $a_\beta{}^* = (a^*)_{-\beta} \neq (a^*)_\beta$.

So we have an automorphism which is not symmetric.
By generalizing the techniques for Hilbert algebras used for the finite system (here we do not have a Hilbert-algebra) we find again:

a symmetric representation (isomorphism) $a \rightarrow U_a$ (the ordinary Gel'fand-Segal representation),

a symmetric anti-representation $a \rightarrow V_a$, (anti-isomorphism) with the properties: $V(\mathcal{A})' = U(\mathcal{A})''$
a conjugation C with $CU_aC = V_a{}^*$.

Furthermore we find unbounded self-adjoint positive definite operators T and T^{-1} such that

$$\left.\begin{aligned} T\,U_a\,T^{-1} &= U_{a_\beta} \\ T\,V_a\,T^{-1} &= V_{a_\beta} \end{aligned}\right\} \text{ for all } a \in \tilde{\mathcal{A}}$$

and

$$(\Omega, U_a\Omega) = \omega(a) = (\Omega, V_a\Omega)$$

$T\Omega = \Omega$ (Ω is the cyclic vector).

We remark further that in the finite case, representation and commutant where simply left and right multiplication. This simple relation ceases to exist for the infinite case.

The automorphism $a \to a_\beta$ of $\tilde{\mathfrak{a}}$ is implemented in the representation-space by an unbounded operator T.

In the finite and the infinite case we found an anti-isomorphism between the representation of the algebra and its commutant, whereas Araki and Woods find an isomorphism. In "their" commutant however time runs backward, so a time reversal in that commutant reveals the connection between their case and ours.

In the treatment presented here we made nowhere use of the Bose or Fermi-character of the system. So the results are expected to hold equally well for Bosons and Fermions.

REFERENCES

1. R. Haag, N. M. Hugenholtz and M. Winnink, to be published.
2. See e. g. Dixmier, Les. C*-algebres et leur representations, Gauthier-Villars, Paris, 1964.
3. H. Araki and E. J. Woods, J. Math. Phys. 4, 637 (1963).

DISCUSSION

Verboven: Is the use of non-commuting algebra so important? Can commuting algebra be used?

Winnink: The use of a non-commuting algebra is indeed important if you want to consider quantum-statistical mechanics. I don't know how, for the case of a commuting algebra, one could prove similar things.

Van Kampen: What does this have to do with statistical mechanics?

Winnink: One usually treats finite systems and then takes limits. We want to treat in a consistent way, infinite systems from the beginning. We hope to gain insight into phase transitions.

Wergeland: In quantum mechanics there was some talk about exotic representations which are possible for infinite systems. However, they were discharged by von Neumann on physical grounds. Are there, nevertheless, physical reasons for admitting these representations?

Verboven: There are powerful methods of group representation theory which can be used in infinite systems. Solid state has had great advances due to the study of infinite crystals. We hope this will happen here also for the more general treatment of matter, perhaps, including phase transitions. Actually, van Kampen and others, have explained phase transitions in the van der Waals theory by making the system infinite.

Wergeland: The Einstein model is not a simplification of a linear dynamical system but rather an enormous complication. I think it is not possible at all to choose a coupling matrix such that the whole frequency spectrum collapses into a line.

Verboven: In this treatment it is the simplest example one can consider.

Fröhlich: There is an important case, namely phase transitions, when W(a) has a singularity.

Sewell: Am I correct in thinking that if this method leads to a theory of phase transitions then there will be superselection rules preventing microscopic transitions between microstates belonging to different phases?

Verboven: Certain symmetries are broken in the irreducible representation, however, not in the reducible representations.

Sewell: If there are superselection rules then it would appear that there could be no possibility of a description of the dynamics of the phase transition within the context of this theory.

Verboven: This is not the case.

Jancovici: Why not use periodic boundary conditions to obtain translational invariance? For that purpose, it is not necessary to have infinite systems.

Winnink: We have not treated any translations in space.

Singh: Have any new results or physical insight been obtained from this approach?

Winnink: In field theory this approach has led to some insight into some of the fundamental problems that exist there.
We hope this will be the case here also.

Jackson: First, if I may say, I would like to go back to the comment of Dr. Jancovici which I think was not fully appreciated. As I understand his point, his statement was in reply to the argument of Verboven that it was necessary to treat infinite systems in order to avoid surface effects. Thus one has only to take periodic boundary conditions for a finite system and one no longer has any trouble with the surface.
Now, the question I wish to ask could perhaps have been more properly asked by Dr. van Leeuwen as he has calculated a relevant example. Suppose you could carry out a calculation for a system with N finite and take it as large as you wish. Suppose

also you could do the calculation for N infinite. If the results obtained for the same quantity in the case $N \rightarrow \infty$ did not agree with the result of the calculation for infinite N, which would you believe to be the applicable one to the real system.

Winnink: If I saw the actual problem, hopefully, I could tell you from the precise form of the limiting process.

Weidlich: We can always ask for an appropriate representation for a given Hamiltonian.

Yang: Let me say something in defence of the general line of research represented by the last two papers as far as I have understood them. In the first place, the study of different representations in elementary particle theory is a necessary one. But one could still raise the question, why does one want to do it in statistical mechanics, where one knows, at least for equilibrium statistical mechanics, that the problem we are dealing with is, we believe, well formulated, and we want to approach the limit starting from a finite system. But one has known through experience that there exists for a given finite system, extremely good approximations such as quasi-excitations and so forth, and in studying these approximate Hamiltonians, which approximate the real finite degree system, one has found that this question of studying the various representations is a very useful one. As a matter of fact we all know that in the late 1950's there were lots of calculations, for example, of the Bose system near zero temperature, and one always found it a little puzzling that if you asked the question, what is the life time of a state which has a given superfluid structure, one does not know how to compute it. In order to investigate such questions, one must investigate what happens for an infinite system, and I think the approach that people are now following is to lay the foundation work of studying such systems. What I am a little puzzled about is what is the next stage that one expects to arrive at? In other words, I see that there is a very complicated physical problem to be solved, and I see that it is important to attack it, and maybe through c-star algebra. The question is, does one see yet some glimpses of what one might expect to arrive at through such approaches?

Winnink: We consider equilibrium states by a few conditions and hope, from this, to learn more about non-equilibrium states.

ON THE ASYMPTOTIC EQUIVALENCE OF VARIOUS ENSEMBLES FOR A REAL SYSTEM

P. MAZUR
Instituut-Lorentz, Leiden,
The Netherlands.

ABSTRACT

A number of thermodynamic limit problems of statistical mechanics are investigated on the basis of very general assumptions concerning the interaction ("stability" and "strong tempering"). In particular a proof is given of the asymptotic equivalence of the three main formalisms of statistical mechanics (microcanonical, canonical and grand-canonical). The method used may be extended to include other generalized ensembles (e.g. the isothermal-isobaric ensemble).

1. INTRODUCTION

The problem of the equivalence of various statistical ensembles has up to fairly recent years only been considered for so-called separable systems[1]. For real systems the problem of the equivalence is intimately related to the problem of the existence of the thermodynamic limit for certain statistical functions. Over the past years significant progress has been made with respect to this last problem[2)3)4)] (e.g. proof of the Van Hove theorem). A proof of the equivalence of the canonical and the grand canonical formalism was also given[3]. Van der Linden has made further progress proving both the existence of the thermodynamic limit of additional quantities and the equivalence of the microcanonical formalism[5]. In this paper on the asymptotic equivalence of various ensembles for a real system we shall essentially follow the treatment developed in his work.

2. THE ASYMPTOTIC PROBLEM

Consider a system of N point particles with mass m and Hamiltonian $\mathcal{H}_N$ given by

$$\mathcal{H}_N(r^N, p^N) = \frac{(p^N)^2}{2m} + U_N(r^N) \; . \tag{1}$$

Here $r^N \equiv (r_1, r_2, \dots, r_N)$ and $p^N \equiv (p_1, p_2, \dots, p_N)$ are the sets of canonical momenta and coordinates; U_N is the potential energy of interaction. The positions $r_i (i = 1, 2, \dots, N)$ are restricted to the volume V of the system.

In classical statistical mechanics one then determines, given the Hamiltonian (1), the Gibbsian analogies for the thermodynamic functions of the system. The following thermodynamic quantities will be considered: besides N and V, E the internal energy, S the entropy divided by k (Boltzmann's constant), β the inverse absolute temperature divided by k, F the free energy multiplied by $-\beta$, μ the chemical potential multiplied by $-\beta$ and p the pressure multiplied by β. Instead of V, E, S and F we shall also use their specific values $v = V/N$, $e = E/N$, $s = S/N$ and $f = F/N$, so that according to the definitions of the various quantities

$$f = s - \beta e, \tag{2}$$

$$\mu = f - pv. \tag{3}$$

We shall discuss here three alternative formalisms most commonly used in statistical mechanics to determine thermodynamic functions (analogies). These are the microcanonical, the canonical and the grand canonical formalisms.

In the microcanonical formalism the central quantity is the phase space volume Y_N, defined as

$$Y_N(E, V) = \frac{1}{N!} \iint dr^N \, dp^N \, \sigma\{E - \mathcal{H}_N(r^N, p^N)\} \,, \tag{4}$$

where σ is the unit step function. In the canonical and grand canonical formalisms the central quantities are the partition function ϕ_N and the grand partition function Ξ_V respectively:

$$\phi_N(\beta, V) = \frac{1}{N!} \iint dr^N \, dp^N \, e^{-\beta \mathcal{H}_N(r^N, p^N)} \,, \tag{5}$$

$$\Xi_V = \sum_{N=0}^{\infty} e^{-\mu N} \phi_N(\beta, V) \,. \tag{6}$$

According to the microcanonical formalism the logarithm of the function (4) is the analogy $S_N^{(m)}$ of S as a function of N, E and V, or with specific quantities

$$s_N^{(m)}(e, v) = \frac{1}{N} \log Y_N(Ne, Nv) \,. ^{*)} \tag{7}$$

The remaining thermodynamic functions are derived within this formalism, from the basic one, by means of the thermodynamic formulae:

$$\beta_N^{(m)}(e, v) = \frac{\partial s_N^{(m)}(e, v)}{\partial e} \,, \tag{8}$$

$$p_N^{(m)}(e, v) = \frac{\partial s_N^{(m)}(e, v)}{\partial v} \,, \tag{9}$$

and formulae (2) and (3) applied to these quantities. In the canonical formalism, the logarithm of the partition function (5), is the analogy $F_N^{(c)}$ of F as a function of N, β and V:

---

*) The more conventional entropy definition, according to the microcanonical formalism is

$$s_N^{(m)}(e, v) = \frac{1}{N} \log \frac{\partial Y_N(Ne, Nv)}{\partial (Ne)} = \frac{1}{N} \log \Omega_N(Ne, Nv) \,,$$

where Ω_N is the so-called structure function. For our purpose the definition (7) is the most convenient. It can be shown that the two alternative definitions lead to the same asymptotic value for the entropy.

$$f_N^{(c)}(\beta, v) = \frac{1}{N} \log \phi_N(\beta, Nv) \tag{10}$$

and one derives from this canonical free energy the canonical specific energy and the canonical pressure according to the thermodynamic formulae:

$$e_N^{(c)}(\beta, v) = - \frac{\partial f_N^{(c)}(\beta, v)}{\partial \beta}, \tag{11}$$

$$p_N^{(c)}(\beta, v) = \frac{\partial f_N^{(c)}(\beta, v)}{\partial v}, \tag{12}$$

Finally in the grand canonical formalism the logarithm of the grand partition function (6), is the analogy $p_V^{(g)}V$ of the quantity pV as a function of β, μ and V:

$$p_V^{(g)}(\beta, \mu) = \frac{1}{V} \log \Xi_V(\beta, \mu), \tag{13}$$

while one obtains from this last function, again according to thermodynamic formulae, the grand canonical specific volume and the grand canonical specific energy:

$$\frac{1}{v_V^{(g)}(\beta, \mu)} = - \frac{\partial p_V^{(g)}(\beta, \mu)}{\partial \mu}, \tag{14}$$

$$\frac{e_V^{(g)}(\beta, \mu)}{v_V^{(g)}(\beta, \mu)} = - \frac{\partial p_V^{(g)}(\beta, \mu)}{\partial \beta}. \tag{15}$$

Now the validity of these formalisms to determine thermodynamic functions is based on the following assumptions.

1. The various "thermodynamic functions" determined in each formalism all have a "thermodynamic limit": e.g. the sequence of functions $s_N^{(m)}(e, v)$ by (7) tends to a finite limit $s^{(m)}(e, v)$ as N tends to infinity.

2. The various formalisms are equivalent in the thermodynamic limit, i.e. the various limit functions obtained for the same

quantity in the various formalisms are identical if expressed in the same variables.

3. The thermodynamic limit functions are the true thermodynamic functions.

It is the purpose of investigations dealing with the foundations of statistical mechanics to justify these assumptions as consequences of the properties of the interaction between the particles. Thus the third assumption is part of the ergodic problem of statistical mechanics. In the absence of a complete and satisfactory solution of this problem and independently of such a solution, it is of importance to justify the first two assumptions which constitute the asymptotic problem of statistical mechanics.

We shall list now the asymptotic problems to be discussed. First one must show that the following limit exists

$$\lim_{N \to \infty} s_N^{(m)}(e, v) = s^{(m)}(e, v) , \qquad \text{(Problem I)}$$

where $s^{(m)}(e, v)$ must be concave in e and v.

One then has to show that this limit may be interchanged with differentiation with respect to e and v, so that

$$\lim_{N \to \infty} \beta_N^{(m)}(e, v) = \beta^{(m)}(e, v) \equiv \frac{\partial s^{(m)}(e, v)}{\partial e} , \qquad \text{(Pr. II)}$$

$$\lim_{N \to \infty} p_N^{(m)}(e, v) = p^{(m)}(e, v) \equiv \frac{\partial s^{(m)}(e, v)}{\partial v} . \qquad \text{(Pr. III)}$$

Similar problems arise in the two other formalisms. Thus one mxx must show that

$$\lim_{N \to \infty} f_N^{(c)}(\beta, v) = f^{(c)}(\beta, v) \qquad \text{(Pr. IV)}$$

with $f^{(c)}(\beta, v)$ convex in β and concave in v,

$$\lim_{N\to\infty} e_N^{(c)}(\beta, v) = e^{(c)}(\beta, v) \equiv -\frac{\partial f^{(c)}(\beta, v)}{\partial\beta}, \quad \text{(Pr. V)}$$

$$\lim_{N\to\infty} p_N^{(c)}(\beta, v) = p^{(c)}(\beta, v) \equiv \frac{\partial f^{(c)}(\beta, v)}{\partial v}; \quad \text{(Pr. VI)}$$

$$\lim_{V\to\infty} p_V^{(g)}(\beta, \mu) = p^{(g)}(\beta, \mu) \quad \text{(Pr. VII)}$$

with $p^{(g)}(\beta, \mu)$ convex in both β and μ,

$$\lim_{V\to\infty} v_V^{(g)}(\beta, \mu) = v^{(g)}(\beta, \mu) \equiv -1/\frac{\partial p^{(g)}(\beta, \mu)}{\partial\mu} \quad \text{(Pr. VIII)}$$

and

$$\lim_{V\to\infty} e_V^{(g)}(\beta, \mu) = e^{(g)}(\beta, \mu) = -v^{(g)}(\beta, \mu)\frac{\partial p^{(g)}(\beta, \mu)}{\partial\beta}$$

(Pr. IX)

In addition one has the following two equivalence problems: show that

$$s^{(m)}(e, v) = f^{(c)}(\beta(e, v), v) + \beta(e, v)e, \quad \text{(Pr. X)}$$

where $\beta(e, v)$ is the solution of the equation

$$e^{(c)}(\beta, v) = e,$$

and that

$$f^{(c)}(\beta, v) = p^{(g)}(\beta, \mu(\beta, v))v + \mu(\beta, v), \quad \text{(Pr. XI)}$$

where $\mu(\beta, v)$ is the solution of the equation

$$v^{(g)}(\beta, \mu) = v.$$

We are mainly concerned here with the solutions to problems X and XI, i.e. with the equivalence problem. However, in order to establish these equivalences, we first have to establish the three basic thermodynamic limits (Problems I, IV and VII) as well as the limits of problems V and VIII. The last two limits, as well as the limit to be established in IX follow in a simple way once problems I, IV and VII have been solved. As for the limits of problems II, III and VI, which are not directly needed to derive the equivalences X and XI, they will be discussed in van der Linden's paper.

3. PROPERTIES OF THE INTERACTION AND BASIC INEQUALITIES

Let the potential energy of interaction of the system have the following properties:

1. the interaction is stable, i.e. there exists a finite positive number u_0 such that

$$U_N(r^N) \geqq -Nu_0 \quad \text{for all } N . \tag{16}$$

2. The interaction is strongly tempered, i.e. there exists a finite positive number r_0 such that for any division of N into N_1 and $N-N_1$

$$U_N(r^N) - U_{N_1}(r^{N_1}) - U_{N-N_1}(r^{N-N_1}) \leqq 0 \tag{17}$$

whenever $|r_i - r_j| \geqq r_0$ for all pairs (i, j) with $i = 1, \dots N_1$ and $j = N_1+1, \dots N$. An interaction energy $U_N(r^N)$ which is the sum over all pairs of Lennard-Jones type potentials has both properties (16) and (17).

As a consequence of property (16) one obtains from (4) and (5), performing first the integration over momentum space, and from (6), the inequalities

$$Y_N(E, V) \leqq \frac{V^N}{N!} \{2\pi m(E + Nu_0)\}^{3N/2} / \Gamma(\tfrac{3N}{2} + 1) , \tag{18}$$

$$\phi_N(\beta, V) \leqq \frac{V^N}{N!} \left(\frac{2\pi m}{\beta}\right)^{3N/2} e^{N\beta u_0} , \tag{19}$$

$$\Xi_V(\beta, \mu) \leqq \exp \{(\frac{2\pi m}{\beta})^{3/2} V e^{-\mu+\beta u_0}\}. \tag{20}$$

From property (17), on the other hand, one obtains for the function (4) the following basic inequality for a division of the volume V in two subvolumes V_1 and $V-V_1$:

$$Y_N(E, V) \geqq \sum_{N_1=0}^{N} \int dx \, \Omega_{N_1}(x, V_1) \, Y_{N-N_1}(E-x, V-V_1), \tag{21}$$

where the structure function $\Omega_N(x, V)$ is defined as

$$\Omega_N(x, V) = \frac{\partial Y_N(x, V)}{\partial x} = \frac{1}{N!} \iint dr^N \, dp^N \, \delta(x \;\; \mathcal{H}_N). \tag{22}$$

Similarly one obtains either from (5) and (17), or directly by taking the Laplace transform with respect to E of (21), the inequality

$$\phi_N(\beta, V) \geqq \sum_{N_1=0}^{N} \phi_{N_1}(\beta, V_1) \, \phi_{N-N_1}(\beta, V-V_1). \tag{23}$$

Finally it follows from the last inequality and from (6) that the function Ξ_V obeys the inequality

$$\Xi_V(\beta, \mu) \geqq \Xi_{V_1}(\beta, \mu) \, \Xi_{V-V_1}(\beta, \mu). \tag{24}$$

For the derivation of the inequalities (21), (23) and (24) one has added to the Hamiltonian (1) a "wall potential" such that the smallest allowed distance of a particle to the boundary of the volume V is $\frac{1}{2} r_0$ (r_0 is the finite number occurring in condition (17)), but such that the particles are otherwise free from any influence of the wall. The actual volume occupied by the point particles is therefore smaller by a finite amount than the volume V (or V_1 and $V-V_1$). The inclusion of such a wall potential does not change the value of the thermodynamic limits to be discussed in the next section. For the rigorous discussion of this point and the detailed derivation of the above inequalities see ref. 5).

From the basic inequality (21) it follows that

$$Y_N(E,V) \geqq \int dx\,\Omega_{N_1}(x,V_1)\,Y_{N-N_1}(E-x,V-V_1) \geqq$$

$$Y_{N_1}(E_1,V_1)Y_{N-N_1}(E-E_1,V-V_1)\,, \tag{25}$$

for $N_1 \leqq N$ and $E_1 \leqq E$. The first inequality follows by retaining only one term of the sum on the right-hand side of (21), the second inequality by using also the fact that $Y_N(E',V) \geqq Y_N(E,V)$ if $E' \geqq E$. The inequalities (25) imply that

$$\log Y_N(E,V) \geqq \log Y_{N_1}(E_1,V_1) + \log Y_{N-N_1}(E-E_1,V-V_1)\,. \tag{26}$$

Similarly it follows from (23) that

$$\log \phi_N(\beta,V) \geqq \log \phi_{N_1}(\beta,V_1) + \log \phi_{N-N_1}(\beta,V-V_1)\,, \tag{27}$$

and from (24) that

$$\log \Xi_V(\beta,\mu) \geqq \log \Xi_{V_1}(\beta,\mu) + \log \Xi_{V-V_1}(\beta,\mu)\,. \tag{28}$$

The last three inequalities will enable us to solve a number of thermodynamic limit problems.

We shall also need the following inequalities of a different type:

$$\frac{\partial^2 \log \phi_N(\beta,V)}{\partial\beta^2} \geqq 0\,, \tag{29}$$

$$\frac{\partial^2 \log \Xi_V(\beta,\mu)}{\partial\beta^2} \geqq 0\,, \tag{30}$$

$$\frac{\partial^2 \log \Xi_V(\beta,\mu)}{\partial\mu^2} \geqq 0 \qquad (31)$$

These inequalities are a direct consequence of the definitions (5) and (6) for ϕ_N and Ξ_V respectively and do not depend on any special properties of the Hamiltonian.

4. THERMODYNAMIC LIMITS

We shall now take the case that the volume V is of cylindrical shape with a cross section of area A and height H. The division of the volume V into the volumes V_1 and $V-V_1$ is effected in such a way that V_1 and $V-V_1$ are again cylinders with cross sections of area A and heights H_1 and $H-H_1$ respectively.

Let us consider then the function $f_N^{(c)}(\beta, v)$ defined by (10). With $V/N = V_1/N_1 = v$, the inequality (27) implies that

$$Nf_N^{(c)}(\beta, v) \geqq N_1 f_{N_1}^{(c)}(\beta, v) + (N-N_1)\, f_{N-N_1}^{(c)}(\beta, v). \qquad (32)$$

In view of our choice for the shape of the volumes V, V_1 and $V-V_1$, (32) represents an inequality for a function $f_N^{(c)}(\beta, v)$ which still depends parametrically on the constant area A. This inequality expresses the fact that, at constant β and v (and constant value of A), $-Nf_N$ is a subadditive function of N. Therefore application of the limit theorem for subadditive functions ref. 6 leads to

$$\lim_{N\to\infty} f_N^{(c)}(\beta, v) = \sup_{N\to\infty} f_N^{(c)}(\beta, v) \equiv f^{(c)}(\beta, v)\,. \qquad (33)$$

The possibility that the limit function is infinite may be excluded. Indeed, according to (19),

$$f_N^{(c)}(\beta, v) \leqq \log\left(\frac{2\pi m}{\beta}\right)^{3/2} v + 1 + \beta u_0\,. \qquad (34)$$

Hence $f_N^{(c)}(\beta, v)$ is finite for all N (for a more detailed discussion see ref. 5)).

Since in taking the limit $N \to \infty$ in (33), both v and A were kept constant, we have in fact taken the thermodynamic limit in such a way that $N \to \infty$, $H \to \infty$, $H/N = v/A$ constant i.e. by letting the system become infinite in one dimension only. Our result implies that there exists already a finite thermodynamic limit in this case. However, the limit function $f^{(c)}(\beta, v)$ still depends parametrically on A. This is in agreement with thermodynamics since the free energy per particle is not the same function of the specific volume v for a cappillary and for a cylinder with macroscopic cross section. It can be shown 7) that a subsequent limit, such that $A \to \infty$, yielding a finite value, can be taken and that this limit is identical with the thermodynamic limit obtained for an all-sided expansion of the volume V[3]. These considerations of course also apply to the further thermodynamic limits to be derived here which all depend parametrically on A.

The convexity of $f^{(c)}$ in β follows from (29). As for the concavity of $f^{(c)}$ in v, it is again a consequence of the inequality (27), which also implies (for N even and with $N_1 = \frac{1}{2}N$)

$$f_N^{(c)}(\beta, \tfrac{1}{2}(v_1+v_2)) \geqq \tfrac{1}{2}\{f_{\frac{1}{2}N}^{(c)}(\beta, v_1) + f_{\frac{1}{2}N}^{(c)}(\beta, v_2)\} . \quad (35)$$

When we apply the limit (33) to this inequality we obtain

$$f^{(c)}(\beta, \tfrac{1}{2}(v_1+v_2)) \geqq \tfrac{1}{2}\{f^{(c)}(\beta, v_1) + f^{(c)}(\beta, v_2)\} . \quad (36)$$

Consequently $f^{(c)}(\beta, v)$ is concave and therefore also continuous in v. The results (33) and (36) (together with (29)) thus provide the solutions of the thermodynamic limit problem IV. It may furthermore be shown[5], that the limit (33) is uniform in v.

In an analogous way one can show, using the inequalities (26) and (28) (together with (30) and (31)), that

$$\lim_{N \to \infty} s_N^{(m)}(e, v) = s^{(m)}(e, v) , \quad (37)$$

with $s^{(m)}(e, v)$ concave and therefore continuous in both e and v, (furthermore the limit is uniform in both variables), and that

$$\lim_{V \to \infty} p_V^{(g)}(\beta, \mu) = p^{(g)}(\beta, \mu) , \tag{38}$$

with $p^{(g)}(\beta, \mu)$ convex (and continuous) in both variables. The two results (37) and (38) are the solutions of the thermodynamic limit problems I and VII.

Let us state now a theorem due to Griffiths[4)8)]:
If a sequence of functions $\varphi_N(x)$ is such that

$$\lim_{N \to \infty} \varphi_N(x) = \varphi(x) \text{ finite,} \tag{39}$$

and

$$\frac{\partial^2 \varphi_N(x)}{\partial x^2} \geqq 0 \text{ for all } N, \tag{40}$$

and is therefore such that φ_N and φ are convex, so that $\partial \varphi_N / \partial x$ and $\partial \varphi / \partial x$ have at most a countable number of jump discontinuities, then

$$\lim_{N \to \infty} \frac{\partial \varphi_N(x)}{\partial x} = \frac{\partial \varphi(x)}{\partial x} \tag{41}$$

in all points where $\partial \varphi / \partial x$ is continuous.

In view of (33) and (29), the sequence $f_N^{(c)}(\beta, v)$ has the required property (39) and the property (40) with respect to its dependence on β. Therefore, according to (41), we have with (11):

$$\lim_{N \to \infty} e_N^{(c)}(\beta, v) = e^{(c)}(\beta, v) \equiv - \frac{\partial f^{(c)}(\beta, v)}{\partial \beta} , \tag{42}$$

in all points where $\partial f^{(c)} / \partial \beta$ is continuous in β.

Similarly the sequence $p_V^{(g)}(\beta, \mu)$ possesses the properties (39) and (40) according to (38), (30) and (31), so that one gets from (41) with (14) and (15):

$$\lim_{V\to\infty} v_V^{(g)}(\beta,\mu) = v^{(g)}(\beta,\mu) \equiv -1/\frac{\partial p^{(g)}(\beta,\mu)}{\partial\mu} \tag{43}$$

in points where $\partial p^{(g)}/\partial\mu$ is continuous in μ, and

$$\lim_{V\to\infty} e_V^{(g)}(\beta,\mu) = e^{(g)}(\beta,\mu) \equiv - v^{(g)}(\beta,\mu)\,\frac{\partial p^{(g)}(\beta,\mu)}{\partial\beta} \tag{44}$$

in points where in addition $\partial p^{(g)}/\partial\beta$ is continuous in β.

According to thermodynamics, the (countable number of) jump discontinuities of $\partial f^{(c)}/\partial\beta$ must be interpreted as first order phase transitions in the e-β diagram at constant v, and those e.g. of $\partial p^{(g)}/\partial\mu$ as first order phase transitions in the v-μ diagram at constant β. Thus (42), (43) and (44) are established outside such first order phase transition points and represent solutions to the thermodynamic limit problems V, VIII and IX.

With the results of this section we are now able to establish the equivalences X and XI.

5. EQUIVALENCE OF THE VARIOUS FORMALISMS

Let us return to the inequality (25). Replacing N by 2N, N_1 by N, V by 2V, V_1 by V, E by 2E and E_1 by E, we get

$$Y_{2N}(2E, 2V) \geqq \int dx\, \Omega_N(x, V) Y_N(2E-x, V) \geqq \{Y_N(E, V)\}^2. \tag{45}$$

By simple generalization one obtains

$$Y_{nN}(nE, nV) \geqq Y_{nN}^{(n)}(nE, nV) \geqq \{Y_N(E, V)\}^n \tag{46}$$

with

$$Y_{nN}^{(n)}(nE, nV) = \int \prod_{i=1}^{n-1} dx_i\, \Omega_N(x_i, V) Y_N(nE - \sum_{i=1}^{n-1} x_i, V). \tag{47}$$

In (46) $Y_{nN}(nE, nV)$ represents the phase space volume for the system composed of nN particles having a total energy nE and occupying a (cylindrical) container of volume nV (height nH, cross section A); $Y^{(n)}_{nN}(nE, nV)$ is the phase space volume for a system composed of n (non-interacting) subsystems, each composed of N particles and occupying a subvolume V (of cylindrical shape with cross section A and height H), with total energy nE; finally $Y_N(E, V)$ is the phase space volume of a subsystem with energy E.

The function $Y^{(n)}_{nN}(nE, nV)$ given by (47) may be evaluated asymptotically for n tending to infinity with the help of the central limit theorem of probability theory[1)5)]. The familiar result is

$$\lim_{n\to\infty} \frac{1}{n} \log Y^{(n)}_{nN}(nE, nV) = \log \phi_N(\beta, V) + \beta E , \tag{48}$$

where ϕ_N, the partition function of a subsystem, is given by (cf. also (5) and (22))

$$\phi_N(\beta, V) = \int dE\, \Omega_N(E, V)\, e^{-\beta E} , \tag{49}$$

and where β is the solution of the equation

$$\frac{\partial \log \phi_N(\beta, V)}{\partial \beta} = -E . \tag{50}$$

On the other hand we have according to (7) and (37)

$$\lim_{n\to\infty} \frac{1}{n} \log Y_{nN}(nE, nV) = N \lim_{n\to\infty} \frac{1}{nN} \log Y_{nN}(nNe, nNv)$$

$$= N \lim_{n\to\infty} s^{(m)}_{nN}(e, v) = Ns^{(m)}(e, v) . \tag{51}$$

Taking logarithms of all members of (46), dividing by nN, and letting n tend to infinity we therefore have with (48) and (51)

$$s^{(m)}(e, v) \geqq f^{(c)}_N(\beta, v) + \beta e \geqq s^{(m)}_N(e, v) , \tag{52}$$

where we have also used (7) and (10). In (52) β is according to (50) the solution of the equation

$$\frac{\partial f_N^{(c)}(\beta, v)}{\partial \beta} \equiv -e_N^{(c)}(\beta, v) = -e . \tag{53}$$

Alternatively we therefore also have, if all functions are expressed in terms of β and v as independent variables,

$$s^{(m)}(e_N^{(c)}(\beta, v), v) \geqq f_N^{(c)}(\beta, v) + \beta e_N^{(c)}(\beta, v) \geqq s_N^{(m)}(e_N^{(c)}(e, v), v). \tag{54}$$

We may now study this result in the limit as N tends to infinity for constant β and v, i. e. in the thermodynamic limit of a subsystem. We then obtain with (33), (37) and (42), since the first and the last member of (54) tend to the same limit,

$$s^{(m)}(e^{(c)}(\beta, v), v) = f^{(c)}(\beta, v) + \beta e^{(c)}(\beta, v) \text{ for } \beta \neq \beta_t(v) , \tag{55}$$

where $\beta_t(v)$ is any of the (countable number of) points where $\partial f^{(c)}/\partial\beta$ has a jump discontinuity as a function of β at constant v (where a first order phase transition occurs). We have used here also the fact that $s^{(m)}(e, v)$ is continuous in e, and that the limit (37) is uniform in e. Now, at a point β_t, $e^{(c)}$ jumps from $e_{t,1}$ to $e_{t,2}$. Therefore in terms of the variables e and v (55) becomes (cf. (53))

$$s^{(m)}(e, v) = f^{(c)}(\beta(e, v), v) + \beta(e, v)e \tag{56}$$

for e not in an interval $e_{t,1} \leqq e \leqq e_{t,2}$. In addition one can then show that (56) must hold for all values of e.

Indeed we have from (56)

$$s^{(m)}(e_{t,1}, v) = \lim_{e \uparrow e_{t,1}} s^{(m)}(e, v) = f^{(c)}(\beta_t, v) + \beta_t e_{t,1} , \tag{57}$$

since $s^{(m)}$ is continuous in e, $f^{(c)}$ in β and β in e (For the continuity of β in e see ref. [5]). On the other hand differentiating with respect to e (cf. (53)) we obtain

$$\beta^{(m)}(e, v) = \beta(e, v)$$

for e not in an interval $e_{t,1} \leqq e \leqq e_{t,2}$. However, for all e in such an interval the function β has as the inverse function of $e^{(c)}$ at constant v the value β_t. Since furthermore $s^{(m)}$ has been shown to be concave in e, the function $\beta^{(m)}$ (which is therefore nonincreasing in e), must be equal to β_t within such an interval or in other words (58) holds for all e. Then we obtain by means of integration and (57) the equivalence relation

$$s^{(m)}(e, v) = \beta_t(e-e_{t,1}) + s^{(m)}(e_{t,1}, v)$$

$$= \beta_t e + f^{(c)}(\beta_t, v) \quad \text{for} \quad e_{t,1} \leqq e \leqq e_{t,2} \,. \qquad (59)$$

Thus the equivalence X of the microcanonical and the canonical formalism has been established.

The equivalence XI between the canonical and the grand canonical formalism can be established in an analogous way, using as a starting point of the analysis the inequality (23) instead of the inequality (25) (or (21)).

Finally we wish to mention that along similar lines one can also establish the equivalence of the isothermal-isobaric ensemble formalism and the other three formalisms considered here[7].

REFERENCES

1. Khinchin, A. I., Mathematical Foundations of Statistical Mechanics (New York, 1949).

2. Van Hove, L., Physica 15 (1949) 951.
Yang, C. N. and Lee, T. D., Phys. Rev. 87 (1952) 404

3. Ruelle, D., Helv. phys. Acta 36 (1963) 183.
Fisher, M. E., Archive for Rational Mechanics and Analysis 17 (1964) 377.

4. Griffiths, R. B., J. math. Phys. 5 (1964) 1215.

5. Van der Linden, J., Physica 32 (1966) 642; thesis (Leiden, 1966).

6. Hille, E., Functional Analysis and Semigroups (New York, 1948).
Fisher, M. E., The Van Hove Theorem (unpublished).

7. Van der Linden, J. and Mazur, P., Physica (to be published).

8. An alternative proof of "Griffiths' theorem" has been given by Fisher, M. E., J. math. Phys. 6 (1965) 1643; according to Lebowitz, J. L., and Penrose, O., J. math. Phys. 7 (1966) 98, the theorem is a corollary of an inequality which may be found in Hardy, G., Littlewood, J. and Polýa, G., Inequalities (London and New York, 1959).

RIGOROUS RESULTS FOR SOME THERMODYNAMIC LIMIT PROBLEMS

J. VAN DER LINDEN *
Instituut-Lorentz, Leiden,
The Netherlands

ABSTRACT

Once the thermodynamic limit of a statistical function has been established, one wants to show furthermore the interchangeability of this limit and differentiation with respect to one of the parameters. In certain cases (e.g. that of the "canonical energy") this question can be resolved directly with the help of a theorem due to Griffiths. It is shown that also for the other cases (e.g. that of the "microcanonical temperature") a solution of this asymptotic problem can be given, depending on (very general) assumptions about the interaction.

Consider for a classical system of N point particles in a volume V the "canonical free energy" per particle

$$f_N^{(c)}(\beta, v) = \frac{1}{N} \log \phi_N(\beta, Nv) \tag{1}$$

where

$$\phi_N(\beta, V) = \frac{1}{N!} \iint dr^N \, dp^N \exp\{-\beta \mathcal{H}_N(r^N, p^N)\}, \; (\beta > 0). \tag{2}$$

If for any kind of Hamiltonian function $\mathcal{H}_N$ it has been shown that

* Research Associate of the "Stichting voor Fundamenteel Onderzoek der Materie (F.O.M.)", The Netherlands.

$$\lim_{N\to\infty} f_N^{(c)}(\beta, v) = f^{(c)}(\beta, v) \tag{3}$$

exists, then for the "canonical internal energy" per particle

$$e_N^{(c)}(\beta, v) = -\frac{\partial f_N^{(c)}(\beta, v)}{\partial \beta} \tag{4}$$

we have

$$\lim_{N\to\infty} e_N^{(c)}(\beta, v) = -\frac{\partial f^{(c)}(\beta, v)}{\partial \beta} \equiv e^{(c)}(\beta, v), \tag{5}$$

except in "first order transitions". This property is, according to Griffiths[1], a consequence of the inequality

$$\frac{\partial^2 f_N^{(c)}(\beta, v)}{\partial \beta^2} \equiv -\frac{\partial e_N^{(c)}(\beta, v)}{\partial \beta} > 0 \quad \text{for all } N, \tag{6}$$

which follows from (1) and (2). When all functions $f_N^{(c)}$ are convex in β, then also the limit function (3) is convex in β, or $e^{(c)}$ decreasing in β. Hence this function $e^{(c)}$ may have jump discontinuities at only a countable number of points β, which are the excluded points in (5).

This theorem of Griffiths has been used in the preceding paper on the asymptotic equivalence of the various formalisms of statistical thermodynamics. The system considered there has a Hamiltonian function

$$\mathcal{H}_N(r^N, p^N) = \mathcal{K}_N(p^N) + U_N(r^N) = \frac{(p^N)^2}{2m} + U_N(r^N) \tag{7}$$

with stable and strongly tempered potential energy U_N. As a typical result we quote that, besides (3) and (5), we have, with α the inverse function of $e^{(c)}$ at constant v,

$$\lim_{N\to\infty} s_N^{(m)}(e, v) = s^{(m)}(e, v) = f^{(c)}(\alpha(e, v), v) + \alpha(e, v)e \tag{8}$$

for the "microcanonical entropy" per particle

$$s_N^{(m)}(e, v) = \frac{1}{N} \log Y_N(Ne, Nv) . \tag{9}$$

Here the occurrence of the function

$$Y_N(E, V) = \frac{1}{N!} \iint dr^N \, dp^N \, \sigma \{E - \mathcal{H}_N(r^N, p^N)\}, \tag{10}$$

with the unit-step function σ, is somewhat unusual. Usually the "microcanonical entropy" is defined with

$$\Omega_N(E, V) = \frac{\partial Y_N(E, V)}{\partial E} = \frac{1}{N!} \iint dr^N \, dp^N \, \delta \{E - \mathcal{H}_N(r^N, p^N)\} \tag{11}$$

instead of Y_N. Now suppose that we may interchange the limit (8) with differentiation with respect to e,

$$\lim_{N\to\infty} \beta_N^{(m)}(c, v) = \frac{\partial s^{(m)}(e, v)}{\partial e} \equiv \beta^{(m)}(e, v) = \alpha(e, v) , \tag{12}$$

where

$$\beta_N^{(m)}(e, v) = \frac{\partial s_N^{(m)}(e, v)}{\partial e} = \frac{\Omega_N(Ne, Nv)}{Y_N(Ne, Nv)} \tag{13}$$

is the "microcanonical temperature". Then this would imply, with (8), that

$$\lim_{N\to\infty} \frac{1}{N} \log \Omega_N(Ne, Nv) = \lim_{N\to\infty} \frac{1}{N} \log Y_N(Ne, Nv) = s^{(m)}(e, v), \tag{14}$$

or that both definitions are asymptotically equivalent.

In this paper we will give a proof of (12), which result is of course of interest in itself. Although the step from (8) to (12) resembles that from (3) to (5), a simple application of "Griffiths' theorem" is not possible in this case, and the proof again depends on the assumptions about the interaction: stability and strong tempering of the potential energy. There are two other thermodynamic limit problems, connected with the "microcanonical" and the "canonical pressure"

$$p_N^{(m)}(e, v) = \frac{\partial s_N^{(m)}(e, v)}{\partial v} \quad \text{and} \quad p_N^{(c)}(\beta, v) = \frac{\partial f_N^{(c)}(\beta, v)}{\partial v}, \tag{15}$$

which show the same features. Here too, results have been obtained, which will be stated briefly at the end. The solution of the problem (12) will be indicated more extensively, but for all details see reference[2].

Using the expression for the kinetic energy in (7), the functions (2) and (10) may be written as

$$\phi_N(\beta, V) = \frac{1}{N!} \left(\frac{2\pi m}{\beta}\right)^{3N/2} \int dr^N \exp\{-\beta U_N(r^N)\}, \tag{16}$$

$$Y_N(E, V) = \frac{1}{N!} (2\pi m)^{3N/2} \int dr^N \frac{\{E - U_N(r^N)\}^{3N/2}}{\Gamma(\frac{3N}{2} + 1)} \sigma\{E - U_N(r^N)\}. \tag{17}$$

From these formulae the following inequalities can be derived for (1) and (9):

$$\frac{\partial^2}{\partial \beta^2} \{ f_N^{(c)}(\beta, v) + \frac{3}{2} \log \beta \} > 0, \tag{18}$$

$$\frac{\partial^2 s_N^{(m)}(e, v)}{\partial e^2} \equiv \frac{\partial \beta_N^{(m)}(e, v)}{\partial e} > -\frac{2}{3} \{\beta_N^{(m)}(e, v)\}^2. \tag{19}$$

Since the property of convexity is conserved in the limit, it follows from (3) and (18) that

$$\frac{3}{2\beta^2} \leqq \frac{\partial^2 f^{(c)}(\beta, v)}{\partial \beta^2} \leqq \infty \tag{20}$$

(the value infinity characterizes the first order phase transitions). We see that the derivative of $e^{(c)}$ with respect to β does not vanish, so that the inverse function $\alpha = \beta^{(m)}$ of $e^{(c)}$ is continuous in e. Note that (20) corresponds to

$$- \frac{2}{3} \{ \beta^{(m)}(e, v) \}^2 \leqq \frac{\partial \beta^{(m)}(e, v)}{\partial e} \leqq 0 , \qquad (21)$$

where, according to (19), the first inequality is already "fore-shadowed" in $\beta_N^{(m)}$. If this would also be the case with the second inequality of (21), one could write down (12) at once, applying "Griffiths' theorem" to the sequence of functions $-s_N^{(m)}$ (cf. (6)). Since this is not so in general, we will establish an upper bound to the sequence of functions $\beta_N^{(m)}$, so that, according to (19), the functions $s_N^{(m)} + \frac{1}{2} Ce^2$ are convex in e for some positive constant C and all N. The application of "Griffiths' theorem" to the latter sequence also reduces to the result (12). Due to the continuity of $\beta^{(m)}$ in e, there are no excluded points e.

In order to prove the required boundedness of $\beta_N^{(m)}$ we introduce auxiliary functions

$$\Lambda_N(\varkappa, E, V) = \frac{1}{N!} \iint dr^N \, dp^N \, \sigma\{E - \mathcal{H}_N(r^N, p^N)\} \exp\{-\varkappa \mathcal{K}_N(p^N)\}, \qquad (22)$$

$$\Psi_N(\varkappa, \beta, V) = \frac{1}{N!} \iint dr^N \, dp^N \exp\{-\beta \mathcal{H}_N(r^N, p^N) - \varkappa \mathcal{K}_N(p^N)\}, \quad (\varkappa > -\beta), \qquad (23)$$

where $\varkappa$ is a real parameter, and $\mathcal{K}_N$ the kinetic energy. We see that for $\varkappa = 0$ these functions reduce to (10) and (2) respectively. For $\varkappa \neq 0$ they may be considered as generalizations of these functions in the sense that the asymptotic equivalence of the microcanonical and the canonical formalisms for a system with stable and strongly tempered potential energy can be established just as well with

$$l_N(\varkappa, e, v) = \frac{1}{N} \log \Lambda_N(\varkappa, Ne, Nv) \qquad (24)$$

and

$$g_N(\varkappa, \beta, v) = \frac{1}{N} \log \Psi_N(\varkappa, \beta, Nv) \qquad (25)$$

instead of (9) and (1) respectively. Note that for (23) we have, using (7) and (16),

$$\Psi_N(\varkappa, \beta, V) = \left(\frac{2\pi m}{\beta+\varkappa}\right)^{3N/2} \int dr^N \exp\{-\beta U_N(r^N)\} \, x$$

$$= \left(\frac{\beta}{\beta+\varkappa}\right)^{3N/2} \phi_N(\beta, V), \tag{26}$$

so that (cf. (3) and (8))

$$\lim_{N\to\infty} g_N(\varkappa, \beta, v) = g(\varkappa, \beta, v) = f^{(c)}(\beta, v) + \frac{3}{2}\log\frac{\beta}{\beta+\varkappa} \tag{27}$$

and

$$\lim_{N\to\infty} l_N(\varkappa, e, v) = l(\varkappa, e, v) = g(\varkappa, \gamma(\varkappa, e, v), v) + \gamma(\varkappa, e, v)e, \tag{28}$$

with γ the inverse function of $-\partial g/\partial\beta$ at constant $\varkappa$ and v.

In addition to this "generalized equivalence" at constant $\varkappa$, we use the convexity of the function (24) in $\varkappa$

$$\frac{\partial^2 l_N(\varkappa, e, v)}{\partial\varkappa^2} > 0 \quad \text{for all } N, \tag{29}$$

which follows from (22). For points $\varkappa$ where $\partial l/\partial\varkappa$ is continuous in $\varkappa$, this property enables us to conclude from (28) that

$$\lim_{N\to\infty} \frac{\partial l_N(\varkappa, e, v)}{\partial\varkappa} = \frac{\partial l(\varkappa, e, v)}{\partial\varkappa} = -\frac{3}{2}\,\frac{1}{\gamma(\varkappa, e, v)+\varkappa}, \tag{30}$$

according to "Griffiths' theorem". For our purpose we need this result for $\varkappa = 0$, so that we must investigate whether γ approaches α continuously for $\varkappa \to 0$. Indeed this can be shown[2)] to be the case due to the continuity of α in e. Therefore, with $\partial\Lambda_N/\partial\varkappa$ for $\varkappa = 0$ equal to

$$\frac{1}{N!}\iint dr^N dp^N \,\sigma\{E - \mathscr{H}_N(r^N, p^N)\}\mathscr{K}_N(p^N) = \frac{3N}{2}\,\frac{(2\pi m)^{3N/2}}{N!}\int dr^N$$

$$\frac{\{E - U_N(r^N)\}^{3N/2+1}}{\Gamma(\frac{3N}{2}+2)} \cdot \sigma\{E - U_N(r^N)\} = \frac{3N}{2}\,\Theta_N(E, V), \tag{31}$$

we obtain

$$\lim_{N \to \infty} \frac{\Theta_N(Ne, Nv)}{Y_N(Ne, Nv)} = \frac{1}{\alpha(e, v)} . \tag{32}$$

Moreover, this limit can be shown[2)] to be uniform in e.

Comparing (17) and (31), we notice that Y_N is the first partial derivative of Θ_N with respect to E. Hence we may write for some positive constant δ, using also (11), the Taylor expansion up to third order in δ:

$$\Theta_N(E+\delta, V) = \Theta_N(E, V) + \delta Y_N(E, V) + \frac{1}{2}\delta^2 \Omega_N(E, V) + \text{remainder}. \tag{33}$$

Here all terms on the right-hand side are positive, so that for (13) we have the inequality

$$\beta_N^{(m)}(e, v) < \frac{2}{\delta^2} \frac{\Theta_N(Ne+\delta, Nv)}{Y_N(Ne, Nv)} . \tag{34}$$

Let us define

$$t_N(e, v) = \frac{1}{N} \log \Theta_N(Ne, Nv), \tau_N(e, v) = \frac{\partial t_N(e, v)}{\partial e} = \frac{Y_N(Ne, Nv)}{\Theta_N(Ne, Nv)} . \tag{35}$$

Then, with $0 < \vartheta_N < 1$, we have

$$\Theta_N(Ne+\delta, Nv) \equiv \exp Nt_N(e+\frac{\delta}{N}, v) = \exp \{Nt_N(e, v) + $$

$$+ \delta\tau_N(e+\vartheta_N \frac{\delta}{N}, v)\} \equiv \Theta_N(Ne, Nv) \exp \delta\tau_N(e+\vartheta_N \frac{\delta}{N}, v) , \tag{36}$$

and hence (34) may be written as

$$\beta_N^{(m)}(e, v) < \frac{2}{\delta^2} \frac{1}{\tau_N(e, v)} \exp \delta\tau_N(e+\vartheta_N \frac{\delta}{N}, v) . \tag{37}$$

Since the sequence of functions τ_N converges to α uniformly in e (cf. (32)), we see that indeed the sequence of functions $\beta_N^{(m)}$ can be bounded from above. This completes the proof of (12).

If now, because of (14), the "microcanonical entropy" is defined with Ω_N instead of Υ_N, then the "microcanonical temperature" is also redefined. It can be argued, however, that for reasons similar to those given above, its thermodynamic limit is still $\beta^{(m)}$.

Finally we want to mention our results[3)] concerning the interchange of the limit (3) and differentiation with respect to v (cf. (12))

$$\lim_{N \to \infty} p_N^{(c)}(\beta, v) = \frac{\partial f^{(c)}(\beta, v)}{\partial v} \equiv p^{(c)}(\beta, v) . \tag{38}$$

We are able to indicate a negative lower bound to the sequence of functions $\partial^2 f^{(c)}/\partial v^2$ on the basis of (5), if, in addition, the potential energy U_N has the property that positive constants c_1 and c_2 may be found such that

$$c_1 U_N(r^N) - r^N r^N : \frac{\partial^2 U_N(r^N)}{\partial r^N \partial r^N} \geqq - Nc_2 \tag{39}$$

for all configurations and all N. (This property means stability of an altered potential energy, and it applies e. g. to Lennard-Jones type pair interactions: the pair potentials u and $c_1 u - r^2 u''$ are both of that type if c_1 is large enough). Hence we can use again "Griffiths' theorem" to derive (38) from (3). There are no excluded points v, as we can also show (using as before only the stability and strong tempering of U_N) that $p^{(c)}$ is continuous in v. To this end we establish, by means of two different generalizations of the equivalence between the canonical and the grand canonical formalisms, the thermodynamic limits

$$\lim_{N \to \infty} \frac{\phi_{N-1}(\beta, Nv)}{\phi_N(\beta, Nv)} = \lim_{N \to \infty} \frac{\phi_N(\beta, Nv)}{\phi_{N+1}(\beta, Nv)} = e^{-\mu^{(c)}(\beta, v)} , \tag{40}$$

together with the continuity of $\mu^{(c)}$ in v. Since here $\mu^{(c)}$ is equal to $f^{(c)} - p^{(c)}v$, $p^{(c)}$ is also continuous in v.

1) Griffiths, R. B., J. math. Phys. 5 (1964) 1215.

2) Van der Linden, J., Physica 32 (1966) 642.

3) Van der Linden, J. and Mazur,P., Physica (to be published).

DISCUSSION

Penrose: This type of theorem can be generalized to systems with electrostatic or magnetostatic interactions, for example, a plasma or a ferromagnet. The stability condition for such potentials was first obtained by Onsager. His work has been recently extended by Fisher and Ruelle. The strong tempering condition is not satisfied here, but instead we may use a special type of boundary condition which, for the magnetic case, corresponds to enclosing the system in a superconducting wall. Such a wall has the required property that if a system is split into two parts by inserting a partition made of wall material then the energy is increased since the lines of force are pushed inside. These two properties are sufficient to lead to thermodynamic functions with all the usual properties including shape independence.

Fröhlich: It must be remembered that the total charge must be zero.

Penrose: The boundary condition I spoke of does have the implication that the total electric charge (or magnetic pole strength) inside the container is zero. On the other hand, Onsager's lower bound on the energy works even if the total charge is not zero.

Mayer: It has always seemed to me to be preferable to use the energy surface definition of the microcanonical partition function.

<u>Van der Linden:</u> The energy volume definition is used only for our special treatment and we prove that both definitions are equivalent in the limit.

<u>Mazur:</u> It is possible that the limit can be established directly for the energy surface definition but not by using the theorem for subadditive functions. We do not know how to achieve this.

<u>Uhlenbeck:</u> Are the requirements you imposed on the intermolecular potential in some sense minimum requirements?

<u>Mazur:</u> It is possible to prove the limits of the statistical functions for a weakly tempered potential (which decreases faster than the inverse third power) but we are not able then, to demonstrate the equivalence and the limit of the microcanonical temperature.

<u>Uhlenbeck:</u> Is it really necessary to assume the additivity property of the intermolecular potential?

<u>Van der Linden:</u> We may be able to remove it.

<u>Uhlenbeck:</u> Although I think one is close to a general proof, the really "true" proof should show what the minimum requirements on the forces are.

Lebowitz: Fisher did include more general potentials. I would also like to mention that Dyson and Lenard have given a proof that general Coulomb systems, i.e. no hard cores, are stable if at least one type of the charges are fermions.

CONVERGENCE OF FUGACITY EXPANSIONS FOR CLASSICAL SYSTEMS

O. PENROSE
Imperial College,
London S. W. 7, England.

There are various ways[1)2)3)] of establishing a lower bound on the radius of convergence of Mayer's fugacity expansions for the pressure, density and correlation functions of an imperfect classical gas. Here I describe a new method which proceeds directly from the Mayer graphs, without the use of integral equations or recurrence relations. The method provides a simple derivation for some of the known bounds on the radius of convergence, and also leads to a new upper bound on the two-body distribution function.

Mayer's fugacity expansions for the pressure and density are

$$p = kT \sum_{l=1}^{\infty} b_l z^l , \qquad \rho = \sum_{l=1}^{\infty} l b_l z^l \tag{1}$$

where

$$b_l = (1/l!) \int \dots \int u_l(\underline{x}_1 \dots \underline{x}_l) \, d^\nu \underline{x}_2 \dots d^\nu \underline{x}_l \tag{2}$$

and the cluster function u_l is defined by

$$u_l = \sum_{\Gamma} \prod_{(ij)\subset\Gamma} f_{ij} . \tag{3}$$

The sum covers all connected graphs with l vertices labelled

1 .... l; the product covers all bonds in the graph Γ; and f_{ij} means $f(|\underline{x}_i - \underline{x}_j|)$ where

$$f(r) \equiv \exp\left[-\varphi(r)/kT\right] - 1 \qquad (4)$$

and $\varphi(r)$ is the two-body interaction potential.

To estimate the sum (3) we associate with each graph Γ a unique Cayley tree obtained by deleting bonds from Γ in the following way (see Fig. 1):

a) To each vertex i in Γ we assign a <u>weight</u> w_i, defined as the number of bonds in the shortest path joining vertex i to vertex 1, and we delete from Γ all the bonds joining two vertices of equal weight. This deletion does not affect the values of the weights, and leaves a graph Γ' in which every bond joins two vertices whose weights differ by 1.

b) From each vertex $\underline{i}$ in Γ', except for the vertex 1, there are one or more bonds leading to vertices of weight $w_i - 1$; we delete all of these except the one for which the label on the vertex of weight $w_i - 1$ is least.

This deletion again does not affect the values of the weights, and leaves a graph Γ'' which is a Cayley tree. Conversely, from any Cayley tree T we can construct the set S(T) consisting of all graphs Γ with the property $\Gamma'' = T$. The minimal graph in this set is T itself; the maximal graph, which we shall denote by T*, is obtained by adding bonds to T

a) joining all pairs of vertices of equal weight, and
b) joining every vertex $\underline{i}$ (except $\underline{i} = 1$) to all the vertices of weight $w_i - 1$ with labels greater than the vertex of weight $w_i - 1$ to which $\underline{i}$ is already joined in T. (see Fig. 1). (5)

The remaining graphs in S(T) can be obtained by adding to T only some of the bonds that are in T* but not in T, in all possible ways. The total number of graphs in S(T) is thus 2^n where n is the number of bonds in T*- T. See Fig. 1.

The sum (3) may now be rearranged by grouping together all terms for which $\Gamma'' = T$; this gives

$$u_1 = \sum_T \Big[\prod_{(ij)\subset T} f_{ij} \Big] \sum_{\Gamma\subset S(T)} \prod_{(ij)\subset\Gamma - T} f_{ij}$$

$$= \sum_T \Big[\prod_{(ij)\subset T} f_{ij} \Big] \prod_{(ij)\subset T^* - T} (1 + f_{ij}) \,. \tag{6}$$

An upper bound on $|u_1|$ is most easily obtained for the case where the two-body potential $\varphi(r)$ is non-negative, for then (4) implies that $|1 + f_{ij}| \leqq 1$ and hence (6) leads to the estimate

$$|u_1| \leqq \sum_T \prod_{(ij)\subset T} |f_{ij}| \,. \tag{7}$$

A similar upper bound applies in the case of <u>hard-core</u> potentials, satisfying the condition

$$\begin{aligned} \varphi(r) &= +\infty & r < a \\ |\varphi(r)| &\leqq A\, r^{-\nu-\epsilon} & r > a \end{aligned} \tag{8}$$

where A, a and ϵ are positive constants, and ν is the number of space dimensions. For such potentials it can be shown[3)] that a constant ϕ' exists with the property

$$\sum_{j=2}^{n} \varphi(|\underline{y}_1 - \underline{y}_j|) \geqq -2\phi' \,, \tag{9}$$

that is,

$$\prod_{j=2}^{n} (1 + f_{1j}) \leqq q \equiv \exp(2\phi'/kT) \,, \tag{10}$$

for all $n \geqq 2$ and all configurations $(\underline{y}_1 \ldots \underline{y}_n)$ such that n-1 spheres of diameter a centred at the points $\underline{y}_2 \ldots \underline{y}_n$ would not overlap.

For each vertex i in T, we define a set of vertices S_i, comprising all those vertices j connected to i by a bond of $T^* - T$ and satisfying either

$$\begin{aligned} & w_j = w_i + 1 \\ \text{or} \quad & \\ & w_j = w_i \text{ and } j > i . \end{aligned} \tag{11}$$

There are at most l-2 non-empty sets of this type, for S_i is empty if i = 1, because no bonds of T*- T contain the vertex 1, and it is also empty by (11), if i is the largest of the labels on the vertices having the maximum weight. For each i, the vertices j belonging to S_i are themselves all joined by bonds in T*- T; for, by (11), any pair of them either have equal weights and are therefore joined because of (5a), or else they have weights w_i and w_i+1 in which case they are joined because of (5b), which implies that every vertex of weight w_i+1 that is joined to i by a bond of T is joined by a bond of T*- T to every vertex of weight w_i and label greater than i. These bonds of T*-T, joining every pair of vertices in S_i, correspond to factors 1 + f in the product and because of the hard core condition these factors ensure that if the product differs from zero then the points $\underline{x}_j$ with j in S_i constitute a possible configuration for the centres of a set of non-overlapping spheres of diameter a. Consequently, by (10) with $\underline{y}_1 = \underline{x}_i$ etc., the contribution to this product from factors with j in S_i has the upper bound q. As we showed immediately after (11), there are at most l-2 non-empty sets of the form S_i, and so the last product in (6) has the upper bound q^{l-2}, and the whole expression has the bound

$$|u_l| \leqq q^{l-2} \sum_T \prod_{(ij)\subset T} |f_{ij}| . \tag{12}$$

Evidently (7) is a special case of this formula, since q=1 for non-negative potentials.

As a first application of this result we use it to estimate the radius of convergence of the series (1). Substituting (12) into (2) and carrying out the integrations (starting at the extremities of the tree T) we obtain

$$|b_l| \leqq (1/l!)\, q^{l-2} \sum_T B^{l-1} \tag{13}$$

where

$$B \equiv \int |f_{ij}|\, d^\nu \underline{x}_j = \int |f(r)|\, d^\nu \underline{r}\,.$$

Since the number of labelled Cayley trees with l vertices is[4)]l^{l-2}, the estimate (13) reduces to

$$|b_l| \leqq (ql)^{l-2}\, B^{l-1}/l! \tag{14}$$

from which it follows by Cauchy's nth root convergence test that

$$|z| < 1/eqB \tag{15}$$

is a sufficient condition for the convergence of the power series (1). For non-negative potentials the result (14) was obtained by Groeneveld[1)]. It is a special case of a more general result due to Ruelle[5)].

As a second consequence of (12), we derive an upper bound on the pair correlation function G(r), based on the formula[6)]

$$\rho^2 G(r) \equiv n_2(\underline{x}_1, \underline{x}_2) - \rho^2$$

$$= \sum_{l=2}^{\infty} z^l \int \cdots \int u_l(\underline{x}_1, \underline{x}_2, \underline{x}_3, \ldots \underline{x}_l)\, d^\nu \underline{x}_3 \ldots d^\nu \underline{x}_l/(l-2)! \tag{16}$$

where $\underline{x}_1$ and $\underline{x}_2$ must satisfy $|\underline{x}_1 - \underline{x}_2| = r$ and are otherwise arbitrary. Substituting the bound (12) into this formula, we obtain

$$\rho^2 |G(r)| \leqq q^{-1} \sum_l \sum_T \int \cdots \int \prod_{(ij)\subset T} |q\, f_{ij}|\, d^\nu x_3 \ldots d^\nu x_l\; z^l/(l-2)! \tag{17}$$

where the sum covers all trees with l vertices labelled 1, 2, . . . , l.

The summation can be simplified by Mayer's reduction method, in which z is replaced by a 'renormalized' fugacity, and the sum is reduced to a sum over irreducible graphs only. In the full Mayer theory this renormalized fugacity would be the density, which by (3) and (1) has the expansion

$$\rho = \sum_{l} \sum_{\Gamma} \int \cdots \int \prod_{(ij)\subset\Gamma} f_{ij}\, d^\nu \underline{x}_2 \ldots d^\nu \underline{x}_l \; z^l/(l-1)! \qquad (18)$$

where Γ denotes any connected labelled graph with l vertices. Here, however, only Cayley trees are included in the sum, and moreover f_{ij} must be replaced by $|q\, f_{ij}|$; consequently the appropriate renormalized fugacity is

$$w = \sum_{l=1}^{\infty} \sum_{T} \int \cdots \int \prod_{(ij)\subset T} |q\, f_{ij}|\, d^\nu \underline{x}_2 \ldots d^\nu \underline{x}_l \; z^l/(l-1)!$$

$$= \sum_{l=1}^{\infty} l^{l-2} (qB)^{l-1}\, z^l/(l-1)! \qquad (19)$$

This power series satisfies[7] the functional equation

$$w e^{-qBw} = z\,. \qquad (20)$$

Since the only irreducible trees are simple chains, Mayer's process reduces (17) to

$$\rho^2 |G(r)| \leqq q^{-1} \sum_{n=2}^{\infty} \int \cdots \int q^{n-1} f_{13} f_{34} \ldots f_{(n-1)n} f_{n2}\, d^\nu \underline{x}_3 \ldots d^\nu \underline{x}_n \; w^n$$

(21)

since there are just (n-2)! labelled chains with end vertices 1 and 2 and with n vertices in all. Evaluating the convolution integral by means of Fourier transforms we finally obtain[8] the upper bound on the pair correlation function:

$$\rho^2 |G(r)| \leqq w^2 \int \frac{\phi(\underline{k})}{1 - qw\phi(\underline{k})} \exp(2\pi i\, \underline{k}\cdot\underline{r})\, d^\nu \underline{k} \qquad (22)$$

where

$$\phi(k) \equiv \int f(r) \quad \exp(-2\pi i\, \underline{k} \cdot \underline{r}) d^{\nu} \underline{r} \,, \tag{23}$$

all integrals being ν -dimensional. A simple corollary of (22) is that, provided (15) is satisfied, G(r) tends to zero as $r \to \infty$, so that the usual criterion for a fluid phase is satisfied.[8)]

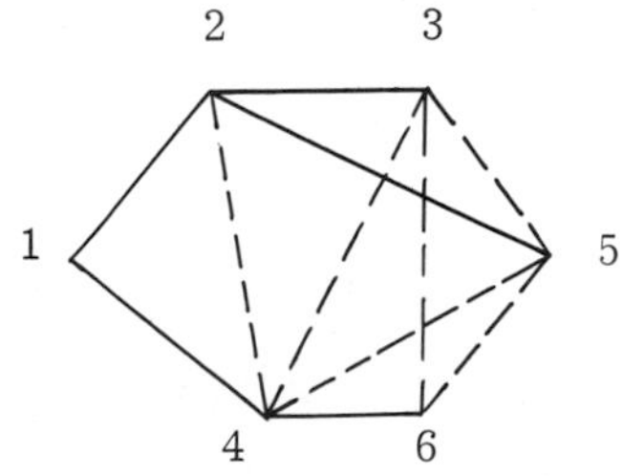

Fig. 1. The solid lines form a labelled Cayley tree T. The weights of the various vertices are $w_1 = 0$, $w_2 = w_4 = 1$, $w_3 = w_5 = w_6 = 2$. By adding bonds at any or all of the dotted lines, a new graph Γ is formed, whose reduced graph Γ'' is T (that is to say, Γ is in the set S(T)). The contribution of T to the sum (6) is a product of factors f_{ij} from the solid bonds and $1 + f_{ij}$ from the dotted bonds.

REFERENCES

1. J. Groeneveld, Phys. Letters 3, 50 (1962).

2. D. Ruelle, Ann. Phys. 29, 109 (1963).

3. O. Penrose, J. Math. Phys. 4, 1312 (1963).

4. G. E. Uhlenbeck and G. W. Ford, Studies in Statistical Mechanics, (North Holland, 1962) Vol. 1, p. 127.

5. D. Ruelle, Rev. Mod. Phys. 36, 580 (1964).

6. G. Stell, The Equilibrium Theory of Classical Fluids (ed. H. L. Frisch and J. L. Lebowitz), eqns 4-6 and 5-5.

7. G. Pólya and G. Szegö, Aufgaben und Lehrsätze aus der Analysis (Springer, Berlin, 1925), Vol. I, part III, Ch. 5, No. 209.

8. For non-negative potentials, this was proved by Groeneveld in 1963 (unpublished).

DISCUSSION

Lebowitz: Penrose and I have extended these results to the convergence of the virial expansion.

Mayer: I suppose the lower bound on the density is not the same as that obtained by taking the derivative of the lower bound of P/kT with respect to the logarithm of the fugacity?

Penrose: No, it is smaller. We were only able to show that the Mayer series $P/kT = \rho - \sum_K \frac{K}{K+1} \beta_K \rho^{K+1}$ converges if

$$|\rho| < \frac{0.28952}{(q+1)B}$$

Siegert: What fraction of the closest packing density does this correspond to in a hard sphere gas?

Penrose: About 1/14 of the closest packing in one dimension.

Brush: Does the virial expansion converge for higher densities than the fugacity expansion?

Penrose: Yes, that is correct, at least in some cases. For a hard sphere gas in one dimension you get

$$\frac{P}{KT} = \frac{\rho}{1-a\rho}$$

which converges all the way up to the point of closest packing corresponding to z = ∞, but the z series diverges for $|z| > \frac{1}{ae}$, owing to a singularity on the negative real axis in the complex z plane, as pointed out by Groeneveld.

RIGOROUS BOUNDS FOR THE EQUATION OF STATE AND PAIR CORRELATION FUNCTION OF CLASSICAL MANY-PARTICLE SYSTEMS

J. GROENEVELD
Instituut voor Theoretische Fysica, Universiteit van Amsterdam

ABSTRACT

The activity and density expansions of thermodynamic quantities, distribution functions and pair correlation function are studied from the point of view of obtaining "best possible" upper and lower bounds.

A general procedure is suggested for deriving such bounds. It is based on a simplification of the Mayer graphs and on a use of recurrence relations or integral equations. Two ways of simplifying graphs have proved useful:

I) For activity and density expansions: Removal of lines,
II) For density expansions: Removal of subgraphs.

It is found that, to several of the existing approximation methods, there can be constructed a "corresponding estimation method". By this is meant a set of bounds involving the same set of graphs as the approximation method.

A survey is given of the present state of the theory. New results to be presented comprise:

1. Bounds for the pair correlation function in terms of chain graphs; asymptotic behaviour.
2. Recent results from density expansions.

§ 1. INTRODUCTION

In this lecture I should like to discuss a group of rigorous results*) which have been obtained, in recent years, in connection with several well-known types of series expansion (the "Mayer expansions") of thermodynamic quantities and distribution functions of classical many-particle systems. These results refer to a grand canonical ensemble with parameters T (temperature) and z (activity)**) associated with a ν-dimensional system ($\nu = 1, 2, 3$) of identical, classical particles with mass m, without internal degrees of freedom. The centers $\vec{r}_1, \vec{r}_2 \ldots$ of the particles (assumed to be continuously variable) are confined to a ν-dimensional spatial region V. The potential energy is assumed to be equal to a sum of pair energies $\phi_{ij} = \phi(\vec{r}_i - \vec{r}_j)$***). Some further conditions on the potential will be introduced in § 4.1.

The Mayer f-function is defined by

$$f(\vec{r}) = e^{-\beta\phi(\vec{r})} - 1 \tag{1.1}$$

where $\beta = (k_B T)^{-1}$ and k_B is Boltzmann's constant.

The k-particle distribution function ($k = 1, 2, 3, \ldots$) is denoted by $n^{(k)}(\vec{r}_1, \ldots \vec{r}_k)$, the pair correlation function $G(\vec{r}_1, \vec{r}_2)$ is defined by the relation

$$n^{(2)}(\vec{r}_1, \vec{r}_2) = n^{(1)}(\vec{r}_1) \,.\, n^{(2)}(\vec{r}_2) \,.\, (1 + G(\vec{r}_1, \vec{r}_2)) \tag{1.2}$$

If there is translational symmetry (i.e. in the limit $V \to \infty$) then $n^{(1)}(\vec{r}_1)$ is equal to the particle number density n. Similarly, in this case, the function $G(\vec{r}_1, \vec{r}_2)$ depends only on $\vec{r}_1 - \vec{r}_2$ and is denoted by $G(\vec{r}_1 - \vec{r}_2)$.

---

*) Cf. Refs[1-10] and, this lecture, § 4.4.4, § 4.5.2 and § 5.

**) See, e.g., Hill[13], p.130; z is also called "the fugacity".

***) The results to be discussed in this lecture can all easily be extended to the case where there are external forces (in addition to those due to the walls) and to lattice systems. In these cases the conditions stated here should be relaxed accordingly (Cf., e.g., Penrose[4]).

The following three well-known types of series expansion[11-15] are considered:

A) Expansion of the grand canonical partition function $Z_{gr}(z, V)$ in powers of the activity z:

$$Z_{gr}(z, V) = \sum_{N=0}^{\infty} Q_N(V)\, z^N \qquad (1.3)$$

where $Q_N(V)$ is the "configurational partition function" *).

B) Expansion of the pressure p in powers of the activity z:

$$\beta p = \lim_{V \to \infty} \sum_{l=1}^{\infty} b_l(V)\, z^l \qquad (1.4)$$

where the $b_l(V)$ are Mayer's finite-volume cluster integrals.

It will be discussed unter what (sufficient) conditions the above relation (1.4) may be rewritten as

$$\beta p = \sum_{l=1}^{\infty} b_l\, z^l \qquad (1.5)$$

where

$$b_l = \lim_{V \to \infty} b_l(V)$$

C) Expansion of the pressure p in powers of the number density n (the "virial" expansion):

$$\beta p = n \left[1 - \sum_{k=1}^{\infty} \frac{k}{(k+1)} \beta_k\, n^k\right] \qquad (1.6)$$

where n is sufficiently small and the β_k's are Mayer's irreducible cluster integrals.

The result to be discussed fall into four categories.

(I) Convergence of series expansions: Upper and lower bounds on R (§ 4.3.1) and $\mathcal{R}$ (§ 4.4) which are the radii of convergence of the series (1.5) and (1.6) respectively.

---

*) The notation used here is that of Ref.[12], eq. (5.4a).

(II) "Thermodynamic limit": Results of this category are e.g. sufficient conditions (§ 4.3.1) that in (1.4) the limit and the summation may be interchanged so that (1.5) is valid. This will also yield lower bounds on z_t, where z_t is defined as the activity of the first phase transition of the system, or, if there is no transition, by: $z_t = \infty$.

Other results of this category are lower bounds (§ 4.4.3) on n_t, where n_t is defined as the gas phase density at the first transition point, or, if there is no transition, by: n_t = the maximum density of the system.

(III) Asymptotic behaviour of the pair correlation function $G(\vec{r})$ for $|\vec{r}| \to \infty$ (§ 5).

(IV) More general, upper and lower bounds for coefficients, thermodynamic quantities and distribution functions (§ 4 and § 5).

We shall first, in § 2, discuss the Mayer theory on which the present work is based, introduce the terminology to be used and, in § 2.3, give a motivation of the present kind of research. Then, in § 3, a brief summary will be given of the methods used. The main part of this lecture, § 4, consists of a survey of the present state of the theory, of the results obtained thus far and of some of the difficulties encountered. New results are stated, without proof, in § 4.4.4 and § 4.5.2. Finally, in § 5, some as yet unpublished results on the pair correlation function are presented.

§ 2. GRAPHICAL METHODS

Let us first recall here some very well-known facts and, at the same time, introduce the concepts and the terminology to be used later in this lecture.

§ 2.1 Mayer expansions

In the theory of the equation of state of classical many-particle systems we have at our disposal a beautiful and rigorous theory, due to Ursell, Mayer and others[11-17] which, in principle, could provide us with all information concerning the system in equilibrium which we might want to obtain. This "Mayer theory" is essentially a prescription for calculating each coefficient in any of the three types of power series expansion A, B and C of § 1. Each coefficient is given as a finite sum of terms, each of which is an integral, with respect to a set of coordinates, of a product of Mayer f-functions. To each of these integrals there is associated a particular kind of linear graph*), called "the corresponding (Mayer) graph" which completely characterizes the product of f-functions and hence also the integral.**) In general, an integral with respect to a set of coordinates of a product of functions (which need not be f-functions) will be called here a "configurational integral".

The configurational integral which, in a series expansion, corresponds to a certain graph is also called "the contribution of the graph in the given series expansion".

With this latter concept one also naturally arrives at the concept of "a graphical series expansion", as opposed to that of a power series expansion, of a certain quantity. By a graphical series expansion is understood here a series expansion, each term of which is the contribution of a single graph. If this series converges, the quantity which is expanded is equal to "the sum (taken in a well-defined order***)) of the contributions of all graphs of a certain, well-defined set of graphs."****)

---

*) See e.g. Ref.[15] p. 123.

**) We shall always consider "labelled" (see Ref.[15] p. 125) graphs only: This has the advantage that there exists a one-to-one relation between graphs and the products of f-functions that occur in these expansions.

***) The order of the summation is important if, as is often the case, a graphical expansion converges only conditionally, but not absolutely.

****) See e.g. Ref.[17].

The "connectivity, $\varkappa$"*) of a graph is the minimum number of points whose omission, together with the lines incident upon them, would make the graph disconnected. Connected graphs are characterized by: $\varkappa \geqq 1$, biconnected graphs[x)] by: $\varkappa \geqq 2$ and triply connected graphs[+)] by: $\varkappa \geqq 3$.

Graphical expansions may be classified according to the minimum connectivity of the graphs that occur in it. By lack of a better word, we shall call this number here "the degree, d" of the graphical expansion (Cf. Table I).

At present at least four different types of graphical expansion are in use: These are expansions of degrees 0, 1, 2 and 3. The first three of these are closely related to the three types of (power series) expansion A, B and C respectively, of § 1. Expansions of degree 3 will not be considered here.

The following notation will be useful: The set of all graphs which occur in the graphical expansion of degree d of a given quantity (e. g. thermodynamical quantity or a distribution function) will be denoted by the symbol Γ_d.

If G and H are linear graphs such that either H = G or H can be obtained from G by omitting from G some of its lines, then H will be called here**) "simpler than G".

The subset of Γ_d consisting of all graphs which are "simplest" within the set Γ_d is denoted by Σ_d.

According to this definition, Σ_o is the set of all graphs without lines, and Σ_1 is the set of all Cayley trees.***) Two examples of graphs of the set Σ_2 are given in Fig. II.

---

*) This definition differs slightly (only for "complete graphs") from the one given by Uhlenbeck (Ref.[18] p. 24) and Berge (Ref.[19] p. 203), but is in accordance with the one used by Friedman (Ref.[14], pp. 46-48). It is used here since it leads, in the present context, to simpler results.

x) Also called "irreducible graphs"[11-14] and "stars"[15, 18, 20, 21].

+) Also called "basic graphs"[22, 25], "prototype graphs"[23] and "wider sense irreducible graphs"[24]. See also Ref.[17], p. 221.

**) The more usual name for this relation is "H is a partial graph of G" (see Ref.[19], p. 6).

***) See e. g. Ref.[19] p. 152, Ref.[18] p. S 18 or Ref.[15] p. 124.

A list of these four types of graphical expansion is given in Table I, stating, as far as is relevant here, the degree d, the sets Γ_d and Σ_d, the expansion parameter and the related theory.

Table I. Four types of graphical expansion*)

Degree d	Γ_d	Σ_d	Expansion in terms of	Related theory
0	The set of all graphs	The set of all graphs without lines	$z, f(\vec{r})$	
1	The set of all connected graphs	The set of all Cayley trees	$z, f(\vec{r})$	First Mayer theorem**)
2	The set of all biconnected graphs		$n, f(\vec{r})$	Second Mayer theorem***)
3	The set of all triply connected graphs			"HNC-theory"+)

*) The symbols d, Γ_d and Σ_d have been defined in the text of § 2.1.

**) See e.g. Refs[18, 20, 21].

+) See, for further references, e.g. Refs[17, 25].

§ 2.2 Approximation methods

Unfortunately, and this is also very well-known, the actual evaluation and summation of all terms in any of the graphical expansions considered here, is in general not possible.

Many of the approximation methods that have been developed in order to meet this difficulty are of a special type: They can be regarded as procedures which consist in taking into account, in a graphical expansion of degree d, only the contributions of those graphs which belong to a certain subset Λ of the set Γ_d of all graphs of the expansion. All other terms, i.e. those corresponding to the graphs of the set $\Gamma_d \setminus \Lambda$, are neglected.

An approximation method of this type is fully characterized by the pair (d, Λ). The graphs of the set Λ will be called the "<u>integrable</u>" graphs of the approximation method.

For later reference a few examples have been listed in Table II.

Degree d	Set of integrable graphs, Λ	Approximation method
0	Σ_o	The "ideal gas law approximation"
1	Σ_1	The "Cayley tree approximation"
2	Λ_{Ch} Λ_{PY} Λ_{HNC}	The chain approximation[16)] The Percus-Yevick approximation[26)] The hypernetted chain approximation[**)]

*) The symbols d, Λ, Σ_o and Σ_1 have been defined in the text of § 2.1 and § 2.2; Λ_{Ch} is the set of all chain graphs (an example of a chain graph is graph H of Fig. II); Λ_{PY} and Λ_{HNC} are the sets of PY-graphs and HNC-graphs respectively (see e.g. Refs[17, 25)]).

**) See e.g. Refs[17, 22, 25, 27)].

§ 2.3 Estimation methods

We may now recall*) the comparatively great success of some of these approximation methods: In the first place of the PY-approximation and, perhaps to a less extent, of the HNC-approximation.

The origin of this success however is not very well understood**). Also lacking is some a-priori knowledge of how good these methods are and which, in given circumstances, is best.

One way to improve this situation would be to try to find rigorous and preferably narrow bounds for the error which is involved in these approximation methods.

An alternative approach which turns out to be an easier one and which is adopted here, is to try to construct an exact theory which is as close as possible to one of the more successful approximation methods. Such a theory should consist of a set of rigorous bounds (for thermodynamic quantities, distribution functions, etc.), which bounds should have the same mathematical character, as the approximation method considered. By this we mean that these bounds and the approximate expressions should be expressible in terms of the graphs of the same set Λ.

In this way one arrives at the following program: To construct, to each of the existing approximation methods characterized by a pair (d, Λ), a "corresponding estimation method", which is a set of bounds in terms of graphs of the set Λ. The only difference between the two, i.e. between the approximation method and a corresponding estimation method, would lie in the counting factors which are associated with each graph of the set Λ. (See e.g. § 5.2, Remark (b)). It will turn out that, in order to construct an estimation method with a given set Λ, the counting factors can be chosen in many different ways.

---

*) See, e.g. Ref. [17] p. 264 and Ref. [27].

**) Mention should be made here however of Percus' method[28]. See also Ref. [17] Ch. 12 and Ref. [29].

One might have the hope that in an ideal case, i.e. if these counting factors would have been chosen in "a best possible manner", the resulting estimation method would have a precision and a region of validity which are comparable to those of the corresponding approximation method.

For this reason the most interesting part of the above described program would be, in view of the success of the PY- and HNC-approximation methods mentioned above, to construct "best possible" PY- and HNC-estimation methods.

These however are problems which appear to be too difficult to start with. It seems necessary first to construct "corresponding estimation methods" in simpler cases. One may hope in this way gradually to acquire the skill and to develop the methods which are needed to solve also these more difficult and more important problems.

The investigations to be discussed here (in § 4) may be regarded as various attempts to construct, in several successively more complicated cases of approximation methods, a "best possible corresponding estimation method".

§ 3. GENERAL PROCEDURE

§ 3.1 Introduction

We give a brief outline of the "general procedure" according to which the estimation methods, to be discussed in § 4, have been (or can be) constructed. This outline must be very schematic. For more details in an important case (that of the "Cayley tree estimation method" to be discussed here in § 4.3.1) we can refer to Dr. Penrose's lecture. Furthermore we refer to the original papers [1-10] and to a forthcoming publication[30].

This "general procedure" consists of the combined application of two "techniques", which we shall discuss now one after the other.

§ 3.2 First technique: f-h-expansions

In addition to the usual graphical expansions in terms of the f-functions only (the "Mayer expansions") one also considers various other ways of expanding the same quantity. In these new kinds of expansion (called "f-h-expansions" here)*), two kinds of function occur: f- and h-functions, where the latter function is defined by:

$$h(\vec{r}_i - \vec{r}_j) = 1 + f(\vec{r}_i - \vec{r}_j) = e^{-\beta\phi(\vec{r}_i - \vec{r}_j)} \quad (3.1)$$

Each term is an integral of a product of f- and h-functions to which there is associated, as usual, a linear graph. Such a graph may contain lines of two kinds, called "f-" and "h-lines".

The purpose of considering these f-h-expansions is to combine as much as possible, in the Mayer expansion, groups of terms which are expected to cancel one another to a large extent.

§ 3.3 Second technique: Simplification of graphs and configurational integrals

Suppose that we are given an f-h-expansion of a certain quantity. What is next to be decided is what kind of graphs one is willing and is able to evaluate rigorously. Let Λ be the set of these graphs. (In most cases this will be "the set of integrable graphs" of some useful approximation method, e. g. one of those listed in Table II).

Then one has to specify, for each "non-integrable" graph G occurring in thc f-h-expansion, a graph H which is "simpler" than G (Cf § 2.1) and which is also "integrable" (i. e. $H \in \Lambda$).

By this coice of H, the (f- and h-) lines of G are again divided into two kinds of lines, into "I-lines" and "E-lines" (referring to "Integration" and "Estimation" respectively). The I-lines of G are also lines of H, the E-lines are all other lines of G. (An example for the case $\Lambda = \Sigma_1$ is given in Fig. I). In this way we

---

*) As far as this "first technique" is concerned, there is a close connection with the method of Ree and Hoover[31].

come to the situation that any graph G which occurs in an f-h-expansion may contain four kinds of lines: f_I-, f_E-, h_I- and h_E-lines.

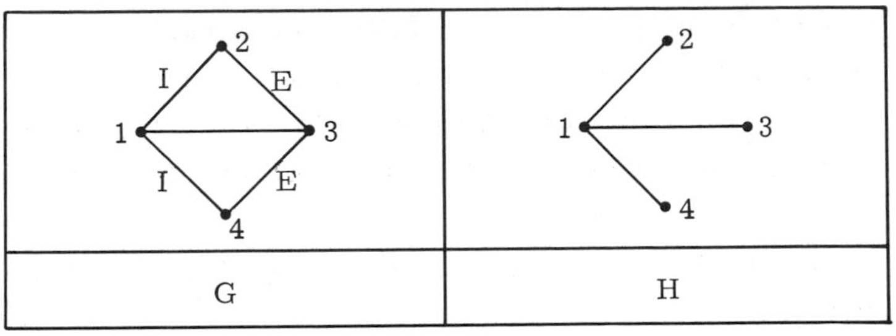

Fig. 1. Simplification of graphs, first method (§ 3).
In this example, Λ is chosen to be equal to Σ_1, the set of Cayley trees. The "non-integrable" graph G ($G \notin \Lambda$) is simplified, by omitting its E-lines. to a Cayley tree H.

Next, the configurational integral corresponding to the "non-integrable" graph G is "simplified" in the following way: The factors in the integrand which correspond to the E-lines of G are replaced by suitably chosen constants and brought before the integral sign. The remaining integrand is separated into a positive and a negative part. Then, using the mean-value theorem of integral calculus, one obtains a rigorous upper and lower bound for the difficult integral considered. Both of these bounds are given as a sum of a finite number of terms, each of which corresponds to the "integrable" graph H. Therefore, these bounds can be calculated in actuality.

Finally one has to sum over all terms in the expansion. It then very much depends on the skill or good luck with which the "two techniques" have been applied, whether the upper and lower bounds thus obtained converge or not and, if they converge, whether it is feasible to calculate these bounds.

§ 4. PRESENT STATE OF THEORY

§ 4.1 Introduction

We shall discuss here one by one the several cases in which our present program. (Cf. § 2.3) of constructing "corresponding estimation methods" has been carried out.

Throughout the remaining part of this lecture we shall make the following assumptions (a) and (b) concerning the pair potential $\phi(\vec{r})$:

(a) The Mayer f-function, defined by (1.1), is absolutely integrable:

$$\int |f(\vec{r})| \, d\vec{r} = B < \infty \tag{4.1}$$

(b) The pair potential $\phi(\vec{r})$ belongs to at least one of the following three classes $\mathcal{N}$, $\mathcal{H}$ and $\mathcal{S}$:

Class $\mathcal{N}$ (nonnegative potentials):

$$\phi(\vec{r}) \geqq 0 \qquad \text{for all } \vec{r}.$$

Class $\mathcal{H}$ *) (hard core potentials): For some $a \geqq 0$, $E \geqq 0$,

$$\left.\begin{array}{l} 1^{o})\ \phi(\vec{r}) = \infty \quad \text{if } |\vec{r}| < a. \\ 2^{o}\ \text{For all } N\ (N = 2, 3, \ldots) \text{ and all } r_1, \ldots r_N, r, \\ \text{if: } |\vec{r}_i - \vec{r}_j| \geqq a \quad (\text{for all } i, j;\ 1 \leqq i < j \leqq N) \\ \text{then } \sum_{i=1}^{N} \phi(\vec{r} - \vec{r}_i) \geqq -E \end{array}\right\} \tag{4.2}$$

It should be noted that (notwithstanding its name) the class $\mathcal{H}$ also includes all nonnegative potentials (which, of course, need not have a hard core). This follows from (4.2) by choosing a = E = 0.

---

*) See Ref. [2]. This class of potentials is very similar to the one considered by Van Hove[32]. A slightly different definition is used by Penrose[4].

<u>Class $\mathcal{S}$</u> (stable potentials)[3,4,33]: There exists a constant $\phi \geqq 0$ such that

$$\left.\begin{array}{l} \sum\limits_{1 \leqq i < j \leqq N} \phi(\vec{r}_i - \vec{r}_j) \geqq -N\phi \\ \text{for all } N \ (N = 2, 3, \ldots) \text{ and all } \vec{r}_1, \ldots, \vec{r}_N. \end{array}\right\} \qquad (4.3)$$

As remarked above, $\mathcal{N}$ is a subclass of $\mathcal{H}$. It is also easy to see[4)] that $\mathcal{H}$ is a subclass of $\mathcal{S}$, so that $\mathcal{S}$ is the most general of the three classes of potentials to be considered here. For stable potentials satisfying (4.3) we shall use the notation

$$u = e^{2\beta\phi} \qquad (4.4)$$

§ 4.2 Expansions of degree 0

4.2.1 Ideal gas law estimation ($d = 0$, $\Lambda = \Sigma_0$)[2,7)]

This is the simplest case of an estimation method*). It arises if d is lowest, i.e. if $d = 0$, and if Λ is chosen to be the smallest subset of Γ_0 that can be chosen, i.e. if $\Lambda = \Sigma_0$. The only graphs which are "integrable" here are the graphs without lines.
The corresponding approximation method is the ideal gas law, where all interactions between the particles are neglected.

A characteristic result obtained in this case is the following:

<u>Theorem</u>[7)]. For stable potentials, the pressure p, regarded as a function p(z) of the activity z, satisfies for all $z_1 \geqq 0$, $z_2 \geqq 0$ the inequality:

$$p(z_1 + z_2) \leqq p(z_1) + p(z_2 \cdot u) \qquad (4.5)$$

---

*) A more complete discussion of this case is given in Ref.[10)].

This result is very general: The equality (4.5) holds for a wide class of potentials and in the entire "physical region" $0 \leqq z < \infty$.

On the other hand, it is a very weak result, as already can be expected from the fact that the inequality (4.5) depends only very weakly on the form of the potential (i.e. only through the parameter u).

4.2.2 "More complicated" estimation methods ($d = 0, \Lambda \supset \Sigma_o$, Lieb's inequalities[1])

If $d = 0$ as in the previous case (§ 4.2.1) but Λ is chosen to be a larger set of graphs (i.e. a larger subset of Γ_o, containing also "more complicated" graphs) then one arrives, for several such choices, at some of Lieb's inequalities[1]. Conversely, as is not difficult to show, each of Lieb's inequalities corresponds to choosing, as a "set of integrable graphs", a particular subset of Γ_o.

Several of these inequalities have an infinite region of validity, i.e. they hold for $0 \leqq z < \infty$, as the inequalities of § 4.2.1. However, they depend more sensitively on the form of the potential and often they are more precise.

It should be mentioned that these inequalities, which originally were derived for nonnegative potentials only, have since then been generalized by Penrose[5] to hard core potentials. A further generalization to the class of stable potentials is not known however.

§ 4.3 Expansions of degree 1 (z-expansions in terms of connected graphs)

4.3.1 Cayley tree estimation for expansions of degree 1 ($d = 1, \Lambda = \Sigma_1$[2, 3, 4])

We now come to a discussion of estimation methods for graphical expansions of degree 1 (z-expansions in terms of connected graphs). The simplest of these methods is the "Cayley tree estimation method", which already has been discussed at this conference in some detail by Dr. Penrose. This estimation method arises if $d = 1$ and if Λ is chosen to be the smallest subset of Γ_1 that can be chosen for Λ, i.e. if $\Lambda = \Sigma_1$ (the set of Cayley trees).

This estimation method has led to the following three groups of results, (a), (b) and (c):

(a) The most important result is a proof[3, 4], for the class $\mathcal{S}$ of stable potentials, that the series in (1.4) converges uniformly in V for all values of z in the interval:

$$0 \leqq z < (e\,u\,B)^{-1} \tag{4.6}$$

This implies that the pressure is, for all z in (4.6), given by

$$\beta p = \sum_{l=1}^{\infty} b_l \cdot z^l \tag{4.7}$$

For future reference we also state two immediate corollaries of this result:

In the first place, a lower bound for R, the radius of convergence of the series in (4.7), is given by:

$$R \geqq (e\,u\,B)^{-1} \tag{4.8}$$

Secondly, (4.7) and (4.8) imply that p(z) is an analytic function of z in the interval (4.6) so that[34] there is no phase transition in this interval. Stated otherwise:

$$z_t \geqq (e\,u\,B)^{-1} \tag{4.9}$$

(b) Also of interest (since they constitute the basis of the above results (a)) are the bounds[4, 3] obtained for the coefficients b_l, $b_l(V)$, etc., for thermodynamic functions and for the distribution functions $n^{(k)}(1, \ldots, k)$ $(k = 1, 2, \ldots)$.

Of interest for another reason are the bounds*) obtained for the pair correlation function G(r) and for several related functions. These bounds have the useful property of approaching to zero for $|\vec{r}| \to \infty$, which makes it possible to study the asymptotic behaviour of the $G(\vec{r})$-function for large $|\vec{r}|$.

A limitation of all these results is that z is restricted to the rather small z-region given by (4. 6).

(c) For nonnegative potentials several results have been obtained[2], of which it is not yet known whether they can be generalized to larger classes of potentials. Of these results the following two are relevant to our subsequent discussion:

(c_1) $R \leqq B^{-1}$ **) (4.10)

(c_2) The analytic function p(z), defined by (4. 7) has a singularity at z = -R.

The first of these, (c_1), tells us that the series expansion (4. 7) for p already diverges for rather small values of z (viz. for z > R, where R satisfies $(e\,B)^{-1} \leqq R \leqq B^{-1}$). For hard spheres one can show***) that the activity z = R above which this occurs corresponds to a density between 4, 5 % and 16, 9 % of the density of closest face-centered cubic packing, i. e. to a rather low density.

The second result, (c_2), states that this divergence is caused by a singularity of p(z) near to the origin on the negative real z-axis, i. e. in a "non-physical" region.

---

*) See Refs[8, 30]. Some of these latter results are stated in § 5.

**) For other upper bounds, see Ref.[4].

***) Using the inequalities $n \leqq z$[1, 2] and $n \geqq z \cdot (1 + zB)^{-1}$[1].

4.3.2 More complicated estimation methods for expansions of degree 1 ($d = 1, \Lambda \supset \Sigma_1$)

For completeness' sake we also mention the existence (thus far only for nonnegative potentials) of four other, "more complicated" estimation methods for expansions of degree 1[35]. These methods arise by choosing for Λ four successively larger sets of connected graphs (i.e. subsets of Γ_1).

In each of these four cases a set of integral equations is obtained for the upper and lower bounds. In the first and second case these equations can be solved and explicit expressions for the bounds are obtained.

Somewhat paradoxically however, these bounds are only more precise than those of the Cayley tree estimation in a region of very low activities. Also, these bounds have a smaller region of convergence.*)

We have not tried to continue this line of research much further, partly for reasons to be discussed in the next two subsections § 4.3.3 and § 4.4.1.

4.3.3 Discussion

It seems likely that any bound, derived from a z-expansion (of degree 1), by estimating each term separately, already diverges for rather small values of z. For this we have the following argument:

It may be surmised that R is rather small, not only for nonnegative potentials (Cf. § 4.3.1, (c_1)), but also in general.

Also it seems plausible to assume[30] that any bound of this type has a radius of convergence R' which is at most equal to R:

$$R' \leqq R$$

*) A very recent further development in this field is due to F. H. Ree[36].

Therefore, if R would be small, so would be any R' and the bound already would diverge for small values of z.

§ 4.4 Expansions of degree 2 (n-expansions in terms of irreducible graphs)

4.4.1 Introduction

We now turn to a consideration of graphical expansions in terms of irreducible graphs. It may be expected that these expansions are much better suited to our present purpose of deriving bounds, than are the z-expansions considered in the preceding subsection § 4.3, for the following reason:

Numerical results on virial coefficients[31)] indicate that $\mathfrak{R}$, the radius of convergence of the virial expansion (1.4), might very well be large. (A suggestive example in this respect is the 1-dimensional system of hard rods, where the virial series (1.4) converges up to the maximum density of the system.)

If $\mathfrak{R}$ would be large also in general, then one might hope to be able to derive, from n-expansions, bounds which remain convergent (and valid) up to considerably high densities.

4.4.2 A difficulty

If one tries to apply the general procedure of § 3 to n-expansions a difficulty arises which can only briefly be indicated here. It is related to the fact that Σ_2, the set of "simplest" biconnected graphs, contains many graphs corresponding to integrals which are very difficult to evaluate. In other words, Σ_2 is not (a subset of) the "set of integrable graphs" of an existing approximation method.

(An example is given by the graph G of Fig. II. This graph belongs to the set Σ_2 but it is not a HNC-graph so that, in a sense, it is "non-integrable". Examples of other, arbitrarily more complicated graphs of Σ_2 can also be given.)

Two ways out of this difficulty have been found practicable. One of these will be discussed in § 4.5. The other consists in choosing Λ not as a subset of Γ_2, i.e. such that

$$\Sigma_2 \subset \Lambda \subset \Gamma_2$$

but as a subset of Γ_1, i.e. such that

$$\Sigma_1 \subset \Lambda \subset \Gamma_1$$

Such a procedure can be shown to introduce an extra large "error" into the bounds. It is very well possible that, in this way, part of the advantage (Cf. § 4.4.1) of n-expansions over z-expansions (of degree 1) might disappear.

Thus far this procedure has only been tried, (with some success) in the case $\Lambda = \Sigma_1$. This case will be considered in § 4.4.4.

4.4.3 Results from indirect methods

We first mention two results concerning n-expansions which have been reached by what may be called here "indirect methods". These results are based almost entirely on the inequalities for the b_l's and the $b_l(V)$'s obtained previously by means of the Cayley tree estimation method for z-expansions, discussed in § 4.3.1.

a) "Convergence"

By a method of contour integration, Lebowitz and Penrose derived[9], from the inequalities for the b_l's referred to in § 4.3.1, the following inequality:

For stable potentials

$$\mathfrak{R} \geqq \frac{0.14476}{B} \cdot \frac{2}{(1+u)} \qquad (4.11)$$

b) "Thermodynamic limit"

These same authors also proved[9]:
For stable potentials

$$n_t \geqq \frac{0.14476}{B} \cdot \frac{2}{(1+u)} \tag{4.12}$$

For hard core potentials a stronger result has been reached[9] which, for simplicity, is reproduced here only for the case of nonnegative potentials:

For nonnegative potentials,

$$n_t \geqq \frac{1}{(1+e)B} = \frac{0.26894}{B} \tag{4.13}$$

4.4.4 Cayley tree estimation method for expansions of degree 2 ($d = 2$, $\Lambda = \Sigma_1$)

By a direct analysis of the irreducible graphs occurring in the cirial expansion (1.6), according to the "general procedure" of § 3 (choosing $\Lambda = \Sigma_1$), one can prove[30)*)]:

Theorem. For nonnegative potentials

$$|\beta_k| \leqq \frac{B^k}{2k} \cdot \frac{1}{(2\pi i)} \oint_{0^+} \frac{d\xi}{\xi^k} \cdot (2e^{\xi} - 1)^{k-1} \qquad (k = 2, 3, \ldots) \tag{4.14}$$

Corollaries.

From (4.14) the following simpler, but weaker, inequalities can be derived:

$$|\beta_k| \leqq \frac{(2B)^k}{4} \cdot \frac{(k-1)^{k-1}}{k!} \qquad (k = 2, 3, \ldots) \tag{4.15}$$

---

*) Use is made here of a modified form[30] of Kirkwood's integral equations[13].

and

$$|\beta_k| \leqq \frac{1}{2k} \cdot \frac{B^k}{c^{k-1}} \tag{4.16}$$

where c = 0.23197 is the smallest positive root of:

$$c \cdot e^{-c} = (2e)^{-1}$$

From (4.16) follows:

$$\mathcal{R} \geqq \frac{0.23197}{B} \tag{4.17}$$

4.4.5 Discussion

For nonnegative potentials (in which case u = 1) the result (4.17) compares favourably with the result (4.11) of the indirect method. However, a considerable further progress may even be expected to be possible along these lines. This optimism is based on the assumption that $\mathcal{R}$ itself is large (Cf. § 4.4.1) and on the circumstance that the estimation method, used in § 4.4.4 in order to derive (4.17), is not very efficient (Cf. § 4.4.2).

§ 4.5 An extension of the general procedure of § 3

4.5.1 Introduction

Very recently a second way out of the difficulty mentioned in § 4.4.2 has been found practicable[30]. It consists in an extension of the general procedure of § 3, in particular of the "second technique" of § 3.3: According to this new method a graph of the set Γ_2 can be "simplified" (and made "integrable") not only by omitting lines but also by omitting larger subgraphs (containing also points), provided that also the remaining graph belongs to the set Γ_2 (i.e. is irreducible). An example is given in Fig. II.

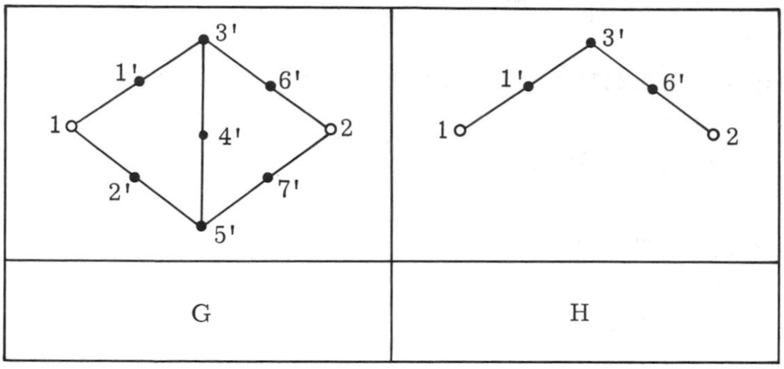

Fig. II. Simplification of graphs, second method (§4. 5).
In this example, Λ is chosen to be equal to Λ_{Ch}, the set of chain graphs. The "non-integrable" graph G ($G \notin \Lambda$) is simplified, by omitting lines and points, to a chain graph H.

The graphs G and H both occur in the n-expansion of the pair correlation function $G(\vec{r}_1, \vec{r}_2)$. These graphs also belong to the set Σ_2 (Cf §2.1 and §4.4.2). The points 1 and 2 are the reference points (see e.g. Ref. [22]), (also called "vertex points"[16]) and "white circles" [37,17]) of the graphs G and H.

This new method seems to open many new perspectives which for the largest part still have to be explored. Only a few definite results have been obtained thus far, which however are felt still to be incomplete. *) One such result is the following:

4.5.2 Chain estimation method ($\Lambda = \Lambda_{Ch}$)

Theorem[30]. For nonnegative potentials, if there is no phase transition in the interval:

$$0 \leqq n < \frac{1}{2B} \tag{4.18}$$

*) See the remark (b) in § 4.5.2.

then, for all such values of n and for all $\vec{r}$:

$$G^-(\vec{r}) \leqq G(\vec{r}) \leqq G^+(\vec{r}) \tag{4.19}$$

where the functions $G^{\pm}(\vec{r})$ are defined by:

$$G^+(\vec{r}) = f(\vec{r}) \cdot \left\{ \frac{1}{(1-A)} + \frac{1}{A} \log \frac{1}{1+A(\exp \frac{A}{1-A} - 1)} \right\}$$

$$+ \frac{1}{A} \log \frac{1}{(1-A)} \cdot \sum_{k=1}^{\infty} f^{[2k]}(\vec{r}) \cdot \frac{n^{2k-1}}{(1-A)^{2k-1}}$$

and (4.20)*)

$$G^-(\vec{r}) = \frac{1}{A} \log \frac{1}{(1-A)} \cdot \sum_{k=o}^{\infty} f^{[2k+1]}(\vec{r}) \cdot \frac{n^{2k}}{(1-A)^{2k}}$$

where

$$A - nB$$

Remarks

a) The method also yields (less precise) bounds for the pair correlation function and for thermodynamic quantities in the (larger) interval:

$$0 \leqq n < \frac{1}{B} \tag{4.21}$$

b) Still lacking in the above results is a proof that there is no phase transition in the region (4.21), i.e. that

$$n_t \geqq \frac{1}{B} \tag{4.22}$$

If such a proof can be given (and it is expected to be possible) then the result (4.22) would constitute an improvement, by a factor (1 + e), of the previous result (4.13) of § 4.4.3.

---

*) The functions $f^{[k]}(\vec{r})$ are defined in § 5.1.

4.5.3 More complicated estimation methods ($\Lambda \supset \Lambda_{Ch}$)

The next problem to be considered is the construction of a PY- and HNC-estimation, i.e. of bounds in terms of PY- and HNC-graphs respectively. The construction of such bounds now seems to be well within reach of the present methods[30].

As remarked above (in § 2.3) one may hope that such bounds will have a precision and a region of validity comparable to those of the corresponding approximations. But perhaps this is expecting too much of these methods.

§ 4.6 Conclusion

The most serious limitations of the estimation methods constructed thus far (and discussed here) are the following: In the case d = 0 (§ 4.2) the bounds obtained are rather wide. On the other hand, in the case d = 1 (§ 4.3) and d = 2 (§ 4.4 and § 4.5), the regions where the bounds are valid (and non-trivial) are always rather small. To illustrate this we may compare, for the system of hard spheres, the density

$$n = \frac{1}{B}$$

which is probably the maximum density within reach of the estimation methods discussed here (Cf. §4.5.2), to the density of closest face-centered cubic packing:

$$n = \frac{5.924}{B}$$

which is (presumably) the maximum density of the system.

In table III we have listed the estimation methods discussed here, together with the kinds of result to which they have led.

Notes for table III

*) The sumbols d, Λ , Γ_d, Σ_d and Λ_{Ch} are defined in § 2.

**) The classes of potentials $\mathcal{S}$, $\mathcal{H}$ and $\mathcal{N}$ are defined in § 4.1.

+) The Roman numerals I-IV refer to the four types of result mentioned in § 1. The quantities R and z_t are defined in § 1, and B by eq. (4.1).

++) The quantities u and B are defined by eqs. (4.4) and (4.1) respectively; R is defined in § 1.

') Cf. § 4.3.3.

***) A more general result, for the class $\mathcal{H}$, is not stated here (Cf. § 4.4.2).

Table III. Present state of the theory.

1st Method (§ 3): Simplification by omission of lines.

degree d*)	set of "integrable" graphs*) Λ	Corresponding approximation method	Class of potentials**)	Type of results+)	Region of validity of bounds++)	Reference
d = 0	Σ_o	Ideal gas law	$\mathcal{S}$	IV	$0 \leqq z < \infty$	§ 4.2.1
	Several larger subsets of Γ_o		$\mathcal{H}$	IV (Lieb's inequalities)	Sometimes: $0 \leqq z < \infty$, sometimes: finite	§ 4.2.2
d = 1	Σ_1	Cayley tree approximation	$\mathcal{S}$	I, II, III, IV	$0 \leqq z < (euB)^{-1}$	§ 4.3.1
			$\mathcal{N}$	$R \leqq B^{-1}$; A singular point at $z=-R$		
	Several larger subsets of Γ_1		$\mathcal{N}$	Incomplete results	$0 \leqq z < R'$ where, very probably '), $R' \leqq R$	§ 4.3.2
d = 2	(Indirect methods)		$\mathcal{S}$	I, II, IV	$0 \leqq n < \frac{0.1448}{B} \cdot \frac{2}{(1+u)}$	§ 4.4.2
			$\mathcal{N}$ ***)	II, IV	$0 \leqq n < \frac{0.2689}{B}$	
	Σ_1		$\mathcal{N}$	I, IV	$0 \leqq n < \frac{0.2316}{B}$	§ 4.4.3

2nd Method (§ 4.5): Simplification by omission of subgraphs.

d = 2	Λ_{Ch}	Chain approximation	$\mathcal{N}$	Incomplete results	$0 \leqq n < \frac{1}{B}$	§ 4.5.2

APPENDIX

§ 5. BOUNDS ON CORRELATION FUNCTIONS

In this section some results are presented concerning the pair correlation function $G(\vec{r})$ and some related functions. These results consist of bounds in terms of chain graphs; they belong to the group of results discussed in § 4.3.1.

§ 5.1 Definitions and notations

The functions $S(\vec{r})$ and $C(\vec{r})$ are defined, in terms of the $G(\vec{r})$-function, by the relations:

$$1 + G(\vec{r}) = (1 + f(\vec{r})) \cdot e^{S(\vec{r})} \qquad (5.1)$$

and

$$C(\vec{r}) = (\tfrac{n}{z})^2 \cdot G(\vec{r}) \qquad (5.2)$$

The function $\underline{C}(\vec{r})$*) is defined by:

$$C(\vec{r}) = (1 + f(\vec{r}))\, \underline{C}(\vec{r}) + (\tfrac{n}{z})^2 f(\vec{r}) \qquad (5.3)$$

It follows from (5.1) - (5.3) that:

$$\underline{C}(\vec{r}) = (\tfrac{n}{z})^2 \cdot (e^{S(\vec{r})} - 1) \qquad (5.4)$$

The functions $f^{[j]}(\vec{r})$ $(j = 1, 2, \ldots)$ are defined, in terms of the function $f(\vec{r})$, by

$$f^{[1]}(\vec{r}) = f(\vec{r})$$

$$f^{[j+1]}(\vec{r}) = \int d\vec{r}'\, f^{[j]}(\vec{r}')\, f(\vec{r} - \vec{r}') \qquad (j = 1, 2, \ldots) \qquad \text{(xx}$$

The functions $\dot{f}^{[j]}(\vec{r})$ $(j = 1, 2, \ldots)$ are defined similarly in terms of $\dot{f}(\vec{r})$, where the latter function is defined by

*) The bar here should indicate that none of the graphs contributing to $\underline{C}(\vec{r})$ has a direct f-bond between the two reference points.

$$\dot{f}(\vec{r}) = |f(\vec{r})|$$

The ν-dimensional Fourier transform $\tilde{F}(\vec{k})$ of a function $F(\vec{r})$ is defined by:

$$\tilde{F}(\vec{k}) = \int F(r)\, e^{-i\vec{k}\,\vec{r}}\, d\vec{r}$$

The function $H(x)$ is defined, for $|x| < e^{-1}$, by:

$$H(x) = \sum_{l=0}^{\infty} \frac{(l+1)^{l-1}}{l!} x^{l} \qquad (5.5)$$

Abbreviation to be used are:

$$v = z\,\tilde{f}(\vec{0}) \qquad \dot{v} = z\,\tilde{\dot{f}}(\vec{0})$$

$$\lambda = \tilde{f}(\vec{k})/\tilde{f}(\vec{0}) \qquad \dot{\lambda} = \tilde{\dot{f}}(\vec{k})/\tilde{\dot{f}}(\vec{0}) \qquad (5.6)$$

$$H = H(uv) \qquad \dot{H} = H(u\dot{v})$$

§ 5.2 Bounds on $C(\vec{r})$*)

Theorem[30)**)]. If $0 \leqq z < (euB)^{-1}$, then the function $\underline{C}(\vec{r})$ and its partial derivatives with respect to z (at constant $\vec{r}$ and $\beta = (k_B T)^{-1}$) satisfy the inequalities

$$\left(\frac{\partial}{\partial z}\right)^m \underline{C}^-(\vec{r}) \leqq \left(\frac{\partial}{\partial z}\right)^m \underline{C}(\vec{r}) \leqq \left(\frac{\partial}{\partial z}\right)^m \underline{C}^+(\vec{r}) \qquad (m = 0, 1, 2, \ldots)$$

(5.7)

*) Bounds for $\underline{C}(\vec{r})$, which approach to zero for $|\vec{r}| \to \infty$, have also been obtained, by a very simple method, by Ruelle[8)]. These bounds however are restricted to finite range potentials.

**) The method used is a generalization of an earlier, simpler method[10)] which can be used only for nonnegative potentials. This generalization is based to a large extent on the work of Penrose[4)] and Ruelle[3)]. The method also yields bounds, similar to those given by (5.7) and (5.8), for the function $S(\vec{r})$.

where the functions $\underline{C}^{\mu}(\vec{r})$ ($\mu = +, -$) are defined, in terms of their Fourier transforms $\tilde{\underline{C}}^{\mu}(\vec{k})$ ($\mu = +, -$), by:

$$\tilde{\underline{C}}^{\mu}(\vec{k}) = \frac{u}{2z} \cdot \left\{ \frac{\lambda^2 v^2 H^3}{1 - \lambda v u H} + \mu \frac{\dot{\lambda}^2 \dot{v}^2 \dot{H}^3}{1 - \dot{\lambda} \dot{v} u \dot{H}} \right\} + \frac{1}{2z} \left\{ \frac{\lambda^2 v^2}{(1 - v)(1 - \lambda v)} - \mu \frac{\dot{\lambda}^2 \dot{v}^2}{(1 - \dot{v})(1 - \lambda \dot{v})} \right\} \qquad (5.8)$$

where u, v, $\dot{v}$, λ, $\dot{\lambda}$, H and $\dot{H}$ are defined by (4.4) and (5.6).

Remarks.

a) Simpler, but weaker, inequalities are obtained if, in the right hand side of (5.8), the second bracket-term is replaced by zero.

b) The interpretation of the bounds $\underline{C}^{\mu}(\vec{r})$ in terms of chain graphs is perhaps made more evident if (5.8) is written in the form:

$$\underline{C}^{\mu}(\vec{r}) = \sum_{j=2}^{\omega} \{ \underline{C}^{[j]} f^{[j]}(\vec{r}) + \mu \, \dot{\underline{C}}^{[j]} \dot{f}^{[j]}(\vec{r}) \} \qquad (5.9)$$

where $\underline{C}^{[j]}$ and $\dot{\underline{C}}^{[j]}$ ($j = 2, 3, \ldots$) are independent of $\vec{r}$.

It may be instructive to compare (5.9) with the expression for $\underline{C}(\vec{r})$ in the "Cayley tree approximation" ("CTA"):

$$\underline{C}^{CTA}(\vec{r}) = \sum_{j=2}^{\infty} z^{j-1} H^{j+1} f^{[j]}(\vec{r}) \qquad (5.10)$$

From (5.9) and (5.10) it is seen that the bounds (5.9) of the estimation method and the approximate expression (5.10) of the approximation method only differ in the counting factors which are associated with each (chain-)graph.

§ 5.3 Corollaries

For simplicity it is assumed here that $\phi(\vec{r})$ is spherically symmetric. We shall write: $\phi(\vec{r}) = \phi(r)$, $f(\vec{r}) = f(r)$, $\tilde{f}(\vec{k}) = \tilde{f}(k)$ etc., where $r = |\vec{r}|$ and $k = |\vec{k}|$. We consider two cases A and B:

5.3.1 Case A

If $\tilde{f}(k)$ is an entire function of k (e.g. if $\phi(r)$ has a finite range), then the bounds $\underline{C}^{\mu}(r)$ (μ = +, -) satisfy*)

$$\underline{C}^{\mu}(r) = \mu\, \underline{C}_o\, r^{-\frac{1}{2}(\nu-1)}\, e^{-\kappa_o r} + O(e^{-\kappa_1 r}) \quad (r \to \infty) \tag{5.11}$$

where κ_o, κ_1, $\underline{C}_o$ are independent of r (but they are functions of z), where $\kappa_1 > \kappa_o$ and where κ_o is the positive root, for κ, of:

$$\tilde{f}(i\kappa) = \frac{1}{zuH} \tag{5.12}$$

Also $\underline{\tilde{C}}_o (\underline{\tilde{C}}_o > 0)$ can be calculated from (5.8).

It follows that the Fourier transforms $\underline{\tilde{C}}(k)$, $\tilde{G}(k)$ and $\tilde{S}(k)$ are holomorphic functions of k in the strip

$$|\mathrm{Im}\, k| < \kappa_o \tag{5.13}$$

5.3.2 Case B

If

$$\phi(r) \backsim \phi_o / r^m \tag{5.14}$$

where ϕ_o and m are constants, $\phi_o \neq 0$ and $m > \nu$, then the bounds $\underline{C}^{\mu}(r)$ (μ = +, -) satisfy:

$$\underline{C}^{\mu}(r) \backsim \underline{C}^{\mu}_o / r^m \qquad (r \to \infty) \tag{5.15}$$

where $\underline{C}^{\mu}_o$ (μ = +, -) are nonvanishing constants which can be calculated from (5.8).

---

*) Bounds with an exponential decay have also been found by Ruelle[8].

It follows that

$$\underline{C}(r) = O(\frac{1}{r^m}) \tag{5.16}$$

and

$$G(r) = O(\frac{1}{r^m}) \tag{5.17}$$

5.3 Discussion

In the literature[38-40] one can find various views regarding the asymptotic behaviour, in the case B, of the function $\underline{C}(r)$. An exponential decay has been suggested by Widom[38], whereas the analysis of Johnson, Hutchinson and March[39] and of Enderby, Gaskell and March[40] suggests that $\underline{C}(r)$ is asymptotically proportional to r^{-m}.

This question has been investigated in the following manner[30]. One writes:

$$\underline{C}(r) = \underline{C}'(r) + \underline{C}''(r) \tag{5.18}$$

where $\underline{C}'(r)$ is the sum of the contributions, to $\underline{C}(r)$, of the "chain-like" graphs, and $\underline{C}''(r)$ that of all other graphs. These chain-like graphs are defined by the property that there exists precisely one path between the two "reference points".

The function $\underline{C}'(r)$ is known. Its Fourier transform is given by:

$$\tilde{\underline{C}}'(k) = (\frac{n}{z})^2 \frac{n\tilde{f}(k)^2}{(1 - n\tilde{f}(k))} \tag{5.19}$$

For the function $\underline{C}''(r)$ one can find bounds, by means of a method similar to the one used for $\underline{C}(r)$. By studying the asymptotic behaviour of $\underline{C}'(r)$ and of the bounds for $\underline{C}''(r)$ it is found that, for sufficiently small $z > 0$:

$$\underline{C}(r)^{-1} = O(r^m) \qquad (r \rightarrow \infty) \tag{5.20}$$

Stated otherwise: $\underline{C}(r)$ does not decrease faster than proportional to r^{-m} for $r \to \infty$.

It seems likely from the above results (5.16) and (5.20) that $r^m \underline{C}(r)$ and hence also $r^m G(r)$) has a limit, for $r \to \infty$. A proof has as yet not been found.

ACKNOWLEDGEMENTS

I am much indebted to Professors J. L. Lebowitz, D. Ruelle, G. Stell and G. W. Ford and to Dr. O. Penrose for encouragement, discussions and correspondence.

---

*) However, see also Ref. [44].

REFERENCES

1. E. Lieb, J. Math. Phys. 4 (1963), 671.

2. J. Groeneveld, Physics Letters 3 (1962), 50.

3. D. Ruelle, Ann. Phys. 25 (1963), 109.

4. O. Penrose, J. Math. Phys. 4 (1963), 1312.

5. O. Penrose, J. Math. Phys. 4 (1963), 1488.

6. J. L. Lebowitz and J. Percus, J. Math. Phys. 4 (1963), 1495.

7. D. Ruelle, Lecture notes of the Theoretical Physics Institute (1963), University of Colorado, Boulder.

8. D. Ruelle, Rev. Mod. Phys. 36 (1964), 580.

9. J. L. Lebowitz and O. Penrose, J. Math. Phys. 5 (1964), 841.

10. J. Groeneveld, Lecture notes of Conference on Graph Theory and Theoretical Physics, Frascati, Italy, Summer 1964. These are hoped to appear in the Proceedings of that Conference, edited by F. Harary (Academic Press, New York).

11. J. E. Mayer and M. G. Mayer, Statistical Mechanics (Wiley, New York, 1940).

12. J. de Boer, Repts. Progr. Phys. 12 (1949), 305.

13. T. L. Hill, Statistical Mechanics (McGraw-Hill, New York, 1956).

14. H. L. Friedman, Ionic Solution Theory (Wiley, New York, 1962), pp. 46-48.

15. G. E. Uhlenbeck and G. W. Ford, The Theory of Linear Graphs with Applications to the Theory of the Virial Development of the Properties of a Gas, in Studies in Statistical Mechanics, Vol. 1, edited by J. de Boer and G. E. Uhlenbeck, North-Holland Publishing Company, Amsterdam, 1962.

16. E. E. Salpeter, Ann. Phys. 5 (1958), 183.

17. G. Stell, _Cluster Expansions for Classical Systems in Equilibrium,_ in H. L. Frisch and J. L. Lebowitz, eds., _The Equilibrium Theory of Classical Fluids_ (Benjamin, New York, 1964).

18. G. E. Uhlenbeck, in the Proceedings of the International Congress on Many-Particle Problems, Utrecht 1960 (Supplement to Physica, 1960) pp. S 17-27.

19. C. Berge, _The Theory of Graphs and its Applications,_ (Methuen, London and Wiley, New York, 1962).

20. G. E. Uhlenbeck and G. W. Ford, _Lectures in Statistical Mechanics,_ American Math. Soc. 1963 (Boulder Lectures 1960).

21. G. E. Uhlenbeck, _Selected Topics in Statistical Mechanics,_ Brandeis Summer Institute, 1962 (Benjamin, New York, 1963).

22. J. M. J. van Leeuwen, J. Groeneveld and J. de Boer, Physica 25 (1959), 792.

23. E. Meeron, J. Math. Phys. 1 (1960), 192.

24. M. S. Green, J. Chem. Phys. 33 (1960), 1403.

25. G. Stell, Physica 29 (1963), 517.

26. J. K. Percus and G. L. Yevick, Phys. Rev. 110 (1958), 1.

27. G. J. Throop and R. J. Bearman, Physica 32 (1966), 1298.

28. J. K. Percus, Phys. Rev. Letters 8 (1962), 462 and _The Pair Distribution Function in Classical Statistical Mechanics,_ in H. L. Frisch and J. L. Lebowitz, eds., _The Equilibrium Theory of Classical Fluids_ (Benjamin, New York, 1964).

29. L. Verlet, Physica 30 (1964), 95.

30. J. Groeneveld, to be published.

31. F. H. Ree and W. G. Hoover, J. Chem. Phys. 40 (1964), 939.

32. L. van Hove, Physica 15 (1949), 951.

33. M. E. Fisher, Arch. Rat. Mech. Anal. 17 (1964), 377.

34. C. N. Yang and T. D. Lee, Phys. Rev. 87 (1952), 404.

35. J. Groeneveld, unpublished results.

36. F. H. Ree, Bounds on the Fugacity and Virial Series of the Pressure, Preprint, UCRL 70050, University of California, Livermore, California.

37. T. Morita, Progr. Theor. Phys. 23 (1960), 829.

38. B. Widom, J. Chem. Phys. 41 (1964), 74.

39. M. D. Johnson, P. Hutchinson and N. H. March, Proc. Roy. Soc. (London) A 282 (1964), 283.

40. J. E. Enderby, T. Gaskell and N. H. March, Proc. Phys. Soc. 85 (1965), 217.

DISCUSSION

Anon.: You were concerned with a singularity. It may be that this is a pole which may be able to be subtracted so that the remaining series converges in much larger region.

Groeneveld: The singularity is a branch point for the case of hard rods. One might be able to remove this singularity by using another (a uniformizing) variable.

Anon.: You should look at the coefficient to know the behavior near the singularity.

Groeneveld: It is worth while to do this but it has not yet been done.

Lieb: I understand that your bound on G went up to the radius of convergence of the power series.

Groenenveld: The bound has a radius of convergence which never exceeds the radius of convergence of the power series. For hard rods it is a factor of two smaller.

Lieb: Have you definitely established the radius of convergence of the power series for the bounds?

Groeneveld: Yes, that is easy.

Lieb: Was it obtained in the same way as Penrose?

Groeneveld: In a similar way, but using a different set of recurrence relations.

Lieb: What kind of bound did you have?

Groeneveld: I did it first for the positive potential. Independently, Penrose and Ruelle did it for more general potentials and this generalized my upper bound for $|b_1|$ but not my lower bound.

Lieb: There are two kinds of bounds on G. Method B gives a power series expansion which is limited by the radius of convergence and this gives G = 0 at infinity. Alternatively, one can use method A which means G looks like the ratio of two partition functions. The bounds on G obtained in this way are valid for much larger values of the fugacity (possibly all values) but they have the disadvantage that $G \neq 0$ at infinity.

CONVERGENCE OF THE FUGACITY EXPANSIONS FOR QUANTUM SYSTEMS

J. GINIBRE

University of Paris,
Faculty of Science, Orsay

INTRODUCTION

The problem of the convergence of the fugacity expansions of the pressure, density and correlation functions of classical gases described in the grand canonical formalism, has been considered by several authors [(1-5)]. They have used several methods, based upon integral equations for the correlation functions, like the Kirkwood-Salsburg (K. S.) and Mayer-Montroll equations[6)], or upon majorization of the Mayer graphs[3, 4)]. Typical results, obtained under suitable assumptions on the interaction potentials, are the following:

1) The correlation functions, both for finite and infinite volume, are analytic functions of the fugacity z in a neighbourhood $|z| < R$ of the origin in the complex z-plane. Expressions for R, which is a lower bound on the radius of convergence, can be given in terms of the interaction potential.

2) When the volume V becomes infinite, the correlation functions tend to well defined limits. The limit is uniform for $|z| \leqq R' < R$. In the same region, the quantity $(\beta V)^{-1} \log Z$, where Z is the grand partition function, tends to a well defined analytic function of z, which is the analytic continuation of the pressure[1)].

3) For $|z| < R$, the correlation functions have a cluster property (C. P.) in the sense that the Ursell functions are absolutely in-

tegrable functions of the differences between their arguments[5]. In the case of the two-point function, Groenveld has given stronger results[4].

In this lecture, we shall consider the corresponding problem in quantum statistical mechanics, and show that the same methods can be applied to this case, where they lead to similar but somewhat weaker results, after one has taken into account the two additional difficulties which distinguish the quantum mechanical problem from the classical one. These are:

a) The replacement of functions by operators. This problem arises in particular for the hamiltonian H_m of m particles and the statistical factor $\exp(-\beta H_m)$, where $\beta = (kT)^{-1}$. Such an operator will have a convenient representation in the form of a Wiener integral (Section 2), as was suggested long ago by Kac.

b) The introduction of quantum statistics, which complicates the algebra.

The two difficulties are independent in the sense that one can also consider the intermediate case where the first one appears and not the second. This is the case of a gas of quantum particles with Boltzmann statistics; it will be referred to as (BS) in the following, as opposed to the full quantum case, referred to as (Q.S).

The basic object of investigation will be the infinite sequence of the reduced density matrices (RDM), which are the analogues of the classical correlation functions. We shall define them in Section 3, and represent them as Wiener integrals. The situation will then turn out to be very similar to the classical one, and we shall be able to use quantum analogues of the K.S. equations to obtain the results listed above under (1) and (2). (Section 4). We shall then state a C.P. which can be proved by using recurrence relations (Section 5).

Before proceeding further, we state conditions on the interaction, which are sufficient to obtain our results.

1. CONDITIONS ON THE POTENTIAL

We consider systems of identical particles with mass 1 in ν dimensional euclidean space, interacting by two body forces described by a potential ϕ, which is a real, symmetric, translation invariant function of the positions x and x' of the two interacting particles: $\phi(x, x') = \phi(x-x') = \phi(x'-x)$. However, we do not assume spherical symmetry. We impose on ϕ the following conditions:

A. ϕ satisfies either A1 or A2.

A1. ϕ is a continuous function, except for point singularities if $\nu \geqq 2$. (Physically, one is interested in a point singularity at the origin).

A2. ϕ has a hard core, and is continuous outside of the core. Condition A is of a technical nature, and has no particular physical meaning.

B. ϕ is stable. For any family of n distinct points $x_1, \ldots, x_n$ (such that the hard cores do not overlap if there is any),

$$\sum_{i<j} \phi(x_i - x_j) \geqq -nB \tag{1 - 1}$$

where $B \geqq 0$ does not depend on n.

Condition B is essential, as was stressed in the four preceding lectures.

C. ϕ is absolutely integrable at infinity.

$$\int_{|x| \geqq r_0} |\phi(x)| \, d^{\nu} x < +\infty \tag{1 - 2}$$

For technical reasons, we need in fact a slight refinement of C, but we shall omit this point here[7].

Conditions A, B and C allow an arbitrary repulsive singularity of ϕ near the origin, including a hard core. However, in the rest of this lecture, we shall restrict ourselves to a smaller class of potentials, for two reasons:

1) The problem is technically much simpler.
2) Only for that restricted class are we able to give explicit expressions for the lower bounds of the radius of convergence of the z series. In the general case, these lower bounds are defined by an eigenvalue problem.

The restricted class is defined by conditions A1, B and C':

C'. ϕ is absolutely integrable in the whole space

$$\int | \phi(x) | \, d^{\nu} x < +\infty \qquad (1-3)$$

Condition C' excludes hard core potentials and the usual Lennard-Jones potential. It allows a behaviour of the type $\phi(r) \underset{r \to 0}{\cong} r^{-\nu+\epsilon}$ near the origin.

2. WIENER INTEGRAL REPRESENTATION OF exp(-βH)

The problem is to find a convenient representation of the operator $\exp(-\beta H)$ where H is of the form:

$$H = -\frac{1}{2}\Delta + W(x) \qquad (2-1)$$

H is the hamiltonian operator of a family of m particles, Δ is the Laplace operator in $l = m\nu$ dimensions, $W(x)$ is the potential energy of the m particles. The units are such that $\hbar = 1$ and the common mass of the particles is 1.

If $\varphi_o(x)$ is any sufficiently regular function of x, then the function

$$\varphi_{\beta}(x) = e^{-\beta H} \varphi_o(x) \qquad (2-2)$$

is the solution of the differential equation

$$\frac{\partial \psi}{\partial \beta} = -H\psi \qquad (2-3)$$

which reduces to $\varphi_o(x)$ as $\beta \to 0^+$.

Consider first the case where $W(x) \equiv 0$. Then (2 - 3) has the elementary solution

$$\psi_\beta(x - y) = (2\pi\beta)^{-1/2} \exp\left[-|x - y|^2 / 2\beta\right] \qquad (2 - 4)$$

which reduces to $\delta(x - y)$ as $\beta \rightarrow 0^+$. In this case:

$$\varphi_\beta = \psi_\beta * \varphi_o . \qquad (2 - 5)$$

In other words, $\exp[-\beta H]$ is represented as the convolution with the propagator ψ_β.

In the general case $W(x) \neq 0$, it is convenient to use the Wiener integral, which we now define in analogy with the Lebesgue integral. In the latter case, one is given a real variable $s \in [0, 1]$, and for every continuous function f of the variable s, one defines a number:

$$I(f) = \int f(s)\, ds \qquad (2 - 6)$$

I is a positive linear form on the linear space of such functions. The notation in the r. h. s. of (2 - 6) exhibits the name of the variable s. We now turn to the Wiener integral. Let x, y be two fixed points in euclidean dimensional space R^1 and β be a positive number. The variable s which appears above is now replaced by a continuous function from $[0, \beta]$ to R^1, such that $\omega(0) = x, \omega(\beta) = y$. For any function $f(\omega)$ which is continuous in an appropriate sense, we define a number:

$$P_{xy}(f) = \int P_{xy}(d\omega)\, f(\omega) \qquad (2 - 7)$$

which is the Wiener integral of f. As an example, which is also the starting point for a correct definition, we consider the following case: let $0 < t_1 < \ldots < t_n < \beta$ be a finite sequence of distinct real numbers in $(0, \beta)$, and let $F(x_1, \ldots, x_n)$ be a bounded continuous function of n variables in R^1. This defines a particular function f by:

$$f(\omega) = F(\omega(t_1), \ldots, \omega(t_n)) \qquad (2 - 8)$$

The Wiener integral of f is defined by:

$$\int P_{xy}(d\omega)f(\omega) = dx_1 \ldots dx_n \Psi_{t_1}(x_1 - x)\Psi_{t_2 - t_1}(x_2 - x_1)\ldots$$

$$\Psi_{\beta - t_n}(y - x_n)\, F(x_1, \ldots, x_n) \qquad (2 - 9)$$

where Ψ_β is defined by (2 - 4).

In the Wiener as well as in the Lebesgue case, the integral can be extended from continuous to integrable functions by limiting procedures.

The basic result which we shall use is the following representation of the operator $\exp(-\beta H)$, which we write as an integral kernel:

$$\left[\exp(-\beta H)\right](x, y) = \int P_{xy}(d\omega)\, \exp\left[-\int_0^\beta W(\omega(t))\, dt\right] \qquad (2 - 10)$$

(Equation (2 - 10) is in fact taken as the definition of a self adjoint extension of H, but we do not insist on this point).

3. DEFINITION AND REPRESENTATION OF THE RDM

We briefly recall the definition of the RDM of a system of identical particles in the grand canonical formalism. From now on and until otherwise stated, the system is assumed to be enclosed in a bounded region Λ with volume V. Let $F_m = L^2(\Lambda^m)$ be the space of wave functions of m particles, i. e. of square integrable functions of m points in Λ. Let $F = \oplus F_m$ be the Hilbert direct sum of the F_m's. If we had not neglected statistics F would be the usual Fock space. The system is defined by a density matrix σ, which is a hermitian positive operator in F with trace one. σ is assumed to commute with the number operator and can therefore be written as $\sigma = \oplus \sigma_m$. The RDM of the system are defined in terms of σ by:

$$\bar{\rho}_m = \sum_{p \geqq m} \frac{p!}{(p - m)!}\, \mathrm{Tr}_{p - m}\, \sigma_p \qquad (3 - 1)$$

where we use the notation $\bar{\rho}_m$ or $\bar{\rho}_\Lambda(x^m, y^m)$ for the m-particle RDM; in the last notation, $\bar{\rho}_m$ is written as an integral kernel, and x^m and y^m are families of m points in R^ν: $x^m = (x_1, \ldots, x_m)$, $y^m = (y_1, \ldots, y_m)$.

The notation Tr_{p-m} in (3 - 1) means partial trace over p - m particles. In the grand canonical formalism, σ is given by:

$$\sigma_p = Z^{-1} \frac{z^p}{p!} \exp\left[-\beta H_p\right] \qquad \text{(B.S. case)} \qquad (3 - 2)$$

$$\sigma_p = Z^{-1} \frac{z^p}{p!} S^p_\epsilon \exp\left[-\beta H_p\right] \qquad \text{(Q.S. case)} \qquad (3 - 3)$$

where $z = \exp(\beta\mu)$ is the fugacity, $\epsilon = +1$ (Bose statistics) or -1 (Fermi statistics), S^p_ϵ is the appropriate symmetrisation operator, Z and Z_ϵ are the partition functions corresponding to the various cases.

Substitution of (2-10) in (3-1, 2, 3) will give Wiener integral representations of the RDM. We first express $\exp\left[-\beta H_m\right]$ by means of (2-10). The starting point and endpoint of the trajectory are points in R^l, where $l = m\nu$, or equivalently, families of m points in R^ν. They are connected by m trajectories ω^m in R^l. Therefore

$$\exp\left[-\beta H_m\right](x^m, y^m) = \int P_{x^m, y^m}(d\omega^m) \exp\left[-U(\omega^m)\right] \qquad (3 - 4)$$

where

$$U(\omega^m) = \sum_{i<j} \int_0^\beta dt\, \phi\left[\omega_i(t) - \omega_j(t)\right] \qquad (3 - 5)$$

We first consider the (B.S.) case. The partial trace which appears in (3 - 1) can be represented as follows: the factor $\exp(-\beta H_p)$ in σ_p is represented by p trajectories, m of which connect the points x^m and y^m which appear in $\bar{\rho}_\Lambda(x^m, y^m)$. The partial trace amounts to identify the endpoints of the p - m = n other trajectories, and integrate over these points. This can be interpreted in terms of graphs as in fig. 1. We now split the integrations over trajectories into two successive steps. The second one will consist in

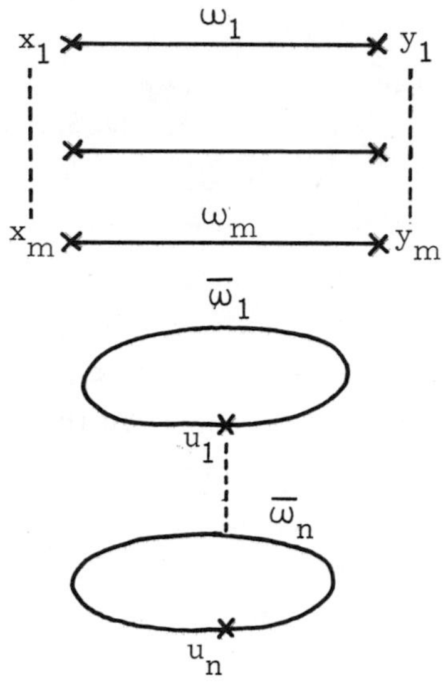

Fig. 1. B.S. case.

integrating over the m trajectories with free ends x^m, y^m. This will be a completely harmless operation, and will contain no reference to the volume Λ or to the z expansion. The difficulties connected with these two features will appear exclusively in the first step, which will include the summation over p and the integration over the closed trajectories. Finally we obtain:

$$\bar{\rho}_\Lambda(x^m, y^m) = \int P_{x^m, y^m}(d\omega^m)\ \rho_\Lambda(\omega^m) \tag{3 - 6}$$

$$\rho_\Lambda(X) = Z^{-1} \sum_{n=0} \frac{1}{n!} \int dY\ z^{m+n} \exp\left[-U(X+Y)\right] \alpha_\Lambda (X+Y) \tag{3 - 7}$$

where:

$X \equiv \omega^m = (\omega_1, \ldots, \omega_m)$

$Y = \bar{\omega}^n = (\bar{\omega}_1, \ldots, \bar{\omega}_n)$ is a family of closed trajectories.

$$\int dY = d\overline{\omega}^{n}, \text{ with:}$$

$$\int d\overline{\omega} = P_{uu}(d\overline{\omega})\, du \qquad (3 - 8)$$

The factor $\alpha_{\Lambda}(X+Y)$ makes the dependence on Λ explicit. It is equal to one if all the trajectories stay in Λ and to zero if at least one of them has a point outside of Λ.

We now turn to the quantum case (Q. S.). The algebraic manipulations, which are slightly more complicated, are well known, especially in connection with perturbation theory[8]. The symmetrization operator S^p_ϵ which takes statistics into account gives a sum of terms obtained by permutation of the end points of the p trajectories in $\exp(-\beta H_p)$. One then takes a partial trace. Therefore, starting for instance from x_1, instead of going to y_1 as previously, one may go to one of the integration points u_i, then to another one u_k, etc... and finally reach a point y_l (with, in general, $l \neq 1$). This has the effect that several elementary trajectories may be inserted between x_1 and the corresponding y to build a composite trajectory of length $j\beta$ (where by length we mean the length of the interval of variation of the parameter).

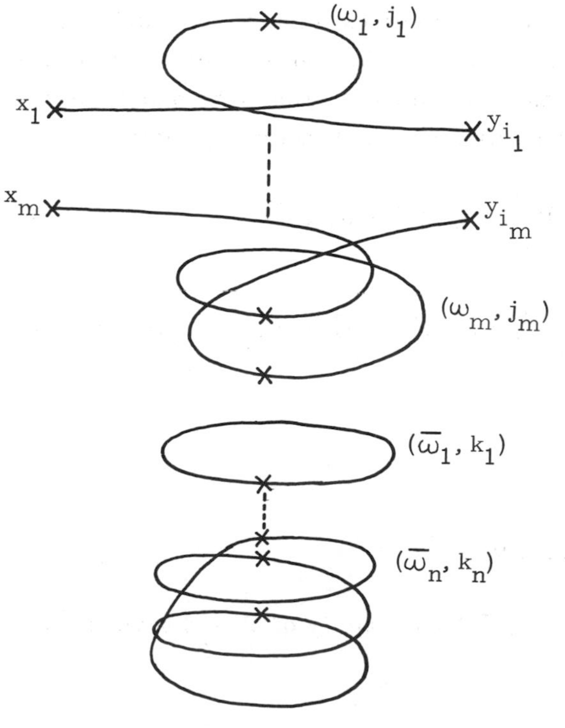

Fig. 2. Q.S. case.

Here $j_1 = 2$, $j_m = 3$,

$k_1 = 1$, $k_n = 3$.

Similarly, the elementary trajectories which are not used in composite trajectories connecting x^m to y^m, combine together to form composite closed loops, as represented in fig. 2. This leads to:

$$\bar{\rho}_\Lambda(x^m, y^m) = S_\epsilon^m \sum_{j_1=1}^{\infty} \dots \sum_{j_m=1}^{\infty} \epsilon^{q+m} \int P^{j^m}_{x^m, y^m}(d\omega^m)\rho_\Lambda(\omega^m, j^m) \tag{3 - 9}$$

$$\rho_\Lambda(X) = Z_\epsilon^{-1} \sum_{n=0}^{\infty} \frac{1}{n!} \int dY \; z^{q+r} \; \exp\left[-U(X+Y)\right] \alpha_\Lambda(X+Y) \tag{3 - 10}$$

where: $X = (\omega^m, j^m)$ is the family of m composite trajectories going from x^m to y^m, ω_i having the length $j_i\beta$.

$Y \equiv (\bar{\omega}^n, k^n)$ is a family of n composite closed loops of length $k_i\beta$.

$$q = \sum_{i=1}^{m} j_i, \quad r = \sum_{i=1}^{n} k_i \, .$$

$$\int dY = d\bar{\omega}^n \quad \text{where now:}$$

$$\int d\bar{\omega} = \sum_{j=1}^{\infty} \frac{\epsilon^{j+1}}{j} \int p^j_{uu}(d\bar{\omega}) \, du \, . \tag{3 - 11}$$

We now observe that the formulas (3 - 7) and (3 - 10) are very similar to the formulas which define the classical correlation functions, and differ from them mainly by the replacement of the integration over points ($\int dx$) by integration over trajectories ($\int d\bar{\omega}$) defined by (3 - 8) and (3 - 10).

This enables us to use exactly the same methods as in classical mechanics to study the analyticity in z and the limit of infinite volume. This will be done in the next section.

4. THE K.S. EQUATIONS

This part of the discussion is a close transcription of the work of Ruelle[1)] in classical mechanics. In the latter case, one makes use of the K.S. equations, which constitute an infinite sequence of coupled linear integral equations for the correlation functions of classical gases. One can write similar equations for the sequence of the $\rho_\Lambda(X)$. In the (B.S.) case, they are formally identical with the classical equations, integrations being now carried on according to (3 - 8). In the (Q.S.) case, the situation is basically the same, although the algebra is more complicated. In all cases, these equations can be considered as the components of one linear equation:

$$\rho^+_\Lambda = A_\Lambda(\zeta + K\,\rho^+_\Lambda) \tag{4 - 1}$$

where: ρ_Λ is the infinite sequence of functionals $\rho_\Lambda(X)$:

$$\rho_\Lambda = (1, \rho_\Lambda(\omega), \ldots, \rho_\Lambda(X), \ldots) \tag{4 - 2}$$

ρ_Λ can be considered as a vector in the linear space E of sequences of functions of an increasing number of trajectories.

ρ^+_Λ is the vector in E obtained by replacing the first component 1 by 0. ζ is the vector $\zeta = (0, z, 0, \ldots)$ in E.

K is a linear operator in E. K is the product of z by an operator which does not depend on z or Λ. The whole dependence on Λ is contained in the operator A_Λ, which simply multiplies each component h(X) of a vector $h \in E$ by $\alpha_\Lambda(X)$. It is then appealing to use (4 - 1) as a definition of ρ^+_Λ by:

$$\rho^+_\Lambda = (1 - A_\Lambda K)^{-1} A_\Lambda \zeta = (1 + A_\Lambda K + (A_\Lambda K)^2 + \ldots) A_\Lambda \zeta \tag{4 - 3}$$

This can be made rigorous by defining in a subspace of E a norm which makes it to a Banach space (complete normed space). One can then prove that $A_\Lambda K$ is a bounded operator in this space.

Therefore, there exists $R > 0$ such that for $|z| < R$, $A_\Lambda K$ has a norm smaller than 1, and (4 - 1) has a unique solution given by the expansion (4 - 3). Moreover, the solution will be an analytic function of z for $|z| < R$. R thus obtained is therefore a lower bound of the radius of convergence of the z expansion of the R.D.M. Typical values of R obtained in this way are the following:

B.S. case:

$$R = \xi \exp\left[-2\beta B - \xi C(\beta)\right] \tag{4 - 4}$$

where:

$$C(\beta) = \lambda^{-\nu}\left(\beta \int \phi_+(x)\, dx + \frac{e^{2\beta B} - 1}{2B} \int \phi_-(x)\, dx\right)$$

$$\leqq \lambda^{-\nu}\beta\left(\int \phi_+(x)\, dx + e^{2\beta B} \int \phi_-(x)\, dx\right) \tag{4 - 5}$$

$$\lambda = \sqrt{2\pi\beta}$$

$$\phi_{\pm}(x) = \max(0, \pm\phi(x)).$$

B is the constant which appears in (1 - 1).

ξ is an arbitrary strictly positive real number. The best possible value, which gives the largest R, is $\xi = C(\beta)^{-1}$.

Q.S. case:

$$R = \xi \exp\left[-2\beta B - D(\xi, \beta)\right]. \tag{4 - 6}$$

$$D(\xi, \beta) = \lambda^{-\nu}\left\{\beta \int \phi_+\, dx\, g_{\nu/2}(\xi) + \frac{1}{2B}\int \phi_-\, dx\left[g_{\nu/2+1}(\xi e^{2\beta B}) - g_{\nu/2+1}(\xi)\right]\right\}$$

$$\leqq \lambda^{-\nu}\beta\left[\int \phi_+\, dx\, g_{\nu/2}(\xi) + \int \phi_-\, dx\, g_{\nu/2}(\xi e^{2\beta B})\right] \tag{4 - 7}$$

where

$$g_\alpha(y) = \sum_{l=1}^{\infty} \frac{y^l}{l^\alpha}$$

ξ must satisfy: $0 < \xi e^{2\beta B} < 1$. The maximization of R as a function of ξ is no longer elementary.

Until now we considered systems with a finite volume. However, the bounds (4 - 4) and (4 - 6) do not depend on the volume. Therefore, equation (4 - 1) is suitable to study systems with an infinite volume. In particular the infinite volume RDM can be defined by the equation:

$$\rho^{+} = \zeta + K \rho^{+} \tag{4 - 8}$$

The analyticity properties proved above still hold for infinite systems. Moreover, one can show that for $|z| < R$, the RDM for a finite system tend in a certain sense to the RDM of the infinite system as defined by (4 - 8). The convergence is uniform for $|z| \leqq R' < R$. In the same region, the function $V^{-1}\beta^{-1} \log Z$ converges to an analytic function of z, which is the analytic continuation of the pressure. From this and the analyticity of the density for $|z| < R$, it follows by elimination that the virial expansion, that is, the expansion of the pressure as a power series of the density, converges in a neighbourhood of the origin.

5. FURTHER RESULTS

Other properties of the classical systems remain valid for quantum systems. In particular, one can use recurrence relations analogous to the classical ones[2, 5] and prove a cluster property in the following form. We define the quantum analogues of the Ursell functions $\overline{\chi}(x^m, y^m)$, by:

$$\overline{\rho}(x, y) = \overline{\chi}(x, y)$$

$$\overline{\rho}(x_1 x_2, y_1 y_2) = \overline{\chi}(x_1 x_2, y_1 y_2) + \overline{\chi}(x_1, y_1)\overline{\chi}(x_2 y_2) + \epsilon \overline{\chi}(x_1, y_2)\overline{\chi}(x_2, y_1)$$

The general definition can be found elsewhere. (9. see also 7c). ϵ is +1 for Bose statistics, -1 for Fermi statistics, and the corresponding term is to be omitted ($\epsilon = 0$) in the B.S. case. One can then show that for $|z| < R$, the functions $\bar{\chi}$ are absolutely integrable functions of the differences of their arguments:

$$\int |\bar{\chi}(x^m, y^m)| \, dx^m \, dy^{m-1} < + \infty \qquad (5-1)$$

In the Q.S. case, this property, besides its own intrinsic interest, is strongly reminiscent of the cluster property of the truncated vacuum expectation values in Quantum Field Theory[10. See also 7a].

REFERENCES

1. D. Ruelle, Ann. Phys. 25, 109 (1963).
2. O. Penrose, J. Math. Phys. 4, 1312 (1963).
3. O. Penrose, Lecture 10, in these Proceedings.
4. J. Groeneveld, Lecture 11, in these Proceedings.
5. D. Ruelle, Rev. Mod. Phys. 36, 580 (1964).
6. T. L. Hill, Statistical Mechanics, McGraw Hill, New York (1956).
7. J. Ginibre a) Thesis. Paris (1965) unpublished.
   b) J. Math. Phys. 6, 238 (1965).
   c) - - 6, 252 (1965).
   d) - - 6, 1432 (1965).
8. C. Bloch. Diagram expansions in quantum statistical mechanics in: Studies in Statistical Mechanics, Vol III, North Holland Company, Amsterdam (1965).
9. C. N. Yang and T. D. Lee, Phys. Rev. 113, 1165 (1959).
10. R. Streater and A. Wightman, TCP, Spin and Statistics, and all that. Benjamin, New York (1964).

DISCUSSION

De Dominicis: Is it possible to carry out this formal treatment in going from the fugacity to the density expansion?

Ginibre: The first thing you may think of doing is to interpret the formulas for $\rho(\omega^m)$ in terms of Mayer graphs, where now the vertices are trajectories. If you then introduce irreducible graphs as in the classical case, you obtain a functional expansion in a series of the one particle functional $\rho(\omega)$. In classical statistical mechanics, instead of $\rho(\omega)$, you get $\rho(x)$ which is constant and equal to the density, due to translational invariance; therefore you end up with the usual series in powers of the density, d. But here $\rho(\omega)$ is not a constant and this does not give an expansion in powers of the density.

Isihara: Together with Montroll and Fujita I approached this problem using propagators. I did not use Feynman path integrals but various products of these propagators come in the theory corresponding to many possible paths from one point to another. In this sence one can rewrite our results in the form which Ginibre presented. Concerning the question Ginibre raised, the case of classical fluids has been studied by Rushbrook and Scoins. In the general case, since the coefficients of the fugacity expansion of the reduced density matrices are different from that of the density, it is rather difficult to derive the density expansion in a similar way to the case of pressure of a classical gas. The problem is somewhat similar to the case of classical multicomponent systems.

Lebowitz: You can eliminate algebraically though and get bounds.

Ginibre: Yes, this proves in particular that for the class of potentials described here (which includes hard spheres) for any fixed finite temperature the expansion of the pressure as a series in the density has a non zero radius of convergence.

Singh: Can you calculate R explicitly in a few particular cases, say $\beta \to \infty$?

Ginibre: As $\beta \to \infty$, the lower bound R on the radius of convergence of the z expansion shrinks to zero, at least for non purely repulsive potentials.

RIGOROUS TREATMENT OF SYSTEMS WITH LONG RANGE POTENTIALS AND OTHER TOPICS*

J. L. LEBOWITZ
Belfer Graduate School of
Science, Yeshiva University,
New York, New York 10033.

1. RIGOROUS TREATMENT OF SYSTEMS WITH LONG-RANGE POTENTIALS

1.a. Equilibrium States

Rigorous upper and lower bounds were obtained[1] for the thermodynamic free-energy density $a(\rho, \gamma)$ of a classical system of particles with two-body interaction potential $q(\underline{r}) + \gamma^{\nu}\varphi(\gamma\underline{r})$ where ν is the number of space dimensions and ρ the density, in terms of the free-energy density $a^{o}(\rho)$ for the corresponding system (reference system) with $\varphi(\underline{x}) \equiv 0$. When $\varphi(\underline{x})$ belongs to a class of functions, which includes those which are non-positive and those whose ν-dimensional Fourier transforms are non-negative, the upper and lower bounds coincide in the van der Waals limit $\gamma \to 0$ and $\lim_{\gamma \to 0} a(\rho, \gamma) = CE\{a^{o}(\rho) + \frac{1}{2}\alpha\rho^{2}\}$:

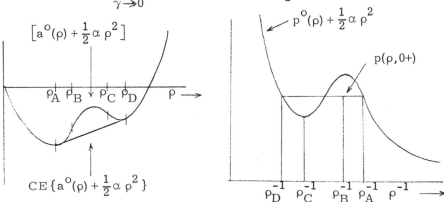

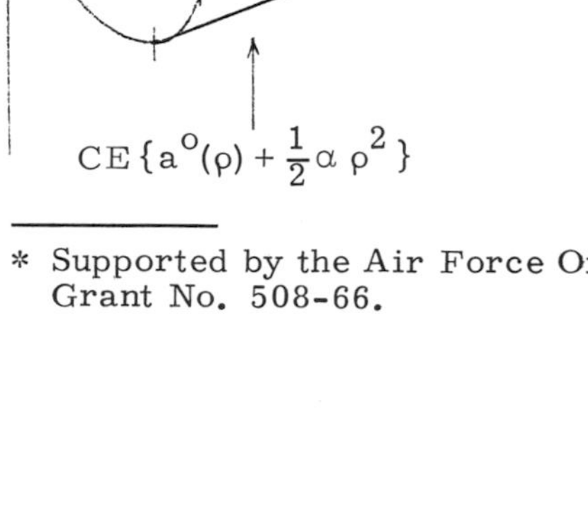

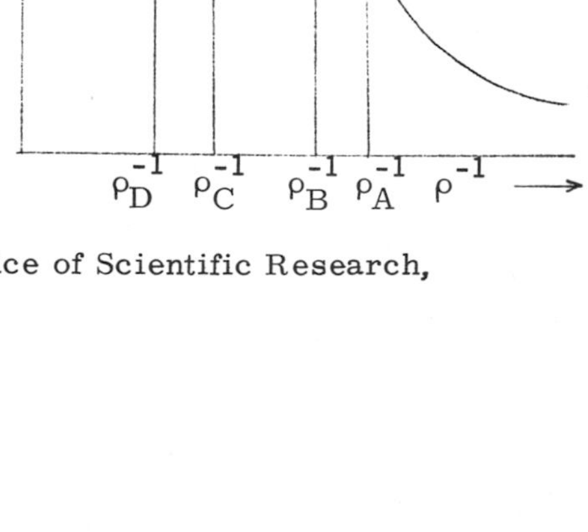

* Supported by the Air Force Office of Scientific Research, Grant No. 508-66.

the maximal convex function of ρ not exceeding $a^o(\rho) + \frac{1}{2}\alpha\rho^2$, where $\alpha \equiv \int \varphi(\underline{x})d\underline{x}$. The corresponding equation of state is given by Maxwell's equal-area rule applied to the function $p^o(\rho) + \frac{1}{2}\alpha\,\rho^2$ where $p^o(\rho)$ is the pressure of the reference system for which $\varphi(\underline{x}) \equiv 0$. If $a^o(\rho) + \frac{1}{2}\alpha\,\rho^2$ is not convex the behavior of the limiting free energy indicates a first-order phase transition.

These results are easily generalized to lattice gases and thus apply also to Ising spin systems. This was used[2] incidently to test an idea of Fisher's that in comparing the specific beats of lattice gases with continuum fluids near the critical point it should be done on the basis of their value per unit volume per particle at close packing $C^*(T) = \rho\, C^{(T)}_{conf} / \rho_{max}$, where C_{conf} is the configurational specific heat per particle and $\rho = \rho_{critical}$ along the critical isochore. Using then for our reference system an "ideal" lattice gas $q(\underline{r}) = \begin{cases} \infty, & \underline{r} = 0 \\ 0, & \underline{r} \neq 0 \end{cases}$ or a continuum system of hard rods, discs or spheres we find the following results for the specific heat discontinuity at the critical point (using Padé equations of state for $\nu = 2,3$)

	Lattice gas	Continuum		
	$\nu = 1,2,3$	$\nu = 1$	$\nu = 2$	$\nu = 3$
ρ_c/ρ_{max}	.5	1/3	.233	.176
$\Delta C^*/k$	1.5	1.5	1.465	1.480
$(\frac{\beta p}{\rho})_c$	.386	.376	.366	.359

The constancy of ΔC^* is remarkable and unexplained.

The generalization of our results to quantum systems[3] requires only very mild additional assumptions. This permits[4] explicit calculations of the properties and critical parameters of a one dimensional quantum system of hard rods with long range attraction, i.e. $q(r) = \begin{cases} \infty, & r < a \\ 0, & r > a \end{cases}$. The behavior of the critical temperature, pressure and density as a function of the quantum parameter λ, the ratio of the de Broglie wave length to the interparticle separation evaluated at the classical critical point show surprising similarly to that found for real fluids expected to obey the law of corresponding states, i.e. the critical temperature and critical density decrease rapidly with λ (in almost identical manner) while the critical ratio is almost independent of λ.

1.b. Metastable States

In considering the equilibrium properties of these systems no meaning at all is attached to that part of the curve $a^o(\rho) + \frac{1}{2}\alpha\rho^2$ which lies above the curve $CE\{a^o(\rho) + \frac{1}{2}\alpha\rho^2\}$ or to the corresponding part of the pressure curve $p^o(\rho) + \frac{1}{2}\alpha\rho^2$. Traditionally however the parts of these curves (actually of similar curves obtained from the original van der Waals-Maxwell theory) are assumed to represent the properties of metastable states of uniform density corresponding to the supercooled vapour and the superheated liquid respectively. It is possible[5] to give a rigorous meaning to these states by considering the properties of our system when it is confined to a restricted region of the configuration space. This is done by a simple extension of the method used to obtain bounds on the equilibrium free energy. The cubical box of volume Ω to which our system consisting of N particles is confined is divided up into M cells of volume ω. We can now restrict the configuration space of our system by imposing restrictions on the densities $\rho_i = N_i/\omega$ of the various cells: $N_i = N$, $i = 1,\ldots M$. The simplest such restriction is

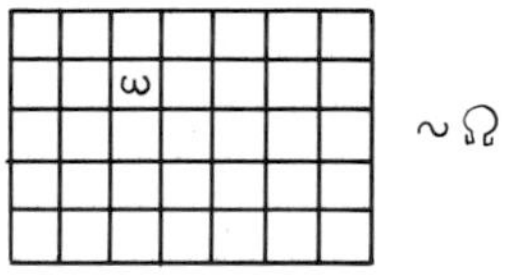

$$\rho_- \leqq \rho_i \leqq \rho_+$$

where $\rho_- \leqq \rho \leqq \rho_+$. Let $\mathcal{R} = \mathcal{R}(\Omega, \omega, \rho_-, \rho_+)$ the region in configuration space where these restrictions are satisfied and $a'(\rho, \gamma : \omega, \mathcal{R})$ the corresponding free energy per unit volume (in the thermodynamic limit $\Omega \rightarrow \infty$. o fixed). When $\rho_- = 0$, $\rho_+ = \infty$, $\mathcal{R}$ coincides with the whole configuration space and $a' = a(\rho, \gamma)$ while letting ρ_- and ρ_+ approach ρ corresponds to restricting the system to be completely uniform on the scale of ω. It is then shown[5] that in the limit $\gamma \rightarrow 0$ followed by the limit $\omega \rightarrow \infty$, i.e.

the cell size $\omega^{1/\nu} << \gamma^{-1}$ the range of $\varphi(\gamma r)$,

$$\lim_{\omega \to \infty} \lim_{\gamma \to 0} a'(\rho, \gamma : \omega, \mathcal{R}) \equiv a'(\rho, 0+ : \mathcal{R}) = CE\{a^o(\rho) + \frac{1}{2}\alpha\rho^2 + g(\rho)\} \tag{2}$$

where

$$g(\rho) = \begin{cases} 0, & \rho_- \leqq \rho \leqq \rho_+ \\ \infty, & \text{otherwise} \end{cases} \tag{3}$$

Thus if $a^o(\rho) + \frac{1}{2}\alpha\rho^2$ is convex in the interval $\rho_- \leqq \rho \leqq \rho_+$, a' coincides with $a^o(\rho) + \frac{1}{2}\alpha\rho^2$. This will be true when ρ and the interval (ρ_-, ρ_+) surrounding it is confined to the stable and/or "metastable" parts of the graph $a^o(\rho) + \frac{1}{2}\alpha\rho^2$; e.g., $0 \leqq \rho_- \leqq \rho \leqq \rho_+ \leqq \rho_B$ or $\rho_C \leqq \rho_- \leqq \rho \leqq \rho_+ \leqq \infty$ in Fig. 1. The precise value of ρ_- and ρ_+ are then not important, and the interval can be shrunk to the point ρ, i.e. the system will actually be in a completely uniform state. When ρ is however, in the unstable part of the graph of $a^o(\rho) + \frac{1}{2}\alpha\rho^2$, i.e. $\frac{d^2}{d\rho^2}\left[a^o(\rho) + \frac{1}{2}\alpha\rho^2\right] \leqq 0$, $\rho_B < \rho < \rho_C$ in Fig. 1, then $a'(\rho; \mathcal{R})$ coincides with $a^o(\rho) + \frac{1}{2}\alpha\rho^2$ only when the interval (ρ_-, ρ_+) is shrunk to a point. We thus see, as expected, that the uniform state coincides with a minimum (maximum) of the constrained free energy in the metastable (unstable) region of $a^o(\rho) + \frac{1}{2}\alpha\rho^2$. (In the stable region where $a^o(\rho) + \frac{1}{2}\alpha\rho^2$ coincides with $CE\{a^o(\rho) + \frac{1}{2}\alpha\rho^2\}$, $0 \leqq \rho \leqq \rho_A$ or $\rho_D \leqq \rho \leqq \infty$, in Fig. 1, the uniform state is, of course, the state of minimum free energy).

1.c. Metastable States for $\gamma \neq 0$

We have seen that in the van der Waals limit, $\gamma \to 0$, when the range of the potential becomes infinite it is possible to give a complete physical characterization of the metastable state. This state also coincides with the analytic continuation of the equilibrium isotherm in the p - ρ plane. We could also construct a restricted grand partition function $\Xi'(z, \gamma, \Omega, \omega, \mathcal{R})$, where z is the fugacity, obtaining in the triple limit

$$\beta p'(z; \mathcal{R}) = \lim_{\omega \to \infty} \lim_{\gamma \to 0} \lim_{\Omega \to \infty} \ln \equiv \Xi/\Omega \tag{4}$$

the analytic continuation of the equilibrium pressure into the metastable region. (There is a singularity of $p'(z;\mathcal{R})$ at the end of the metastable region where the uniform state is no longer stable against small perturbations).

The question arises however, of whether there is any way of defining metastable states for systems with realistic (non infinite-range) potentials, i.e. $\gamma \neq 0$. It seems quite possible[6] (on the basis of the droplet model) that for such potentials the isotherm $p(\rho)$ (and $p(z)$) has an essential singularity at the onset of condensation $\rho = \rho_A$. It is however, possible that there might still be some sort of analytic continuation which will define the metastable state[7]. Even if this were the case there would still be the question of how to characterize the metastable state physically, i.e. how to define a region $\mathcal{R}$ in configuration space in which the metastable state would be a local minimum for the free energy.

We may gain some insight into this problem by considering the case of very small γ, i.e. $\gamma^{-1} >> r_o$ where r_o is the effective range of $q(r)$. Making the dimensions of the cell ω of $0(\gamma^{-1+\delta})$, $0 < \delta < 1$, we then have from our inequalities[1] that

$$a(\rho, \gamma) = CE\{a^o(\rho) + \frac{1}{2}\alpha\rho^2\} + o(\gamma) \tag{5}$$

while

$$a'(\rho, \gamma; \omega, \mathcal{R}) = a^o(\rho) + \frac{1}{2}\alpha\rho^2 + o(\gamma) \tag{6}$$

where ρ_- and ρ_+ are again chosen in such a way that $a^o(\rho) + \frac{1}{2}\alpha\rho^2$ is convex in that interval. It is thus seen that if ρ is in the metastable portion of $a^o(\rho) + \frac{1}{2}\alpha\rho^2$, (for $\gamma = 0$), then for sufficiently small γ, and hence $\omega^{1/\nu} >> r_o$, restricting the system to a region in configuration space where it cannot be very non-uniform on the scale of γ^{-1} leads to a free energy per unit volume very close to that of van der Waals, $\gamma = 0$, metastable value, corresponding to the system being uniform. The free energy for the unrestricted system $a(\rho, \gamma)$ will, on the other hand, be close to the flat portion of the curve, corresponding to the system being in two phases. This is true both in one and higher dimensions. In the latter case, we expect the system to have a first order phase transition even for finite γ while a one dimensional system will not have a phase transition[8] for $\gamma \neq 0$. The difference between (5) and (6) in one dimension thus indicates a tendency to form clusters on the scale of γ^{-1}, with densities close to those of liquid and vapour phases (something found numerically by Andrews[8]). The fact that in one dimension $a(\rho, \gamma)$ is a differentiable function[7] of ρ for $\gamma \neq 0$ (at least for some forms of q and φ) also indicates that the "metastable" or uniform state for finite γ cannot come from simple analytic continuation in ρ of the equilibrium uniform state, i.e. while $a'(\rho, \gamma; \omega, \mathcal{R})$ is "close" to $a(\rho, \gamma)$ for $\rho < \rho_A$ it is not close for $\rho_A < \rho < \rho_B$ to an analytic continuation of $a(\rho, \gamma)$ as would be the case in the limit $\gamma \to 0$, where $a'(\rho, 0+; \mathcal{R})$ is the analytic continuation of $a(\rho, 0+)$. This would be consistent with the conjecture[5, 6] that in higher dimensions also (where there is a phase transition for finite γ) the metastable state is not a simple analytic continuation of the equilibrium state. It is however possible, and even probable, that $a'(\rho, \gamma: \omega, \mathcal{R})$ is analytic for $\rho < \rho_B$ or $\rho > \rho_C$.

These considerations, while suggestive of the meaning of the metastable state for very small but, finite γ are not entirely satisfactory in that a' depends somewhat on the choice of ω which is not an intrinsic parameter of the problem (simple considerations seen to indicate that the choice $\omega^{1/\nu} \sim \gamma^{-1/2}$ gives the best bounds for a' in (5)). There are two possible ways which occur to me about how it might be possible to "uniquely" define the metastable state:

(1) Let $\gamma^{\nu}\varphi(\gamma r) = \alpha\gamma^{\nu}\psi(\gamma r)$ with $\int \psi(y)dy = 1$ and $\psi(y)$ independent of α and satisfying the conditions, $\psi(k) \geq 0$, $\underset{k}{\mathrm{Max}}\, \tilde{\psi}(\underline{k}) = \psi(0)$, where $\tilde{\psi}(k)$ is the Fourier transform of $\psi(y)$ e.g., $\psi(y) = (2\pi)^{-\nu/2} e^{-1/2\, y^2}$. Then in the limit $\gamma \to 0$ the metastable (and unstable) state for $\alpha < \alpha_o$ is the analytic continuation of the equilibrium state for $\alpha > \alpha_o$. It is now <u>possible</u> that for $\gamma \neq 0$ there might also be an analytic continuation in the complex α-plane from $\alpha > \alpha_o$ to $\alpha < \alpha_o$ for the metastable state. (We are assuming here throughout that $a^o(\rho)$ does not have a phase transition in the

range of densities of interest). This is suggested in part by considering "formal" expansions[10] in powers of γ of $a(\rho, \gamma)$ (or correlation functions). The coefficients of this expansion which are functions of ρ and α appear to behave well for the stable and metastable states, the zero order term being $\overline{a^{o}(\rho) + \frac{1}{2}\alpha\rho^2}$, diverging however at the unset of the unstable region.

2) Another possibility which is in principle applicable also to systems with short range potentials is to consider regions $\mathcal{R}$ not in configuration space but in the function space of possible correlation functions a la Ruelle[10]. The metastable state might then be characterized as the state of minimum free energy in the restricted region where the pair distribution function $n_2(\underline{r}_1, \underline{r}_1, +\underline{r})$ approaches ρ^2 asymptotically.

Using the results of reference 1 it is indeed possible to show (c.f. also ref. 11) that when the free energy of the reference system $a^{o}(\rho)$ (where $q(r)$ is "essentially" stable potential and contains a hard core or $q(r) \geqq 0$) is strongly convex in an interval surrounding ρ (e.g. $\frac{d^2 a^{o}(\rho)}{d\rho^2} > 0$ in $(\rho - \delta, \rho + \delta)$) then

$$\lim_{\gamma \to 0} \lim_{\Omega \to \infty} \frac{\gamma^{\nu}}{\Omega} \iint \psi(\gamma r) \left[n_2^{o}(\underline{r}_1, \underline{r}_1 + \underline{r} : \rho, \Omega) - \rho^2 \right] d\underline{r}_1 \, d\underline{r} = 0 \tag{7}$$

where $\psi(y)$ satisfies the conditions of the last paragraph. Eq. (7) follows from the inequality (sec. VIII, ref. 1).

$$a(\rho, \gamma) \leqq a^{o}(\rho) + \tfrac{1}{2}\alpha\rho^2 + \tfrac{1}{2}\alpha\gamma^{\nu} \lim_{\Omega \to \infty} \frac{1}{\Omega} \iint \psi(\gamma r) \left[n_2^{o}(\underline{r}_1, \underline{r}_1 + \underline{r} ; \rho, \Omega) - \rho^2 \right] d\underline{r}_1 d\underline{r} \tag{8}$$

which holds for all α and ψ. Now taking the limit $\gamma \to 0$ we have, under the above conditions on ψ that

$$CE\{a^{o}(\rho) + \tfrac{1}{2}\alpha\rho^2\} \leqq a^{o}(\rho) + \tfrac{1}{2}\alpha\rho^2 + \frac{\alpha}{2} \lim_{\gamma \to 0} \lim_{\Omega \to \infty} \frac{\gamma^{\nu}}{\Omega} \iint \psi(\gamma r) \left[n_2^{o} - \rho^2 \right] d\underline{r}_1 d\underline{r} \tag{9}$$

However under the condition on $a^o(\rho)$ mentioned before $CE\{a^o(\rho) + \frac{1}{2}\alpha\rho^2\} = a^o(\rho) + \frac{1}{2}\alpha\rho^2$ for sufficiently small (but finite $|\alpha|$, since $a^o(\rho)$ is convex). Q.E.D.

1. OTHER TOPICS

2.a. Kinetic Equations and Density Expansions: Exactly Solvable One Dimensional System

We have made a tetailed study of the time evolution of the distribution function $f(q, v, t)$ of a labelled (test) particle in a one-dimensional system of hard rods of diameter a. The system has a density ρ and is in equilibrium at $t = 0$. (Some properties of this system were studied earlier by Jepsen.) When the distribution function f at $t = 0$ corresponds to a delta function in position and velocity, then $f(q, v, t)$ is essentially the time-displaced self distribution function f_s. This function f_s (which can be found in an explicit closed form), and all of the system properties which can be derived from it, depend on ρ and a only through the combination $n = (\rho/(1 - \rho a))$. In particular, the diffusion constant D is given by $D^{-1} = \lim_{s \to 0}[\tilde{\psi}(s)]^{-1} = (2\pi\beta m)^{1/2}n$, where $\tilde{\psi}(s)$ is the Laplace transform of the velocity auto-correlation function $\psi(t) = \langle v(t)v\rangle$. An expansion of $[\tilde{\psi}(s)]^{-1}$ in powers of n on the other hand has the form $\sum B_l n^l/s^{l-1}$, leading to divergence of the density coefficients for $l \geq 2$ when $s \to 0$. This is similar to the divergences found in higher dimensional systems. Similar results are found as well in the expansion of the collision operator describing the time evolution of $f(q,v,t)$. The lowest order term in the expansion is the ordinary (linear) Boltzmann equation, while higher terms are $0(\rho^l t^{l-1})$. Thus any attempt to write a Bogoliubov, Choh-Uhlenbeck type of Markoffian kinetic equation as a power series in the density leads to divergences in the terms beyond the Boltzmann equation. A Markoffian collision operator can however be constructed, without using a density expansion, which e.g. describes the stationary distribution of a charged test particle in the system in the presence of a constant electric field. The distribution of the test particle in the presence of an oscillating external field is also found. Finally, the short and long time behavior of the self-distribution is examined.

2.b. Properties of a Harmonic Crystal in a Stationary Non-Equilibrium State

The stationary nonequilibrium Gibbsian ensemble representing a harmonic crystal in contact with several idealized heat reservoirs at different temperatures is shown to have a Gaussian Γ-space distribution for the case where the stochastic interaction between the system and heat reservoirs may be represented by Fokker-Planck type operators. The covariance matrix of this Gaussian is found explicitly for a linear chain with nearest neighbor forces in contact at its ends with heat reservoirs at temperatures T_1 and T_N, N being the number of oscillators. We also find explicitly the covariance matrix, but not the distribution, for the case where the interaction between the system and the reservoirs is represented by very "hard" collisions. This matrix differs from that for the previous case only by a trivial factor. The heat flux in the stationary state is found, as expected, to be proportional to the temperature difference $(T_1 - T_N)$ rather than to the temperature gradiant $(T_1 - T_N)/N$. The kinetic temperature of the jth oscillator T(j) behaves, however, in an unexpected fashion. T(j) is essentially constant in the interior of the chain decreasing exponentially in the direction of the hotter reservoir rising only at the end oscillator in contact with that reservoir (with corresponding behavior at the other end of the chain). No explanation is offered for this paradoxical result.

2.c. A Note on the Ensemble Dependence of Fluctuations with Application to Machine Computations

The standard theory of fluctuations in thermodynamic variables in various ensembles is generalized to non-thermodynamic variables: e.g., the mean square fluctuations of the kinetic energy K in a classical micro-canonical ensemble at fixed energy E is given for large systems by $\langle(\delta K)^2\rangle/\langle K\rangle = T(1-3/2C)$ where T is the temperature (corresponding to the energy E) and C is the specific heat per particle (in units of Boltzmann's constant). The general results may be expressed in terms of the asymptotic behavior of the Ursell functions in various ensembles. Applications are made to molecular dynamic computations where time averages correspond (via ergodicity) to phase averages in an ensemble with fixed energy and momentum. The results are also useful for time dependent correlations.

REFERENCES

1. J. L. Lebowitz and O. Penrose, J. Math. Phys. 7, 98 (1966).

2. J. L. Lebowitz, S. Baer and G. Stell, Phys. Rev. 141, 198 (1966).

3. E. Lieb, J. Math. Phys. 7, 1016 (1966).

4. T. Burke, J. L. Lebowitz and E. Lieb, Phys. Rev. 149, 118 (1966).

5. J. L. Lebowitz and O. Penrose, "Rigorous Treatment of Equilibrium and Metastable States in the van der Waals-Maxwell Theory of First Order Phase Transitions", to appear in the Proceedings of 5th Eastern Theoretical Physics Conference; M. Dresden, editor.

6. Andreev, J. Exp. and Theor. Phys. (U.S.S.R.) 12, (1963); M. E. Fisher, Proceedings of the Centennial Conference on Phase Transformations at the University of Kentucky, 1965, to be published.

7. J. S. Langer, "Theory of the Condensation Point", Proceedings of the 5th Eastern Theoretical Physics Conference; M. Dresden, editor.

8. M. Kac, Phys. Fluids 2, 8 (1959).

9. F. C. Andrews, Phys. Lett. 10, 17 (1966).

10. J. L. Lebowitz, G. Stell and S. Baer, J. Math. Phys. 6, 1282 (1965).

11. D. Ruelle, J. Math. Phys. 6, 201 (1965).

12. J. L. Lebowitz and J. K. Percus (to be published in Phys. Rev.)

13. Z. Rieder, J. L. Lebowitz and E. Lieb (to be published in J. Math. Phys.)

14. J. L. Lebowitz, J. K. Percus and L. Verlet (to be published in Phys. Rev.)

DISCUSSION

Hajdu: Can you generalize your equations to the case where there is an external field?

Lebowitz: You can generalize to terms linear in the field.

Hajdu: Will the kernel depend on the field?

Lebowitz: No, the kernel will not depend on the field, even though you have only one time scale.

Hajdu: If you calculate a static conductivity do you obtain any influence due to the non-Markovian behavior of this equation?

Lebowitz: The d.c. conductivity is related to the diffusion coefficient by the usual Einstein relation.

Bedeaux: You said about the strange temperature behavior along the chain of oscillators in the stationary state

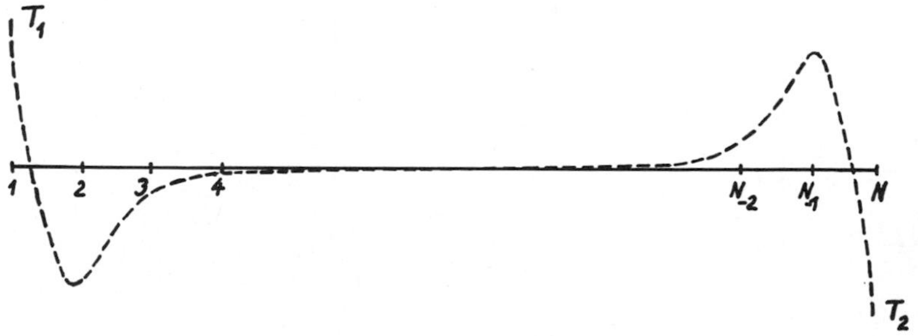

that you should intuitively think that oscillator 2 will have a temperature more or less the same as 1 (anyway at least higher than the average temperature) because 1 is much nearer than N. This intuitive idea is bound to the case (in my opinion) of finite conductivity. In this case the conductivity is infinite and therefore the distance is of no importance. The conductivity of the chain as a whole (seen as a possibility to transport heat from heatbath T_1 to heatbath T_2) has a finite value independent of the length of the chain. This will be caused by a finite resistance for heat to be extracted from heatbath T_1 by oscillator 1 and the same for heat to be absorbed by heatbath T_2 from oscillator N. In the left hand side of the chain you therefore have the following situation. It is easier for heat to flow away to the right than to enter the chain from the left. In the stationary state you should therefore expect that the heatflow near oscillator 1 has a lower density and a higher speed (the flux is naturally the same at any point of the chain) than the rest of the chain. This corresponds to a situation in which the temperature is lower than the average temperature in the chain. The reverse argument gives in the same way higher temperature at the other end of the chain.

Fröhlich: Could you introduce a small anharmonic term?

Lebowitz: I cannot solve that problem.

Stecki: Is the Résibois-Prigogine destruction term (functional of the initial distribution) missing?

Lebowitz: It is in the kernel K.

Uhlenbeck: The problem of the heat conduction in a linear harmonic chain is, I think, analogous to the heat conduction in a Knudsen gas where one also has a constant temperature between the plates and some sort of boundary layer near the plates.

Lebowitz: But the jump doesn't actually go below.

Uhlenbeck: No, but you have the boundary layer which is just of this length.

Lebowitz: I wouldn't be at all surprised if there is a boundary layer, but it is surprising that it goes below the average. By the way I should mention one thing, not the exact solution but the general result for the problem was also done by Dr. Olaf Bills, from Australia using the Wang-Uhlenbeck method for a linear chain. He did not get an explicit stationary solution but he considered more the time dependent solution.

Uhlenbeck: Is the distribution you obtained the same as found long ago by E. Einstein and by Epstein?

Lebowitz: I do not believe so.

ON THE THREE-DIMENSIONAL ISING MODEL

D. C. MATTIS *)
Belfer Graduate School of
Science, Yeshiva University
New York, N.Y. 10033

ABSTRACT

The 3-dimensional Ising model is reduced to a problem on a 2-dimensional net involving non-commuting operators, by use of the standard transfer-matrix method. This is then solved by an approximate reduction to boson operators (i.e. approximate second-quantization), reduction to normal modes, summation of all the terms in the Baker-Hausdorff expansion of the exponentials and solution of the appropriate eigenvalue equations.

The result of this is the free energy and specific heat of the 3-dimensional Ising model as a function of temperature, with or without a magnetic field, or of the equivalent lattice-gas problem, at arbitrary density.

This paper will serve to introduce a new method of solving the Ising model, in an approximation which we hope will prove adequate in three (or more) dimensions. Briefly stated, the method is as follows:

(a) Use of the transfer-matrix method, which reduces the 3-dimensional partition sum to the solution of an eigenvalue problem on a 2-dimensional grid, without approximation.

---

*) Work supported by U.S. Air Force under A.F.O.S.R. grant # 1075-66.

(b) Replacement of the Pauli spin operators by boson field operators, after choosing σ_x, σ_y and σ_z in a suitable cartesian frame. The transfer matrix which, in the exact formulation is the product of exponentials of quadratic forms in spin operators, becomes in our approximation, products of exponentials of quadratic forms in boson operators.

(c) Exact diagonalization of these products of exponential operators.

Let us discuss these steps in order. Step (a) extracts maximum advantage of the spinor operators and of the nearest-neighbor character of the interplanar forces. Note that if, instead of (b) we follow it by what might be designated step (b'), (b') Replacement of the Pauli spin operators by (certain) fermion field operators, we can then proceed to an exact solution of the 2-dimensional Ising model and recover all the well known results of Onsager[1)] and others[2)]. In three or more dimensions, however, step (b') leads to insoluble expressions for well known reasons[3)], but step (b) is then a reasonable approximation. Conversely step (b) is not too good for the 2-dimensional Ising model because in the one-dimensional transfer matrix which results, it is quite important to take the "hard core" into account; in the 2- or higher-dimensional transfer matrices, the "hard core" is of lesser importance due to the possibility of two spin disturbances going around one another without colliding. Once (b) is justified, step (c) follows exactly because the Baker-Hausdorff expansion can be exactly and explicitly carried out. Products of exponential operators are combined into a single exponential and then diagonalized.

Below we shall principally discuss formulas valid for isotropic nearest-neighbor forces in a simple cubic lattice, in the absence of an applied magnetic field and at temperatures T greater than the Curie temperature T_c. (We can generalize to arbitrary magnetic fields, temperatures below T_c, and other crystal structures. But aside from indicating what is to be done, we shall limit ourselves to the restrictions outlined above in the present, introductory, paper.)

For details of step (a) the reader is first referred to an article by Schultz, Lieb and the present author[2)] in which it is shown that the partition function Z,

$$Z = \exp - \frac{F}{kT}$$

$$= \mathrm{Tr}\{\exp \sum_{a=1}^{N_1} \sum_{b,c=1}^{N_2} K\sigma_{a,b,c}(\sigma_{a+1,b,c} + \sigma_{a,b+1,c} + \sigma_{a,b,c+1})\} \tag{1}$$

(where K = J/kT, F = free energy, and σ = Pauli spin matrix) can be determined as the solution of an eigenvalue problem:

$$V\,\psi = z\,\psi \tag{2}$$

Here V is the transfer matrix, ψ is an eigenfunction of V, and z is the l a r g e s t eigenvalue of V. Then it is proved[2)] that

$$Z = \exp - F/kT = z^{N_1} \tag{3}$$

A solution of the eigenvalue problem (2) thus fixes Z and F, hence all the thermodynamic properties of the system. As is well known V involves two non-commuting operators[2)]:

$$V = V_1^{1/2}\, V_2\, V_1^{1/2} \tag{4}$$

where

$$V_1 = (2 \cosh K)^{N_2^2} \exp(-2K^* \sum_{b,c=1}^{N_2} \sigma^+_{b,c}\, \sigma^-_{b,c}) \tag{5}$$

and

$$V_2 = \exp\left[K \sum_{b,c=1}^{N_2} \sigma^x_{b,c}\, (\sigma^x_{b+1,c} + \sigma^x_{b,c+1})\right] \tag{6}$$

with K* defined by:

$$\tanh K^* = \exp - 2K \quad (\text{or } \tanh K = \exp - 2K^*). \tag{7}$$

The choice of σ_x in (6) is the appropriate one for $T \geqq T_c$; below

T_c, a linear combination of σ_z and σ_x is more appropriate, the amount of σ_z being a function of the magnetization. As the present discussion is limited to temperatures higher than T_c the formulation given above imposes itself. We recall the definitions:

$$\sigma^+ = \begin{pmatrix} 0 & 1 \\ 0 & 0 \end{pmatrix}, \quad \sigma^- = \begin{pmatrix} 0 & 0 \\ 1 & 0 \end{pmatrix} \text{ and } \quad \sigma_x = \sigma^+ + \sigma^- . \tag{8}$$

The commutation relations are:

$$\begin{aligned} &[\sigma_i^{\pm}, \sigma_j^{\pm}] = 0 \qquad , \qquad i \neq j \\ &[\sigma_i^-, \sigma_i^+] = 1 - 2\sigma_i^+ \sigma_i^- \qquad , \qquad i \neq j \end{aligned} \tag{9}$$

Step (b) consists of obeying these commutation relations on the average, i.e., averaging the right-hand-side of (9).

In V_2, Eq. (6), we replace σ_x as follows:

$$\sigma_i^+ \rightarrow a_i^* \sqrt{1 - 2\bar{n}}, \quad \sigma_i^- \rightarrow a_i \sqrt{1 - 2\bar{n}}, \quad \sigma_i^x \rightarrow (a_i + a_i^*) \sqrt{1 - 2\bar{n}} \tag{10}$$

In V_1, the number-counting operator $n_i = \sigma_i^+ \sigma_i^-$ is replaced as follows:

$$n_i \rightarrow a_i^* a_i \tag{11}$$

which is exact for $n_i = 0$ or 1 but not for larger values. The reliability of the present method stems from the fact that the average n_i which appears in (10) and in the body of this work will be small compared to 1, and it is plausible that spurious values $n_i = 2, 3, \ldots$ do not play any significant role in the solution, even at $T = T_c$.

The self-consistent determination of $\bar{n}$ is the next important step. One first evaluates the internal energy U:

$$\begin{aligned} U &= \frac{-3}{2} N_1 J \sum_{b,c} \langle \psi | \sigma_{b,c}^x (\sigma_{b+1,c}^x + \sigma_{b,c+1}^x) | \psi \rangle \\ &\rightarrow \frac{-3}{2} N_1 J(1-2\bar{n}) \sum_{b,c} \langle \psi | (a_{b,c}^* + a_{b,c})(a_{b+1,c}^* + a_{b,c+1}^* + \text{h.c.}) | \psi \rangle \\ &= U_1(\bar{n}, T) . \end{aligned} \tag{12}$$

This quantity we denote $U_1(\bar{n}, T)$ indicating the functional dependence on $\bar{n}$ and T, and distinguishing it by a subscript from a second evaluation of the internal energy which we next perform. We turn back to Eqs. (2) and (3), and having determined z and F by methods discussed in the body of the paper, we may obtain U by the familiar thermodynamic relationship:

$$U = \partial(F/T)/\partial(1/T) = U_2(\bar{n}, \partial\bar{n}/\partial T, T) \tag{12'}$$

We then solve, numerically if necessary, the self-consistency equation $U_1 = U_2$ for $\partial\bar{n}/\partial T$ and obtain the equation,

$$\frac{\partial \bar{n}}{\partial T} = g(\bar{n}, T) \tag{13}$$

in terms of a known and calculable function g. In the present case, it can be shown that g is always finite[5]. Thus the solution of the differential equation above, subject to the obvious boundary condition $\bar{n} = 0$ at $T = \infty$, yields the thermodynamically self-consistent $\bar{n}(T)$.

Because of the tedious nature of this calculation, it is convenient to have an approximate formula for $\bar{n}$, valid at high temperatures but not in the critical region $T = T_c$, viz.,

$$\bar{n} \cong \frac{1}{N_2^2} \Sigma < \psi | a_i^* a_i | \psi > \tag{14}$$

Unfortunately, it turns out that this formula gives an infinite derivative $\partial\bar{n}/\partial T$ at T_c even though $\bar{n}$ itself is small. Because this feature is not in agreement with (13), the rigorous formula (13) *must* be used in studying critical point phenomena.

We now turn to the body of this work, the determination of the ground state ψ and z. By translational invariance the normal modes are plane waves. Explicitly, let us introduce the Fourier-transformed operators as follows:

$$a_q = \frac{1}{N_2} \Sigma\, a_i\, e^{iq\cdot r_i}, \quad a_q^* = \frac{1}{N_2} \Sigma\, a_i^*\, e^{-iq\cdot r_i} \tag{15}$$

where $r_i = (b_i, c_i)$ is again a lattice point in the typical plane. We then find directly:

$$Z = (2 \cosh K)^{N_1 N_2^2} \exp (N_1 \sum_{q_2 \geqq 0} \log z_q) . \qquad (16)$$

where z_q is the largest eigenvalue of the qth normal mode transfer matrix given by

$$V_q \equiv V_{1q}^{1/2} V_{2q} V_{1q}^{1/2} \qquad (17)$$

with

$$V_{1q} = \exp \{-2K^* (n_q + n_{-q})\}, \quad n_q = a_q^* a_q , \qquad (17a)$$

and

$$V_{2q} = \exp \{K(1 - 2\bar{n})\omega_q (n_q + n_{-q} + a_q^* a_{-q}^* + a_{-q} a_q\} \qquad (17b)$$

where

$$\omega_q = \sum_{\substack{\delta = \\ \text{near. neighb.}}} \exp i q \cdot \delta, \qquad \delta = (\pm 1, 0), (0, \pm 1) . \qquad (18)$$

From (16) we deduce F, hence U_2, once z_q is found. U_1 is simply the expectation value of the operator

$$-\frac{3}{2} N_1 J(1 - 2\bar{n}) \sum_{q_z \geqq 0} \omega_q (n_q + n_{-q} + a_q^* a_{-q}^* + a_{-q} a_q) \qquad (19)$$

in the ground state, Ψ. Thus, to proceed, we must find this state. It will be necessary to manipulate arbitrary quadratic forms, for which the following nomenclature will be found helpful:

$$h_k(x) \equiv n_k + n_{-k} + x(a_k a_{-k} + h. c.) . \qquad (20)$$

For example, (19) involves the particular quadratic form $h_k(1)$. We shall also require 2 distinct ways of writing exponential operators: the "canonical form" (on the left, below) and the "normal ordered form" (on the right):

$$\exp(y\, h_k(x)) = (\exp C)(\exp A a^*_k a^*_{-k})(\exp B(n_k + n_{-k}))(\exp A a_{-k} a_k) \tag{21}$$

It can be shown[4] (here we omit all proofs) that these two expressions are indeed equal provided x and y are suitably restricted, which will inevitably be the case here, and that the (real) parameters A, B and C are related to the parameters x, y by:

$$\left.\begin{aligned} &\exp(-B) = \{\cosh \epsilon\}\{1 - (1 - x^2)^{-1/2} \tanh\epsilon\} \\ &\quad \text{where we introduce the abbreviation: } \epsilon \equiv y\,(1 - x^2)^{1/2} \\ &A \exp(-B) = x(1 - x^2)^{-1/2} \sinh\epsilon, \quad \exp(-C) = (\exp y)\exp(-B) \\ &\quad \cosh\epsilon = \cosh B - \tfrac{1}{2} A^2 \exp(-B) \end{aligned}\right\} \tag{22}$$

These formulas have the simple limiting form when $x = 1$:

$$\exp(-B) = 1 - y, \quad A\exp(-B) = y \quad \text{and} \quad \exp(-C) = (1-y)\exp y. \tag{23}$$

The procedure for diagonalizing V_q has been found to be the following:

(i) Cast V_{2q} into normal order

(ii) Combine it with V_{1q}, so that $V_{1q}^{1/2}\, V_{2q}\, V_{1q}^{1/2}$ is in normal order.

(iii) Put the combined expression in canonical form.

(iv) Diagonalize $h_k(x)$ by the procedure described below.

The procedure for diagonalizing h is the familiar Bogolubov transformation, which consists of picking real parameters u and v subject to $u^2 - v^2 = 1$, and letting

$$\left.\begin{aligned} a_k &\rightarrow u_k\, a_k + v_k\, a^*_{-k} \\ a^*_k &\rightarrow u_k\, a^*_k + v_k\, a_{-k} \end{aligned}\right\} \tag{24}$$

in such a manner as to diagonalize h:

$$h_k(x_k) \rightarrow (1 - x_k^2)^{1/2} (n_k + n_{-k}) + (1 - x_k^2)^{1/2} - 1 \,. \tag{25}$$

After step (iii) the appropriate x_k is found to be

$$x_k \equiv \frac{\Omega_k \sinh 2K}{\Omega_k \cosh 2K - 1} \,, \quad \text{where } \Omega_k = \omega_k(1 - 2\bar{n})K \,. \tag{26}$$

The Bogolubov parameters are thus

$$\left. \begin{aligned} u_k^2 &= \frac{1}{2} (1 - x_k^2)^{-1/2} + \frac{1}{2} \\ v_k^2 &= \frac{1}{2} (1 - x_k^2)^{-1/2} - \frac{1}{2} \end{aligned} \right\} \tag{27}$$

and the various ground state expectation values are

$$\langle n_k \rangle = \frac{1}{2} (1 - x_k^2)^{-1/2} - \frac{1}{2} \tag{28}$$

$$\langle h_k(x_k) \rangle = (1 - x_k^2)^{1/2} - 1 \tag{29}$$

$$\langle h_k(1) \rangle = \frac{1 - x_k}{1 + x_k}^{1/2} - 1 \,. \tag{30}$$

where $h_k(1) = (a_k + a_{-k}^+)(a_k^+ + a_{-k}) - 1.$

Finally, we have z_k to be inserted into (16) to yield Z and F:

$$z_k = \{\cosh 2K - \Omega_k - \sqrt{1 + \Omega_k^2 - 2\Omega_k \cosh 2K}\} \{\exp \Omega_k\} \{\cosh 2K - 1\}^{-1} \tag{31}$$

With the help of (30) the internal energy is found to be

$$U_1 = \frac{-3}{2} N_1 \; J(1 - 2\bar{n}) \sum_{q_z > 0} \omega_q \left\{ \frac{1 - \Omega_q \exp - 2K}{1 - \Omega_q \exp 2K} \right\}^{1/2} \tag{32}$$

With (28) the (approximate) valuation of $\bar{n}$ is readily carried out:

$$\bar{n} \cong -\frac{1}{2} + \frac{1}{2N_2^2} \sum \frac{1 - \Omega_k \cosh 2K}{\{1 + \Omega_k^2 - 2\Omega_k \cosh 2K\}^{1/2}} \tag{33}$$

Note that within the range of validity of this expression, ($T_c >> T$) we may approximate Ω_k by $\omega_k K$ on the right-hand side and thus have a direct, albeit approximate, valuation of $\bar{n}$.

The above completes the technical aspects of the program outlined at the beginning of the paper. While numerical results are not yet available, some features of the method are already apparent and we shall briefly mention them here. The Curie temperature is found by the vanishing of the denominator in (32) at $q = 0$, i.e.,

$$4(1 - 2\bar{n})\, J/kT_c = \exp -2J/kT_c \tag{34}$$

with the exact $\bar{n}$ determined by the method[5] of Eqs. (12) and (13). While the determination of T_c by this method will await the numerical work, we may already use the value of T_c known from numerical series extrapolation methods[2)], viz. $kT_c \doteq 4.5$ J, to estimate $\bar{n}(T_c)$.

$$1 - 2\bar{n}(T_c) \doteq \frac{4.5}{4} \exp - \frac{2}{4.5} \doteq 0.72$$

or

$$\bar{n}(T_c) \doteq 0.14 \quad . \tag{35}$$

This is much smaller than the "dangerous" value $\frac{1}{2}$, and as this is an estimate of the <u>maximum</u> $\bar{n}$ we may conclude that the "unphysical" region $n_i = 2, 3, \ldots$ introduces little error in the entire range of temperatures $T \geqq T_c$. While it would be particularly desirable to have a method valid in the critical region, we have here at the very least a calculation which must be valid at high temperatures and which we hope soon to test against high-temperature expansions such as have been given by Rushbrooke and others over the past years.

Finally it should be noted that despite the divergence of the summand in U_1 at T_c the internal energy remains finite because of the restricted phase space at $k = 0$. The specific heat, however, does diverge (but not for a five- or higher-dimensional Ising model due to the ever more restricted phase space at $k = 0$). The two- and three-dimensional (and possibly the four-dimensional) Ising models are thus found to be unique in having a specific heat infinity at T_c, although for different reasons.

The present method can be extended to the case of finite applied magnetic field, and will eventually permit calculations on the "lattice gas" problem which is so closely related to the central study of statistical mechanics.

FOOTNOTES AND REFERENCES

1. L. Onsager, Phys. Rev. 65, 117 (1944).
2. Such as the spontaneous magnetization, due to Onsager and later C. N. Yang, Phys. Rev. 85, 808 (1952). Note that the magnetization in finite magnetic field has never been found exactly. For reviews see: G. Newell and E. Montroll, Revs. Mod. Phys. 25, 353 (1953), C. Domb. Adv. in Phys. 9, 151 (1960), and for the transfer matrix formalism: T. Schultz, D. Mattis and E. Lieb, Revs. Mod. Phys. 36, 856 (1964).
3. See the related discussion in the book by E. Lieb and D. Mattis, Mathematical Physics in One Dimension-Exactly Soluble Models of Interacting Particles, Academic Press, New York, 1966.
4. The derivations have been partly carried out with the collaboration of E. Lieb.
5. Note added in proof: A simpler method than this one has been found since the paper was delivered at the Conference, which consists essentially of evaluating $U_3(\overline{n}, T)$ = energy of bonds connecting two planes *via* the transfer matrix. Consequently $\overline{n}$ can be found algebraically without solving Eq. (13), by setting $U_1 = U_3$.

DISCUSSION

Martin: Since the approximation with the Bose commutation relations is uncontrolled, have you tested it in the known case of two dimensions?

Mattis: Because of the "hard core", a boson (rather than a fermion) approximation to what is essentially a linear chain problem may yield crazy results. None the less if one insists on trying it, he will see that the specific heat of the two-dimensional net is more singular than that of the three-dimensional net, which in turn is more singular than the four-dimensional, etc.

Jancovici: Average field methods like this one, usually work better the higher the number of dimensions.

STRUCTURE OF THE FERMION DENSITY MATRIX

LOUIS WITTEN
RIAS, Baltimore, Md.
21227; June 20, 1966.

ABSTRACT

One of the key problems involved in understanding the structure of the p'th order density matrix has been called the ensemble N-representability problem. It is the problem of how to recognize whether a given p'th order reduced density matrix is derivable by integrating the density matrix formed from an ensemble of dynamically possible states of the system (antisymmetric wave functions for fermions) over all but p coordinates. This problem is equivalent to asking for the dynamically permitted structure of reduced density matrices; i. e. the allowed sets of eigenvalues and eigenfunctions. The possible structure of the one particle reduced density matrix is understood and described. The two particle reduced matrix is of much greater interest and of correspondingly greater complexity. The possible structure of this matrix is partially understood and a description is presented which permits many families of allowed two particle reduced matrices to be specified.

STRUCTURE OF THE PERMION DENSITY MATRIX

1. INTRODUCTION; REPRESENTABILITY PROBLEM

The density matrix of a many-particle system of Fermions with fixed number of particles, N, is defined by

$$\rho = | \psi > < \psi | \tag{1}$$

for a system in the normalized state $|\psi>$ and by

$$\rho = \sum_i P_i |\psi_i><\psi_i| \tag{2}$$

for a system which is described as being in one or another dynamical state $|\psi_i>$ according to a probability distribution P_i $(0 \leqq P_i \leqq 1 ; \Sigma P_i = 1)$. The expectation value of an operator, H, is given by

$$< H > = \mathrm{Tr}\, \rho H. \tag{3}$$

For a 1, 2, ... particle operator this reduces to $\mathrm{Tr}\rho_1 H$, $\mathrm{Tr}\rho_2 H$, ... respectively where the reduced density matrices ρ_1, ρ_2, ... are defined by

$$< j | \rho_1 | i > = \mathrm{Tr}\, \rho a_i^+ a_j \tag{4}$$

$$< kl | \rho_2 | ij > = \mathrm{Tr}\, \rho a_j^+ a_i^+ a_k a_l , \tag{5}$$

a_i, a_j^+ represent the annihilation, creation operators for single particle states i and j.

For many problems only one and two particle operators are of interest, for calculating the expectation value of these it is sufficient to have a knowledge only of ρ_1 and ρ_2 (henceforth one-matrix and two-matrix[(1)]). If for example one were interested in estimating the ground state energy (E_g) of a system which interacted therough two body interactions alone, one would calculate it by finding the expectation value of the Hamiltonian operator, H, and would need to use only ρ_2. A usual approximation scheme is given by varying possible state functions $|\psi>$ (varying over a class of antisymmetric state functions). Under this variation, an upper bound to the ground state energy is given by

$$<\psi | H\psi> = \mathrm{Tr}\, \rho H \geqq E_g . \tag{6}$$

depends on the coordinates of N particles. Actually the inequality involving ρ would be formally true for variations of ρ over mixed states as well. One could hope to simplify the approximation by using

$$\mathrm{Tr}\ \rho_2 H \geqq E_g \tag{7}$$

for all variations of the trial two-matrix, ρ_2. This would be an enormous simplification since ρ_2 depends only on four sets of coordinates. The difficulty is that not any function of four sets of coordinates could be included in the class over which ρ_2 is varied. We must vary ρ_2 only under the class of N-representable or, more specifically, ensemble N-representable(2) two matrices. A two matrix, σ, is N-representable (ensemble N-representable) if there exists an antisymmetric $|\psi\rangle$ (or family $|\psi_i\rangle$ and probabilities, P_i) such that the resultant density matrix, ρ, satisfies

$$\langle kl\,|\sigma|\,ij\rangle = \mathrm{Tr}\ \rho a_j^+ a_i^+ a_k a_l\ . \tag{8}$$

The variation (7) is only valid if the constraint of ensemble N-representability is imposed on the trial two matrices. No practical way has been discovered to test the ensemble N-representability of a trial two matrix other than through the defining relation (8). However, the corresponding problem for trial one-matrices has been solved. We shall reconstruct this solution in section II and discuss the two-matrix in section III.

Obviously necessary conditions that trial one matrices, $\langle j\,|\,\rho_1\,|\,i\rangle$, satisfy are that they be Hermitian, non-negative matrices with trace equal to N. Obviously necessary conditions on $\langle kl\,|\,\rho_2\,|\,ij\rangle$ are that they be antisymmetric in an interchange of i with j or k with l, have trace equal to N(N-1), be non-negative and Hermitian. Hermiticity means

$$\langle kl\,|\,\rho_2\,|\,ij\rangle = \overline{\langle ij\,|\,\rho_2\,|\,kl\rangle}\ , \tag{9}$$

the bar denoting complex conjugation.

If we were interested in making calculations with a different set of single particle states

$$b_i = \sum_i U_{ij} a_j\ , \tag{10}$$

U being a unitary matrix, we would use a transformed set of reduced density matrices. The transformation properties are exemplified by that of the two-matrix

$$< kl|\rho_2|ij >' = \mathrm{Tr}\,\rho b_j^+ b_i^+ b_k b_l = \sum_{pqrs} < pq|\rho_2|rs > \overline{U}_{ri}\overline{U}_{sj}U_{kp}U_{lq}. \qquad (11)$$

The p-particle reduced density matrix can be considered to be a tensor of rank 2p in a unitary space. Being Hermitian matrices, they have spectral decompositions. For example,

$$< j|\rho_1|i > = \sum_{u=1}^{M} \lambda_u \overline{f}_i^u f_j^u ; \quad \sum_i f_i^u \overline{f}_i^v = \delta_{uv} \qquad (12)$$

$$< kl|\rho_2|ij > = \sum_u \nu_u \overline{f}_{ij}^u f_{kl}^u ; \quad \sum_{ij} f_{ij}^u \overline{f}_{ij}^v = \delta_{uv} \qquad (13)$$

λ_u and ν_u are the set of eigenvalues of the one and two matrix respectively; f_i^u and f_{ij}^u are the corresponding sets of orthonormal eigenfunctions; M is the rank of the one matrix.

Under the transformation (10),

$$f_i^u \rightarrow f_j^{u'} = \sum_i U_{ji} f_i^u$$

$$(14)$$

$$f_{ij}^u \rightarrow f_{ij}^{u'} = \sum_{kl} U_{ik} U_{jl} f_{kl}^u$$

One would expect that the constraints of N-representability and ensemble N-representability should be characterizable in terms of constraints on the eigenvalues and eigenfunctions. This is expected as well for the corresponding representability problems for the general p-order reduced density matrix. Quite probably an understanding of the representability problems would yield the allowed sets of reduced density matrix eigenfunctions and eigenvalues that systems may have. Such an understanding, especially if an allowed set of eigenproperties of a p-matrix can be correlated with a corresponding system Hamiltonian, would be a great help in understanding any strictly quantum mechanical properties that a system may exhibit. For example, Yang has shown[3] that the existence of a quantum mechanical phase tranition (e.g. superconductivity) corresponds to the existence of off diagonal long range order of reduced density matrices in coordinate space representation. He has demonstrated that such order corresponds to the existence of a large eigenvalue, of the order of N, for one of the reduced density matrices and for all the higher order reduced density matrices (e.g. starting with the two-matrix for superconductivity).

II. THE REPRESENTABILITY PROBLEM FOR THE ONE MATRIX

Call $\overline{\mu}$ the space of all Hermitian non-negative matrices, $< j | \mu | i >$, with trace equal to N. Let $\overline{\mu}^N$ be the ensemble N-representable subspace of $\overline{\mu}$. $\overline{\mu}$ and $\overline{\mu}^N$ are both convex spaces this means that if μ_1 and μ_2 are elements of $\overline{\mu}$ so is

$$\mu = \alpha\mu_1 + (1-\alpha)\mu_2, \quad 0 \leqq \alpha \leqq 1. \tag{15}$$

If $\mu_1{}^N$ and $\mu_2{}^N$ are ensemble N-representable, there are density matrices ρ^1 and ρ^2 that

$$\begin{aligned} < j | \mu_1{}^N | i > &= \mathrm{Tr}\rho^1 a_i^+ a_j \\ < j | \mu_2{}^N | i > &= \mathrm{Tr}\rho^2 a_i^+ a_j \end{aligned} \tag{16}$$

Hence

$$\mu^N = \alpha\mu_1{}^N + (1-\alpha)\mu_2{}^N, \quad 0 \leqq \alpha \leqq 1, \tag{17}$$

is ensemble N-representable with density matrix $\alpha\rho^1 + (1-\alpha)\rho^2$. $\mu_E{}^N$ is called an extreme point of $\overline{\mu}_N$ if whenever

$$\mu_E{}^N = \alpha\mu_1{}^N + (1-\alpha)\mu_2{}^N, \quad 0 < \alpha < 1, \tag{18}$$

both $\mu_1{}^N$ and $\mu_2{}^N$ are equal to $\mu_E{}^N$. According to the Krein-Millman theorem, a compact convex set is completely determined by its extreme points; that is, any member of the set may be expressed by a linear combination of the extreme points. The set $\bar{\mu}^N$ is a compact convex set; the N-representability problem would be solved if we could characterize all the extreme points of $\bar{\mu}^N$. This characterization has been made for the case of ensemble N-representability.

By a suitable choice of basis the one matrix can be diagonalized. Hence we can imagine that the general one matrix in a certain representation takes the form

$$\{\text{diag } \lambda_1, \lambda_2 \ldots \lambda_M\}, \ \lambda_i \leqq 1. \tag{19}$$

λ_i are the eigenvalues and the restriction, $\lambda_i \leqq 1$, is obvious from the definition of the one matrix. Our problem is to find the extreme points of a compact convex space characterized by (19) with $\Sigma_i \lambda_i = N$. The extreme points are given by the sets

$$\mu_E^N = \{\text{diag } 1, 0, 1, 1 \ldots\}$$

which contain N unit elements and M-N zeros with the unit elements taking all possible distributions successively.

It is clear that every point, μ_E^N, of the type (20) is an extreme point of the set (19). We must show that all extreme points are included in (20). Because of the restrictions, $\lambda_i \leqq 1$, and $\Sigma_i \lambda_i = N$, any other possible extreme point would have more than N non-zero entries. Suppose μ_x^N is assumed to be extreme and not of the form (20). Hence at least two of its non-zero entries x_1 and x_2 are less than 1. So, for example,

$$\mu_x^N = \{\text{diag: } \lambda_1, \lambda_2, 0, 1, 1, 0 \ldots\} \tag{21}$$

where the two non-zero elements λ_1 and λ_2 are less than one. But,

$$\mu_x^N = \tfrac{1}{2}\{\text{diag: } \lambda_1 + \epsilon, \lambda_2 - \epsilon, 0, 1, 1, 0 \ldots\} + \tfrac{1}{2}\{\text{diag: } \lambda_1 - \epsilon, \lambda_2 + \epsilon, 0, 1, 1, 0 \ldots\} \tag{22}$$

For small enough ϵ ($\epsilon > 0$), both expressions in brackets are members of the set (19), and hence μ_x^N cannot be an extreme point.

We next must show that all extreme elements, μ_E^N, are N-representable. We do this by taking the example

$$\{\text{diag: } 1, 1, 1 \ldots 1, 0, 0, 0 \ldots\}; \tag{23}$$

the first N positions have unit elements. Physically this corresponds to a state of the N-particle system in which the first N-states are occupied.

$$\begin{aligned} \Psi &= a_N^+ a_{N-1}^+ \cdots a_1^+ \mid 0 > , \\ \rho &= |\Psi > < \Psi| \end{aligned} \tag{24}$$

yields (23) for a one-matrix. (23) is a one-matrix which can be represented by a density matrix constructed from a single Slater determinant. It is practically obvious and can be formally proved[2] that the state (24) is the only way of producing the one-matrix (23). We have proved the theorem that a non-negative Hermitian one-matrix with trace equal to N is ensemble N-representable if and only if the eigenvalues are less than or equal to one.[4]

III. STRUCTURE OF THE TWO-MATRIX

We have found all the extreme points in the space of ensemble N-representable one-matrices and should like to find all the extreme points in the convex space of ensemble N-representable two-matrices. This is still an unresolved problem. Let $\bar{\sigma}$ be the space of all Hermitian, non-negative matrices, with trace equal to N(N-1), and with the symmetry properties of ρ_2. Any $\sigma \epsilon \bar{\sigma}$ permits a spectral decomposition,

$$< kl \mid \sigma \mid ij > = \sum_u \nu_u \bar{f}_{ij}^u f_{kl}^u \tag{25}$$

For each σ and corresponding f_{ij},

$$< kl \mid \sigma \mid ij > f_{ij} = \nu f_{kl} . \tag{26}$$

The indices range over the positive integers from 1 to M. If σ is a candidate for ensemble N-representability, it may be considered as a fourth rank tensor in a unitary space; the antisymmetric eigenfunctions, f_{ij}, are second rank tensors transforming according to (14). One would expect that the ensemble N-representability problem can be settled only by considering a complete set of independent unitary invariants of σ. In the case of the one-matrix, the eigenvalues represent such a complete set, and in fact the ensemble N-representability problem has a solution which we stated in terms of allowed properties of its eigenvalues.

Under the transformation (14), an antisymmetric tensor, f_{ij}, can be brought to the canonical form in which it is zero everywhere except for 2 x 2 diagonal blocks of the form[5]

$$\begin{pmatrix} 0 & a_\alpha \\ -a_\alpha & 0 \end{pmatrix}; \qquad \alpha = 1, 2, \ldots r , \tag{27}$$

where all a_α are real and positive and the number, r, of non-vanishing a_α is one-half the rank of f_{ij}. The a_α are unitary invariants of f_{ij}, as is the rank. Any eigenfunction of σ can be transformed to the canonical form. However, in general, two eigenfunctions cannot simultaneously be brought to such a canonical form. The maximum number of linearly independent orthonormal eigenfunctions is M(M-1)/2. An understanding of the possible reduction to a simple canonical set by a unitary transformation would be of great value in understanding the nature of the two-matrix.

Suppose in equation (25), the summation is ordered in the order of decreasing rank of the eigenfunctions; rank $f^1_{ij} \geqq$ rank $f^2_{ij} \geqq$ ... . The rank of f^1_{ij} may be 2, 4, 6 ..., or M. For each possibility we shall find a family of extreme elements of $\bar{\sigma}^N$, the class of ensemble N-representable $\bar{\sigma}$. Consider first the case that rank $f^1_{ij} = M$. What is the largest eigenvalue that a representable two-matrix can have if rank $f^1_{ij} = M$. This question has been answered and the largest eigenvalue has f^1_{ij} as eigenvector and is

$$B = \frac{N}{M}(M - N + 2) \tag{28}$$

for M even, N even and

$$B = \frac{(N-1)}{M}(M - N + 3) \tag{29}$$

for M odd and N odd[6]. Consider for definiteness that M and N are both even; the maximum eigenvalue (28) can be reached by the system in <u>one and only one way,</u> its wave function must be of the form

$$|\Psi> = CA^{N/2}| >; \quad C = \left[\frac{(\frac{N}{2})!\,(\frac{M}{2} - \frac{N}{2})!}{(\frac{M}{2})!}\right]^{1/2}$$

$$A = \sum_{i=1}^{M/2} a^+_{2i-1}\, a^+_{2i} \;. \tag{30}$$

$| >$ is the vacuum state. The two-matrix $< kl\,|\,\sigma\,|\,ij >$ for the system in the state $|\Psi >$ can be divided into four parts according to whether $k \gtrless l$ and $i \gtrless j$; any one is obtainable from any other by the symmetry properties. One such part is

$$\underset{k<l,\; i<j}{< kl\,|\,\sigma\,|\,ij >} = \begin{pmatrix} D_{11} & 0 \\ 0 & D_{22} \end{pmatrix},$$

$$D_{11} = \begin{pmatrix} \ddots & & \frac{N(M-N)}{M(M-2)} \\ & \frac{N}{M}. & \\ & & \ddots \end{pmatrix}, \tag{31}$$

$$D_{22} = \begin{pmatrix} \ddots & & 0 \\ & \frac{N(N-2)}{M(M-2)} & \\ 0 & & \ddots \end{pmatrix}.$$

D_{11} is an $M/2$ by $M/2$ sub-matrix and corresponds to kl and ij taking the sequence of values $2i - 1$, $2i$ ($i = 1, \ldots M/2$). Each diagonal element is N/M and each non-diagonal element is $N/M-N)/M(M-2)$. D_{22} corresponds to other values of the pairs kl and ij and is a diagonal sub-matrix with each diagonal element equal to $N(N-2)/M(M-2)$[7]. The matrix, σ, described by the form (31) is an extreme element of $\overline{\sigma}^N$.[2] Since σ is the only two-matrix that will yield the eigenvalue (28) and since it is representable (i. e. obtained by a system in state (30)), it is necessarily extreme. f^1_{ij} has rank M as can easily be verified (of course $M > N$).

Consider the case where the rank of f^1_{ij} is equal to J, $J < M$. Suppose $J = 2$. A wave function corresponding to a single Slater determinant

$$|\Psi> = a_1^+ \ldots a_N^+ | > \tag{32}$$

gives rise to a two-matrix

$$\begin{matrix} < kl | \sigma | ij > = \\ k < l \leqq N; \; i < j \leqq N. \end{matrix} \quad \begin{pmatrix} 1 & & & & 0 \\ & \cdot & & & \\ & & \cdot \; 1 & & \\ & & & \cdot & \\ 0 & & & \cdot & 1 \end{pmatrix} \quad . \tag{33}$$

The matrix, σ, described by the form (33) is an extreme element of $\overline{\sigma}_N$. This follows from the observation that the only way to produce the two-matrix, σ, of (33) is from a system in the state (32)[2].

Suppose $2 < J < M$ and we work in a representation where f^1_{ij} takes the canonical form (27) with $r = J/2$. What is the maximum eigenvalue the system can have? By following exactly the same type of argument as that in the appendix of the paper by Yang[3] in which he deduced relation (28), we can come to some conclusions. The maximum eigenvalue is given by

$$B = \frac{N'}{J}(J - N' + 2) \tag{34}$$

with the system in a state

$$|\Psi\rangle = CA^{N'/2}|\Psi_o\rangle ; \qquad C = \left[\frac{\frac{N'}{2}!\,(\frac{J}{2}-\frac{N'}{2})!}{(\frac{J}{2})!}\right]^{1/2}$$

$$A \equiv \sum_{i=1}^{J/2} a^+_{2i-1}\, a^+_{2i} \tag{35}$$

N' and $|\psi_o\rangle$ have the following significance. There are N' particles distributed among the first J states of the system. $|\psi_o\rangle$ is a state corresponding to M-J allowed single particle states (not including the first J) and N-N' particles; hence $|\psi\rangle$ has N particles and M allowed single particle states. To maximize B for fixed J, we choose $N' = (J+2)/2$; this is possible if $M-J \geqq N-N'$,

$$M \geqq N + \frac{J}{2} - 1 . \tag{36}$$

Since $J_{max} = M-2$, it is possible for all J if

$$M \geqq 2N - 4 . \tag{37}$$

Assume this inequality holds; the maximum possible value of B is given by $(J+2)^2/4J$(8). It can be reached only by systems having wave functions of the type (35) where $|\Psi_o\rangle$ represents an arbitrary N-1-J/2 particle wave function distribution among M-J states. If M-J = N-1-J/2 this is possible in only one way and hence we have the result that <u>any σ produced from (35) with $|\Psi_o\rangle$ corresponding to an N-1-J/2 Slater determinant is extreme in $\bar{\sigma}^N$</u>.

The two matrix σ corresponding to (35) has a structure like

$$\underset{k<l;\ i<j}{\langle kl|\sigma|ij\rangle} = \begin{pmatrix} (\sigma_1) & & \\ & (\sigma_2) & \\ & & (\sigma_3) \end{pmatrix} \tag{38}$$

σ_1 is a two-matrix for a system of $N' = (J+2)/2$ particles distributed in J possible states; σ_1 is analogous to the extreme matrix, (31). σ_2 corresponds to the two-matrix of the state $|\Psi_o>$. σ_3 is diagonal and has a contribution $< kl|\sigma| kl >$ $(k < l)$ when k appears in the set 1, 2, ... J and the state l is at least partially occupied in $|\Psi_o>$. If σ_2 is an extreme set of $\overline{\sigma}^{N-N'}$ (in the space of M-J single particle functions), then σ as given by (38) is an extreme element of $\overline{\sigma}^N$. This is so because the wave function (35) is unique for the form (38), and having σ_2 extreme in its space eliminates the arbitraries of $|\Psi_o>$.

Suppose o is an extreme element of $\overline{\sigma}^N$ and we perform a unitary transformation $\sigma \rightarrow \sigma'$,

$$< kl | \sigma' | ij > = \sum_{pqrs} < pq|\sigma| rs > \overline{U}_{ri}\overline{U}_{sj}U_{kp}U_{lq} \ . \quad (39)$$

U is an arbitrary unitary matrix whose indices range over the range of non-vanishing indices of σ. If σ is extreme in $\overline{\sigma}^N$ so is σ'. Proof:

Suppose

$$\sigma' = \sum < pq|\sigma| rs > \overline{U}_{ri}\overline{U}_{sj}U_{kp}U_{lq} = \alpha\sigma_1 + (1 - \alpha)\sigma_2. \quad (40)$$

Multiply by $U^{-1}_{tl}\, U^{-1}_{sk}\, \overline{U}^{-1}_{iw}\, \overline{U}^{-1}_{jy}$,

$$< vt|\sigma| wy > = \alpha < kl|\sigma_1 | ij > U^{-1}_{tl}\, U^{-1}_{vk}\, \overline{U}^{-1}_{iw}\, \overline{U}^{-1}_{jy} \quad (41)$$

$$+ (1 - \alpha) < kl|\sigma_1 | ij > U^{-1}_{tl}\, U^{-1}_{vk}\, \overline{U}^{-1}_{iw}\, \overline{U}^{-1}_{jy} \ .$$

Because σ is extreme,

$$< kl|\sigma_1 | ij > U^{-1}_{tl}\, U^{-1}_{vk}\, \overline{U}^{-1}_{iw}\, \overline{U}^{-1}_{jy} = < vt|\sigma| wy > , \quad (42)$$

and a similar relation for σ_2. By multiplying again by the product of two U's and two $\overline{U}$'s, we deduce that $\sigma_1 = \sigma_2 = \sigma'$. (Q. E. D.).

For any possible value of the rank of the eigenvector with the largest rank, we have found families of extreme two-functions. If the restriction $M \leqq 2N-4$ is relaxed, the appropriate modifications in the results can probably be readily made. It is quite possibly true that we have found all possible extreme ensemble N-representable two-functions.

NOTES AND REFERENCES

1. We shall also use the terms one-matrix and two-matrix to refer to matrices having the same number of indices and same symmetries as ρ_1 and ρ_2 but not satisfying relations (1) and (2). Since our main problem is to determine when such matrices can be made to satisfy these relations, no ambiguity in meaning should result.

2. The nomenclature, N-representable and ensemble N-representable, is due to A. J. Coleman, Rev. Mod. Phys., 35, 668 (1963).

3. C. N. Yang, Rev. Mod. Phys., 34, 694 (1962).

4. This theorem has probably been conjectured by many people. The ensemble N-representable problem for the one-matrix was to my knowledge first discussed in the literature by S. Watanabe, Zeitschrift für Physik, 113, 482 (1939). He showed the sufficiency of the conditions in the eigenvalues. The proof given here is substantially that of H. W. Kuhn, Proc. Symp. in Appl. Math., 10, 141 (1960). After being conjectured by L. H. Thomas, the theorem was independently proved by Coleman (ref. 1).

5. The existence of this canonical form was demonstrated recently by Yang (ref. 3) and by Coleman (ref. 2). It follows also readily from well known methods in the Theory of Algebraic Invariants. (See e.g. the book by that title written by G. B. Gurevich, translated by J. R. M. Radok and A. J. Spencer, P. Noordhoff, Ltd., Groningen, The Netherlands, 1964).

6. F. Sasaki, Quantum Chemistry Group, Uppsala, Report No. 77, 1962 (unpublished), apparently first deduced (28) and (29). See also reference (2) and (3).

7. A. J. Coleman, Structure of the Fermion Density Matrix II, J. Math. Phys., 6, 1425 (1965), has also obtained this two-matrix.

8. The text assumes that $(J+2)/2$ is an even integer. I have not yet worked out the modifications necessary when it is an odd integer.

DISCUSSION

Girardeau: Would you care to comment on the probability that, within the foreseeable future, someone will find useable necessary and sufficient conditions which will ensure that conjectured one and two particle density matrices are actually derivable from an N-body wave function.

Witten: The problem has already been solved for the one particle reduced density matrix. I think it will also be solved for the two particle reduced density matrix.

Girardeau: I would like to present a verbal "proof" that the probability is exactly zero. Suppose that useable necessary and sufficient conditions existed. Then the solution for the exact ground state energy of all N-body systems with 2-particle interactions would become trivial, since the energy functional would involve functions of only one and two variables. But it would be a miracle if all N-body problems were exactly soluble. By definition, a miracle is an event of probability zero.

Lieb: You posed the problem of showing that your extreme one particle reduced density matrix comes from determinantal wave functions. Was this not essentially solved by Foldy in a paper in the Journal of Mathematical Physics? (Jour. Math. Phys. 3, 531, (1962)).

Witten: The problem I posed was not to show that the extreme one particle reduced density matrix comes from a single Slater determinant wave function. This has been rigorously shown, but the proof I know is, in my opinion, complicated. I posed the problem of presenting a simple transparent proof. I do not remember that Foldy has done so in his paper, I will have to check it.

Lieb: Hasn't Garrard given a characterization of the necessary and sufficient conditions - but they were rather unuseable.

Witten: Yes, he did give a set of necessary and sufficient conditions which are unuseable. His approach was entirely different from the one I described.

THERMAL PROPERTIES OF LINEARLY ASSOCIATED SYSTEMS WITH RANDOM ELEMENTS: HELIX-COIL TRANSITION IN DNA

GUY W. LEHMAN
North American Aviation
Science Center, Thousand
Oaks, California, USA.

ABSTRACT

New mathematical techniques are developed for determining the thermal properties of an ensemble of disordered linearly associated systems. The method is used to compute (i) the magnetization of a quenched Ising ferromagnet involving two types of magnetic moments randomly distributed and (ii) the melting curve for copolymeric DNA composed of randomized A-T and G-C base pairs.

The above mentioned problems are also examined for the case of non-random nearest-neighbor correlated sequences and a vector functional equation is derived from which the thermal properties can be calculated. In particular, it is suggested that the transition breadth can be increased beyond that obtained by random sequences of A-T and G-C base pairs in DNA.

The configurational heat capacity for typical DNA composed of 50% G-C is estimated to be 1000 cal/mole/deg at 363°K falling rapidly to 160 cal/mole/deg at 369°K and should allow one to measure the transition breadth directly for dilute DNA-solvent solutions.

1. INTRODUCTION

The purpose of this paper is to: (i) present a new technique for treating the thermal properties of linearly associated systems with nearest-neighbor coupling when compositional randomness is present and (ii) obtain the exact temperature dependence of denaturation, θ, for the model of copolymeric DNA recently studied by Reiss, McQuarrie, McTague, and Cohen[1] and independently by Goel[2] and Montroll and Goel[3]. The MG approach and its mathematical equivalence to the RMMC model will be discussed in this section.

The properties of the partition function, Q, which are independent of base-pair sequences are discussed in Sec. II. Averaging techniques leading to integral and functional equations enabling one to compute the ensemble average of the logarithm of the partition function, $\langle \ln Q \rangle$, are developed in Sec. III. In Sec. IV, numerical solutions of the integral and functional equations are presented and θ computed for random base pair sequences. In Sec. V, the extension of the techniques of Sec. II to non-random sequencing is discussed and a vector functional equation is derived from which θ can be calculated.

A. Relationship between MG and RMMC models

The MG ferromagnet is composed of two types of magnetic atoms (characterized by two magnetic moments) and exchange coupled through a single nearest-neighbor interaction energy, U. The energy in the MG model is

$$E([J], [\mu]) = - \sum_{n=1}^{N} J_n \mu_n - U \sum_{n=2}^{N} \mu_n \mu_{n-1} \qquad (1)$$

for a given assignment of J_n's and $\mu_n = \pm 1$. (For a real ferromagnet, we would take $J_n = Hg_n$, where H is the applied external magnetic field and g_n the magnetic moment of the atom at the nth site). The probability of finding a ferromagnet with the spin configuration $[\mu]$ when the sequence $[J]$ is specified is simply

$$P([J], [\mu]) = \exp\{-\beta E([J], [\mu])\} / Z_{MG}([J]) ,$$

where $Z_{MG}([J])$ is the partition function for a single ferromagnet. In the above equation, $\beta = 1/kT$, where k and T are the Boltzmann factor and temperature, respectively

$$Z_{MG}([J]) = \sum_{[\mu]} \exp\{-\beta E([J], [u])\} \tag{2}$$

In order to calculate the thermodynamic properties of an ensemble of independent ferromagnets, we must compute

$$z = \frac{1}{N} \langle \ln Z_{MG}([J]) \rangle_{[J]} \tag{3}$$

For example, the fraction of sites containing + spins, is

$$\Theta_+ = \frac{1}{N} \langle \sum_{n=1}^{N} \langle \frac{1}{2}(1+\mu_n) \rangle_{[\mu]} \rangle_{[J]} = \frac{1}{2}\left[1 + \beta^{-1}\left(\frac{\partial}{\partial J_1} + \frac{\partial}{\partial J_2}\right) z\right], \tag{4}$$

for a system with two types of J_n's. Similarly, the average internal energy per atom is obtained from

$$E_{AVE} = -\frac{\partial}{\partial \beta} z. \tag{5}$$

If $\mu_n = +1$ refers to bonded base pairs of adenine-thymine (A-T) groups or guanine-cytosine (G-C) groups, then θ_+ in Eq. (4) can be used to calculate the melting curve of copolymeric DNA as MG describe provided we use J_1, J_2, and U as disposable parameters. In particular, MG use

$$-\beta J_n = A_n(T - T_n), \qquad n = 1,2. \tag{6}$$

If we are dealing with poly A-T or poly G-C, i.e., only one type of J_n, $T = T_n$ would correspond to zero magnetic field and melting of the molecule would correspond to 50% of the bonded bases being broken. $T < T_n$ corresponds to a positive applied magnetic field, i.e., parallel to the spins at absolute zero. By analogy, $T > T_n$ corresponds to a reversal of the magnetic field which tends to disorder the spin system.

In the case of copolymeric DNA, the above mentioned analogy with the ferromagnet in an applied field breaks down, at least physically, since we have a mixture of interacting groups with two different T_n's. For this reason, the physical basis of the DNA model of RMMC is much more appealing in spite of the formal analogy with the MG ferromagnetic model. Briefly, the RMMC model is a generalization of a model which takes the standard state of the polynucleotide as the completely unbonded one (neglecting strand separation), and its free energy is taken to be zero. A bonded base pair of A-T or G-C groups in the interior of a helical segment has a free energy $\underline{\Delta}F$ and contributes a factor (the internal partition factor)

$$s = \exp(-\beta\Delta F) \tag{7}$$

to the partition function. The contribution of the internal degrees of freedom to the partition function arising from a helical segment of j base pairs is s^j. The end of each helix is characterized by a factor σ, (the nucleation parameter) which accounts for the entropy corrections associated with the relative motion of the two free strands and an absence of a stacking energy here.

The model proposed by RMMC represents DNA as a linear sequence of A-T and G-C pairs with A-T = T-A and G-C = C-G. Furthermore, the stacking interaction between two base pairs is assumed to be independent of the sequence and composition and hence a single σ is used. The internal partition functions s_A and s_B are used for bonded A-T and G-C groups respectively.

The contribution to the partition function of a configuration in which there are n_A bonded A-T's, n_B bonded G-C's and h helices is then

$Q = s_A^{\ n_A} s_B^{\ n_B} \sigma^h$. Hence, the DNA partition function is

$$Q = \sum s_A^{\ n_A} s_B^{\ n_B} \sigma^h \tag{8}$$

where the sum extends over all configuration in which n_A, n_B and h are compatible. The fraction of bonded bases is

$$\Theta = \frac{1}{N} \left\langle \left(s_A \frac{\partial}{\partial s_A} + s_B \frac{\partial}{\partial s_B}\right) \ln Q \right\rangle_{[s]} . \tag{9}$$

A comparison of RMMC and the MG models [Cf. Eqs. (1) and (2)] shows that

$$s_n = e^{-2J_n\beta}, \quad \sigma = e^{-4\beta U} \tag{10}$$

and

$$Q_{RMMC}([s]) = e^{-NU\beta} \, e^{-\beta \sum_n J_n} Z_{MG}([J]) \tag{11}$$

thereby showing the mathematical equivalence of the two models.

II. PROPERTIES OF Q_{RMMC} INDEPENDENT OF [s]

We now establish some general results independent of the s_n sequence. From Eqs. (1) and (2),

$$Z_{MG}([J] \equiv Z_{MG}(-[J]) , \tag{12}$$

simply by replacing μ_n by $-\mu_n$. Hence, from EQ. (11)

$$\ln Q_{RMMC}([s]) = \ln Q_{RMMC}([s^{-1}]) + N_A \ln s_A + N_B \ln s_B \tag{13}$$

where N_A and N_B are the total number of A-T and G-C pairs, re-referred to as A and B respectively. Let $\Theta(s_A, N_A; s_B, N_B)$ denote the fraction of bonded bases for a molecule of N_A s_A's and N_B s_B's, then it follows from Eqs. (10), (11), (12) and (13) that

$$\Theta(s_A, N_A; s_B, N_B) = 1 - \Theta(s_A^{-1}, N_A; s_B^{-1}, N_B), \tag{14}$$

regardless of the sequence of s_n's. Following RMMC,

$$s_n = \exp\{\Delta H_n [T_n^{-1}]/R\}, \quad n = A, B. \tag{15}$$

Here, $\Delta H_A/RT_A = \Delta H_B/RT_B$. T_A and T_B are, respectively, the transition temperatures of poly A-T and poly G-C DNA.

Since $\Theta(s_A, N_A; s_B, N_B) = \Theta(s_B, N_B; s_A, N_A)$ we have from Eq. (14) that

$$\Theta(s_A, N_A; s_A^{-1}, N_B) = 1 - \Theta(s_A, N_B; s_A^{-1}, N_A). \tag{16}$$

This expression is valid at a single temperature, namely,

$$T = (T_A + T_B)/2$$

and allows us to relate the fraction of bonded bases at this temperature and composition N_A to the fraction bonded having composition N_B. In particular, $\Theta \equiv 1/2$ at $N_A = N_B = N/2$, regardless of the sequencing. Equation (16) provides us with a valuable check on numerical calculations.

III. AVERAGING TECHNIQUES

In general, we recall that the partition function Q, for a system whose energy is

$$E([\mu]) = \sum_{n=2}^{N} E_{n,n-1}(\mu_n; \mu_{n-1}),$$

that is, a linearly associative system which has two states $\mu_n = \pm 1$ and is nearest-neighbor coupled, can be obtained from [Cf. Eq. (2) for the MG model]

$$Q_N = \sum_{\mu_N} \Phi_N(u_N), \tag{17}$$

where

$$\Phi_N(u_N) = \sum_{\mu_{N-1}} \exp\{-\beta E_{N,N-1}(\mu_N; \mu_{N-1})\} \Phi_{N-1}(\mu_{N-1}) \tag{18}$$

with

$$\Phi_2(u_2) = \sum_{\mu_1} \exp\{-\beta E_{2,1}(\mu_2; \mu_1)\}. \tag{19}$$

In particular, for the RMMC model, if

$$U_n = \Phi_n(1), V_n = \Phi_n(-1), \tag{20}$$

then

$$\begin{pmatrix} U_n \\ V_n \end{pmatrix} = \begin{pmatrix} s_n & s_n\sigma \\ 1 & 1 \end{pmatrix} \begin{pmatrix} U_{n-1} \\ V_{n-1} \end{pmatrix} \tag{21}$$

where

$$U_2 = s_2(1+\sigma), \qquad V_2 = 2. \tag{22}$$

Hence,

$$\frac{1}{N}\ln Q_N = \frac{1}{N}\ln(U_N + V_N) \equiv \frac{1}{N}\ln\left[1+(U_N/V_N)\right] + \frac{1}{N}\sum_{n=3}^{N}\ln(V_n/V_{n-1}) + \frac{1}{N}\ln V_2 \tag{23}$$

Note that Eq. (23) is simply an identity. From Eqs. (21) and (22)

$$W_n \equiv U_n/V_n = s_n \frac{W_{n-1}+\sigma}{W_{n-1}+1} \tag{24}$$

and

$$V_n/V_{n-1} = 1 + W_{n-1}\,. \tag{25}$$

Hence, Eq. (23) becomes

$$N^{-1}\ln Q_N = N^{-1}\ln(2) + N^{-1}\sum_{n=2}^{N}\ln(1+W_n), \tag{26}$$

with $W_2 = s_2(1+\sigma)/2$. Since $s_n > 0$, $0 < \sigma < 1$, we see that $0 < W_n < s_n$. Consequently, the W_n's are bounded for any sequence of s_n's.

A. Integral Equation Approach For Randomized Sequences[4].

Using two integral identities,

$$\ln(y+W_n) = \ln(y) + 2\int_0^\infty du\, u^{-1}\, e^{-u^2 y}\left[1 - e^{-u^2 W_n}\right] \tag{27}$$

$$e^{u^2 K} = 1 + 2u\int_0^\infty dv\, I_1(2uv)\, e^{-v^2 K^{-1}}, \tag{28}$$

where $I_1(z)$ is a modified Bessel function, we readily find using Eq. (24) that

$$C_N(y) \equiv N^{-1} \langle \sum_{n=2}^{N} \ln(y+W_n) \rangle$$

$$= \ln(y) + 2 \int_0^\infty du\, u^{-1}\, e^{-u^2 y} \left[1 - H_N(u)\right]. \qquad (29)$$

Here,

$$H_N(u) = N^{-1} \langle \sum_{n=2}^{N} e^{-u^2 W_n} \rangle \qquad (30)$$

$$\equiv N^{-1} \langle \sum_{n=2}^{N} e^{-s_n u^2} \{1 + 2\alpha_n u \int_0^\infty dv\, I_1(2\alpha_n uv) e^{-v^2 W_{n-1}}\} \rangle \qquad (31)$$

whcrc

$$\alpha_n = \left[s_n(1-\sigma)\right]^{1/2}. \qquad (32)$$

In order to proceed further, the s_n sequence must be specified. In particular, if the s_n's are uncorrelated, then

$$\langle f(s_n) e^{-v^2 W_{n-1}} \rangle = \langle f(s_n) \rangle \langle e^{-v^2 W_{n-1}} \rangle \qquad (33)$$

with

$$\langle f(s_n) \rangle = x_A f(s_A) + x_B f(s_B), \qquad (34)$$

$x_A = N_A/N$ and $x_B = N_B/N$ being the fraction of A-T and G-C bases respectively. For brevity, we use $x_1 = x_A$, $x_2 = x_B$, $s_1 = s_A$, and $s_2 = s_B$. Then

$$H_N(u) = \sum_{m=1}^{2} x_m e^{-u^2 s_m} \{1 + 2\alpha_m u \int_0^\infty dv\, I_1(2\alpha_m uv) e^{-v^2} H_N(v)\}$$

$$+ N^{-1} \sum_{m=1}^{2} x_m \{e^{-u^2 s_m} - \exp(-u^2 s_m \frac{W_N + \sigma}{W_N + 1})\} \qquad (35)$$

We can now pass to the limit of infinite N with an error that is bounded by $N^{-1}0(1)$. Our principal results for random or uncorrelated sequences are that

$$C_\infty(y) = \ln(y) + 2\int_0^\infty du\, u^{-1}\, e^{-u^2 y}\left[1 - H_\infty(u)\right], \tag{36}$$

with

$$H_\infty(u) = F(u) + \int_0^\infty dv K(u,v) H_\infty(v), \tag{37}$$

where

$$F(u) = \sum_m x_m e^{-s_m u^2} \tag{38}$$

$$K(u,v) = 2\sum_m x_m e^{-s_m u^2} \alpha_m u I_1(2\alpha_m uv) e^{-v^2}. \tag{39}$$

Finally,

$$\lim_{N\to\infty} N^{-1}\langle \ln Q_N \rangle = C_\infty(1). \tag{40}$$

The reason for defining the auxiliary function $C_N(y)$, Eq. (29), will become clear in a subsequent section. The point is that $C_\infty(y)$ can be calculated from $H_\infty(u)$.

B. Solution for $H_\infty(u)$ with $s_A = s_B = s$

When $s_A = s_B = s$,

$$H_\infty(u) = e^{-u^2 W_\infty}, \tag{41}$$

with

$$W_\infty = s\frac{W_\infty + \sigma}{W_\infty + 1} \tag{42}$$

according to Eqs. (24) and (30). Consequently, we find

$$W_\infty = \frac{s-1}{2} + \left[\left(\frac{s-1}{2}\right)^2 + s\sigma\right]^{1/2}. \tag{43}$$

Using Eq. (28), we find that Eq. (41) is a solution of Eq. (37) as the case must be. Similarly,

$$C_\infty(y) = \ln(y + W_\infty) \tag{44}$$

so that

$$C_\infty(1) = \ln\left(\frac{s+1}{2} + \left[\left(\frac{s-1}{2}\right)^2 + s\sigma\right]^{1/2}\right) \tag{45}$$

agreeing with the solution obtained by RMMC.

C. Solution for $H_\infty(u)$ by Fredholm Construction

Since one can show that

$$M \equiv \left[\int_0^\infty \int_0^\infty du\, dv\, [K(u,v)]^2\right]^{1/2} = \sigma^{-1/4}\, O(1) \tag{46}$$

the Fredholm construction(5) is valid and forms a basis for solving Eq. (37). From the work of Michlin(6), e.g., one can show that the solution of

$$H(\lambda, u) = F(u) + \lambda \int_0^\infty dv\, K(u,v)\, H(\lambda,v) \tag{47}$$

is given by

$$H(\lambda, u) = F(u) - \lambda\left[D_0(\lambda)\right]^{-1} \int_0^\infty dv\, D(\lambda; u, v) F(v), \tag{48}$$

where

$$D(\lambda; u,v) = \sum_{n=1}^{\infty} \lambda^n D_n(u,v), \tag{49}$$

$$D_n(u,v) = -\sum_{r=0}^{n-1} d_r K_{n-r}(u,v) \tag{50}$$

$$d_n = -\frac{1}{n}\sum_{r=0}^{n-1} d_r t_{n-r}, \qquad n = 1, 2, \ldots \tag{51}$$

$$K_{n+1}(u,v) = \int_0^\infty dz\, K_n(u,z)\, K(z,v) \tag{52}$$

$$K_1(u,v) = K(u,v), \qquad d_0 = 1 \tag{53}$$

$$t_n = \int_0^\infty du\, K_n(u,u) \tag{54}$$

$$D_0(\lambda) = 1 + \sum_{n=1}^{\infty} \lambda^n d_n . \tag{55}$$

The zeros of $D_0(\lambda)$ give the eigenvalues of the operator $K(u,v)$.

We have inserted the eigenvalue parameter λ in Eq. (47) in order to check out our machine calculations since we know the eigenvalues of $K(u,v)$ for the special case $s_A = s_B = s$. For this case, it is possible to show that[7]

$$\lambda_m = (\lambda_+/\lambda_-)^m , \qquad m = 1, 2, \dots , \tag{56}$$

where

$$\lambda_{\pm} = \frac{1+s}{2} \pm \left[\left(\frac{s-1}{2}\right)^2 + s\sigma \right]^{1/2} \tag{57}$$

are the two eigenvalues of the 2 x 2 matrix appearing in Eq. (21). From Eq. (54), it follows that

$$t_n = \sum_{m=1}^{\infty} (\lambda_m)^{-n} = \frac{1}{(\lambda_+/\lambda_-)^n - 1} . \tag{58}$$

The d_n's are given by Eq. (51) from which one can show that

$$d_n = (-1)^n \prod_{r=1}^{n} \left[(\lambda_+/\lambda_-)^r - 1 \right]^{-1} . \tag{59}$$

For $\sigma > 0$, $D_0(\lambda)$ defined by Eq. (55) is absolute convergent for all λ and s since $\lambda_+/\lambda_- > 1$.

This last remark simply illustrates the power and elegance of the Fredholm construction. For the case $s_A \neq s_B$, we must construct various terms appearing in Eqs. (48-55). Fortunately, it is not necessary to perform the integrations indicated in Eqs. (52) and (54) to construct $K_n(u,v)$ and t_n. We define

$$K(a,b,c;\, u,v) = 2bu\, e^{-au^2} I_1(2buv)\, e^{-cv^2} , \tag{60}$$

so that

$$K(u,v) = x_A K(s_A, \alpha_A, 1; u,v) + x_B K(s_B, \alpha_B, 1; u,v) \qquad (61)$$

from Eq. (39). Using the well-known integrals involving Bessel functions, one can show that

$$\int_0^\infty dz\, K(a_1,b_1,c_1; u,z)\, K(a_2,b_2,c_2; z,v) = K(a_3,b_3,c_3; u,v), \qquad (62)$$

where

$$a_3 = a_1 - (b_1)^2 \gamma_{12},\ b_3 = b_1 b_2 \gamma_{12},\ c_3 = c_2 - (b_2)^2 \gamma_{12} \qquad (63)$$

and

$$\gamma_{12} = \left[c_1 + a_2\right]^{-1}.$$

Similarly,

$$\int_0^\infty du\, K(a,b,c; u,u) = \left\{2\left[\beta^2 - 1\right]^{1/2} (\beta + \left[\beta^2 - 1\right]^{1/2})\right\}^{-1}, \qquad (64)$$

where

$$\beta = (a+c)/(2b). \qquad (65)$$

Finally, using

$$\int_0^\infty dv\, K(a,b,c; u,v)\, e^{-gv^2} = e^{-\rho u^2} - e^{-gu^2}, \qquad (66)$$

where

$$\rho = a - b^2(c+g)^{-1}, \qquad (67)$$

we have all the items necessary to construct

$$D_0(\lambda) \text{ and } \int_0^\infty dv\, D(\lambda; u,v)\, F(v).$$

When the above mentioned prescription is followed one obtains a solution for $H_\infty(u)$ in the following form

$$H_\infty(u) = \sum_{r=1}^{\infty} A_r\, e^{-\Lambda_r u^2}, \qquad (68)$$

where

$$\sum_{r=1}^{\infty} A_r = 1 . \qquad (69)$$

From Eqs. (68), (36), and (69), one finds

$$C_\infty(y) = \sum_{r=1}^{\infty} A_r \ln(y+\Lambda_r) . \qquad (70)$$

This procedure has been programmed on the IBM 7094 using Fortran IV double precision arithmetic. If the Fredholm construction is stopped at N terms then Eqs. (68) and (70) will contain 2^{N+1} terms. When $s_A^{x_A} s_B^{x_B}$ is near unity, some of the low order t_n's become much larger than unity for $\sigma \lesssim 10^{-3}$. In these cases N simply has to be increased to achieve convergence. The maximum N used to date has been 16. Numerical solutions will be presented in Sec. IV.

D. Functional Equation Approach For Random Sequences

In order to compute z or $C_\infty(1)$ for $\sigma < 10^{-3}$ without using large amounts of computer time, we have been forced to seek another approach. In fact, we obtain a functional equation for $C_\infty(y)$ in an almost trivial way. Starting with the definition of Eq. (29) for $C_N(y)$ and using Eq. (24) one obtains

$$C_n(y) = N^{-1} \left\langle \sum_{n=2}^{N} \{\ln(y+s_n) + \ln(\frac{y+s_n\sigma}{y+s_n} + W_{n-1}) - \ln(1+W_{n-1})\} \right\rangle$$

(71)

For uncorrelated s_n sequences, we can decouple the s_n and W_{n-1} terms as we did in Eq. (33). As before [Cf. Eq. (35)], we can pass to the limit of $N \to \infty$ and obtain, using the defining equation for $C_\infty(y)$,

$$C_\infty(y) = \sum_{m=1}^{2} x_m \{\ln(y+s_m) + C_\infty(L_m y) - C_\infty(1)\} , \qquad (72)$$

where L_m is an operator which is defined by

$$L_m y = (y+s_m \sigma) / (y+s_m) . \qquad (73)$$

In the special case, $s_1 = s_2 = s$, $L_m = L$,

$$C_\infty(y) = \ln(y+s) + C_\infty(Ly) - C_\infty(1) \tag{74}$$

has the solution given by Eq. (44) as one can see by direct substitution. Functional equations of the type shown in Eq. (74) have been studied by Laplace and are discussed in detail by Boole[8]. In many respects Eq. (74) has a special structure since it involves $C_\infty(1)$. Moreover,

$$\sigma \leqq Ly \leqq 1, \qquad 0 \leqq y \leqq \infty \tag{75}$$

and Eq. (74) or Eq. (72) need only be solved in the internal $0 \leqq y \leqq 1$. The problem of computing $C_\infty(1)$ from (74) is trivial since one and only one point $0 < y_o < 1$ exists such that $y_0 = Ly_0$, namely

$$y_0 = W_\infty + 1 - \sigma, \tag{76}$$

W_∞ being given by Eq. (43). Hence, $C_\infty(1) = \ln(y_0 + s)$ which is again Eq. (44).

One can also solve Eq. (74) by iteration. By k successive substitutions, one has

$$C_\infty(y) = \sum_{r=0}^{k-1} \ln(L^r y + s) + C_\infty(L^k y) - kC_\infty(1). \tag{77}$$

Using methods described by Boole,

$$L^r y = \lambda_+ \left\{ \frac{I_-(y) - \varkappa^{r+1} I_+(y)}{I_-(y) - \varkappa^r I_+(y)} \right\} - s, \tag{78}$$

where

$$I_\pm(y) = y + s - \lambda_\pm, \quad \varkappa = \lambda_- / \lambda_+, \tag{79}$$

λ_+ being given by Eq. (57). Since $L^k 1 \rightarrow \lambda_+ - s = W_\infty + 1 - s$ as $k \rightarrow \infty$, we can set $y = 1$ in Eq. (77), solve for $C_\infty(1)$ and again recover Eq. (45). If we attempted to use this procedure as a basis for solving Eq. (74) numerically, we would find the convergence to be quite slow in the transition region about $s = 1$ for $\sigma < 0.01$.

As far as we know, Boole's approach cannot be used to solve Eq. (72) when $s_1 \neq s_2$. From a formal point of view our Fredholm construction described previously does provide a solution of Eq. (72) but is not computationally satisfactory if $\sigma < 10^{-3}$.

In the earlier stages of this work, an abortive attempt was made to replace Eq. (72) be an equivalent matrix problem. That is, we defined $C_\infty(y)$ at N mesh points $0 \leqq y_n \leqq 1$, $n = 1, 2, \ldots N$ and used Lagrange interpolation to construct $C_\infty(L_m y_n)$ from the $C_\infty(y_p)$'s in the neighborhood of the point $L_m y_n$. As one might expect, we found that our matrix was nearly singular whenever we were in the transition region where $C_\infty(1)$ is changing rapidly with temperature. This approach was abandoned owing to severe round-off problems and our inability to obtain accurate solutions to Eq. (74). At this juncture, the Fredholm construction was pushed and satisfactorily programmed for $\sigma > 10^{-3}$ and provided us with considerable insight. We discovered that we could fit the Fredholm results in the region $\Theta \cong 0.5$, i.e. the transition region, with

$$C_\infty(1) \cong \ln(1 + W_e) \tag{80}$$

where

$$W_e = \frac{\hat{s} - 1}{2} + \left[\left(\frac{\hat{s} - 1}{2}\right)^2 + \hat{s}\,\sigma_e \right]^{1/2} . \tag{81}$$

Here,

$$\hat{s} = s_A^{\ x_A} \, s_B^{\ x_B} \tag{82}$$

is the geometric mean as discussed by RMMC and σ_e is an effective σ which is composition dependent and larger than the true σ. Consequently, we set

$$C_\infty(y) = \ln(y + W_e) + \ln\left[D(y)\right] \tag{83}$$

and find that [Cf. Eq. (72)]

$$D(y) = \left[D(1)\right]^{-1} \{G_A(y)D(L_A y)\}^{x_A} \{G_B(y)D(L_B y)\}^{x_B} \tag{84}$$

where

$$G_m(y) = (y + s_m \frac{W_e + \sigma}{W_e + 1}) / (y + W_e). \tag{85}$$

Here, of course, m = 1 or A and 2 or B and L_A and L_B are given by Eq. (73).

To solve Eq. (84), we divide the interval $0 \leqq y \leqq 1$ into N parts using

$$y_n = \sigma \{ \exp [(\frac{n-1}{N-1}) \ln(1+\sigma^{-1})] - 1 \}, \tag{86}$$

n = 1, 2, ... N. [Note that $y_1 = 0$ and $y_N = 1$]. The coice of this nonlinear subdivision of the y scale is dictated by the fact that the most rapid variation of $C_\infty(y)$ or D(y) occurs in the neighborhood of $y = \sigma << 1$. We solve Eq. (84) by iteration starting with some initial guess for D(y) usually unity. The points $L_m y_n$ lie between σ and 1. The values of $D(L_m y_n)$ are computed by use of a 5 point Lagrange interpolation formula from previously computed values of $D(y_n)$. For appropriately chosen σ_e, we found that $0.1 \lesssim D \lesssim 1.5$ and the iteration was halted when two successive iterations differed by 5×10^{-6} at any point. The mesh size was varied from N = 20, 40, 50, 80, and 200. This scheme works satisfactorily for $10^{-5} < \sigma < 1$ and was programmed in Fortran IV language using double precision arithmetic to prevent loss of significant figures in the small y range. The denaturation curve was constructed from Eq. (9) by numerical differentiation of $C_\infty(1)$, i.e.

$$\Theta = \{ s_A [C_\infty(1; s_A + \Delta s, s_B) - C_\infty(1; s_A - \Delta s, s_B)] + s_B [C_\infty(1; s_A, s_B + \Delta s) - C_\infty(1; s_A, s_B - \Delta s)] \} / (2\Delta s). \tag{87}$$

IV. NUMERICAL RESULTS FOR RANDOM SEQUENCES: $C_\infty(1), \Theta$

The machine programs for computing $C_\infty(1)$ by the Fredholm construction were checked out by taking $s_A = s_B = s$ for which the solutions are known. When $s = 0.5$, $\sigma = 10^{-2}$, the smallest zero of $\mathscr{D}_0(\lambda)$ [Eq. (55)] is $\lambda_1 = 2.0600231$. Our double precision program gives $\sum_{r=0}^{10} \lambda_1^r d_r = -7 \times 10^{-10}$, with $d_8 \sim 1.6 \times 10^{-11}$, $d_9 \sim -2.4 \times 10^{-14}$, $d_{10} \sim 1.8 \times 10^{-17}$. By contrast, for s = 1.2, $\sigma = 10^{-2}$, $d_8 \sim 3.5 \times 10^{-3}$, $d_9 \sim -3.3 \times 10^{-4}$, $d_{10} \sim 2.3 \times 10^{-5}$, $d_{11} \sim -1.3 \times 10^{-6}$, $d_{12} \sim 5 \times 10^{-8}$, $d_{13} \sim -2 \times 10^{-9}$, $d_{14} \sim 3.5 \times 10^{-11}$, $d_{15} \sim -6 \times 10^{-13}$, and $d_{16} \sim 8 \times 10^{-15}$. Convergence is rapid once a sufficiently large N is reached.

The subsequent calculations reported in this paper are based upon $T_A = 342.5$, and $T_B = 383.5$ °K as being appropriate for copolymeric DNA. [These values were suggested by McTague.] Hence, by Eq. (15),

$$s_n = \exp\{(\Delta H_A/RT_A)\left[1-(T_n/T)\right]\}, \quad n = A, B. \qquad (88)$$

The approximate melting curves shown in Fig. 1 of RMMC were computed for $\Delta H_A/R = -3800$°K. However, according to Eq. (14), $\theta([s]) \equiv 1 - \theta([s^{-1}])$ so that the sign of ΔH_A is irrelevant; i.e., $H_A > 0$ refers to a standard state in which the base pairs are completely bonded, while $\Delta H_A < 0$ refers to the standard state being unbonded.

A comparison of numerical solutions for $C_\infty(1)$ derived from the Fredholm construction and from the functional equation [Eq. (83) and (84)] is given in Table I for $\sigma = 10^{-3}$ and $x_A = x_B = 0.5$. For this composition, the transition temperature is T = 363°K independent of σ.

Table I. $C_\infty(1)$ and θ for $x_A = x_B = 0.5$; $\sigma = 10^{-3}$; $\Delta s = 0.01$; $\Delta H_A/R = 3800^\circ K$. Columns labeled FC and FE refer to Fredholm construction and functional equation approaches. IT denotes number of iterations to achieve convergence (see text).

T	FC N=14	FE				IT
		N=20 (10^{-4} to 10^{-5})		N=40 (5×10^{-6})		
	$C_\infty(1)$	$C_\infty(1)$	θ	$C_\infty(1)$	θ	
376	0.38766	0.38767	0.9772			
374	0.33181	0.33182	0.9652			
372	0.27633	0.27634	0.9434			
370	0, 22205	0.22207	0.9032			
368	0.17045	0.17047	0.8333	0.17044	0.8351	67
366	0.12366	0.12372	0.7235	0.12368	0.7258	63
364	0.08372	0.08431	0.5771	0.08427	0.5793	63
363			(0.5000)		(0.5000)	
362	0.05352	0.05407	0.4158	0.05406	0.4174	57
360	0.03317	0.03302	0.2709	0.03318	0.2713	48
358	0.02006	0.01976	0.1636	0.02006	0.1621	42
356	0.01235	0.01182	0.0960			
354	0.00798	0.00710	0.0572			
352	0.00546					
350	0.00398					

The first column of Table I shows the values of $C_\infty(1)$ computed by means of the Fredholm construction, FC, using 14 terms. The values of $C_\infty(1)$ at 364 and $362^\circ K$ are not accurate to the number of figures given. The functional equation [Eq. (84)] was solved for N = 20 and 40 as shown. The N = 20 calculations were terminated when difference between successive iterates were less than 10^{-5} in magnitude at any point or the number of iterations exceeded 50. The N = 40 calculations were terminated when the error was less than 5×10^{-6} and the number of iterations to achieve this is shown by IT in the last column. The fraction of bonded bases, θ, was computed from Eq. (87) using $\Delta s = 0.01$ as indicated. The agreement among the calculated values of $C_\infty(1)$ by the FC method and the FE method is very satisfactory. Similarly, the agreement between the θ's for N = 20 and N = 40 is also satisfactory.

Table II shows the results $\sigma = 10^{-2}$ and $x_A = 0.5$. For this case, convergence is very rapid. Tables III and IV show results for $\sigma = 9 \times 10^{-5}$ with $x_A = 0.97$, 0.7, 0.6, 0.5, 0.4, and 0.3. In particular, we note that the transition temperature is essentially given by $\hat{s} = s_A^{x_A} s_B^{x_B} = 1$; that is, the melting temperature is

$$T_M \cong x_A T_A + x_B T_B.$$

Table II. $C_\infty(1)$ and θ For $\Delta H_A/RT_A = -11.1678830$; $\sigma = 10^{-2}$; $x_A = 0.5$ (FE Approach); $N = 40$ (5×10^{-6}); $\Delta s = 0.01$. IT denotes number of iterations to converge with error indicated above.

T	$C_\infty(1)$	θ	IT
363	0.13866	0.4991	35
362	0.15496	0.5420	24
360	0.19180	0.6252	23
358	0.23405	0.7016	19
354	0.33286	0.8215	26
352	0.38812	0.8642	23

Table III. $C_\infty(1)$ and θ For $\Delta H_A/R = 3800^\circ K$, $x_A = 0.97$, $\Delta s = 0.005$, $\sigma = 9 \times 10^{-5}$; $N = 40\ (5 \times 10^{-6})$ FE Approach. $\sigma_e = \sigma$.

T	$C_\infty(1)$	θ	IT
343.23	0.00784	0.3131	262
343.73	0.01468	0.5315	252
344.23	0,02489	0,7209	227

Table IV. $C_\infty(1)$ and θ For $\Delta H_A/R = 3800^\circ K$, $\Delta s = 0.01$, $\sigma = 9 \times 10^{-5}$; $N = 40\ (5 \times 10^{-6})$ FE Approach. $\sigma_e = 10^{-3}$.

	$x_A = 0.7$				$x_A = 0.6$		
T	$C_\infty(1)$	θ	IT	T	$C_\infty(1)$	θ	IT
350.8	0.00427	0.0757	117	354.9	0.00592	0.0945	114
352.8	0.01335	0.2358	45	356.9	0.01595	0.2514	79
354.8	0.03643	0.5139	81	358.9	0.03901	0.5057	106
356.8	0.07682	0.7725	114	360.9	0.07792	0.7520	103
358.8	0.12924	0.9132	105	362.9	0.12867	0.8993	104

	$x_A = 0.5$				$x_A = 0.4$		
T	$C_\infty(1)$	θ	IT	T	$C_\infty(1)$	θ	IT
360	0.01057	0.1638	83	363.1	0.00641	0.0968	79
362	0.02631	0.3671	100	365.1	0.01619	0.2428	83
363	0.03947	0.4975	113	367.1	0.03793	0.4897	126
364	0.05659	0.6282	128	369.1	0.07532	0.7458	130
366	0.10124	0.8329	130	371.1	0.12502	0.9034	121

	$x_A = 0.3$					
	$N=40\ (5\times10^{-6})\ \Delta s=0.01$			$N=80\ (10^{-6})\ \Delta s=0.005$		
T	$C_\infty(1)$	θ	IT	$C_\infty(1)$	θ	IT
367.2	0.00540	0.0825	112			
369.2	0.01398	0.2215	99	0.01395	0.2224	169
371.2	0.03449	0.4815	114	0.03447	0.4835	129
373.2	0.07182	0.7624	121	0.07182	0.7654	158
375.2	0.12220	0.9224	115			

Table V. Symmetry Check at $T = 0.5\ (T_A + T_B) = 363^\circ K$. Same parameters as Table IV. $s_A = s_B^{-1} = 1.87118$; $\Delta s = 0.01$. $C_\infty(1, x_A) = (2x_A - 1)\ \ln(s_A) - C_\infty(1, 1-x_A)$. $\theta(x_A) + \theta(1-x_A) = 1$.

x_A	$C_\infty(1)$	θ	$(2x_A-1)\ln s_A$
0.3	0.00107	0.0101	-0.25028
0.4	0.00612	0.0921	-0.12514
0.5	0.03947	0.4975	0
0.6	0.13140	0.9041	0.12514
0.7	0.25168	0.9878	0.25028

In Table III, $T_M \cong 343.73$. Similarly, T_M is always approximately given by the third row for each x_A in Table IV. Finally, Table V shows that the symmetry check at $T = 363^\circ K$ is numerically satisfied for the case $\sigma = 9 \times 10^{-5}$.

We have also computed θ for $\sigma = 10^{-5}$ and $x_A = 0.5$. The results are listed here as a pair of (T, θ) numbers for brevity: (358, 0.0187), (360, 0.0892), (362, 0.3178), (364, 0.6743), (366, 0.9054), (368, 0.9778). N = 40 was used and the maximum number of iterations required was 212 to achieve an accuracy of 5×10^{-6}.

An examination of our tables shows that the transition breadth is compositional dependent in a manner similar to Fig. 2 of RMMC. They found that it was possible to fit the experimental transition breadths by using $\sigma = 10^{-6}$ based upon their approximate partition function. Our calculations are numerically exact for randomized sequences and one finds that

$$\left.\frac{d\theta}{dT}\right|_{\substack{T=363 \\ x_A=0.5}} \cong -0.046 - 0.044 \ln_{10}\sigma$$

If we take the experimental breadth, defined by $\Delta T_M = |\theta(0.7) - \theta(0.3)|$, at $x_A = 0.5$ to be $2.9^{\circ}K$, then the appropriate σ from the above equation is found to be $\sigma \approx 7 \times 10^{-5}$. The value $\sigma = 9 \times 10^{-5}$ leads to a transition breadth, at 50% G-C, of $\Delta T_M \cong 3.1^{\circ}K$.

In concluding our remarks on calculating DNA melting curves for random sequences, it appears that the maximum term method employed by RMMC to arrive at an approximate θ is deficient since the exact randomized θ gives a σ at least 70 times larger than the σ they needed to obtain the experimental ΔT_M.

A brief remark appears to be in order concerning the excess specific heat associated with the melting transition. The configurational energy is approximately given by

$$\Delta E = \Delta H_A \theta$$

so that the change in heat capacity for a mole of DNA molecules is

$$\Delta C \cong R(\Delta H_A/RT_A)\ T_A\left(\frac{d\theta}{dT}\right)$$

For the case 50% G-C, $\Delta T_M \cong 3.1^{\circ}K$ and $(d\theta/dT) \cong 0.13/^{\circ}K$ for $T = 363^{\circ}K$. Hence, $\Delta C \cong 1000$ cal/mole/deg. Empirically, we note that

$$\theta' = \frac{1}{2}\{1 + \tanh[A(T-T_M)]\},$$

so that

$$\frac{d\theta}{dT} = \frac{A}{2} \{ \operatorname{sech} \left[A(T-T_M)\right] \}^2 ,$$

with $A = 0.26/^{\circ}K$. For example, $\theta(366^{\circ}K) = 0.823$ in close agreement with the exact value in Table IV of 0.833. Hence, $\Delta C(366) \cong 570$ cal/mole/deg. and $\Delta C(369) \cong 160$ cal/mole/deg. This suggests the possibility of measuring the transition breadth directly by measuring ΔC for 1% DNA-solvent solution.

V. NON-RANDOM SEQUENCES

In this section, we briefly indicate an approach for determining $C_{\infty}(1)$ for non-random sequences or correlated sequences. We shall restrict our attention to the case of nearest-neighbor correlations as being the simplest but most important. To facilitate the mathematical treatment of our problem, we introduce a normalized probability distribution function[9]

$$P_s([a]) = R_0(a_1) \left[\prod_{n=1}^{N-1} R(a_n, a_{n+1}) \right] R_0(a_N)/\mu_1^{N-1} \mathcal{S}_1^{2}), \tag{89}$$

where $a_n = 0$ or 1 if the nth site contains an A-T group denoted by A or a G-C group denoted by B, respectively. Here, μ_1 in the largest eigenvalue of the symmetric $\underset{\sim}{R}$ matrix

$$\underset{\sim}{R} = \begin{pmatrix} R(0,0), & R(0,1) \\ R(0,1), & R(1,1) \end{pmatrix} \tag{90}$$

belonging to the eigenfunction, $\varphi_1(a_k)$, and

$$\mathcal{S}_1 = \sum_{a=0}^{1} R_0(a)\varphi_1(a). \tag{91}$$

As $N \to \infty$, the P_s distribution function is specified completely by p_A, the probability that any site is occupied by an A group and p_{AB}, the probability that any pair of nearest-neighbor sites be simultaneously occupied by an AB pair. We assume, of course, that $p_{AB} = p_{BA}$, and neglect end effects. It is necessary to have

$$p_A + p_B = 1. \tag{92}$$

If $P_s(a_k, a_{k+1})$ denotes the probability of the nearest-neighbor pair of sites k, k+1 being occupied by AA, AB, BA, or BB groups and if $1 << k << N$, then, by summing Eq. (89) over all a_n's except a_k, a_{k+1}, one has

$$P_s(a_k, a_{k+1}) = \varphi_1(a_k) R(a_k, a_{k+1}) \varphi_1(a_{k+1})/\mu_1. \tag{93}$$

The probability that the kth site be occupied is

$$P_s(a_k) = \sum_{a_{k+1}} P_s(a_k, a_{k+1}) = [\varphi_1(a_k)]^2. \tag{94}$$

Hence, for the components of the eigenfunctions $\varphi_1(a_k)$ belonging to the largest eigenvalue μ_1, we can take

$$\varphi_1(0) = \sqrt{p_A}, \varphi_1(1) = \sqrt{p_B}, \tag{95}$$

and since $\underset{\sim}{R}$ is symmetric, it can be diagonalized by a unitary transformation leading at once to

$$\varphi_2(0) = -\sqrt{p_B}, \varphi_2(1) = \sqrt{p_A} \tag{96}$$

for the components of the eigenfunction belonging to the eigenvalue μ_2. Using the spectral representation

$$R(a_k, a_{k+1}) = \sum_{q=1}^{2} \mu_q \varphi_q(a_k) \varphi_q(a_{k+1}). \tag{97}$$

Hence, from Eqs. (93), (95), (96) and (97), it follows that

$$\Upsilon \equiv \mu_2/\mu_1 = 1 - \frac{p_{AB}}{p_A p_B}, \tag{98}$$

and Eq. (93) is completely specified by p_A and p_{AB} as stated. [For our approach to be rigorously valid, $|\Upsilon| < 1$, but our final equations give the correct results for the two extremes of $\Upsilon = \pm 1$].

If $p_{AB} = p_A p_B$ (i.e. random sequences), $\Upsilon = 0$, and

$$P_s(a_k, a_{k+1}) = P_s(a_k)\, P_s(a_{k+1}). \tag{99}$$

We also obtain from Eq. (93)

$$p_{AA} = p_A - p_{AB}$$

$$p_{BB} = p_B - p_{AB}, \tag{100}$$

so that $p_{AA} = (p_A)^2$ and $p_{BB} = (p_B)^2$ for random sequences.

We are now in a position to derive a vector functional equation which allows us to evaluate $C_\infty(1)$ for sequences described by the nearest-neighbor correlated probability distribution function $P_s([a])$. The key equations are (29), (24), and (71), but now a coupling exists between s_n and W_{n-1}. For convenience in exposition, we put

$$s(a_n) = s_n,\ W_n(a_n, a_{n-1}, \ldots, a_2) = W_n(s_n, s_{n-1}, \ldots, s_2) \tag{101}$$

and define

$$C_{r,\nu}(y) = \lim_{N\to\infty} N^{-1} \sum_{n=1}^{N} \sum_{[a]} \tau_{r,\nu}([a]) \ln| y + W_n(a_n, a_{n-1}, \ldots, a_2)| \tag{102}$$

where

$$\tau_{r,\nu}([a]) = R_0(a_N) R(a_N, a_{N-1}) \ldots R(a_{n+2}, a_{n+1}) \varphi_r(a_{n+1}) \times \varphi_\nu(a_n) R(a_n, a_{n-1}) \quad \ldots R(a_2, a_1) R(a_1)/\mu_1^{N-1} (\varsigma_1)^2 \tag{103}$$

By Eq. (97),

$$\sum_{r=1}^{2} \mu_r \tau_{r,r} \equiv P_s([a])$$

so that

$$C_\infty(1) \equiv \sum_{r=1}^{2} \mu_r C_{rr}(1) \tag{104}$$

is the desired result $\lim_{N\to\infty} \langle N^{-1} \ln Q_N \rangle$.

We can carry out the indicated $[a]$ summation in Eq. (102) for $a_N, a_{N-1}, \ldots, a_{n+1}$, introduce Eq. (97) for the factor $R(a_n, a_{n-1})$ in Eq. (103), use Eq. (24) relating W_n with $s(a_n)$ and W_{n-1}, and show after much labor that

$$C_{2\nu}(y) = 0, \quad (\text{i.e. } N^{-1} 0(1)), \tag{105}$$

and

$$\mu_1 C_{1\nu}(y) = \sum_{a=0}^{1} \varphi_\nu(a) \Big\{ \varphi_1(a) \ln[y + s(a)] + \sum_{k=1}^{2} \mu_k \varphi_k(a)\, C_{1k}\Big(\frac{y+s(a)\sigma}{y+s(a)}\Big)\Big\} - \mu_\nu C_{1\nu}(1). \tag{106}$$

Defining

$$G_\nu(y) = \mu_1 C_{1\nu}(y) \tag{107}$$

and using Eqs. (95), (96) and (98), allows us to write Eq. (106) as a vector equation in $\underset{\sim}{G}(y)$ whose components are $G_\nu(y)$. One finds that

$$\underset{\sim}{G}(y) = \underset{\sim}{\omega}_A \ln(y + s_A) + \underset{\sim}{\omega}_B \ln(y + s_B) + \underset{\sim}{\alpha}\, \underset{\sim}{G}(Ay) + \underset{\sim}{\beta}\, \underset{\sim}{G}(By) - \underset{\sim}{\eta}\, \underset{\sim}{G}(1), \tag{108}$$

where

$$\underset{\sim}{\omega}_A = \begin{pmatrix} p_A \\ -q \end{pmatrix}, \quad \underset{\sim}{\omega}_B = \begin{pmatrix} p_B \\ q \end{pmatrix}, \quad \underset{\sim}{\eta} = \begin{pmatrix} 1 & 0 \\ 0 & \gamma \end{pmatrix}, \tag{109}$$

$$\underset{\sim}{\alpha} = \begin{pmatrix} p_A, & -\gamma q \\ -q, & \gamma p_B \end{pmatrix}, \quad \underset{\sim}{\beta} = \begin{pmatrix} p_B, & \gamma q \\ q, & \gamma p_A \end{pmatrix},$$

$Ay = (y + s_A\sigma)/(y + s_A)$, $\gamma = 1 - (p_{AB}/p_A p_B)$, and $q = (p_A p_B)^{1/2}$.

According to Eqs. (104), (105) and (107),

$$C_\infty(1) \equiv G_1(1). \tag{110}$$

For random sequences, $\Upsilon = 0$ and we recover Eq. (72) for $C_\infty(y)$ with $x_A = p_A$ and $x_B = p_B$.

Equation (108) covers a wide class of sequences ranging from random to a completely ordered ABABAB ... when $p_A = p_B = p_{AB} = 0.5$ since $p_{AA} = p_{BB} = 0$. It is instructive to note that Eq. (108) does give the correct $C_\infty(1)$ although $\Upsilon = -1$. If we define

$$\underset{\sim}{G} = \underset{\sim}{\mathcal{L}}\,\underset{\sim}{G}_T, \quad \sqrt{2}\,\underset{\sim}{\mathcal{L}} = \begin{pmatrix} 1 & 1 \\ 1 & -1 \end{pmatrix}, \tag{111}$$

iterate Eq. (108) once, note that $\underset{\sim}{\alpha}^2 = \underset{\sim}{\beta}^2 = \underset{\sim}{0}$, $\underset{\sim}{\mathcal{L}}\,\underset{\sim}{\alpha}\,\underset{\sim}{\beta}\,\underset{\sim}{\mathcal{L}} = \begin{pmatrix} 0 & 0 \\ 0 & 1 \end{pmatrix}$, and $\underset{\sim}{\mathcal{L}}\,\underset{\sim}{\beta}\,\underset{\sim}{\alpha}\,\underset{\sim}{\mathcal{L}} = \begin{pmatrix} 1 & 0 \\ 0 & 0 \end{pmatrix}$, the components of $\underset{\sim}{G}_T$ decouple and

$$G_{T1}(y) = \frac{1}{\sqrt{2}} \ln\left[(By + s_A)(y + s_B)\right] + G_{T1}(ABy) - \sqrt{2}\, G_1(1).$$

The G_{T2} component satisfies the same equation with A and B interchanged. As before, a single $0 < y < 1$ point exists such that $y_{AB} = ABy_{AB}$. Hence, $G_1(1) = 1/2 \ln\left[(By_{AB} + s_A)(y_{AB} + s_B)\right]$. This is exactly

$$C_\infty(1) = N^{-1} \ln\left[\mathrm{Tr}\left\{\begin{pmatrix} s_A & s_A\sigma \\ 1 & 1 \end{pmatrix}\begin{pmatrix} s_B & s_B\sigma \\ 1 & 1 \end{pmatrix}\right\}^{N/2}\right] =$$

$$= 1/2 \ln(\lambda_{AB+}) \text{ as } N \to \infty,$$

where λ_{AB+} is the largest eigenvalue of the matrix in the braces. One readily finds that

$$\lambda_{AB+} = 1/2\left[1 + s_A s_B + (s_A + s_B)\sigma\right]$$

$$+ \left\{\left(\frac{1 - s_A s_B}{2}\right)^2 + \left[2 s_A s_B + 1/2(s_A + s_B)(1 + s_A s_B)\right]\sigma\right.$$

$$\left. + 1/4(s_A - s_B)^2\sigma^2\right\}^{1/2}.$$

We note that $\lambda_{AB+}(s_A^{-1}, s_B^{-1}) \equiv (s_A s_B)^{-1} \lambda_{AB+}(s_A, s_B)$ as required by the symmetry rule, Eq. (13). For $\sigma = 9 \times 10^{-5}$, $C_{\infty}(1) \cong 0.01$ at the transition point $s_A s_B = 1$ (363°K); by contrast, Table IV shows $C_{\infty}(1) = 0.0395$ for random sequences.

Equation (108) can also be solved exactly for the case of $p_{AB} = 0$ corresponding to infinite sequences like AAAA ... ABBB ... B. For this case $\gamma = 1$, and $\alpha\beta = 0$; consequently, α and β can be simultaneously diagonalized and one finds the expected result

$$C_{\infty}(1) = x_A \ln(\lambda_{A+}) + x_B \ln(\lambda_{B+})$$

with λ_{A+} and λ_{B+} being given by Eq. (57) using s_A and s_B.

If $p_{AB} < p_A p_B$, $p_{AA} > p_A^2$ and $p_{BB} > p_B^2$, we will find a tendency for clustering of the A's and the B's without complete separation. This circumstance would probably produce a broader transition than obtained for random sequences. No detailed numerical investigation of this point has been made yet.

VI. SUMMARY AND DISCUSSION

We have employed some new techniques to construct ensemble averages of $C_{\infty}(1)$, the logarithm of the partition function Q_N, needed to describe the thermal properties of a linear random ferromagnet in an external field composed of two types of g factors with a single exchange parameter. The relationship of this model (first considered by Montroll and Goel) to the Reiss, McQuarrie, McTague and Cohen model for melting of copolymeric DNA was established and the two models shown to be mathematically equivalent.

A Fredholm integral equation approach was derived and solved numerically for $\sigma > 10^{-3}$ when the A-T, G-C groups were randomly sequenced. A functional equation, FE, was constructed for $C_{\infty}(y)$ and solved numerically for a large number of cases ranging from $10^{-5} < \sigma < 1$, $0 \leq x_A \leq 1$. Excellent $C_{\infty}(1)$ agreement was obtained between the Fredholm construction and the FE approach when the FC converged rapidly enough to be useful.

Table IV summarizes the temperature and compositional dependence of $C_\infty(1)$ and θ, the denaturation parameter, for $\sigma = 9 \times 10^{-5}$, giving a transitional breadth $\Delta T_M \cong 3.1^\circ C$ at 50% G-C. The maximum term method used by RMMC to approximate $C_\infty(1)$ and θ required $\sigma \cong 10^{-6}$ for $\Delta T_M \cong 2.9^\circ C$. The exact (random sequence) θ yields $\Delta T_M \cong 2.9^\circ C$ for $\sigma \cong 7 \times 10^{-5}$.

In Sec. V, the averaging technique was extended to the case of non-random sequences by introducing a nearest-neighbor correlated probability distribution function. A vector functional equation [Eq. (108)] was derived from which $C_\infty(1)$ and θ can be calculated. The method was shown to be general enough to treat any situation from ABABAB ... order to random A-B order. The limiting case $p_{AB} = 0$, complete separation of A and B's, was also correctly described and it appears that for $p_{AB} < p_A p_B$, the transition can be broadened more than that obtained by random sequences.

We stress the fact that a transition breadth $\Delta T_M \cong 3^\circ C$ should be directly measurable by specific heat experiments since the calculated $\Delta C \sim 10^3$ cal/mole/deg at $T = T_M = 363^\circ K$ for 50% G-C, decreasing by a factor of 6 at $T = 369^\circ K$.

ACKNOWLEDGEMENTS

The author is indebted to Drs. H. Reiss and J. P. McTague for numerous stimulating discussions on copolymeric DNA. He is also indebted to Dr. R. Futrelle for help with a crucial step in computer logic involved in the Fredholm construction and to Dr. W. F. Hall for a critical reading of the manuscript.

REFERENCES

1. H. Reiss, D. A. McQuarrie, J. P. McTague, and E. R. Cohen. J. Chem. Phys. 44, 4567 (1966). Hereafter referred to as RMMC. This paper should be consulted for reference to previous work relating to DNA.

2. N. S. Goel, Ph. D. Thesis, Univ. of Maryland, Technical Report No. 462 (1965).

3. E. W. Montroll and N. S. Goel, Technical Note BN-425, Univ. of Maryland, Institute for Fluid Dynamics and Applied Mathematics (1965). This work is subsequently referenced as MG. Low field magnetization studies for a dilute Ising Model have been carried out by Katsura and Tsujiyama. (Unpublished).

4. Averaging techniques involving the use of integral and functional equations were first considered by F. J. Dyson, Phys. Rev. 92, 1331 (1953), H. L. Frisch and S. P. Lloyd, Phys. Rev. 120, 1175, (1960), and H. Schmidt, Phys. Rev. 105, 425 (1957). The work presented in this paper is an extension of previous results: See G. W. Lehman, Bull. Am. Phys. Soc. 11, 115 (1966).

5. S. Michlin, Comp. Rend. (Doklady) Acad. Sci. USSR, 42, 373 (1944) proved the convergence of the Fredholm series under the hypothesis that the kernel K belongs only to the class L_2. See also, F. G. Tricomi, Integral Equations, Interscience Publ. NY (1957), pg. 55.

6. Our equations are related to those of Michlin (Ref. 5) by $n!\ D_n(u,v) = (-1)^n B_n(u,v)$, $n!\ d_n = (-1)^n C_n$, and $t_n = A_n$. His C_{n+1} recurrence formula pg. 375 is equivalent to our EQ. (50) obtained by back substitution from C_n, C_{n-1}, ... Our Eq. (51) is his γ_{N+1} equation pg. 376.

7. If $H_n(u) = e^{-Ku^2} \sum_{r=0}^{n} A_r u^r$ is inserted into the homogeneous part of Eq. (47), the coefficient of u^n fixes λ and A_{n-1}, A_{n-2}, ... are subsequently fixed by step-down relations. The resulting H_n's are eigenfunctions of K belonging to λ_n.

8. G. Boole, Calculus of Finite Differences, 4th Ed. Chelsea Pub. Co. N.Y. (1958).

9. The factor $\mu_1^{N-1} \varsigma_1^2$ is a normalization factor required to make $\sum_{[a]} P_s\langle[a]\rangle \equiv 1$ in the limit $N \to \infty$ and can be obtained by the well-known matrix method. See, e.g., E. W. Montroll, J. Chem. Phys. 9, 706 (1941). The factors $R_0(a_1)$ and $R_0(a_N)$ drop out of the analysis when $N \to \infty$. If $R(a_n\,;\,a_{n+1}) = R_0(a_n)R_0(a_{n+1})$, then $[R_0(a_n)]^2$ would represent the relative probability of a site being occupied by an A or B and $P_s([a])$ would be proportional to the uncorrelated product distribution function $\prod_{n=1}^{N} [R_0(a_n)]^2$.

DISCUSSION

Hijmans: Do I understand correctly that it makes a qualitative difference, whether σ goes to zero first and then N goes to infinity or the other way around? In that case would it not be possible to decide from the experimental conditions whether one should take $N\sigma \ll 1$ or $N\sigma \gg 1$?

Lehman: In the transition region, $N\sigma \gg 1$ for the treatment to be correct.

Hijmans: The quantity that goes to infinity fastest is then N ?

Lehman: Yes.

Rice: Shouldn't one be careful in interpreting agreement with experiment because of the neglect of the change in the mean electrostatic energy on going from the helix to the coil configuration?

Hijmans: Yes, this is true.

Rice: That is, I would not worry about whether σ had a specific value or not when an important effect is neglected.

Weiss: Isn't there any other experimental result that can be compared with the theory except the melting curve which is rather insensitive ?

Lehman: No, I do not think so.

Isihara: Experimentally the coiling up of a DNA molecule at the transition is visible under the electron microscope. The one dimensional spin lattice keeps its shape before and after the transition, although the spins flip. How do you explain this configurational change in the entire chain?

Lehman: The spin lattice - DNA analog is physically meaningless here.

THE ENTROPY OF CRYSTALLIZED SOLIDS COMPOSED OF LONG CHAIN MOLECULES

H. G. ZACHMANN
Institut für Physikalische
Chemie der Universität
Mainz

ABSTRACT

In crystallized solids consisting of long chain molecules each molecule usually belongs partly to crystalline and partly to non-crystalline regions. The entropy of such materials is calculated, taking into consideration especially that the ends of the non-crystallized parts of the molecules are fixed and the volume available to these parts is limited by the crystallits. In order to do this calculation one has to solve a random walk problem with absorbing barriers. From the fact that each chain molecule can belong to several regions with different order there arise some interesting thermodynamical consequences, for example the existence of a broad melting range and a folding of the chains during crystallization, as observed experimentally.

A. INTRODUCTION

Substances composed of long chain molecules usually can not be crystallized completely. At the end of the crystallization one obtains a material composed of crystalline regions, where the chains lie parallel to each other, and non-crystalline regions, where the chains show no order and can move quickly changing their conformations. Till now, it has not been completely cleared how these different regions are arranged and connected with each other. The oldest model is the so called fringed micelle model (fig. 1a). In this model each molecule goes through many different crystallites and non-crystalline regions. In other models, which are more in favor today, it is assumed that the molecules are folded. The non-crystalline regions are then formed either by chains connecting different crystals (fig. 1b) or by loops (fig. 1c) hanging out of the surfaces of the crystals[1].

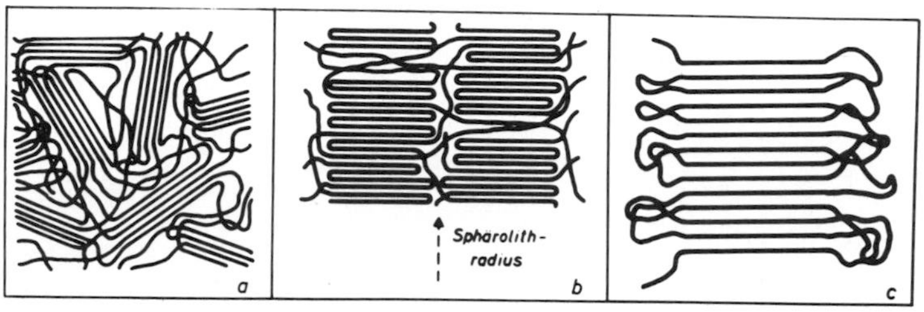

Fig. 1. Different models for the arrangement of the crystalline and non-crystalline regions.

The structures shown in fig. 1 are in a metastable state. A state with higher degree of order would certainly correspond to a lower value of free energy and therefore would be thermodynamical more stable. But this state cannot be formed without a complete melting and rearranging of the chains, which cannot take place at room temperature. Even a few degrees below the melting point, complete equilibrium cannot be attained owing to kinetic hindrances during crystallization.

There arises now the problem of calculating the entropy of the semicrystalline material and to discuss the crystallization and melting behaviour. We have already published some contributions to this problem[2, 3, 4]. In this publication we will be mainly concerned with the basic assumptions and consequences of our investigations and the comparison of our treatment with the quite different treatment given by Flory[5]. We will also use here a better approximation for the "packing" entropy arising from the mutual interference of the chains.

B. DERIVATION OF THE EQUATION

As shown by Flory[6], Huggins[7] and Prigogine[8], the entropy of substances composed of long chain molecules can be calculated by means of a lattice model. For this purpose the molecule is divided in units of suitable length, so that each unit can occupy one lattice cell. From the different contributions to entropy, we will consider here only the configurational entropy, which arises from the fact that the molecules can be arranged in different ways in the lattice. In a first approximation, only this part of entropy leads to special effects in the semicrystalline material[2,4,9].

The configurational entropy is given by the equation

$$S = k \cdot \ln g. \tag{1}$$

g is the so called combinatorial factor, which gives the number of different configurations of the system. In the completely molten material we have a great number of configurations as each chain can assume many different conformations. In the completely crystallized state all molecules have to be extended so that g is one. In the semicrystalline material only the parts of the molecules lying in the non-crystalline regions can assume different conformations. Therefore only the chains in the non-crystalline regions contribute to the configurational entropy.

In difference to the molecules in the molten sample, the chains in the non-crystallized regions

(1) have one or both ends fixed at definite places, and
(2) have to stay in a small volume limited by the adjacent crystallits.

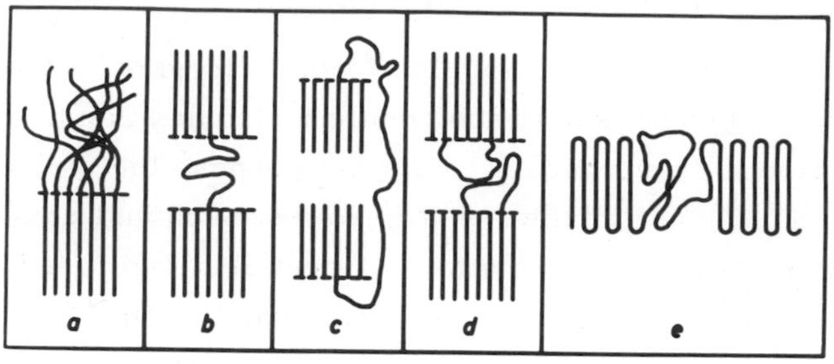

Fig. 2. Simple models for the calculation of the entropy (to avoid confusion, in the figures b to e there is shown only one non-crystallized chain instead of all).

We have to consider these two facts when we calculate the entropy of the semicrystalline material. In order to be able to do so, we have to confine ourself to simple models for the arrangement of the crystals and the non-crystalline regions. One can distinguish different types of non-crystalline regions some of which are shown in fig. 2. In fig. 2a these regions are formed by chains with one free end, in fig. d they are formed by loops hanging out of the surface a. s. o. (In most figures there is shown only one chain of the non-crystalline region instead of all, in order to avoid confusion). We will assume now that in our sample there is only one type of non-crystalline regions present and that all non-crystallized chains have the same length (and, if both ends of the chains are fixed, also the same end-to-end distance). We can then introduce the number of configurations Z belonging in the average to one chain. As each chain contributes to g a factor Z, we then obtain

$$g = Z^{\nu} \qquad (2)$$

ν is the number of chains in the non-crystalline region.

Z can be calculated in the following way: We determine first the number of conformations Z_w of the chain with one respectively both ends fixed assuming that there is only this single chain present in the non-crystalline region and that each lattice site may be occupied by more than one unit; that means that we neglect the volume of the units of the chains. Next we introduce a volume factor f_v in order to consider the fact that each lattice cell can be occupied only by one unit. Last we introduce a packing factor f_p which takes into account the other chains present in the non-crystalline regions. Owing to the competition for space, the number of conformations is reduced by the mutual interference between the different chains. We then obtain

$$Z = f_p \cdot f_v \cdot \hat{Z}_w \tag{3}$$

The conformation number $\hat{Z}_w$ can be determined by solving an equivalent threedimensional random flight problem in the presence of absorbing walls. The walls make allowance for the limitation of the volume and have to be placed at the surfaces of the crystals. This problem has been solved in a previous publication[3] assuming a primitive cubic lattice with the coordination number γ equal to 6. We will give here only the results. If there is no limitation of space, that means in an infinite lattice, one obtains for the number of conformations of a chain with one end fixed

$$\hat{Z}(N) = \gamma^N \tag{4}$$

and for a chain with both ends fixed at two points separated by r, s, and t steps in the three dimensions of space (see fig. 3)

$$\hat{Z}(N, r, s, t) = \sum_{i=0}^{k} \sum_{j=0}^{k-i} \frac{(N+1)!}{(r+i)!\; i!\; (s+j)!\; j!\; (t+k-i-j)!\; (k-i-j)!} \tag{5}$$

with

$$k = \frac{N+1-r-s-t}{2} \tag{6}$$

N is the number of the units in the chain*).

---

*) In the publication cited above we have used the symbols $Z'(N)$ and $Z^*(N, r, s, t)$ instead of $Z(N)$ and $Z(N, r, s, t)$ in order to distinguish more clearly between the chain with one end fixed and the chain with both ends fixed.

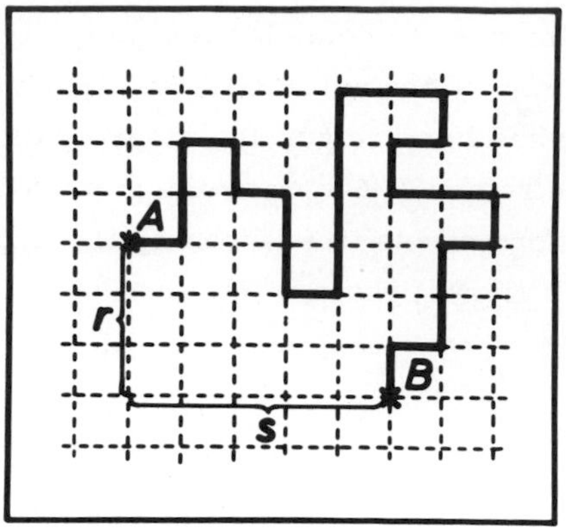

Fig. 3. Projection of the three-dimensional cubic lattice with a chain with fixed ends at the points A and B on the two-dimensional plane.

The subscript w in Z has been omitted in order to indicate that there are no walls present. For the number of conformations of the chain with both ends fixed we have obtained also a simple approximation by introducing a freely jointed model chain. This approximation is given by

$$\hat{Z}(N, r, s, t) = \gamma^N \cdot W(\frac{N+1}{1,5}, h) \cdot V \qquad (6)$$

where W is the wellknown probability function for the end to end distance

$$W(n, h) = (\frac{3}{2\gamma nl^2})^{3/2} \cdot \exp(-\frac{3h^2}{2nl^2}), \qquad (7)$$

$V = a^3$ the volume of one lattice cell, and

$$h = a \cdot \sqrt{r^2 + s^2 + t^2} \qquad (8)$$

the end to end distance.a is the lattice konstant (see fig. 3). If there are walls present, one has to substract from $\hat{Z}(N, r, s, t)$ the numbers of conformations the chain can assume when one of its ends is removed to some mirror image points defined by the geometry of the problem. So, one obtains $\hat{Z}_w(N, r, s, t)$ by simple algebraic processes from the function $\hat{Z}(N, r, s, t)$. For more detail and references see the publication cited above.

For the calculation of the factors f_v and f_p we have to distinguish between chains with one and fixed (fig. 2a) and chains with both ends fixed (fig. 2b to e). If there is only one end fixed we may use in a first approximation the same expressions as in the molten state. These expressions are given by the equations (16) and (18) in the appendix. If there are both ends fixed the factors f_p and f_v depend on the extension ratio of the chains. For example, if the chains are fully extended both factors have to be one as there is no mutual interference between the different units then. For the factor f_v there has not been deduced an exact expression till now. We will use therefore either the average value given by equation (16) or, if the chains are nearly extended, the value 1. For the packing factor f_p we will use an expression derived by DiMarzio[10]:

$$\ln f_p = \frac{1}{N+1} \cdot \ln \frac{1}{N+1} + (N+1) \sum_{i=1}^{3} \left(1 - \frac{N}{N+1} \alpha_i\right) \ln \left(1 - \frac{N}{N+1} \alpha_i\right) \qquad (9)$$

α_1, α_2, and α_3 are the fractions of bonds lying respectively in the three dimensions of space. They can be calculated from the extension ratio $\frac{h}{a(N+1)}$ by means of the equations

$$\alpha_1 = -\frac{1}{3} + \frac{2}{3} \left[1 + \frac{3(h/a)^2}{(N+1)^2}\right]^{1/2}$$

and

$$\alpha_2 = \alpha_3 = \frac{1 - \alpha_1}{2}$$

For the completely molten material the three factors $\hat{Z}$, f_v, and f_p are given in the appendix.

C. RESULTS

By means of the derived equations we have calculated the configurational entropy S_k^{nc} belonging to a chain in the non-crystalline region. As a reference, we have also determined the configurational entropy S_k^{m} of a chain with the same length in the molten sample. Fig. 4 gives the difference between these entropies, for the case that the non-crystalline regions are formed by loops hanging out of the crystals. h is the end-to-end distance of the loop and N the number of units forming one loop.

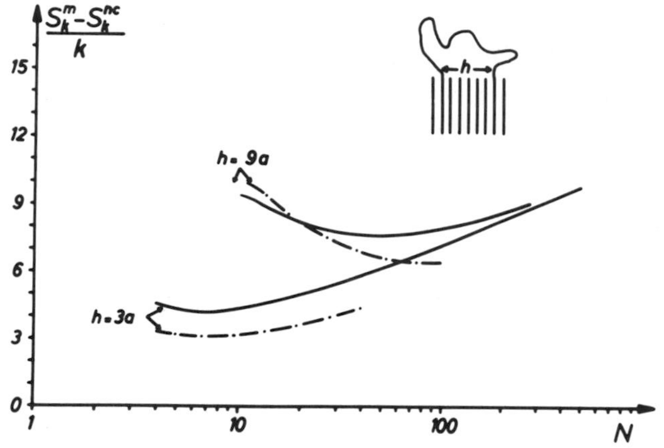

Fig. 4. Difference between the configurational entropies of a chain in the non-crystalline region, S_k^{nc}, and a chain of the same length in the molten material, S_k^{m}. N is the number of units forming the chain. -.-.- by using the exact equation ____ by using the Gaussian approximation.

We see that the entropy of a chain in the non-crystalline region is smaller than the entropy of a chain with the same length in the molten sample by an amount of several k. This difference is of course due to the fact that in the non-crystalline region the ends of the chain are fixed and the volume disposable is limited by the crystals. Fig. 5 shows the results for the case that the non-crystalline regions are formed by chains with one free end. These results are important for the discussion of the crystallization behaviour (see section E).

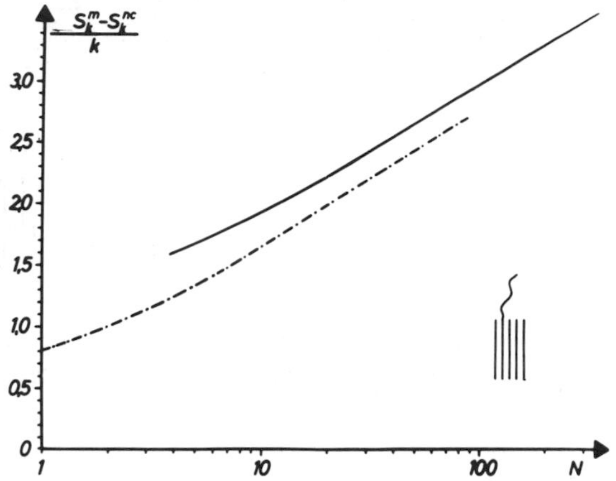

Fig. 5. Difference between the configurational entropies of a chain in the non-crystalline region, S_k^{nc}, and a chain of the same length in the molten material, S_k^m. N is the number of units forming the chain. -. -. - by using the exact equation —— by using the Gaussian approximation.

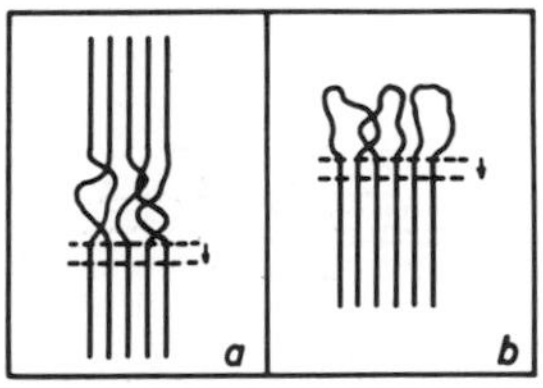

Fig. 6. Two examples for the melting of a small sheet of a crystal. The melting sheet considered lies between the two broken lines in each figure.

We have calculated also the change of configurational entropy occurring when a small sheet of a crystal, with the length of one unit, is melting (see fig. 6). This change of entropy, related to one unit, will be called ΔS_k^o. It has to be compared with the configurational part of the average melting entropy of one unit, $\overline{\Delta S_k^o}$, obtained by dividing the difference of the configurational entropies of the melt and the completely crystallized material by the number of units contained. From equations (1) and (13) one obtains $\overline{\Delta S_k^o} = k \cdot \ln \frac{\gamma - 1}{2,25}$. Fig. 7 gives the results for a crystal with loops hanging out of the surface. The direction in which melting proceeds is indicated by the arrow in the figure. The dotted line gives the average value $\Delta \overline{S_k^o}$. N is the number of units of the loop. When N increases - owing to the proceeding melting of the crystal- ΔS_k^o approaches the average value $\Delta \overline{S_k^o}$.

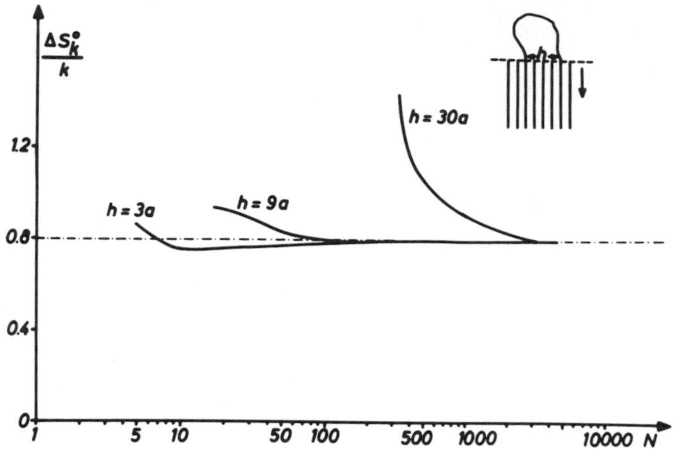

Fig. 7. Change of configurational entropy with the melting of one unit. N is the number of units in a loop and h the end-to-end distance of the loop. The arrow indicates the direction in which the melting proceeds.

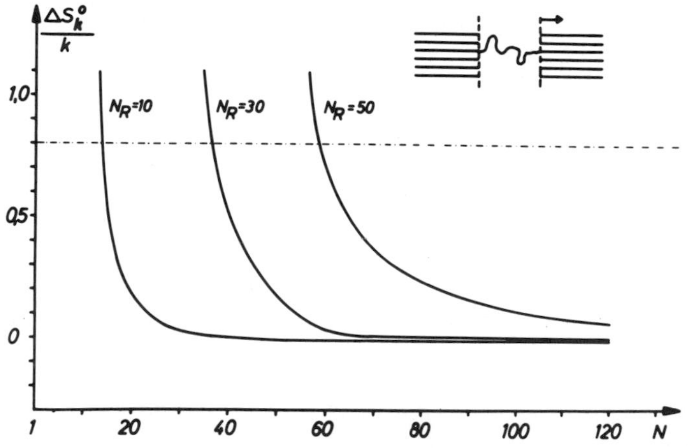

Fig. 8. Change of configurational entropy with the melting of one unit. N is the number of units in the non-crystallized chain, N_R the value assumed by N when the two crystals touch each other. The arrow indicate the direction in which melting proceeds.

Fig. 8 shows the results for another model structure, in which two different crystals are connected by non-crystallized chains. ΔS_k^o is here smaller than the average value. These results determine the melting behaviour of the material (see the following section).

D. CONSEQUENCES FOR THE MELTING BEHAVIOUR

To obtain the condition for equilibrium between the crystals and the adjacent non-crystalline regions*) one has to consider the change in free enthalpy occurring with the melting of a small sheet of the crystal as shown in fig. 6. In equilibrium this change has to be zero. From this condition one obtains for the equilibrium temperature the equation

$$T' = \frac{\Delta H^o}{\Delta S^o} \tag{10}$$

ΔH^o and ΔS^o are the changes of enthalpy and entropy occurring with the melting of one unit of a molecule. ΔS^o consists of two parts, namely the change of configurational entropy ΔS_k^o and the change of the other contributions to entropy ΔS_2^o. The meaning of the equilibrium temperature T' can be interpreted in the following way: If the temperature of the sample is above T' the considered sheet melts; if it is beneath T' crystallization proceeds.

ΔH^o has in a first approximation a constant value. The same is true for ΔS_2^o. ΔS_k^o however is not constant but depends on the structure and changes during the melting as shown in the figures 7 and 8. Therefore T' changes also during melting and the melting behavior becomes very complicated. For the discussion of the melting behavior we will introduce the temperature

$$T_s = \frac{\Delta H^o}{\overline{\Delta S^o}}$$

where $\overline{\Delta S^o}$ is the average melting entropy of one unit. T_s will be called the thermodynamic melting point. Up to this tem-

*) We mean of course metastable equilibrium in the sense stated in the introduction of this publication.

perature an ideal crystal with extended chains is more stable than the melt.

The different possibilities of melting behaviour, depending on the considered structure and also on the considered melting process, are summarized in fig. 9. For the two melting processes shown in the first row in this figure, the entropy change ΔS_k^o is larger than the average value $\overline{\Delta S_k^o}$ and approaches this value with proceeding melting. The equilibrium temperature T' lies then below the melting point T_s. Melting starts at relative low temperatures and one obtains a broad melting range. Such a melting behaviour is found with all unorientented semicrystalline polymers. The dependence of the crystalline fraction on temperature has been calculated on the basis of similar considerations by Fischer[11]. The results have been proved experimentally[12]. Other authors have also explained the broad melting range by entropy effects, but they have used untenable suppositions respectively erraneous equationa for the entropy (for a detailed discussion see reference[2]). Münster[13] has shown that the broad melting range can be treated as a second order transition.

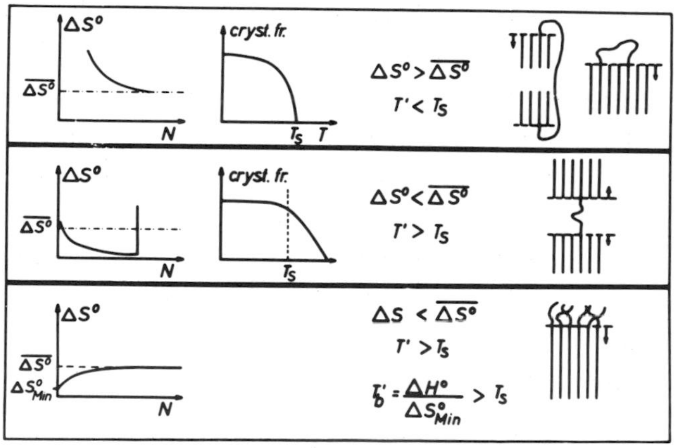

Fig. 9. The different possibilities of melting behaviour.

For the melting processes shown at the models in the second and in the third row of fig. 9, ΔS_k^o lies below the average value

$\overline{\Delta S_k^o}$ and T' is therefore larger than T_s. In the second row T' increases with proceeding melting (except for the last steps of the process); in the third row T' has its highest value T_b' when melting starts. In both cases there arises an interesting situation: If the sample is held at the temperature T', which varies during melting but lies mostly considerable above T_s, the melting proceeds in this way that, in every stage of the melting, the crystal is in metastable equilibrium with the adjacent non-crystalline region. At a constant temperature T*, which lies above T_s but below the momentary equilibrium temperature T' the melting cannot proceed in that way, as there would occur at first an increase of free enthalpy. But now one has to take into consideration that at $T^* > T_s$ the melt obtained at last is more stable than the crystal*); the entropy effect leads here only to a free enthalpy of activation which may be overcome, by means of thermal fluctuation. We can say therefore, that the considered melting process may take place also at the temperatures T*, but one has to wait then for a time long enough.

The models of the second and third row of fig. 9 apply for semicrystalline samples with oriented chains and for completely crystallized samples with extended chains. But the described superheating effects, respectively time delay effects, occur actually with these samples only if the crystals cannot melt by another process, which can take place at lower temperature than that considered in fig. 9. For the extended chain model, it can be shown that ΔS_k^o is smaller than $\overline{\Delta S_k^o}$ for every possible melting process[14]. In agreement with these results, samples crystallized completely with extended chains**) show experimentally detectable superheating effects[15].

---

*) The mentioned increase in free enthalpy is overcompensated at the end of the process (where T' falls below T_s).

**) Such structures can be obtained in some cases by applying high pressure during crystallization.

E. CONSEQUENCES FOR THE CRYSTALLIZATION BEHAVIOUR

We have mentioned that the entropy of the chains in the non-crystallized regions is lower than the entropy of the same parts of the molecules in the completely molten sample. This difference of entropy acts like an additional surface tension[4] (exactly: like an addition to the entropy part of the free energy of the surface). Fig. 10 shows this additional surface tension for same structures. We see that it is relatively high for a bundle-like crystal (fig. 10b) and even higher for a crystal formed by chains which are already partly built in in other crystals (fig. 10c; the crystal considered grows at the place indicated by the arrow). The lowest value of surface tension is obtained for a folded chain crystal with short loops*).

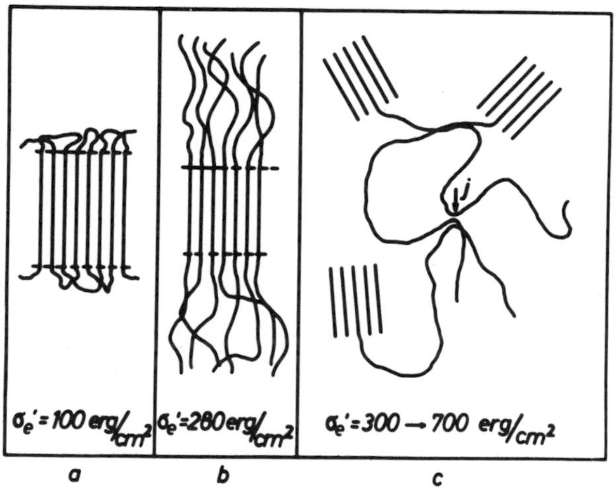

Fig. 10. The additional surface tension for three different structures.

These results are very important for the discussion of the crystallization behaviour. From kinetic considerations it follows that mainly the structure with the smallest surface tension is formed. We conclude therefore that we have to obtain crystals with folded chains. The most stable structure-crystals with extended chains- cannot be formed as the surface tension of the

*) This value contains also an enthalpy term of 60 erg/cm^2 arising from the gauche conformations which appear in the loop.

bundle-like crystal, occurring as an intermediate state, is too large. We see from this, that the considered entropy effects provide a good explanation for the experimentally observed foldind of the chains*).

But these conclusions can be drawn only if supercooling is not too large. The restriction arises from the following fact: In order that the considered entropy effect should act during the time t_o in which the crystal nucleus is formed, the condition $t_o > \tau$ must be fullfilled. τ is the relaxation time, belonging to the process by which equilibrium concerning the distribution of the conformations of the chains is attained. For small supercooling that condition is fullfilled because the critical nucleus is very large so that it will take a comparatively long time until it is formed. For large supercooling the critical nucleus becomes small and may be formed so quickly that the entropy effect does not act. Most units of the molecules crystallize then in the neighbourhood of the places where they are lying in the molten state and one obtains the structure given by the fringed micelle modell in fig. 1a.

F. COMPARISON WITH THE TREATMENT GIVEN BY FLORY

The combinatorial factor g was determined by us under the assumption that the crystallits are situated at definite places and are formed by definite units of the molecules. The different configurations are generated in our treatment by the different conformations of the chains in the non-crystalline regions. In quite a different way the problem was attacked by Flory[5]. Flory determines the number of configurations assuming that only the crystalline fraction is constant. In his treatment, different configurations arise not only by changing the conformations of the chains in the non-crystalline regions, but also by changing the units which form the crystals and changing the places where the

---

*) An attempt to explain the folding of the chains by means of the large surface tension of the bundle-like crystal has been made also by Hoffman and Lauritzen[16].

crystals are situated. In a similar manner he calculates the entropy of crystals with chain loops the end to end distances of which are distributed at random ("switch-board model")[17]. He obtains the results that substances composed of infinite long chains have to crystallize completely and have to show a sharp melting point.

There arises now the question: Which is the more adequate treatment? The answer is the following: Flory does not investigate whether each crystal in a given structure is stable or may be transformed. Further, he ignores in his treatment the fact that the crystals, once formed under the influence of kinetic factors, may prevent the system from attaining complete equilibrium. Flory determines therefore the thermodynamical behaviour the system would show if it was in equilibrium. From this point of view his results are of great interest. But these results describe only an ideal behaviour which is quite different from that really observed. In our treatment, by assuming fixed crystals and fixed ends of the chains in the non-crystalline regions, we investigate the behaviour of a definite given structure. In that way we make allowance for the fact that the system is in a metastable state. We obtain the melting behaviour, which can be really observed and we get an answer to the question which metastable structure is most likely to be formed.

Appendix: Number of configurations of a chain in the molten material

The combinatorial factor of the molten material is given according to Flory[6] by

$$g = \left(\frac{N_o}{2}\right)^{\nu} \cdot \left(\frac{\gamma-1}{e}\right)^{(N_o-1)\nu} \approx \left(\frac{\gamma-1}{e}\right)^{N_o \cdot \nu} \qquad (13)$$

N_o is the number of units forming one molecule, ν is the number of molecules and γ is the coordination number of the lattice.

By means of equation (2) we obtain for the average number of configurations of one molecule

$$Z = \left(\frac{\gamma - 1}{e}\right)^{N_o} \tag{14}$$

Following the derivation of the expression for g given by Flory, it is easy to see that the three factors $\hat{Z}$, f_v, and f_p are given by

$$\hat{Z} = \gamma^{N_o} \tag{15}$$

$$f_v = \left(\frac{\gamma - 1}{\gamma}\right)^{N_o} \tag{16}$$

and

$$f_p = \left(\frac{1}{e}\right)^{N_o} \tag{17}$$

In a better approximation derived especially for a cubic lattice ($\gamma = 6$) DiMarzio[10)] has obtained for the packing factor

$$f_p = \left(\frac{1}{2{,}25}\right)^{N_o} \tag{18}$$

LITERATURE

1. For more detail see: H. G. Zachmann, Advances in Polymer Sci. 3, 581 (1964).
2. H. G. Zachmann, Z. Naturforsch. 19a, 1397 (1964).
3. H. G. Zachmann, and P. Spellucci, Kolloid. Z. u. Z. f. Polymere, 213, 39 (1966).
4. H. G. Zachmann, Z. Naturforsch. 20a, 719 (1965).
5. P. J. Flory, J. Chem. Phys. 17, 223 (1949).
6. P. J. Flory, J. Chem. Phys. 10, 51 (1942).
7. M. L. Huggins, J. Phys. Chem. 46, 151 (1942).
8. I. Prigogine: "The Molecular Theory of Solution", Amsterdam 1957 p. 323 ff.
9. H. G. Zachmann, to be published.
10. E. A. DiMartio, J. Chem. Phys. 36, 1563 (1962).
11. E. W. Fischer, to be published.
12. Y. Nukushima, Y. Itoh, and E. W. Fischer, Polymer Letters 3, 383 (1956).
13. A. Münster, Z. Physik. Chem. N. F. 1, 259 (1954).
14. H. G. Zachmann, Kolloid-Z. u. Z. f. Polymere 206, 25 (1965).
15. E. Hellmuth und B. Wunderlich, J. Appl. Phys. 36, 3039 (1965).
16. J. D. Hoffmann und J. I. Lauritzen, J. Research Natl. Bur. Standards 65A, 297 (1961).
17. P. J. Flory, J. Amer. Chem. Soc. 84, 2857 (1962).

DISCUSSION

Mayer: I believe that it is assumed that in the physical system the chains which have their two ends frozen into crystals have random distances along the crystal faces between the two frozen segments. If this is really the model then the computation of the entropy must be made for chain segments which are constrained to end at fixed surfaces (the crystal faces) rather than at fixed points. In any case it is immaterial that the two chain ends are frozen and cannot change their positions; as long as these positions are randomly distributed their entropies are those of a randomly distributed ensemble.

Zachmann: This corresponds to the treatment given by Flory. That treatment gives no answer to the question wether a special structure is in a metastable state; there is investigated only the behavior in complete thermodynamic equilibrium. How can you introduce in that equilibrium-concept the condition that the system is in a metastable state?

Mayer: The entropy of a random ensemble is the same as the entropy of an ensemble of ergodic systems, and must be calculated as though the system were ergodic. The familar example is the CO crystal (or any other frozen disordered system) in which the random end to end orientation leads to an entropy $kN \ln 2$ at $0^{o}K$, even though the disordered arrangement in any single crystal is frozen in, and cannot change.

Zachmann: I do not think this can be compared exactly with our problem. The equivalent process to the freezing of CO is the "glass" transition in amorphous samples consisting of chain molecules. With this transition, of course, there is no change of entropy in spite of the fact that the motion of the units is freezing. In non-crystalline regions formed by chains with fixed ends all units of the chains (except those of the ends) can move. We consider here an assembly of systems in which only the conformations of the chains change from system to system but not the end-to-end distances. This assembly is ergodic with respect to different conformations. Using this assembly, we can investigate whether the special structure considered is metastable.

Jackson: Di Marzio calculated the packing entropy as a function of stretching. What do you do about stretching?

Zachmann: I need an expression giving the packing entropy as a function of the extension of the chains. If I take the Flory value, obtained for the melt, $\left(\frac{1}{e}\right)^N$, this would not be correct. For extended chains, for instance, the factor has to be 1, because there is in this case no mutual interference between the chains.

Isihara: One way of observing crystallization is to measure the volume change. If you use a lattice model, isn't it difficult to explain the change?

Zachmann: I have to assume that the lattice constant in the melt is larger than in the crystal. This has been neglected as it does not affect essentially the considered entropy-effect.

Jackson: I have a question about the passage to equilibrium. This concerns a calculation done by Fred Gornick and myself. We considered sequences which were too small to take part in the crystallization. Do you take this into account.

Zachmann: I do not. This comes from the special models I have used. In a better approach such effects have to be considered also, of course.

CORRELATION FUNCTIONS IN NON-HOMOGENEOUS CHARGED REGIONS

G. M. BELL
Chelsea College of Science and Technology, University of London
S. LEVINE
University of Manchester

ABSTRACT

We discuss an aqueous electrolyte solution with an adsorbed phase of ions formed near an interface. The adsorbed ion centres are assumed to lie on an adsorption plane, and the water near this plane differs in its properties from bulk water. In the neighbouring region of solution there is a diffuse charge while the mean properties at any point depend on distance from the interface. The sign of the diffuse charge is opposite to that of the adsorbed charge giving a "double layer".

It is necessary to consider correlation functions for the probability of occupation by ion centres, of given species, of sets of points which may be in the diffuse layer or on the adsorption plane or both. The binary correlation functions represent the formation of ionic self-atmospheres. For any double layer ion, part of its self-atmosphere lies on the adsorption plane itself and part in the diffuse layer. By making a simple assumption of additivity for the simultaneous effect of two ions in given positions in the double layer equations for the self-atmosphere potentials may be obtained. An integral equation for the self-atmosphere of an adsorbed ion is derived. Connections with existing theories of ion distribution in bulk electrolyte, the diffuse region and on the adsorption plane are indicated.

1. INTRODUCTION

We are concerned here with the distribution of ions near a phase boundary and suppose that in addition to position dependent concentrations of unbound ions there is a layer of adsorbed ions bound by specific forces to the interface. Such a situation arises in physical systems like metallic electrodes, ionised monolayers at air/water or oil/water boundaries and charged colloidal suspensions. The model assumed here is shown in fig. 1. The

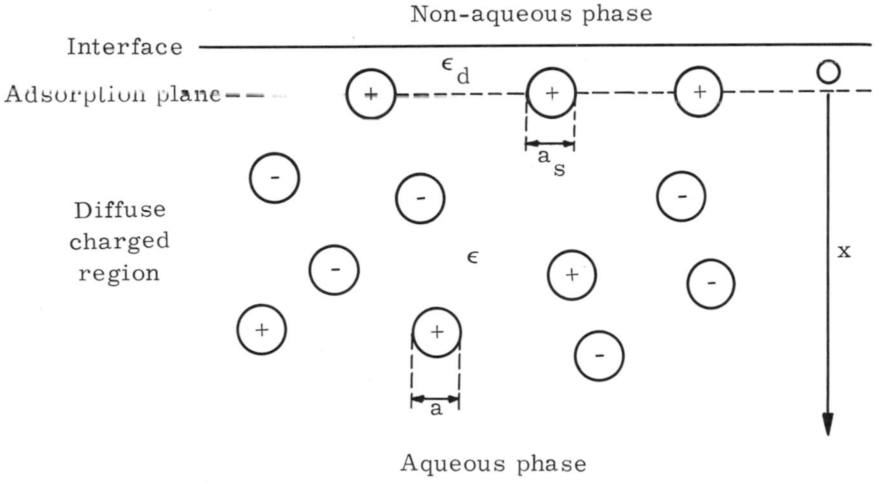

Fig. 1. The charged double layer.

centres of all adsorbed ions lie on the plane $x = 0$ and move freely on this adsorption plane, so that the adsorbing surface is regarded as "smooth". (This is a good approximation where adsorption is on specific sites provided the number of adsorbed ions is considerably less than the number of adsorption sites. The distance of nearest approach as introduced below is then to be interpreted as the shortest distance between a pair of sites.) In the adjacent electrolyte solution there is a diffuse charge density $\rho(x)$ opposite in sign to that on the adsorption plane so that an electrical double layer exists[1]. (For bulk concentrations of 1-1 electrolyte greater than about 1M, $\rho(x)$ may alternate in sign, see § 3.) The water is regarded as a continuous medium but to account for measured double-layer capacities it is usually necessary to suppose that the dielectric constant ϵ_d near the adsorption plane is smaller than the value ϵ in the diffuse region[2].

The mean surface number density of species i (charge e_i) on the adsorption plane is denoted by $\nu^{(i)}$ and the mean volume number density of i at the plane of coordinate x in the diffuse region by $n^{(i)}(x)$, approaching the bulk value $n^{(i)}$ as $x \to \infty$. The mean surface charge density σ on the adsorption plane and the mean volume charge density $\rho(x)$ are thus given by,

$$\sigma = \Sigma_i e_i \nu^{(i)}, \qquad \rho(x) = \Sigma_i e_i n^{(i)}(x) \; [\rho(\infty) = 0]. \tag{1}$$

Formally we take all species as present in both parts of the double layer so that some $\nu^{(i)} = 0$ and, when there are insoluble surface-active ions, some $n^{(i)}(x) = 0$. As $x \to \infty$ the diffuse charge density $\rho(x) \to 0$, since bulk electrolyte is electrically neutral. There is a mean potential $\psi(x)$, varying from $\psi(0)$ on the adsorption plane to 0 at $x = \infty$. For metallic electrodes unbound ion centres cannot penetrate beyond a plane at a given distance from the adsorption plane, but in some ionised monolayers unbound ions may penetrate the adsorption plane[3][4].

An ion of opposite sign is more likely to be found near a given ion than one of the same sign, giving rise to a "self-atmosphere". In bulk electrolytes the self-atmosphere[5] is symmetrical about the given ion centre but in double layers it is modified by the non-uniformity of the mean ion densities and by "image" effects due to the discontinuities in dielectric constant. To obtain adsorption isotherms or diffuse region ion distributions $n^{(i)}(x)$ both the mean potential $\psi(x)$ and the potential at an ion centre due to its own self-atmosphere and interface image effects are needed. Work has been done at the Debye-Huckel level of accuracy on diffuse region self-atmospheres[6-11] but intuitive assumptions have usually been made about the self-atmosphere of an adsorbed ion[12-18]. One aim of the present work is to develop an equivalent treatment for both adsorbed and diffuse region ions.

2. SELF-ATMOSPHERE POTENTIALS AND CORRELATION FUNCTIONS

Each ion is regarded as a point charge at the centre of a hard sphere. For simplicity all diffuse region ions have diameter a and all adsorbed ions (which may lose some of their hydration shell of water molecules) have diameter a_s. The dielectric constant of each ion is the same as that of the environment, ϵ for the diffuse region and ϵ_d for the adsorption region so that we neglect the effect of ionic polarisability on the energy of interaction of two ions, which can be written as

$$u^{(ij)}(12) = u^{(rep)}(r_{12}) + \xi_1 \xi_2 e_i e_j v(12) \tag{2}$$

Here 1 and 2 denote points $\underset{\sim}{r}_1$ and $\underset{\sim}{r}_2$, $r_{12} = |\underset{\sim}{r}_2 - \underset{\sim}{r}_1|$, $u^{(rep)}(r_{12})$ is a hard sphere repulsion term and v(12) is the potential at $\underset{\sim}{r}_2$, due to a point charge at $\underset{\sim}{r}_1$ in the presence of the interfaces; ξ_1 and ξ_2 are charging parameters with values between 0 and 1. Buff and Stillinger give Fourier-Bessel expansion expressions for v(12) with a metallic boundary and a plane of dielectric discontinuity[19].

When it is desirable to distinguish points on the adsorption plane from those in the diffuse region the numbers denoting the former are "dashed". Thus the self-atmosphere potential at a field-point f, with position vector $\underset{\sim}{r}$, due to an ion i with charge $\xi_1 e_i$ at $\underset{\sim}{r}_1$ is defined by

$$\phi_1^{(i)}(\underset{\sim}{r}, \xi_1) = \xi_1 e_i v(1f) + \int_V v(2f)\rho_1^{(i)}(\underset{\sim}{r}_2, \xi_1)d\tau_2 + \int_A v(2'f)\sigma_1^{(i)}(\underset{\sim}{r}'_2, \xi_1)d\tau'_2 \tag{3}$$

V being the electrolyte solution volume and A the adsorption plane area. The contributions to $\phi_1^{(i)}$ are indicated in fig. 2: the first term is the potential due directly to the ion at r_1, the second is due to the self-atmosphere volume charge density $\rho_1^{(i)}(r_2, \xi_1)$, integrated over volume elements $d\tau_2$, and the third to the self-atmosphere surface charge density $\sigma_1^{(i)}(\underset{\sim}{r}_2', \xi_1)$, integrated over surface elements $d\tau_2'$.

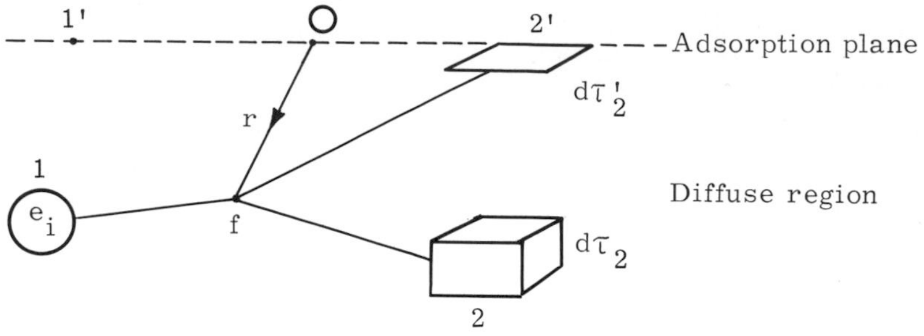

Fig. 2. Contributions to the self-atmosphere potential at a field-point f due to charge e_i at r_1.

The self-atmosphere charge densities can be written in terms of mean number densities and binary correlation functions *). If $n^{[ij]}(12, \xi_1)$ denotes the conditional mean number density of j at $\underset{\sim}{r}_2$ with an i, charge $\xi_1 e_i$, placed at $\underset{\sim}{r}_1$ then $n^{[ij]}(12, \xi_1) - n^{(j)}(x_2)$ is the change in the number density of j due to the presence of the i. Similarly the change in surface number density at a point on the adsorption plane is $\nu^{[ij]}(12'; \xi_1) - \nu^{(j)}$.

Now binary correlation functions $g^{(ij)}(12, \xi_1)$ and $g^{(ij)}(12', \xi_1)$ are given by

$$g^{(ij)}(12, \xi_1) = n^{[ij]}(12, \xi_1)/n^{(j)}(x_2)$$
$$g^{(ij)}(12', \xi_1) = \nu^{[ij]}(12', \xi_1)/\nu^{(j)} , \qquad (4)$$

so that the self atmosphere charge densities can be expressed by

$$\rho_1^{(i)}(\underset{\sim}{r}_2, \xi_1) = \Sigma_j e_j \{n^{[ij]}(12, \xi_1) - n^{(j)}(x_2)\} = \Sigma_j e_j n^{(j)}(x_2)\{g^{(ij)}(12, \xi_1) - 1\} \qquad (5a)$$

$$\sigma_1^{(i)}(\underset{\sim}{r}_2', \xi_1) = \Sigma_j e_j \{\nu^{[ij]}(12'; \xi_1) - \nu^{(j)}\} = \Sigma_j e_j \nu^{(j)}\{g^{(ij)}(12'; \xi_1) - 1\} \qquad (5b)$$

---

*) The notation used is adapted from that of Hill[20].

Formally these are expressions for the self-atmosphere of a diffuse region ion but similar ones for an adsorbed ion are obtained by replacing 1 by 1'. Naturally the relative contributions to the potential from the diffuse part (5a) and the adsorption plane part (5b) differ in the two cases; indeed the adsorption plane part is usually neglected for a diffuse region ion.*) For $r_{12} < a$, $g^{(ij)}(12, \xi_1) = 0$ for all j so that, by (5a) and (1), part of a diffuse region ion's self-atmosphere is a sphere of charge density $-\rho(x)$ and radius a, giving rise to a cavity potential. Similarly part of an adsorbed ion's self-atmosphere is a disc charge of density $-\sigma$ and radius a_s.

The potential at a unit charge at $\underset{\sim}{r}_1$ due to its own image system in the interfaces is

$$v(x_1) = \lim_{r_{1f} \to 0} \{v(1f) - \frac{1}{\epsilon r_{1f}}\} . \tag{6}$$

Hence the image-self-atmosphere potential at the ionic charge $\xi_i e_i$ on an ion at r_1 is

$$\eta^{(i)}(x_1, \xi_1) = \xi_i e_i v(x_1) + \int_V v(21)\rho_1^{(i)}(\underset{\sim}{r}_2, \xi_1)d\tau_2 + \int_A v(2'1)\sigma^{(i)}(\underset{\sim}{r}_2', \xi_1)d\tau_2'$$

$$= \lim_{r_{1f} \to 0} \{\phi^{(i)}(\underset{\sim}{r}, \xi_1) - \frac{\xi_1 e_i}{\epsilon r_{1f}}\} . \tag{7}$$

If the ion lies on the adsorption plane we have

$$\eta^{(i)}(\xi_1') = \xi_1' e_i v(0) + \int_V v(21')\rho_{1'}^{(i)}(\underset{\sim}{r}_2, \xi_1')d\tau_2 + \int_A v(2'1')\sigma_{1'}^{(i)}(\underset{\sim}{r}_2', \xi_1')d\tau_2'$$

$$= \lim_{r_{1'f} \to 0} \{\phi_{1'}^{(i)}(\underset{\sim}{r}, \xi_1') - \frac{\xi_1' e_i}{\epsilon_d r_{1'f}}\} . \tag{8}$$

---

*) This neglect may not be justified. From a diffuse layer ion's viewpoint an adsorption plane with a high density of mobile adsorbed ions tends to behave as a conductor and image forces at a non-metallic interface might be seriously affected.

3. DISTRIBUTIONS IN THE DIFFUSE REGION

Using a Canonical Ensemble, for a given number N_j of each species j in V and N'_j on the adsorption plane A, the product $n^{(i)}(x_1)d\tau_1$ can be expressed as a fraction of the configurational integral Q. If the full charge e_i on the particular ion at r_1 is replaced by $\xi_1 e_i$ in this expression then it may be denoted by $n^{(i)}(x_1,\xi_1)d\tau_1$. Differentiating with respect to ξ_1, and dividing throughout by $n^{(i)}(x_1,\xi_1)$ gives

$$-\beta^{-1}\partial \log n^{(i)}(x_1,\xi_1)/\partial\xi_1 = \xi_1 e_i^2 v(x_1) + e_i\Psi_m(x)$$
$$+ e_i\int_V v(21)\,\Sigma_j e_j n^{[ij]}(12,\xi_1)d\tau_2 - e_i\int_V v(21)\,\Sigma_j e_j n_b^{[ij]}(12,\xi_1)d\tau_2$$
$$+ e_i\int_A v(2'1)\,\Sigma_j e_j \nu^{[ij]}(12',\xi_1)d\tau'_2 \qquad (9)$$

where $\beta^{-1} = kT$ and the suffix b refers to bulk electrolyte. The potential due to the charge at the boundary of a metallic phase is $\Psi_m(x_1)$ and this is replaced by 0 when the non-aqueous phase is not metallic. The mean potential $\Psi(x_1)$ may (analogously to (3)) be written

$$\Psi(x_1) = \Psi_m(x_1) + \int_V v(21)\rho(x_2)d\tau_2 + \int_A v(2'1)\,\sigma\, d\tau'_2 \qquad (10)$$

and then, from (9), (10), (5) and (7),

$$\beta^{-1}\log n^{(i)}(x_1)/n^{(i)} = \beta^{-1}\log \zeta^{(i)}(x_1) - e\Psi(x_1) - e_i\int_0^1 \eta^{(i)}(x_1,\xi_1)d\xi_1$$
$$+ e_i\int_0^1 \eta_b^{(i)}(x_1,\xi_1)d\xi_1 \qquad (11)$$

the last term referring to bulk electrolyte. The symbol ζ_i denotes the ratio $n^{(i)}(x_1, 0)/n^{(i)}$. It has been analysed by the authors[21] and shown to be a volume exclusion term approaching 1 as the electrolyte concentration approaches zero and which is always 1 at $x_1 = \infty$.

The Gouy-Chapman approximation (leading to the well-known Poisson-Boltzmann equation for the diffuse region) consists in replacing $g^{(ij)}$ by 1 everywhere, ignoring the image potential $v(x_1)$ and also putting $\zeta^{(i)}(x_1)$ equal to 1. The second, fourth and fifth terms on the right-hand side of (11) disappear and $n^{(i)}(x_1)$ depends only on $\psi(x_1)$, the mean potential. Another approach is that of Stillinger and Kirkwood[22] who by using a moment expansion in ξ_1 and making various approximations, developed a differential-difference equation (equation (15) below) for the diffuse region. This can be obtained quite easily from the present formalism by making equivalent assumptions which clearly show the physical significance of the terms neglected. We put $v(x_1) = 0$, $\zeta^{(i)}(x_1) = 1$ and replace $g^{(ij)}(12)$ by 0 for $r_{12} < a$ and by 1 for $r_{12} > a$. Hence the image and excluded volume effects are neglected and only the cavity part of the self-atmosphere is retained. (With regard to the self-atmosphere an equivalent assumption is to put $n^{[ij]}(12,\xi_1) = 0$ for $r_{12} < a$ and otherwise put $n^{[ij]}(12,\xi_1) = n^{(j)}(x_2)$ and $v^{[ij]}(12;\xi_1) = v^{(j)}$ in (9)). Denoting the cavity part of $\eta^{(i)}(x_1,\xi_1)$ by $\eta_{cav}(x_1)$, equation (11) becomes

$$-\beta^{-1}\log n^{(i)}(x_1)/n_i = e_i\{\psi(x_1) + \eta_{cav}(x_1)\} = e_i\psi_{cav}(x_1) \qquad (12)$$

where the last relation defines $\psi_{cav}(x_1)$. For a 1-1 electrolyte, $e_1 = -e_2 = e$, $n^{(1)} = n^{(2)} = n$ and, using (10) and (12),

$$d^2\psi/dx^2 = -(4\pi/\epsilon)\rho(x) = (8\pi ne/\epsilon)\sinh\{\beta e\psi_{cav}(x_1)\} = \kappa^2\psi_{cav}(x_1) \qquad (13)$$

where κ is the Debye-Huckel constant $\{8\pi\beta ne^2/\epsilon\}^{1/2}$ and the last member represents Stillinger and Kirkwood's linearisation approximation. These authors replace $v(12)$ by $1/\epsilon r_{12}$ so that

$$\eta_{cav}(x_1) = -\int_{r_{12}<a} \{\rho(x_2)/\epsilon r_{12}\}\, d\tau_2$$

$$= -(2\pi/\epsilon)\int_{x_1-a}^{x_1+a} \{a - |x_2 - x_1|\}\,\rho(x_2)\,dx_2 \qquad (14)$$

Then differentiating (14) twice, and using the last member of (13)

$$d^2\psi_{cav}/dx_1^2 = \kappa^2\psi_{cav}(x_1) + d^2\eta_{cav}(x_1)/dx_1^2$$

$$= \tfrac{1}{2}\kappa^2\{\psi_{cav}(x_1 - a) + \psi_{cav}(x_1 + a)\} \qquad (15)$$

which becomes the linearised Poisson-Boltzmann relation for $a = 0$. The term $\psi_{cav}(x_1 - a)$ must be omitted if the point x_1 is within a distance a of the plane of farthest penetration for unbound ions. Stillinger and Kirkwood solved (15) by Fourier inversion and showed that the charge density $\rho(x)$ alternates in sign when κa is greater than a critical value. Such a result also appears if we approximate the right hand side of (15) by the first three terms of a Taylor expansion about x_1, obtaining

$$d^2\psi_{cav}/dx_1^2 = \{\kappa^2/(1 - \tfrac{1}{2}\kappa^2 a^2)\}\,\psi_{cav}(x_1) \qquad (16)$$

for which alternating solutions appear at $\kappa a = \sqrt{2}$. This compares with the value 1.03 from the accurate solution of (15)[22). [See also Martynov[35)]] . In the next section we consider correlation functions outside the exclusion sphere.

4. THE ADDITIVITY APPROXIMATION FOR CHARGED SYSTEMS

Consider as an example a correlation function $g^{(ij)}(12)$ between two points in the diffuse layer. The joint probability of an i in volume element $d\tau_1$ at r_1 and a j in volume element $d\tau_2$ at r_2 can be written as a fraction of the configurational integral Q and if the full charge e_j on the particular ion at r_2 is replaced by $\xi_2 e_j$ this becomes a function of the charging parameter ξ_2. By varying ξ_2 from 0 to 1 we obtain an integral equation of the Kirkwood type[20)],

$$\log g^{(ij)}(12)/g^{(ij)}(12,\xi_2 = 0)$$

$$= -\beta e_j\Big[e_i v(12) + \int_0^1\int_V v(32)\,\Sigma_k e_k\{n^{[ijk]}(123,\xi_2) - n^{[jk]}(23,\xi_2)\}\,d\tau_3 d\xi_2$$

$$+ \int_0^1\int_A v(3'2)\,\Sigma_k e_k\,\{\nu^{[ijk]}(123';\xi_2) - \nu^{[jk]}(23';\xi_2)\}\,d\tau_3' d\xi_2\Big| \quad (17)$$

The charging parameter ξ_1 for the i at r_1 remains fixed throughout the operation and we put $\xi_1 = 1$; it is easy to replace e_i by $\xi_1 e_i$ on the central ion when necessary. The symbols $n^{[ijk]}(123,\xi_2)$ and $\nu^{[ijk]}(123';\xi_2)$ respectively denote the conditional volume and surface number densities of k given both an i at $\underset{\sim}{r}_1$ and a j at $\underset{\sim}{r}_2$. Thus the relation for second-order distribution functions depends on third-order distribution functions; a similar relation for third-order distribution functions would depend on fourth-order ones and so on. A closed relation for second-order functions results from the additivity approximation

$$n^{[ijk]}(123,\xi_2) - n^{(k)}(x_2) = \{n^{[ik]}(13) - n^{(k)}(x_3)\} + \{n^{[jk]}(23,\xi_2) - n^{(k)}(x_3)\} \quad (18a)$$

$$\nu^{[ijk]}(123';\xi_2) - \nu^{(k)} = \{\nu^{[ik]}(13') - \nu^{(k)}\} + \{\nu^{[jk]}(23';\xi_2) - \nu^{(k)}\} \quad (18b)$$

The change in the local density of k due to both an i at $\underset{\sim}{r}_1$ and a j at $\underset{\sim}{r}_2$ is equated to the sum of the changes due to an i at $\underset{\sim}{r}_1$ and a j at $\underset{\sim}{r}_2$, taken by themselves. After linearisation in the potential of the mean force (18a) and the well-known Kirkwood superposition approximation (see for instance, Hill[20)]) become equivalent. Substitution of (18) in (17) and use of (3) and (5) gives exactly the relation

$$g^{(ij)}(12) = g^{(ij)}(12,\xi_2 = 0)\,\exp\{-\beta e_j \phi_1^{(i)}(\underset{\sim}{r}_2)\} \,. \quad (19)$$

Now $g^{(ij)}(12, \xi_2 = 0) = 0$ for $r_{12} < a$ for hard-sphere repulsion and for $r_{12} > a$ it can be shown that, to the first order in number densities,

$$g^{(ij)}(12, \xi_2 = 0) = 1 - \Sigma_k \int_{\omega_2} \{n^{[ik]}(13) - n^{(k)}(x_3)\} d\tau_3 + \ldots$$

where ω_p denotes the sphere of radius a with centre at r_p. Hence, for $r_{12} > a$, $g^{(ij)}(12, \xi_2 = 0) - 1$ represents an excluded volume effect and, for concentrations of electrolyte which are not too high it is a reasonable approximation to put $g^{(ij)}(12, \xi_2 = 0) = 1$. Then substituting (19) in (5),

$$\begin{aligned} \rho_1^{(i)}(\underset{\sim}{r}) &= \Sigma_j e_j \left[\exp\{-\beta e_j \phi_1^{(i)}(\underset{\sim}{r})\} - 1\right], \quad r_{12} > a ; \\ \rho_1^{(i)}(\underset{\sim}{r}) &= -\rho(x), \quad r_{12} < a . \end{aligned} \qquad (20)$$

For bulk electrolyte (where $\rho(x) = 0$) equation (20) gives the non-linear Debye-Huckel relation. For the diffuse double layer the first relation of (20) is the basis of the treatments of self-atmosphere effects by Loeb[7] and Williams[8], which are thus equivalent to the approximation (18). The second relation of (20) gives the cavity effect pointed out by Buff and Stillinger[19] and implicit in the work of Stillinger and Kirkwood[22] (see §3 above). The author have treated the modifications to the Goüy-Chapman theory (see §3 above) of the diffuse region due to image-self atmosphere effects, including the cavity effect, and also volume exclusion effects, ion polarisation, electrostatic saturation, electrostriction and compressibility. At bulk 1-1 electrolyte concentrations of less than 0.1 M considerable mutual cancellation is found.

G. A. Martynov[35] has based a treatment of the double layer on integral equations of the Bogolubov or Born-Green type. A Kirkwood superposition has been used previously to derive the linear Debye-Huckel relation for bulk electrolytes (see Landau and Lifschitz[25], Meeron[26]. Percus[27] has derived for a bulk solution a relation equivalent to (17) with (18a) substituted (the integral over A being, of course, omitted) by functional expansion of $\log n^{[ij]}(12)$ with respect to the intermolecular potential; $\xi_2 = 0$ now being understood to mean that the entire intermolecular potential is "turned off". He criticises the expression obtained for $g^{(ij)}(12)$ for lack of symmetry with respect to an i-j interchange, but the expression proposed as a substitute is an elaborate one. A lack of symmetry in solutions of the non-linear Debye-Huckel equation has been known for a long time (see Fowler and Guggenheim, §912[28]) but disappears on linearisation.

An improved treatment of the effect of finite ion volumes on the self-atmosphere results if before making the additivity approximation we use the relations (exact for hard sphere repulsion),

$$n^{[ijk]}(123,\xi_2) = 0 \text{ in } \omega_1 \text{ and } \omega_2; \quad n^{[jk]}(23,\xi_2) = 0 \text{ in } \omega_2. \tag{21}$$

As an example we derive an integral equation of Kirkwood and Poirier[29]. Since this concerns bulk electrolyte we can put $v(pq) = 1/\epsilon r_{pq}$, $n^{(k)}(x) = n^{(k)}$ and omit the integral over A. Also we define the potential of mean force $w^{(lm)}(pq)$ as $-\beta^{-1}\log g^{(lm)}(pq)$. After substituting (21) in (17), and then applying (18a) over the region $V-\omega_1-\omega_2$, the integral over $V-\omega_1-\omega_2$ is linearised in the potential of mean force by putting

$$n^{[ik]}(13) - n^{(k)} = n^{(k)}\left[\exp\{-\beta w^{(ik)}(13)\} - 1\right] = -\beta n^{(k)} w^{(ik)}(13)$$

and (17) becomes

$$w^{(ij)}(12) = w^{(ij)}(12,\xi_2 = 0) + \frac{e_i e_j}{\epsilon r_{12}} - \beta\Sigma_k \frac{e_j e_k n^{(k)}}{\epsilon} \int_{V-\omega_1-\omega_2} r_{23}^{-1}\, w^{(ik)}(13)\, d\tau_3$$

$$- \Sigma_k \frac{e_j e_k}{\epsilon} \int_0^1 \int_{\omega_1} r_{23}^{-1}\, n^{[jk]}(23,\xi_2)\, d\tau_3\, d\xi_2 \tag{22}$$

If we ignore an excluded volume term by putting $w^{(ij)}(12,\xi_2 = 0) = 0$ outside ω_1 and if we omit the last term in (22), which arises from the part of the self-atmosphere of the ion at r_2 displaced by the ion at r_1, then (22) becomes identical with equation (27) of Kirkwood and Poirier[29]. The integral equation (47) of Buff and Stillinger[19] for the self-atmosphere of a finite ion in the diffuse region can similarly be related to our equations (17), (18a) and (21).

5. THE SELF-ATMOSPHERE OF AN ADSORBED ION

We now consider the equilibrium of ions on the adsorption plane. By first reducing the charging parameter ξ_1' on an adsorbed ion at r_1' from 1 to 0 and then removing the discharged ion it can be shown that the reduction in Helmholtz free energy due to the removal of an ion of species i from the adsorption plane is

$$\mu_s^{(i)} = \alpha_s^{(i)} + \beta^{-1}\log\{\nu^{(i)}\gamma_{os}^{(i)}\} + e_i\psi(0) + e_i\int_0^1 \eta^{(i)}(\xi_1')d\xi_1' \tag{23}$$

Here $\alpha_s^{(i)}$ depends on T and contains the specific adsorption energy, $\eta^{(i)}(\xi_1')$ is defined by (8) and $\gamma_{os}^{(i)}$ is the activity coefficient for a discharged surface ion and is, in fact, an area exclusion factor which to the first order in $\nu^{(j)}$ is $1+\pi a_s^2\,\Sigma_j\nu^{(j)}$. The adsorption isotherm for species i is obtained by equating $\mu_s^{(i)}$ to the bulk chemical potential of i.

Binary correlation functions with one point on the adsorption plane will now be discussed. Replacing 1 by 1' and, where necessary, 2 by 2' in (17) and (18) it can be shown that substituting the additivity approximation into a Kirkwood-type integral equation leads to

$$\begin{aligned} g^{(ij)}(1'2) &= g^{(ij)}(1'2,\xi_2=0)\exp\{-\beta e_j\phi_1^{(i)}(\underset{\sim}{r}_2')\}\ , \\ g^{(ij)}(1'2') &= g^{(ij)}(1'2',\xi_2=0)\exp\{-\beta e_j\phi_{1'}^{(i)}(\underset{\sim}{r}_2)\}\ . \end{aligned} \tag{24}$$

If we suppose that that unbound ions do not penetrate beyond a plane $x=\gamma$ then $g^{(ij)}(1'2,\xi_2)=0$ for $x<\gamma$ and it is a reasonable approximation to put $g^{(ij)}(1'2,\xi_2=0)=1$ throughout the diffuse region $(x > \gamma)$. From the definition (similar to (3)) of $\phi_{1'}^{(i)}(\underset{\sim}{r})$ it follows that, for $x > \gamma$

$$\nabla^2\phi_{1'}^{(i)} = -(4\pi/\epsilon)\rho_{1'}^{(i)}(\underset{\sim}{r}) = \kappa^2(x)\,\phi_{1'}^{(i)}(\underset{\sim}{r}) \,,$$

$$\kappa^2(x) = 4\pi\beta\,\Sigma_j e_j^2\, n^{(j)}(x)/\epsilon \,, \qquad (25)$$

where we have put $\xi_1 = 1$, substituted (24) in (5a)(1' replacing 1) and linearised in $\phi_{1'}^{(i)}(\underset{\sim}{r})$. Again from the definition of $\phi_{1'}^{(i)}(\underset{\sim}{r})$ and Gauss' electrostatic law

$$(\partial\phi_{1'}^{(i)}/\partial x)_{x=+0} - (\partial\phi_{1'}^{(i)}/\partial x)_{x=-0} = -4\pi\sigma_{1'}^{(i)}(r_{1'f})/\epsilon_d \qquad (26)$$

where we introduce explicitly that on the adsorption plane $\sigma_{1'}^{(i)}$ is a function of $r_{1'f} = |r - r_1'|$. Substituting (24) in (5b) (1' replacing 1), $g^{(ij)}(1'2', \xi_2 = 0) = 0$ for $r_{1'2'} < a_s$ and approximating $g^{(ij)}(1'2', \xi_2 = 0)$ by 1 for $r_{1'2'} > a_s$, which is reasonable for not too high surface densities of adsorbed ions since $g^{(ij)}(1'2', \xi_2 = 0)$ is similar in form to $g^{(ij)}(12, \xi_2 = 0)$,

$$\sigma_{1'}^{(i)}(r_{1'f}) = -\sigma, \qquad r_{1'f} < a_s \,;$$

$$\sigma_{1'}^{(i)}(r_{1'f}) = \Sigma_j e_j \nu^{(j)}\left[\exp\{-\beta e_j \phi_{1'}^{(i)}(r_{1'f})\} - 1\right]$$

$$= -\beta\Sigma_j e_j^2 \nu^{(j)}\phi_{1'}^{(i)}(r_{1'f}) \,, \qquad r_{1'f} > a_s \,, \qquad (27)$$

where only the linear term in $\phi_{1'}^{(i)}$ is retained in the last member of (26). Together with the condition that $\phi_{1'}^{(i)} \rightarrow 1/(\epsilon_d r_{1'f})$ as $r_{1'f} \rightarrow 0$, equations (25), (26) and (27) determine the self-atmosphere potential of an adsorbed ion and are equivalent to the Debye-Huckel equations for a bulk ion.

Since (25) is linear the solution for $\phi_{1'}^{(i)}$ can be developed with the aid of a Green's function $G(\underset{\sim}{r})$[30], which is the potential, satisfying (25) in the diffuse region, with a point charge e_0 at 0 and no other charge on the adsorption plane. Then, with a charge e_i at 0, (25) and (26) with r_1' replaced by 0 are satisfied by the self-atmosphere potential

$$\phi^{(i)}(\underset{\sim}{r}) = \frac{e_i}{e_o} G(\underset{\sim}{r}) + \int_A \frac{\sigma^{(i)}(r')}{e_o} G(|\underset{\sim}{r} - \underset{\sim}{r}'|) d\tau'$$

At a point at a distance r from 0 on the adsorption plane it is useful to define

$$M(r', r) = \frac{\epsilon_d}{2\pi e_o} \int_0^{2\pi} G(|\underset{\sim}{r} - \underset{\sim}{r}'|) \, d\theta \, , \qquad (28)$$

so that $M(r', r)/\epsilon_d$ is the potential, satisfying (25), of a unit charge uniformly smeared over a circle of radius r' and centre 0. Then putting $d\tau' = r'dr'd\theta'$ in (28) and substituting from (27), we obtain an integral equation for $\phi^{(i)}(r)$ on the adsorption plane:

$$\phi^{(i)}(r) = \frac{e_i}{e_o} G(r) - \frac{2\pi\sigma}{\epsilon_d} \int_0^{a_s} M(r', r) r' dr'$$
$$- \frac{2\pi\beta \Sigma_j e_j^2 \nu^{(j)}}{\epsilon_d} \int_{a_s}^{\infty} M(r', r) \, \phi^{(i)}(r') r' dr' \qquad (29)$$

It should be noted that since the local Debye-Huckel constant $\kappa(x)$ is required to obtain G(r), using (25), a solution of the diffuse-layer distribution equations for a given value of σ is assumed; usually a Goüy-Chapman approximation would be sufficient.

Buff and Stillinger[19)] applied the general cluster theory of inhomogeneous fluids[31)] to obtain an elegant formal development of double layer theory at a metallic surface. However, they assumed that the electrostatic forces between adsorbed ions are so weakened by screening that they become negligible beyond the exclusion distance a_s. This would mean that G(r) is not large compared with β^{-1} for $r > a_s$ and that the last term on the right-hand side of (29), which represents the effect of the part of the adsorption plane self-atmosphere due to the region $r > a_s$, is small compared with the second term which represents the "cavity" part due to the region $r < a_s$. This is less likely to be true for non-metallic surfaces than for metallic ones and our preliminary investigations of (29) indicate that it is, in fact, not correct even for metallic surfaces. This confirms results derived by other methods[32)34)].

REFERENCES

1. R. Parsons in "Modern Aspects of Electrochemistry I". (Ed. J. O'M. Bockris), Butterworths (1954).

2. J. R. Macdonald and C. A. Barlow in "Electrochemistry" Pergamon Press (1964).

3. D. A. Haydon and F. H. Taylor, Phil. Trans. Roy. Soc. A, 252, 225 (1960); 253, 255 (1960), Trans. Faraday Soc. 58, 1233 (1962).

4. S. Levine, G. M. Bell and B. A. Pethica, J. Chem. Phys., 40, 2304 (1964).

5. J. C. Poirier in "Chemical Physics of Ionic Solutions" (Ed. B. E. Conway and R. G. Barradas) John Wiley and Sons Inc. (1966).

6. L. Onsager and N. N. T. Samaras, J. Chem. Phys., 2, 528 (1934).

7. A. Loeb, J. Colloid Sci., 6, 75 (1951).

8. W. E. Williams, Proc. Phys. Soc. A, 66, 372 (1953).

9. E. Schmutzer, Z. Phys. Chem., 204, 131 (1958).

10. A. Bellemans, Physica, 30, 924 (1964).

11. G. M. Bell and S. Levine in "Chemical Physics of Ionic Solutions" (Ed. B. E. Conway and R. G. Barradas), John Wiley and Sons Inc. (1966); Faraday Soc. Discussion on "Colloid Stability in Aqueous and Non-aqueous Media" (1966).

12. O. A. Esin and B. F. Markov, Zh. Fiz. Khim., 13, 318 (1939)

13. V. S. Krylov, Electrochim. Acta, 9, 1247 (1964).

14. C. A. Barlow and J. R. Macdonald, J. Chem. Phys., 40, 1535 (1964); 43, 2575 (1965).

15. D. C. Grahame, Z. Electrochem., 62, 264 (1958).

16. S. Levine, G. M. Bell and D. Calvert, Can. J. Chem., 40, 518 (1962).

17. G. M. Bell, S. Levine and B. A. Pethica, Trans. Faraday Soc., 58, 904 (1962).

18. S. Levine, J. Mingins and G. M. Bell, J. Phys. Chem., 67, 2095 (1963).

19. F. P. Buff and F. H. Stillinger, J. Chem. Phys., 39, 1911 (1963).

20. T. L. Hill, Statistical Mechanics, Mc.Graw-Hill, (1956).

21. S. Levine and G. M. Bell, J. Phys. Chem., 64, 1188 (1960).

22. F. H. Stillinger and J. G. Kirkwood, J. Chem. Phys., 33, 1282 (1960).

23. G. A. Martynov and B. V. Derjaguin, Dokl. Alcad. Nauk. S.S.S.R., 152, 767 (1963).

24. V. S. Krylov and V. G. Levich, ZH. Fiz. Khim., 37, 106 (1963).

25. L. D. Landau and E. M. Lifschitz, Statistical Physics, §74 Pergamon Press (1959).

26. E. Meeron in "Electrolytes" (Ed. B. Pesce), Pergamon (1962).

27. J. K. Percus in "Equilibrium Theory of Classical Fluids" (Ed. H. L. Frisch and J. L. Lebowitz), W. A. Benjamin Inc., (1964).

28. R. Fowler and E. A. Guggenheim, Statistical Thermodynamics, Cambridge University Press (1939).

29. J. G. Kirkwood and J. C. Poirier, J. Phys. Chem. 58, 591 (1954).

30. S. Levine, G. M. Bell and J. Mingins, to be published.

31. F. H. Stillinger and F. P. Buff, J. Chem. Phys. 37, 1 (1962).

32. S. Levine, J. Mingins and G. M. Bell, Can. J. Chem., 43, 2834 (1965).

33. G. M. Bell, J. Mingins and S. Levine, Trans. Faraday Soc., 62, 949 (1966).

34. J. R. Macdonald and C. A. Barlow, Can. J. Chem., 43, 2985 (1965).

35. G. A. Martynov, Research in Surface Forces (ed. Derjaguin), Consultants' Bureau, New York, 2; 75, 84 and 94 (1966).

STATISTICAL MECHANICS OF A PARTIALLY IONIZED PLASMA *)

JULIUS L. JACKSON AND
LEWIS S. KLEIN
Howard University.

In this talk we shall present some results and speculations on the problem of the calculation of the equilibrium composition of a partially ionized plasma. In addition we should like to review the basic principles and call attention to some of the interesting aspects of the problem. A rigorous treatment would involve the solution of the many-body problem as well as the answer to subtle questions regarding the distinction between highly excited atomic states and free particle states. No such attempt is made here. Rather what we do here is present a consistent treatment of the problem in a particular approximation, wherein the atom-plasma interaction is handled in the Debye-Hückel approximation.

For simplicity we confine our attention to a hydrogen atom plasma. It is assumed that one has a system with, in all, N_o electrons and N_o protons in equilibrium in a volume V, at temperature T. The object then is to calculate how many of the electrons and protons are combined as atoms as a function of T, V, and N_o. We call N_a the number of atoms, N_e the number of free electrons, and N_p the number of free protons, $(N_o = N_a + N_e = N_a + N_p)$. We assume that these are the only species possible - i.e. molecules are not considered.

The equilibrium equation for the number of atoms is called a Saha Equation and we shall refer to such an equation, with or without refinements and corrections, by that name. The usual procedure followed in deriving a Saha equation for the equilibrium

*) This research was supported in part by the National Science Foundation and the Physics Branch of the Office of Naval Research.

concentrations of species is to evaluate the partition function for a fixed number of atoms (and free electrons and protons) and find the number of atoms corresponding to the maximum volume in phase space. This, of course, is the same as minimizing the free energy as a function of N_a or equating chemical potentials,

$$\mu_o = \mu_p + \mu_e \,. \tag{1}$$

The zeroth order Saha Equation may be obtained by neglecting every possible complication. That is, to obtain the simplest possible equilibrium equation one makes the following assumptions:

1) all interactions among free protons, free electrons and atoms are neglected.

2) the free electrons, free protons, and the center of mass of the atoms are treated classically.

3) only the ground state of the atom is taken into account. One then obtains for the partition function

$$Z(N_e, N_p, N_a) = \frac{1}{N_e!}\left(\frac{V}{\lambda_e^3}\right)^{N_e} \frac{1}{N_p!}\left(\frac{V}{\lambda_p^3}\right)^{N_p} \frac{1}{N_a!}\left(\frac{V}{\lambda_a^3}\right) \tag{2}$$

where for each species

$$\lambda_j = \left(\frac{h^2}{2\pi\, m_j\, kT}\right)^{1/2} , \tag{3}$$

and E_o is the energy of the ground state of hydrogen. If one now maximizes this expression with respect to N_a one obtains

$$\frac{(N_o - N_a)^2}{N_a} = \frac{V}{h^3}\left(\frac{2\pi\, m_p\, m_e\, kT}{m_p + m_e}\right)^{3/2} e^{-\frac{|E_o|}{kT}} \tag{4}$$

Notwithstanding the sweeping simplifications made in arriving at Eq. (4), it is a surprisingly good equation. It gives the correct overall dependence of the degree of ionization on the temperature, volume, and the ground state energy (which may be regarded as a variable by going to different atoms). Furthermore, the equation has the interesting feature that even though it is an equation for a macroscopic quantity, it contains the Planck constant explicitly.

The question of improving Eq. (4) in view of the assumptions that go into its derivation, is simply one of attempting to put back in the things that were left out. It might be added that there is now strong motivation from the experimental side for a more accurate Saha equation, as improving laboratory techniques now enable one to make more detailed quantitative comparisons between theory and experiment. As a first step in improving Eq. (4) one may include the Coulomb interaction among the charged particles. Doing this gives for the leading term, the Debye-Huckel free energy[1)]

$$F^{D.H.} = -(N_p + N_e)\frac{e^2\varkappa}{3} \tag{5}$$

where $\varkappa$ is the reciprocal Debye length, $\sqrt{4\pi(N_p+N_e)e^2/kTV}$. If one includes the above term in the theory, one obtains a modified Saha equation wherein the ionization energy, $|E_o|$ in the exponent on the right hand side of Eq. (4) is replaced by $|E_o| - e^2\varkappa$. This is the well known "lowering of the ionization potential".

To make the theory still more realistic one should treat the atoms according to statistical mechanical principles and attempt to calculate their partition sum, instead of writing only the first term in the sum. One then encounters the well known difficulty of the divergence of the hydrogen atom partition function[2)], i.e.

$$Z_H = \sum_{n=1}^{\infty} 2n^2 e^{-\frac{E_o}{n^2kT}} = \infty \tag{6}$$

There have been many suggestions on how to remedy this situation. The remedies all involve taking into account the fact that the interactions between the atom and other constituents "destroy" highly excited atomic states. Thus the interactions give rise to a cut-off in the partition sum, Eq. (6), and a shift in the levels. The interaction most important in giving rise to a cut-off depends generally on the composition. Under conditions of very low ionization the atom-atom interaction will be most important. In the region of considerable ionization, when one has a "partially ionized plasma", the interaction between the atoms and the changed particles (plasma) are most important. One of the most attractive ways of treating the atom-plasma interaction was suggested by Ecker and Weizel[3)] who noted that the Coulomb interaction of the electron and proton of an atom were on the average shielded by the plasma, so that the effective interaction is the Debye-Huckel potential. They thus replace the hamiltonian of an isolated hydrogen atom, $H_o = K - e^2/r$, by

$$H_1^{eff} = K - e^2 \, e^{-\varkappa r}/r - e^2\varkappa \qquad (7)$$

Here K is the relative kinetic energy operator. The partition sum is then taken over the bound eigenstates of the effective hamiltonian. This automatically takes care of the divergence noted in Eq. (6) as the effective hamiltonian has a finite number of bound states. The additive constant, $-e^2H$, in the Ecker-Weizel hamiltonian was obtained on the basis of a physical argument. Recently, however, a calculation was presented[4)] using for the effective hamiltonian

$$H_2^{eff} = K - \frac{e^2 e^{-\varkappa r}}{r} \qquad (8)$$

Although the quantum mechanics of these two effective hamiltonians is essentially the same, the statistical mechanics is different as the ground state energy of H_2^{eff} is shifted to first order by $e^2\varkappa$. Thus, if one takes the leading term in the atomic partition function implied by $H_{(2)}^{eff}$ one obtains an additional lowering in the ionization potential of the same order of magnitude as the plasma free energy contribution.

Although the physical argument presented for the use of H_1^{eff} is convincing, we however, have asked ourselves how one can decide what is the correct effective hamiltonian on the basis of statistical mechanical first principles. This, of course, is in the context of treating the atom-plasma interaction on the level of the Debye-Hückel approximation.

The particular form of fundamental statistical mechanical theory which we use is one wherein the chemical potential of a constituent is written in terms of the distribution function of its interaction potential with all other particles. For a single component classical fluid it may be shown that the chemical potential is[5)]

$$\mu = \mu_o - kT \ln \int P(\phi)\, e^{-\beta\phi}\, d\phi \tag{9}$$

where $\mu_o = kT \ln \frac{N\lambda^3}{V}$ and $P(\phi)$ is the probability distribution function of the interaction potential at a point for the fluid in equilibrium. Our objective was to derive an analogous expression for the chemical potential of an atom, writing it in terms of the distribution function of the interaction of the atom with the free electrons and protons. The desired formula, which we have derived, is

$$\mu_a \cong kT \ln \frac{N_a \lambda_a^3}{V}$$

$$- kT \ln \left[\sum_n \langle n | \iint d\phi_1 d\phi_2\, P(\phi_1, \phi_2)\, e^{-\beta e(\phi_1(r_1) - \phi_2(r_2))}\, e^{-\beta H_o} | n \rangle \right] \tag{10}$$

Here H_o is the hamiltonian of the atom and ϕ_1 and ϕ_2 are respectively the electrostatic potentials due to the plasma at the positions $\vec{r}_1$ of the atomic proton, and $\vec{r}_2$ of the atomic electron. $P(\phi_1, \phi_2)$ is the joint distribution function of the electrostatic potential in the plasma at the two points $\vec{r}_1$ and $\vec{r}_2$. The equation is indicated to be approximate. The reason for this is that H_o and the interaction potentials do not commute. To derive Eq. (10) one must disentangle these operators. There are thus additional terms on the right hand side involving commutators, which we have not written. These terms may be shown to be small under reasonable assumptions. After doing the integration over ϕ_1 and ϕ_2, one must then re-entangle the operators to get an effective hamiltonian. By the sum over "n" we mean the sum over the bound states of the atom. By the nature of the problem we can decide what the bound states are only after one has obtained the effective hamiltonian by carrying out the statistical average indicated by the integrations over ϕ_1 and ϕ_2. In the Debye-Hückel approximation one may show that the joint distribution of the potential at two points is[6)]

$$P(\phi_1, \phi_2) = \frac{1}{2\pi\varkappa kT(1-\sigma^2)^{1/2}} e^{-\left(\frac{\phi_1^2 + \phi_2^2 - 2\sigma\phi_1\phi_2}{2\varkappa kT(1-\sigma^2)}\right)} \qquad (11)$$

where

$$\sigma = \frac{1 - e^{-\varkappa r}}{\varkappa r} \quad .$$

If one inserts Eq. (11) into Eq. (10) and carries out the integration one finally obtains for the effective hamiltonian

$$H^{eff} = K - \frac{e^2 e^{-\varkappa r}}{v} - \varkappa e^2 \qquad (12)$$

in precise agreement with the result of Ecker and Weizel.

REFERENCES

1. P. Debye and E. Hückel, Phys. Z. 24, 185 (1923).
2. K. Herzfeld, Ann. Phys. 51, 261 (1916), M. Planck, Ann. Phys. 75, 637 (1924), E. Fermi, Ann. Phys. 26, 54 (1924).
3. G. Ecker and W. Weizel, Ann. Phys. 17, 126 (1956).
4. G. Harris, Phys. Rev. 133, 427 (1964).
5. J. L. Jackson and L. S. Klein, Phys. Fluids 7, 228 (1964).
6. J. L. Jackson and L. S. Klein, Phys. Fluids 7, 232 (1964).

DISCUSSION

Van Kampen: The difficulty is that the partition function for a single atom diverges because the large orbitals extend over infinite space. However, the electron ceases to be bound when the orbital extends to the next ion. This suggests that this partition function should be cut-off at those values of n for which the orbital has the size of the ion distance. It is hard to understand why the Debye length should come in as a cut-off, since orbitals of that size do not belong to a single atom.

Jackson: But on the average you have both negative and positive neighbours moving about so it is not clear to me that this is necessarily the right cut-off.

Mayer: Part of the answer is that the Debye terms take care of the ion electron interaction at large distances, and do this essentially for the large contributions that arise from the slowly decreasing r^{-1} potential at distances greater than the Debye length. The specific bound states must then be taken care of but the "effective potential" with which these must be computed now contain the Debye length, and not the intermolecular distance. In the theory the effect of the neutral atomic neighbours in disturbing the higher orbits is neglected.
Incidentially, one might mention that the same type of difficulty arises in the treatment of an imperfect gas of dissociating molecules even when the dissociation products are neutral species with short range interaction.

The imperfections are due to the interactions of the various constituent species which are close to each other, but when they are really close we call them a new molecular species. The cut-off distance is not easily defined.

Martin: Is there some parameter to indicate smallness?

Jackson: The parameter is the Debye-Hückel parameter, $\lambda = \beta e^2 \kappa$.

Lebowitz: What kind of densities are you working at? Are hard core interactions relevant here?

Jackson: The densities, of course, are the densities for which the theory is applicable and of interest, that is densities small enough so that one does not have to treat the free particles quantum mechanically and such that the Debye length is large compared to interparticle distances. These conditions are realized in typical laboratory discharges. However, we have not considered the effect of the hard core interactions.

Lebowitz: Very low densities then.

Jackson: Yes, moderate.

Jancovici: Why does Planck's constant appear in the zeroth

order theory?

Jackson: Planck's constant belongs there as in order to compare the statistical weight associated with the volume of phase space in the continuum with the weight of a single bound atomic state, one must divide the volume of the continuum (of dimensionality, action cubed) by the cell size in the continuum, h^3.

ON THE STATISTICAL THEORY OF ENTROPY-PRODUCTION

F. SCHÖGL,
Technical University of
Aachen, Germany.

In macroscopic thermodynamics of irreversible processes in general the change of entropy of a non-isolated system, is divided in two essentially different parts: exchange of entropy with the environment and entropy produced in the interior of the system. In macroscopic thermodynamics it is an independent basic assumption that the second part is positively definite. In the following it shall be shown that for this entropy-production there exists a general and relatively simple expression in statistical mechanics. The system may be non-isolated and open. That means it can be in interaction and material exchange with its environment.

For convenience let us assume that the microstates of the system be enumerable. This assumption is not necessary and only made for this talk. i shall be the index which counts the microstates. In classical statistics a mixture-state p is described by a probability-distribution p_i over the microstates. To each distribution p corresponds a statistical entropy

$$S = - \sum_i p_i \ln p_i \tag{1}$$

If the system Σ with the microstates i is in interaction with its environment Σ' then the combined system

$$\tilde{\Sigma} = \Sigma + \Sigma' \tag{2}$$

shall be considered. The mixture states $\tilde{p}$ of the total system are described by the joint probabilities $\tilde{p}_{i\alpha}$ that Σ is in the microstate i and Σ' simultaneously in the microstate α. (α may count the microstates of Σ'). Always it is possible to factorize in the following way:

$$\tilde{p}_{i\alpha} = p_i \, p'_\alpha \, \gamma_{i\alpha} \, . \tag{3}$$

Here p_i, p'_α are the distributions for Σ, Σ' respectively and $\gamma_{i\alpha}$ is a factor, which describes correlation between both systems. If all $\gamma_{i\alpha}$ are 1 then exists no correlation at all and vice versa. It shall be possible to define the environment in such a way that $\tilde{\Sigma}$ is isolated. Then the state $\tilde{p}^o$ of maximal entropy is equipartition over all pairs (i, α) which can be reached from a given initial state $\tilde{p}$ in agreement with the conservation-laws of the system. If $\tilde{\Sigma}$ goes over from $\tilde{p}$ to $\tilde{p}^o$ then the change of the total entropy becomes

$$\tilde{S}^o - \tilde{S} = K + K' + \tilde{C} \, . \tag{4}$$

The quantity K is given by

$$K = \sum_i p_i \ln \frac{p_i}{p_i^o} = K(p, p^o) \tag{5}$$

and related to the system Σ only. K' is the analogous quantity for the environment. $\tilde{C}$ vanishes if there exists no correlation between Σ and the environment. $\tilde{C}$ is a contribution in (4) due to correlation. In macroscopic thermodynamics such correlation-terms in general are neglected as comparable small surface-effects and entropy becomes additive for combined systems. In statistics however such correlation-terms as $\tilde{C}$ can be respected.

(4) shows that K is to be interpreted as the entropy produced in the interior of Σ by the transition form $\tilde{p}$ to $\tilde{p}^o$.

It is easy to show that from (5) follows:

$$K \geqq 0 \, . \tag{6}$$

The equality-sign holds only if p and p^o are exactly the same mixture-states.

It may be instructive to consider the special case that p is a thermal equilibrium-state. Such a state is defined by given expectation-value of energy E and eventually of other observables X^v and furthermore by the requirement of maximal entropy under these conditions:

$$p_i^o = C \exp \{ - \frac{1}{T^o} (E_i - y_v^o X_i^v) \} . \qquad (7)$$

(It is to sum over v). T^o, y_v^o are temperature and the other intensity-parameters. K becomes for this case to

$$K = \Delta S - \frac{1}{T^o} (\Delta E - y_v^o \Delta X^v) \geqq 0 \qquad (8)$$

where

$$\Delta E = E^o - E \quad \text{etc.} \qquad (9)$$

If p is a thermal state too then (8) is a well known inequality of macroscopic thermodynamics. It holds however also in case that p is quite different from any equilibrium-state.

There exists in probability-theory also a general interpretation of the quantity K given by (5). - S is the by Shannon given measure of information. It is the adequate measure of the knowledge of the observer connected with p if the microstates have equal apriori-probability. K is the adequate measure if the microstates have apriori-probabilities p_i^o (Compare: A. Renýi, Wahrscheinlichkeitsrechnung, Berlin 1966). If something is known about the state of the environment then in general for the observer the microstates of the system will have apriori-probabilities p^o different from equipartition.

A further fundamental property of K is its behaviour with respect to stochastic motion of the system. The most general changes of the mixture-state p of a system into another $\hat{p}$ at later time can be written in the form

$$\hat{p}_j = \sum_i \gamma_{ji} p_i \tag{10}$$

where γ_{ji} is the transition-probability from i to j. The γ_{ji} in general depend in a complicated way on the previous history of the system and can depend on p itself. The equations (10) thus are in general non-linear. Special cases of (10) are different master-equations, Boltzmann's transport-equations, Fokker-Planck-equation and others.

Let p^o be an invariant distribution with respect to the matrix γ_{ji}, that means

$$p_j^o = \sum_i \gamma_{ji} p_i^o . \tag{11}$$

Then one can show by (10) that there is valid:

$$K(\hat{p}, p^o) \leqq K(p, p^o) . \tag{12}$$

In the special case that (10) describes an homogeneous Marcovian process the equations (10) become linear and the matrix γ_{ji} despends on the time-difference only. p^o then becomes independent of time and (12) gives:

$$\dot{K} \leqq 0 . \tag{13}$$

In the special case that for contact with a large and steady environment (a steady heat-bath) p^o is a thermal equilibrium-state (7) the relation (13) gives:

$$- \dot{K} = \dot{S} - \frac{1}{T^o} (\dot{E} - y_v^o \dot{X}^v) \geqq 0 . \tag{14}$$

It should however be emphasized that (14) holds too in the far more general case that the heat-bath changes its temperature T^o and its intensity-variables y_v^o with time under the assumption that (7) always fulfills (11). The stochastic motion then may be non-Marcovian. To this point Dr. A. Stahl has given an essential contribution.

This general scheme was applied to three problems:

1) Statistical derivation of Le Chatelier-Braun-principle (not yet published). Here inequality (6) alone is needed. The scheme shows precisely what is the correct coordination of conjugate variables. Compared to that result this question is sometimes problematic in macroscopic theory.

2) Statistical derivation of Onsager's symmetry-relations for non-isolated and open systems (F. Schlögl ZS. f. Physik 193, 163 (1966)). Cox has 1950 given a statistical derivation for isolated systems where $\dot{S}$ is the entropy-production per second. In non-isolated systems - $\dot{K}$ is to be taken instead. The result for isolated systems was that microscopic reversibility leads to Onsager's symmetry. In non-isolated systems one has to require the existence of a detailed balance instead.

3) Statistical derivation of a fundamental inequality (A. Stahl und F. Schlögl; in press ZS. f. Physik) for a system in a heat-bath which changes in time:

$$\int_{-\infty}^{t} dt \left[\left(\frac{1}{T^+} - \frac{1}{T} \right) \dot{E} - \left(\frac{y_v^+}{T^+} - \frac{y_v}{T} \right) \dot{X}^v \right] \geqq 0 . \qquad (15)$$

This inequality has been derived within the framework of macroscopic thermodynamics recently by J. Meixner in a more general form. He demonstrated its fundamental importance for non-equilibrium thermodynamics. T, y_v are the time-dependent temperature and other intensity-parameters of the environment. T^+, y_v^+ are their values at time $-\infty$ at which equilibrium is assumed.

DISCUSSION

Meixner: The inequality

$$\int_{-\infty}^{\infty} dt \left[\left(\frac{1}{T_{-\infty}} - \frac{1}{T} \right) \dot{E} - \left(\frac{y_{-\infty}}{T_{-\infty}} - \frac{y_\nu}{T} \right) \dot{X} \right] \geq 0$$

is a special case of a more general inequality which can be derived from the first and second laws of thermodynamics and the conservation of momentum. This inequality can be used to build up non-equilibrium thermodynamics so that the concept of entropy does not enter.

Schlögl: That is an important advantage because the measureability of entropy in non-equilibrium states is problematic.

Waldmann: Entropy has no operational meaning in non-equilibrium states. What we do in kinetic theory is to look for some quantity that always increases in time. Do you assume the existence of temperature in non-equilibrium states?

Schlögl: If there is no more known, a state is given by some mean values of certain observables. We have to find this probability distribution which has maximum entropy under these conditions. If only the mean value of the energy is known, then for the observer the system has a temperature.

Waldmann: You assume the surroundings are in thermal equilibrium. This temperature then has nothing to do with the system.

Schlögl: Yes, that is correct. But it has to do with the expectations.

Mayer: Should one say that your quantity $S = -\sum_i p_i \ln p_i$ is a statistically defined quantity which is never different from the thermodynamically defined entropy when the latter is operationally defined?

Schlögl: I totally agree.

Wergeland: I disagree a little bit on the impossibility of defining entropy for non-equilibrium situations. We are interested in entropy differences. Szilard dealt satisfactorily with this question in the 1920's.

Meixner: With enough information you can obtain kinetic equations and define entropy. Without that, one can still define another quantity which gives upper and lower bounds on the entropy. The more one knows, the closer together these bounds become.

Schlögl: Statistical entropy is uniquely defined. It is a reasonable question to see if its properties agree with those of macroscopic entropy.

ON THE NON-EXISTENCE OF DENSITY EXPANSIONS FOR THE TRANSPORT COEFFICIENTS IN CLASSICAL GASES

E. G. D. COHEN
The Rockefeller University
New York, N.Y. 10021

1. INTRODUCTION

a. Introduction

The problem I would like to discuss is that of the approach to equilibrium of a gas, which is initially not in equilibrium. I shall restrict myself to the case of a classical gas with strong repulsive short range intermolecular forces of finite range r_o (see fig. 1).

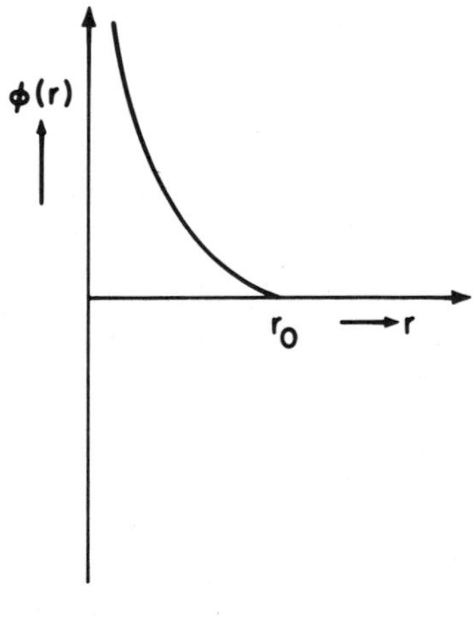

Fig. 1

The neglect of any attraction between the molecules makes this case not quite realistic, but is is hoped that many of the qualitative features of the approach to equilibrium are not changed by this neglect.

b. Dilute Gas

The approach to thermal equilibrium of a dilute gas has been solved to a large degree long ago by Boltzmann (1872)[1] and Chapman and Enskog (1911-1916)[2][3][4].

In this case, when only binary collisions between the molecules occur, the basic assumption of Boltzmann is that the time evolution of the gas can be described by the first distribution function $f(\vec{r}, \vec{v}; t)$ alone and is governed by the equation:

$$\frac{\partial f(\vec{r}, \vec{v}; t)}{\partial t} + \vec{v} \cdot \frac{\partial f}{\partial \vec{r}} = J(ff) \tag{1}$$

Here J is a time independent operator which involves the dynamics of two particles in infinite space only. The particular form of J used by Boltzmann is not essential for the following and I shall not write it down.

Near equilibrium, when the gas is in a hydrodynamical state and can be described by the five hydrodynamical quantities: the local density $n(\vec{r}, t)$, the local velocity $\vec{u}(\vec{r}, t)$ and the local temperature $T(\vec{r}, t)$, the Boltzmann equation has been solved by Chapman and Enskog. They obtained the Navier-Stokes equations with explicit (density independent) expressions for the transport coefficients: the viscosity $\eta(n, T)$ and the heat conductivity $\lambda(n, T)$ in terms of the intermolecular forces:

$$\eta(n, T) = \eta_o(T) \tag{2a}$$

$$\lambda(n, T) = \lambda_o(T) \tag{2b}$$

The temperature dependence has since been checked extensively and has been shown for a realistic intermolecular potential to be in very good agreement with experiment over a wide range of temperatures.

c. Expectation for Dense Gas

The generalization of the Boltzman equation to higher densities, where in addition to binary collisions, also triple-, quadruple-, etc. collisions between the molecules occur, seems straight forward and one expects an equation of the form:

$$\frac{\partial f}{\partial t} + \vec{v} \cdot \frac{\partial f}{\partial \vec{r}} = J(ff) + K(fff) + L(ffff) + \dots \qquad (3)$$

where K, L, ... are time independent operators which depend on the dynamics of 3-, 4-... particles in infinite space. We shall call an equation of the form (3) where $\frac{\partial f}{\partial t} = A(f)$ with A a time independent operator: a kinetic equation. If one solves an equation of the form (3) near equilibrium à la Chapman-Enskog then one obtains a virial - or density expansion of the transport coefficients, which reads for the viscosity for instance:

$$\eta(n, T) = \eta_o(T) + n\eta_1(T) + n^2\eta_2(T) + \dots \qquad (4)$$

Here η_1, contains contributions of triple collisions (from K), η_2 of quadruple collisions (from L) etc.

(4) presents a virial expansion of a macroscopic property of the gas which is analogous to those valid in equilibrium for the thermodynamic properties of the gas.

d. Almost all post war attempts to generalize the Boltzmann equation to the case of dense gases have lead to equations of the form (3). The ideas of Bogolubov (1946)[5)] have been of profound influence on all these developments.

2. DERIVATION OF GENERALIZED BOLTZMANN EQUATION

A generalized Boltzmann equation can be derived by starting from the Liouville equation and by expanding in some way in powers of the density or better in terms of an increasing number of f's.

a. If one integrates the Liouville equation over the phases of all particles but one, one can derive for f an equation of the form:

$$\frac{\partial f}{\partial t} + \vec{v} \cdot \frac{\partial f}{\partial \vec{r}} = O(f_2) \tag{5}$$

where O is a time independent operator and f_2 the pair distribution function.

b. Now f_2 can be obtained in an expansion in terms of an increasing number of f's by generalizing the well-known cluster expansions used in equilibrium statistical mechanics to the case of non-equilibrium[6)7)].

In this way one can obtain as a formal identity the following cluster expansion of $f_2(x_i \equiv \vec{q}_i, \vec{p}_i)$ in terms of f:

$$\begin{aligned} f_2(x_1 x_2; t) &= f_2^{(o)}(x_1 x_2; t) + f_2^{(1)}(x_1 x_2; t) + f_2^{(2)}(x_1 x_2; t) + \dots \\ &= \tilde{\mathcal{S}}_t^{(2)}(x_1 x_2)\, f(x_1; t)\, f(x_2; t) + \\ &+ \int dx_3 \tilde{\mathcal{T}}_t^{(3)}(x_1 x_2 | x_3) \prod_{i=1}^{3} f(x_i; t) + \\ &+ \frac{1}{2!} \int dx_3 \int dx_4 \tilde{\mathcal{T}}_t^{(4)}(x_1 x_2 | x_3 x_4) \prod_{i=1}^{4} f(x_i; t) + \dots \end{aligned} \tag{6}$$

where

$$\tilde{\mathcal{S}}_t^{(s)}(x_1 \dots x_s) = S_{-t}^{(s)}(x_1 \dots x_s)\, a_s(x_1 \dots x_s; 0) \prod_{i=1}^{s} S_t^{(1)}(x_i) \tag{7a}$$

$$\begin{aligned} \tilde{\mathcal{T}}_t^{(3)}(x_1 x_2 | x_3) = \tilde{\mathcal{S}}_t^{(3)}(x_1 x_2 x_3) &- \tilde{\mathcal{S}}_t^{(2)}(x_1 x_2)\, \tilde{\mathcal{S}}_t^{(2)}(x_1 x_3) - \\ &- \tilde{\mathcal{S}}_t^{(2)}(x_1 x_2)\, \tilde{\mathcal{S}}_t^{(2)}(x_2 x_3) + \tilde{\mathcal{S}}_t^{(2)}(x_1 x_2) \end{aligned} \tag{7b}$$

while $\mathcal{T}_t^{(4)}(x_1\, x_2 | x_3\, x_4)$ can be derived immediately from results given elsewhere[6].

In (7):

$$S_{-t}^{(s)}(x_1 \ldots x_s) = \exp - t\mathcal{H}_s(x_1 \ldots x_s) \tag{8a}$$

with

$$\mathcal{H}_s(x_1 \ldots x_s) = \sum_{i=1}^{s} \frac{\vec{p}_i}{m} \cdot \frac{\partial}{\partial \vec{q}_i} - \sum_{1 \leq i < j}^{s} \sum \theta_{ij} \tag{8b}$$

where

$$\theta_{ij} = \frac{\partial \phi(r_{ij})}{\partial \vec{q}_i} \cdot \frac{\partial}{\partial \vec{p}_i} + \frac{\partial \phi}{\partial \vec{q}_j} \cdot \frac{\partial}{\partial \vec{p}_j} \tag{8c}$$

In the expansion (6) the $a_s(x_1 \ldots x_s ; 0)$ contain the contributions to $f_2(x_1\, x_2 ; t)$ of the correlations present in the initial state of the gas at $t = 0$. The a_s are equal to one if there are no correlations at $t = 0$. We shall assume that $a_s(x_1 \ldots x_s ; 0)$ is only different from 1 if two or more of the particles $1 \ldots s$ are within a distance r_o at $t = 0$.

We remark that the $\tilde{\mathcal{S}}$ and $\tilde{\mathcal{T}}$ operators contain (through the a_s as well as through the $\mathcal{H}_s$) only one length: r_o.

To obtain a kinetic equation of the form (3), as had been obtained by Bogolubov and others, from (5) and (6), one would have to show that for a large class of initial conditions for $t >> t_c$ (t_c is the duration of a collision):

a) $a_s(x_1 \ldots x_s ; 0) = 1$ for all $s \geqq 2$ i.e. the initial state is forgotten;

b) $\mathcal{S}_t$ can be replaced by $\mathcal{S}_\infty$ i.e. the whole time dependence of f_2 is through f alone: f_2 is a time independent functional of f.

Due to the nature of the operator O it suffices to demonstrate a) and b) for those phases of particles 1 and 2, where $r_{12} \leqq r_o$.

The validity of a) and b) under the above mentioned conditions is indeed supported by:

1) it is true for $\tilde{\mathcal{S}}_t^{(2)}(x_1\, x_2)$ i.e. for $t \gg t_{coll}$ and $r_{12} \leqq r_o$ $\tilde{\mathcal{S}}_t^{(2)}(x_1\, x_2)$ in (6) can be replaced by $\mathcal{S}_\infty^{(2)}(x_1\, x_2)$. Introducing this into $f_2^{(o)}$ and using this $f_2^{(o)}$ for f_2 in (5) leads essentially to the Boltzmann equation (1) for f.

2) it is true for $\int dx_3 \mathcal{T}_t^{(3)}(x_1\, x_2 \mid x_3)$ i.e. this operator in (6) can be replaced by $\int dx_3 \mathcal{T}_\infty^{(3)}(x_1\, x_2 \mid x_3)$ under the above mentioned conditions. Introducing this with (6) for $f_2^{(1)}$ into (5) leads to a correction to the Boltzmann equation due to triple collisions. Choh and Uhlenbeck[8)9)] solved the so-obtained generalized Boltzmann equation à la Chapman-Enskog and obtained in this way - as expected - density dependent corrections to the Chapman-Enskog values for the transport coefficients.

Thus for instance for the viscosity they found:

$$\eta = \eta_o(T) + n\eta_1(T) \tag{9}$$

with for η_1 an explicit expression in terms of the intermolecular forces.

3) If one assumes a) and b) to be true for <u>all</u> terms in (6) and if in addition, one replaces then on the right hand side of (6) f by the equilibrium distribution function:

$$f \rightarrow f^{eq} = n(2\pi mkT)^{3/2}\, e^{-\vec{p}^2/2mkT} \tag{10}$$

then the expansion (6) reduces term by term to the known virial expansion for f_2 in equilibrium.

Yet in spite of all this and of the fact that all the higher terms in (6) look all right, the expansion (6) for f_2 cannot be used to obtain a generalized Boltzmann equation for f because a) and b) cannot be proved to be true for $f_2^{(2)}(x_1\, x_2\, ; t)$ and for all higher terms. On the contrary these terms all diverge if one takes the limit of $t \rightarrow \infty$ in the $\mathcal{S}_t$-operators.

In fact one finds in 3-dimensions that:

$$f_2^{(2)} \text{ diverges } \sim \log\left(\frac{t}{t_c}\right) \text{ for } t \rightarrow \infty \tag{11a}$$

and

$$f_2^{(\ell)} \text{ diverges} \sim \left(\frac{t}{t_c}\right)^{\ell-2} \quad \text{for } t \to \infty \quad (\ell \geq 3) \tag{11b}$$

while in 2-dimensions:

$$f_2^{(1)} \text{ diverges} \sim \log\left(\frac{t}{t_c}\right) \quad \text{for } t \to \infty \tag{12a}$$

and

$$f_2^{(\ell)} \text{ diverges } \left(\frac{t}{t_c}\right)^{\ell-1} \quad \text{for } t \to \infty \quad (\ell \geq 2) \tag{12b}$$

Therefore the expansions cannot be used term by term to obtain a generalized Boltzmann equation of the form (3).

Proof of Divergences

To illustrate the nature of the difficulties, we shall discuss b) for the case that there are no correlations in the initial state i. e. all $a_s(0) = 1$. The same divergence difficulties occur if one wants to prove a) i. e. the disappearance of the initial state correlations in case the $a_s(0) \neq 1$.

As elaborate discussions have been given elsewhere [7)10)11)], we shall only present the gist of the argument. We restrict ourselves to a discussion of the logarithmic divergence of $f_2^{(1)}$ in two dimensions for the case of hard discs. For fixed phases of the particles 1 and 2 then, with $r_{12} \leqq r_o$, we estimate the volume in the phase space of particle 3 for which $\mathcal{T}_t^{(3)} \neq 0$ for large t for a general f*). Because of the presence of the $\mathcal{S}$ - operators, the analysis involves a dynamical problem viz. the study of the dynamical events between 3 particles in infinite space.

Such an analysis shows that there are non-vanishing contributions to the integrand if in time t sequences of 3 or more binary collisions occur.

---

*) The t-dependence of f is not taken into account here.

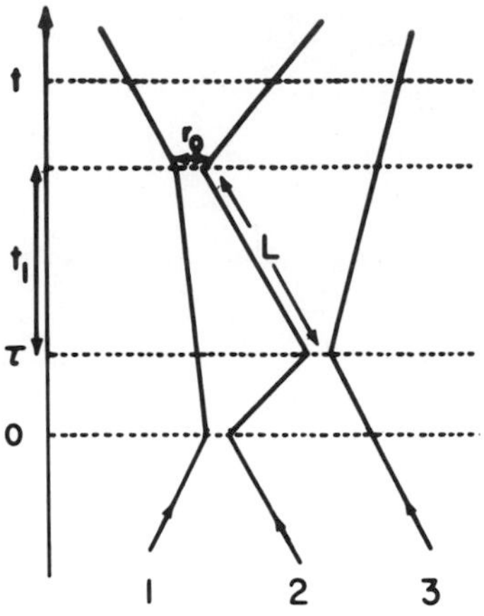

Fig. 2a

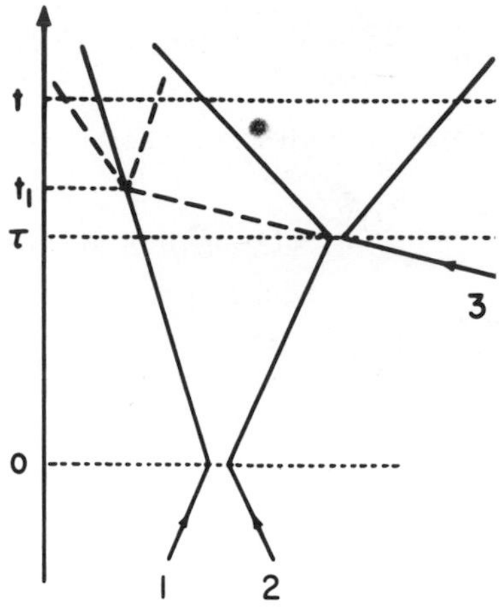

Fig. 2b

As far as $f_2^{(1)}$ is concerned, one of the collisions between particles 1 and 2 takes place at a time t. Without loss of generality we shall denote for convenience in the following, however, that the first collision between the particles 1 and 2 takes place at a time 0, so that between time 0 and t 3 or more successive binary collisions must take place.*) These binary collisions can be of two types: real or imaginary (hypothetical); (cf. fig. 2a and 2b resp.).

As the estimates of the phase space volumes do not depend essentially on whether the collisions are real or imaginary we confine ourselves to the case of 3 real successive binary collisions. On the basis of the following considerations, one easily convinces oneself that the contributions of 4 or more binary collisions remain finite.

We investigate therefore only whether the volume in the phase space of particle 3 associated with events as sketched in fig. 2a remains finite or not in the limit that $t \to \infty$.

It is convenient to choose a coordinate system in which particle

*) This time t = 0 has, of course, nothing to do with the initial time t = 0 at which the gas was first considered.

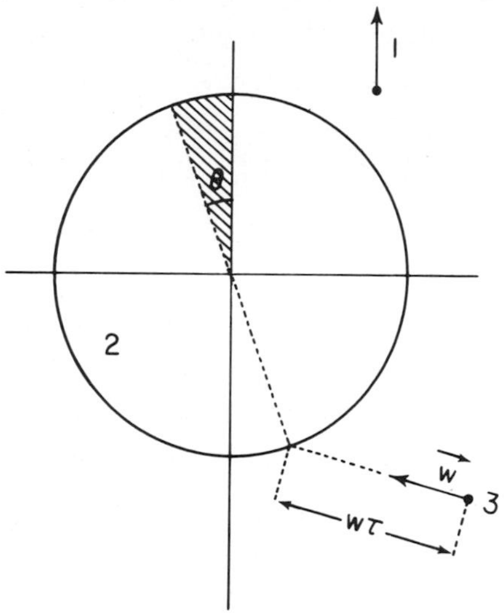

Fig. 3

2 is at rest just after the first binary collision which takes place at t = 0, and in which particle 1 then moves away from particle 2 along the positive z-axis. Introducing instead of the coordinates $\vec{q}_3$ of particle 3 the time τ it takes 3 to collide with 2 and the angle θ of the line of centers of that collision with the positive z-axis and instead of the momenta $\vec{p}_3$ of particle 3 the velocity w of 3 in the chosen coordinate system, one has to estimate an integral of the form:

$$\int d\tau \int d\theta \int d\vec{w} \quad J$$

where the limits of τ, θ and $\vec{w}$ are determined by the condition that a third collision occurs, and where J is the Jacobian of the above mentioned transformation. For such a third collision to occur one clearly must have for large τ i.e. for $\tau > \tau_0$ say, that

$$\frac{\alpha_1}{\tau} \leqq \sin\theta \sim \theta \leqq \frac{\alpha_2}{\tau} \tag{13}$$

As one easily demonstrates that for our estimates J can be treated as independent of θ and τ, one sees immediately that one has to consider the integral

$$\int_{\tau_o}^{\infty} d\tau \int_{\frac{\alpha_1}{\tau}}^{\frac{\alpha_2}{\tau}} d\theta \int d\vec{w}\, J \qquad (14)$$

which clearly leads to a logarithmic divergence $\sim \log \tau$ for $\tau \to \infty$. In the coordinate system considered the divergence is due to head-on collisions of 3 and 2. Therefore, although for increasing τ a third collision becomes increasingly more difficult, it so to speak does not become difficult enough, so that the total volume in the phase space of particles 3 diverges logarithmically when τ is allowed to go to infinity.

The argument presented above also whows immediately that the phase volume remains finite in 3-dimensions. For in that case one has to replace $d\theta$ by $\sin\theta\, d\theta \sim \theta\, d\theta$ which leads at the upper limit to a vanishing contribution, as $\lim_{\tau\to\infty} \frac{1}{\tau} = 0$.

Similar considerations for $f_2^{(2)}$ in 2-dimensions lead for sequences of 4 successive binary collisions such as f. i. shown in fig. 4 to the linear divergence of the combined phase space of the particles 3 and 4, quoted in (12b).

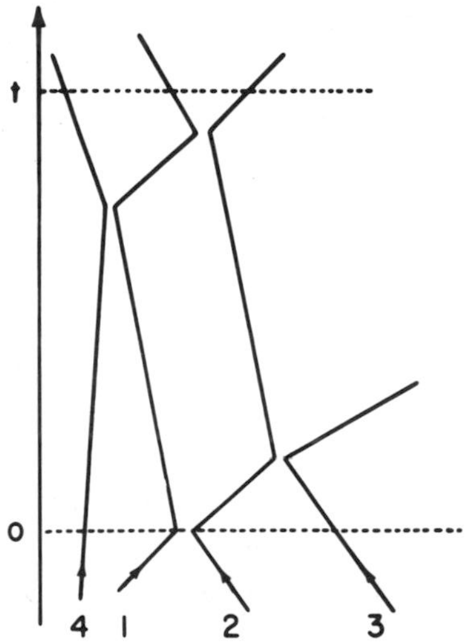

Fig. 4

Although the phase space divergences do not rule out a priori the existence of the $f_2^{(1)}$ for very special classes of initial conditions (and therefore of f's), they rule out the existence of the $f_2^{(1)}$-and therefore also the existence of a kinetic equation of the form (3),-in general for the class of initial conditions considered here.

3. CONSEQUENCES FOR TRANSPORT COEFFICIENTS

If one uses in 2-dimensions for f_2 in equation (5) the (divergent) expression:

$$f_2 = \mathcal{S}_{\infty}^{(2)}(x_1\, x_2) f(x_1;t) f(x_2;t) + \lim_{T\to\infty} \int dx_3 \mathcal{J}_T^{(3)}(x_1\, x_2 | x_3) \prod_{i=1}^{3} f(x_i;t) \tag{15}$$

and if one then solves this equation near equilibrium à la Chapman-Enskog,the divergence in $f_2^{(1)}$ implies also a divergence in the transport coefficients:

$$\eta(n,T) = \eta_o(T) + A\, n\, r_o^2 \lim_{T\to\infty} \log\left(\frac{T}{t_c}\right) + \ldots \tag{16}$$

The coefficient A has been computed by Sengers[11] using for f the solution of the (ordinary) Boltzmann equation for hard discs in first Enskog approximation. Sengers found A = -0.03826 in that case. Again, one cannot rule out entirely the possibility that A = 0, if one would take for f the exact solution of the Boltzmann equation for hard discs.

Although therefore neither for the divergences in f_2 nor for those in η and λ a complete proof exists at the moment their reality is very strongly suggested by the above considerations as well as by a number of simplified models, which can be worked out in considerable detail[12)13)14)].

4. EXPECTATION OF NEW THEORY

a. Origin of divergences

Physically, the divergences discussed in the previous section are due to the fact that for instance, τ or T in eq. (14) or (16) resp. are allowed to approach infinity. This is directly related to the basic idea of the whole expansion (6), viz. the expansion of f_2 in terms of properties of isolated groups of particles in infinite space i. e. to the application of the idea of the virial expansion. Clearly in a real gas the times τ and T should not exceed a few times t_{mfp}, the time to traverse a mean free path in the gas. This restriction of τ and T is due to the presence of all the other molecules in the gas and this should therefore be taken into account in a realistic expansion for f_2.

b. Logarithmic density dependence of transport coefficients

If one assumes then ad hoc that in (16) T should be placed by t_{mfp} and if one then uses that $t_{mfp}/t_c \sim \frac{1}{nr_o^2}$, then one finds immediately that for a 2-dimensional gas of hard discs the viscosity as a function of n contains terms which depend on the density $\sim n \log n$:

$$\eta (n, T) = \eta_o(T) + 0.03826\, n\, r_o^2 \log n\, r_o^2 + B\, n\, r_o^2 + \ldots \quad (17)$$

This shows then that the divergences in f_2 lead (in principle) to experimentally observable consequences in the transport coefficients. *) Similarly in 3-dimensions one would find for the viscosity an expansion of the form:

$$\eta (n, T) = \eta_o(T) + n\eta_1(T) + n^2 \log n\eta_1'(T) + n^2\eta_2(T) + \ldots \quad (18)$$

We would like to point out that from the work of Lebowitz and Percus[12)] on a one dimensional model as well as of Hauge and Cohen[13)] for the (2-dimensional) wind-tree model follows that

---

*) A logarithmic dependence of the transport coefficients on the density follows immediately from an evaluation of the time correlation expressions for the transport coefficients, where similar difficulties occur[7)].

the (time-) divergences in f_2 do <u>not</u> necessarily lead to non-analytic behavior of the transport coefficients as a function of density. The term $\sim n\, r_o^2 \log n\, r_o^2$ in 2-dimensions (or $\sim (n\, r_o^3)^2 \log n\, r_o^3$ in 3-dimensions) in η is due to the logarithmic time divergence in f_2 but would not occur if - as is the case in the above mentioned models - only divergences in $f_2 \sim$ powers of t occur (see also below).

c. Resummation

Mathematically a resummation should be carried out of the expansion (6) of f_2 in terms of f which introduces then in a natural way a cut-off of all paths of the particles at distances of the order of the mean free path and of all "free" times of flight at times of the order of the mean free time.

A partial resummation of the expansion (6) was carried out by Dorfman and Cohen. This resummation only involved in each term of f_2 a certain class of (most divergent) events involving

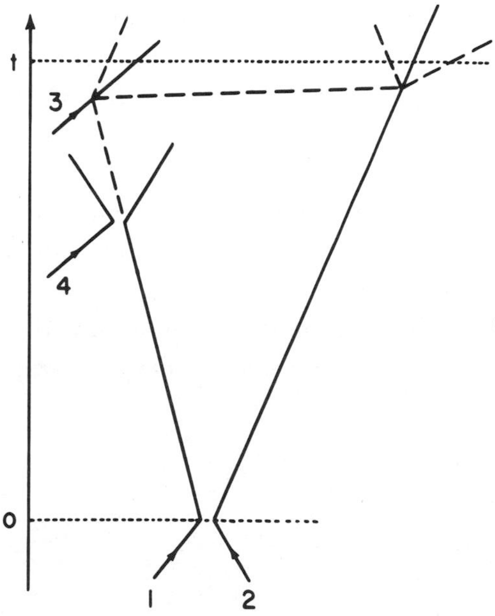

Fig. 5

imaginary collisions, which interrupt the "free" paths of the particles in previous terms. Thus for instance divergent events like in the four particle term $f_2^{(2)}$ in 2-dimensions, interrupt the (free) paths of particle 1 in the three particle event of fig. 5. Similar events will interrupt the free paths of particle 2 in fig. 5. A resummation involving similar events in higher order terms leads then to a rearrangement of the expansion (6), involving finite integrals. Thus for instance the divergent integral for f_2 involving

$$\int_{\tau_o}^{\infty} d\tau \, \frac{1}{\tau}$$

is replaced by the convergent integral of the form:

$$\int_{\tau_o}^{\infty} d\tau \, e^{-\nu\tau} \frac{1}{\tau}$$

where $\nu = n\sigma \int d\vec{p}_3 \, (p_{13} + p_{23}) \, f(\vec{p}_3 \, ; t)$. Here σ is the total cross section for the intermolecular potential considered and $p_{ij} = |\vec{p}_i - \vec{p}_j|$. A resummation as sketched above leaves the coefficient of the logarithmic term in the transport coefficients (viz. for 2-dimensional hard discs Sengers' A = -0.03826) unchanged. Whether this still holds true when a complete resummation is carried out, which eliminates all divergent terms, seems plausible but has not been proved. The only indication one has that this might well be the case is that under very general conditions, a cut-off function $\varphi(\tau)$ (with $\varphi(0) = 1$) obtained from a resummation will leave the coefficient of the logarithmic term in η unchanged viz.:

$$c \int_a^{\infty} \frac{\varphi(\tau)}{\tau} \, d\tau = -c \quad \log a + O(1) \tag{18}$$

for almost any function $\varphi(\tau)$.

d. Results of resummation

Thus one can have good hope that Sengers' coefficient for the logarithmic term is the same also in a resummed theory. The coefficient B in (17) of the term $\sim n r_o^2$ has not yet been found.

Similarly in 3 dimensions although resummation probably leaves also there the coefficient of the logarithmic term $\sim (n r_o^3)^2 \log n r_o^3$ - which stems here from the four body term - unchanged, the computation of the coefficient of the term $\sim (n r_o^3)^2$ not only seems to involve at least the resummation of all most divergent contributions to f_2, but also contributions from the (convergent) three-body term as well.

The above considerations also seem to imply that the convergent contribution $\eta_1(T)$ to η computed by Choh and Uhlenbeck in 3-dimensions will remain unchanged by any resummation.

From all this it will be clear that very little is known with certainty of the general structure of a convergent theory of transport phenomena. In particular the density dependence of the transport coefficients seems to be much more complicated than was previously expected.

e. Mean free path corrections

It might be illustrative to present some elementary considerations, based on the mean free path concept on the basis of which the logarithmic density dependence of the viscosity of a 2-dimensional gas of hard discs, can perhaps be understood. These considerations also give some suggestions about the occurrence in η of other non-analytic terms in the density than those mentioned before.

In the elementary theory of transport coefficients based on the mean free path ℓ the following expression for the viscosity η in terms of ℓ can be derived:

$$\eta = \frac{1}{3} nm \, \ell \, \bar{v} \tag{19}$$

where m is the mass of the molecules and $\bar{v}$ their average velocity. For ℓ one can take for instance the Maxwell mean free path given by:

$$\ell = \frac{1}{n\pi r_o^2 \sqrt{2}} \tag{20}$$

As is well known the expression (20) for ℓ only holds if:

1) only binary collisions occur;
2) no two binary collisions involve the same pair of molecules.

To correct for 1), corrections due to triple-, quadruple-, etc. collisions have to be introduced which are proportional to n^2, n^3, etc. These corrections therefore lead to a density expansion of ℓ of the form:

$$\ell = \frac{1}{n\pi r_o^2 \sqrt{2}\,(1 + a_1 n + a_2 n^2 + \ldots)} = \ell_o + n\ell_1 + n^2\ell_2 + \ldots \tag{21}$$

which with (19) also leads to a density expansion of η of the form (4) (for hard discs the η_i $(i = 0, 1, \ldots)$ do not depend on T, of course).

To correct for 2), corrections due to, for instance, recollisions of particles, as sketched in fig. 2a, have to be considered. Clearly of all collisions between particles 3 and 2 at time τ only those lead to a correction to ℓ_o if particle 2 collides again with particle 1 at a time t_1 later, say. If no such recollision between 1 and 2 occurs, no correction for ℓ_o is needed.

Now for large $t_1 \gg t_c$, there is a fraction $\sim \frac{1}{t_1}$ of all 3-2 collisions which leads to a 1-2 recollision at t_1. For, for such a recollision to occur the direction of the velocity of 2- and therefore also of 3- has to lie within a plane angle $\sim \frac{r_o}{L} = \frac{t_c}{t_1}$ as $L \sim t_1$. Integrating this fraction over t_1 up to $t_1 = \alpha t_{mfp}$ where $\alpha = O(1)$, and using that one considers two particles (viz. 2 and 3) in addition to particle 1, one finds that the correction 2) contains a contribution

$$\sim (n r_o^2)^2 \int_{\ldots}^{\alpha t_{mfp}} \frac{dt_1}{t_1} = (n r_o^2)^2 \log (n r_o) + C(n r_o^2)^2 + \ldots$$

where C is a constant. Therefore correcting ℓ for 1) and 2) leads to an expression of the form:

$$\ell = \frac{1}{n\pi r_o^2\sqrt{2}\,(1+\alpha_1 n r_o^2 + \alpha_2 (n r_o^2)^2 + \ldots \alpha_1'(n r_o^2)\log(n r_o^2) + \ldots)}$$

$$= \ell_o + \sum_{s=1}^{\infty} (n r_o^2)^s \lambda_s + \sum_{p,q}^{\infty} (n r_o^2)^p \log(n r_o^2)^q \lambda_{pq} + \ldots \tag{22}$$

On the basis of these considerations one would expect therefore, with (19) contributions to η not only $\sim(n r_o^2)\log(n r_o^2)$ but $\sim(n r_o^2)^p(\log n r_o^2)^q$ where p, q $\geqq$ 1. The same conclusion has been obtained by Van Leeuwen and Weyland[14] for the self-diffusion coefficient in a two dimensional Lorentz gas.

It will be appreciated that 1) the possibility of the existence of contributions to η of the above mentioned form is at best suggested by these elementary considerations and also that 2) nothing can be said about the existence of other contributions to η of still a different non-analytic character than those considered here, f. i. whether terms $\sim(n r_o^2)\log\log(n r_o^2)$ could occur.

f. Experimental consequences

1) The nature of the divergences in f_2 depend on the intermolecular potential. In particular the divergences cannot be reliably established without taking into account explicitly some details of the intermolecular potential. This is for instance demonstrated by the fact that in a 2 dimensional Lorentz gas, no divergence occurs in the three particle term of f_2 in the wind-tree model of Ehrenfest *)[15], where the (infinitely) heavy (tree) molecules are squares while the same term contains a logarithmic time divergence in case the squares are replaced by circles!

Furthermore, as follows f. i. from the arguments given sub e), the occurrence of logarithmic terms is related to the presence in the system of a continuous set of velocity directions, so that

*) The Ehrenfest wind-tree model consists of light (wind) molecules which can only move in 4 directions, that are parallel to the diagonals of fixed square (tree) molecules, which are with their centers randomly distributed in the plane.

such terms do not seem to occur in 1 dimension f. i., where only 2 velocity directions are possible or in the 2-dimensional wind-tree model, where only 4 velocity directions are possible.

These considerations also suggest under appropriate conditions the possibility to obtain information about the form of the intermolecular potential from the magnitude of the coefficient of contributions to the transport coefficients which depend logarithmically on the density.

2) It should be stressed, however, that there are strong indications that for a real gas the contributions of the non-analytic terms to the transport coefficients is small and only constitutes a few percent of the terms analytic in the density[16].

I would like to conclude by saying that more than 100 years after Boltzmann's equation, not only is the proper generalization of this equation to higher densities still unknown, but not even the first correction term to this equation is reliably known and fully understood!

REFERENCES

1. Boltzmann, L., Lectures on Gas Theory, University of California Press, Berkeley and Los Angeles (1964).
2. Enskog, D., Kinetische Theorie der Vorgange in massig verdunnten Gasen, Dissertation, Uppsala (1917).
3. Chapman, S. and Cowling, T. G., The mathematical theory of non-uniform gases, Cambridge University Press (1953); Waldmann, L., Encyclopedia of Physics, ed. S. Flugge, Vol. XII., Springer-Verlag Berlin, (1958) p. 296.
4. Uhlenbeck, G. E. and Ford, G. W., Lectures in statistical mechanics, In: Vol. I Lectures in Applied Mathematical Society, Providence, R.I. (1963). Chaps IV and VI.
5. Bogolubov, N. N., Problems of a dynamical theory in Statistical physics, In: Studies in Statistical Mechanics Vol. I, ed. de Boer, J., and Uhlenbeck, G. E., North Holland Publishing Company (1962) p. 5;
See also ref. 4) Chap. VII.
6. Cohen, E. G. D., J. Math. Phys. 4, 183 (1963).
7. Dorfman, J. R. and Cohen, E. G. D., J. Math. Phys. Febr. 1967.
8. Choh, S. T. and Uhlenbeck, G. E., The kinetic theory of dense gases, Dissertation, University of Michigan (1958).
9. Cohen, E. G. D., Fundamental Problems in Statistical Mechanics, North-Holland Publishing Company, (1961) p. 110.
10. Cohen, E. G. D., Lectures in Theoretical Physics, (1965), Vol. VIII A, ed. W. E. Brittin, University of Colorado Press, Boulder, (1966) p. 145.
11. Sengers, J. V., Phys. Rev. Letters, 15, 515 (1965); Phys. Fluids, 9, 1685 (1966).
12. Lebowitz, J. L., and Percus, J., to appear.

13. Hauge, E. H., and Cohen, E. G. D., to be published.

14. Van Leeuwen, J. M. M., and Weyland, A., to appear.

15. Ehrenfest, P. and T., Begriffliche Grundlagen der Statistischen Auffassung in der Mechanik, in Collected Scientific Papers, North-Holland Publishing Company, (1959), p. 229.

16. Sengers, J. V., Intern. Journ. of Heat and Mass Transfer, Vol. I, 1103 (1965); see also ref. 10.

DISCUSSION

Fröhlich: Since you use a cut-off potential it is possible to define collisions. However, this may be a significant point in leading to the results you have presented.

Cohen: I take it that you refer to the long range effects which lead to the divergences mentioned and that you want to stress that those effects might be studied more directly if one would start with a potential with an infinite tail instead of with a cut-off potential, as I do. I agree that this might be the case and in this connection I also believe that some kind of analogy could exist with the case of a plasma where long range effects already exist in equilibrium.
However, although I agree that it is quite possible that one might gain in this way a deeper understanding of the nature of long range effects which lead to divergences, a more or less systematic way to incorporate these long range effects together with the short range (individual particle) effects which are also present in a consistent theory, is not clear to me.

Rice: I believe there is a statement by Grad to the effect that, in the mathematical sense, the Boltzmann equation does not have a solution unless a cut-off potential is used. (Prof. Uhlenbeck and Ford have informed me that this statement is incorrect).

Cohen: I can not comment on this.

Lebowitz: How can you say there are no $t^n \log t$ divergences?

Cohen: I only claim that in a given term the most divergent contributions are $\sim t^n$ and not $\sim t^n \log t$. There can, of course, in this same term be less divergent contributions $\sim t^{n-1} \log t$, etc.

LOGARITHMIC TERMS IN THE DENSITY EXPANSIONS OF TRANSPORT COEFFICIENTS *)

K. KAWASAKI **)
and
I. OPPENHEIM
Department of Chemistry
Massachusetts Institute of
Technology, Cambridge,
Massachusetts, U.S.A.

ABSTRACT

Correlation function expressions for the transport coefficients involve integrals of the form

$$\lim_{\epsilon \to 0} \int_0^\infty e^{-\epsilon t} \langle I(t)I(0) \rangle \, dt$$

where I is the appropriate flux and the limiting operation is to be performed last. The ϵ dependences of the terms in the expansion of the transport coefficients in power series in the density are analysed using the binary collision expansion. As $\epsilon \to 0$, the coefficients in the density series involving more than two (three) particles are divergent in two (three) dimensions. These divergences arise from integrations over small values of the Fourier transform variables of the particle coordinates and are most severe in certain ring diagram contributions to the coefficients of each power of the density. Summation over these ring diagrams

*) A portion of this work was supported by the National Science Foundation.

**) Present address: Department of Physics, Faculty of Science, Kyushu University, Fukuoka, Japan.

produces a finite contribution which yields a term containing $\rho^n \log \rho$ (where n = 1 (2) for ρD, η, κ in two (three) dimensions). This summation introduces a renormalized free particle propagator $\overline{G}_o$ where

$$\overline{G}_o = (\epsilon + i\,L_o + \rho\overline{\mathscr{L}})^{-1} ,$$

$i\,L_o$ is the free particle Liouville operator, $\overline{\mathscr{L}}$ is simply related to the Boltzmann collision operator and is positive semi-definite, and the $\rho\overline{\mathscr{L}}$ term introduces a collision damping into the free particle propagator G_o,

$$G_o = (\epsilon + i\,L_o)^{-1} .$$

The analysis of the three particle term in two dimensions confirms the fact that the dynamical event producing the divergence involves essentially a head-on collision and therefore that weak-coupling calculations of transport coefficients in gases may not contain the divergences discussed here.

Since the publication of our paper with the same title[1], there has been some discussion concerning the existence and origin of the divergence in the density series of the transport coefficients as well as regarding our resummation procedure for taming the divergence[2]. In particular, it has been argued that if one performs the k integration in the apparently divergent expressions of I prior to taking the limit $\epsilon \to 0+$, the divergence may disappear. The purpose of this report is to amplify the discussion of the divergence given in I demonstrating that the divergence is real and to give a more convincing argument for choosing the ring diagrams for resummation. It will turn out, indeed, that the divergences come from integration over small values of k as we have indicated in I and it is shown explicitly that the resummation of I is equivalent to the introduction of collision damping to a free particle propagator.

For definiteness, let us consider the term in the development of the self diffusion coefficient which represents the recollision (12)(13)(12) which, according to I (3.1), is (we follow the notation of I and Kawasaki and Oppenheim, Ref. 3 unless stated otherwise),

$$t_{Da}(p_1) \equiv \iint d\underline{p}_2 d\underline{p}_3 \, V^2 (0|T_{12}G_oT_{13}G_oT_{12}|0)\phi(p_2)\phi(p_3)$$

$$= \frac{1}{(2\pi)^2}\int d\underline{k} \iint d\underline{p}_2 d\underline{p}_3 V^3 T_{12}(0|\underline{k}, -\underline{k}, 0) g(\underline{k}, -\underline{k}, 0) \times$$

$$\times T_{13}(\underline{k}, -\underline{k}, 0|\underline{k}, -\underline{k}, 0) g(\underline{k}, -\underline{k}, 0) T_{12}(\underline{k}, -\underline{k}, 0|0)\phi(p_2)\phi(p_3) \tag{1}$$

For short-range intermolecular forces, $T_{ij}(\underline{k}^N|\underline{k}'^N)$ is almost equal to $T_{ij}(0|0)$ if all the k's are much smaller than the inverse of the force range. Since we are interested in the small k region, we replace all the T's appearing in (1) by $T(0|0)$ and we introduce a cut-off k_{max} to eliminate possible divergences coming from large k. Then, defining the binary collision operator t_{ij} by

$$t_{ij} \equiv V\, T_{ij}(0|0) \, , \tag{2}$$

$t_{Da}(p_1)$ becomes

$$t_{Da}(\underline{p}_1) = \frac{1}{(2\pi)^2}\int d\underline{k} \iint d\underline{p}_2 d\underline{p}_3 t_{12}\left[\epsilon + i\underline{k}\cdot\frac{\underline{p}_1 - \underline{p}_2}{m}\right]^{-1}$$

$$t_{13}\left[\epsilon + i\underline{k}\cdot\frac{\underline{p}_1 - \underline{p}_2}{m}\right]^{-1} t_{12}\,\phi(p_2)\phi(p_3) \tag{3}$$

One can show that t_{ij} is essentially a Boltzmann collision operator[3] in three dimensions; its two-dimensional analog is

$$t_{ij}\, F(\underline{p}_i, \underline{p}_j) = \int_{-\infty}^{\infty} d\, b_{ij} \frac{|\underline{p}_i - \underline{p}_j|}{m} \left[F(\underline{p}_i, \underline{p}_j) - F(\underline{p}_i^*, \underline{p}_j^*)\right] \tag{4}$$

where F is an arbitrary function, b_{ij} is the impact parameter which can be negative in two-dimensions, and $\underline{p}_i^*$ and $\underline{p}_j^*$ are the momenta which $\underline{p}_i$ and $\underline{p}_j$ take before the collision $[ij]$, respectively. With this, we obtain

$$t_{Da}(\underline{p}_1)A(\underline{p}_1)\phi(p_1)$$

$$= \frac{1}{(2\pi)^2}\int_0^{k_{max}} kdk \iint d\underline{p}_2 d\underline{p}_3 \int_{-\infty}^{\infty} db_{13} t_{12} \frac{|\underline{p}_1 - \underline{p}_3|}{m} \times$$

$$\times \{I_\epsilon\left(\frac{k|\underline{p}_1-\underline{p}_2|}{m}, \frac{k|\underline{p}_1-\underline{p}_2|}{m}, 0\right)\left[t_{12}A(\underline{p}_1)\phi(p_1)\phi(p_2)\phi(p_3)\right] -$$

$$- I_\epsilon\left(\frac{k|\underline{p}_1-\underline{p}_2|}{m}, \frac{k|\underline{p}_1^*-\underline{p}_2^*|}{m}, \chi\right)\left[t_{12}A(\underline{p}_1)\phi(p_1)\phi(p_2)\phi(p_3)\right]^*\}$$

(5)

where $A(\underline{p})$ is an arbitrary function of $\underline{p}$ and $[\ldots]^*$ means that the momenta in this bracket expression are those before the collision $[13]$, $\underline{p}^*$'s, and χ is the scattering angle for this collision. The function I_ϵ is defined as follows:

$$I_\epsilon(u, u', \chi) \equiv \oint d\phi \frac{1}{\epsilon + iu\cos\phi} \frac{1}{\epsilon + iu'\cos(\phi+\chi)}, \quad [u, u' \geqq 0].$$

(6)

We now focus our attention on this function and investigate its behavior for small u and u' for small but nonzero ϵ. The integration over ϕ can be converted into an integral over the unit circle c by a change of variable, $z = e^{i\phi}$. Eq. (6) becomes

$$I_\epsilon(u, u', \chi) = \frac{4i}{uu'} e^{-i\chi} \oint_c dz \frac{z}{(z^2 - 2\frac{i\epsilon}{u} z + 1)(z^2 - 2\frac{i\epsilon}{u'} e^{-i\chi} z + e^{-2i\chi})}.$$

(7)

Excluding the special case of $\chi = 0$, $u = u'$ which corresponds to no scattering[4)] and noting that $0 \leq \sqrt{1+\chi^2} - \chi \leq 1$ for $\chi \geq 0$, the poles inside the unit circle are $i[\epsilon/u - \sqrt{1+(\epsilon/u)^2}]$, $ie^{-i\chi} \times [\epsilon/u' - \sqrt{1+(\epsilon/u')^2}]$ and (7) becomes after some manipulation:

$$I_\epsilon(u,u',\chi) = -\frac{8\pi}{uu'}\left(\frac{b'}{a} - \frac{a'}{b}\right)(b-a)^{-1}(b'-a')^{-1}\zeta\left(\zeta - \frac{b'}{a}\right)^{-1}\left(\zeta - \frac{a'}{b}\right)^{-1} \tag{8}$$

where

$$\zeta = e^{i\chi} \quad \text{and}$$

$$\begin{aligned} a &= \epsilon/u - \sqrt{1+(\epsilon/u)^2} \\ b &= \epsilon/u + \sqrt{1+(\epsilon/u)^2} \\ a' &= \epsilon/u' - \sqrt{1+(\epsilon/u')^2} \\ b' &= \epsilon/u' + \sqrt{1+(\epsilon/u')^2} \end{aligned} \tag{9}$$

Now, the second term in (5) involves an expression of the form $\frac{i}{(2\pi)^2}\int d\underline{p}_2 d\underline{p}_3 t_{12} J_{2\epsilon}$ where

$$J_{2\epsilon} = \int_0^{k_{max}} kdk \oint d\chi\, I_\epsilon(u,u',\chi)F(\chi) \tag{10}$$

where we have used the result

$$\int_{-\infty}^{\infty} db_{13} \cdots = -\oint d\chi \frac{\partial b_{13}}{\partial \chi} \cdots \tag{11}$$

and

$$F(\chi) = \frac{|\underline{p}_1 - \underline{p}_3|}{m} \frac{\partial b_{13}}{\partial \chi}\left[t_{12}A(\underline{p}_1)\phi(p_1)\phi(p_2)\phi(p_3)\right]^*.$$

Here $u = kv$ and $u' = kv'$ with $v = \frac{|\underline{p}_1 - \underline{p}_2|}{m}$ and $v' = \frac{|\underline{p}_1^* - \underline{p}_2^*|}{m}$. The integral over χ can again be transformed into a contour integral of ζ over the unit circle c:

$$J_{2\epsilon} = \int_0^{k_{max}} kdk \oint_c \frac{d\zeta}{i\zeta} I_\epsilon(u,u',\chi)G(\zeta) \tag{12}$$

where $G(e^{i\chi}) = F(\chi)$. Since for finite u and u' and nonzero ϵ we have $|b'/a| > 1$ and $|a'/b| < 1$ (for $u = u' = \infty$, I_ϵ obviously vanishes), we obtain

$$J_{2\epsilon} = \int_0^{k_{max}} \frac{dk}{k} \frac{(2\pi)^2}{vv'} \left[1 + (\epsilon/kv)^2\right]^{-1/2} \times$$

$$\left[1 + (\epsilon/kv')^2\right]^{-1/2} G(a'/b) , \qquad (13)$$

if we assume that $G(\zeta)$ has no singularity inside the unit circle. The only contributing pole inside the unit circle is at

$$\zeta = \zeta_o = a'/b = \{\epsilon/u' - \sqrt{1 + (\epsilon/u')^2}\} / \{\epsilon/u + \sqrt{1 + (\epsilon/u)^2}\}$$

$$(14)$$

The integration in Eq. (13) can be analyzed from several different, but equivalent, points of view. We note that the indefinite integral of the interesting part of the integrand of (13) is given by

$$\int \frac{dk}{k} \left[1 + (\epsilon/kv)^2\right]^{-1/2} \left[1 + (\epsilon/kv')^2\right]^{-1/2}$$

$$= -\ln \left[(k^2 + (\epsilon/v)^2)^{1/2} + (k^2 + (\epsilon/v')^2)^{1/2}\right] . \qquad (15)$$

First, we break up the integration over k in Eq. (13) into two parts: from 0 to $\alpha\epsilon/v$ and from $\alpha\epsilon/v$ to k_{max} where α is chosen such that α and $\alpha v'/v >> 1$. In the integration from $\alpha\epsilon/v$ to k_{max}, a'/b given by Eq. (14) is approximately -1 and $G(a'/b)$ can be replaced by $F(\pi)$. It is easily demonstrated that the integral from 0 to $\alpha\epsilon/v$ remains finite as ϵ approaches zero. Thus, since we are interested in the singular behavior of $J_{2\epsilon}$, we can write Eq. (13) as

$$J_{2\epsilon} \cong - \frac{(2\pi)^2}{vv'} F(\pi) \ln \frac{\epsilon}{v} \left[\frac{(\alpha^2+1)^{1/2} + (\alpha^2 + (\frac{v}{v'})^2)^{1/2}}{(k_{max}^2 + (\epsilon/v)^2)^{1/2} + (k_{max}^2 + (\frac{\epsilon}{v'})^2)^{1/2}}\right]$$

$$(15a)$$

As $\epsilon \to 0$, $J_{2\epsilon}$ contains a divergence proportional to $-\ln\epsilon$; this divergence has been discussed by Haynes et al.[5]. It is clear that it is the integration over small values of k, as discussed in I, which gives rise to this divergence. We could also have introduced a cut off k_o at small values of k in the integration in Eq. (13). In this case, for small ϵ,

$$J_{2\epsilon} \cong -\frac{2\pi^2}{vv'} F(\pi) \ln \frac{(k_o^2+(\epsilon/v)^2)^{1/2} + (k_o^2+(\epsilon/v')^2)^{1/2}}{(k_{max}^2+(\epsilon/v)^2)^{1/2} + (k_{max}^2+(\epsilon/v')^2)^{1/2}} \tag{15b}$$

As $\epsilon \to 0+$, Eq. (15b) contains a term proportional to $-\ln k_o$. This again clearly demonstrates that the divergence as $\epsilon \to 0+$ arises from the contribution at small values of k. We note that the first term of (5) possesses no divergence[4].

In order to understand the physical origin of this divergence, we present an alternative evaluation of the integral $J_{2\epsilon}$. Let us first consider the case when ϵ is much smaller than u and u', and we neglect $(\epsilon/u)^2$ and $(\epsilon/u')^2$ in the square roots in (9). Eq. (8) becomes

$$I_\epsilon(u,u',\chi)$$

$$\cong \frac{4\pi}{uu'} e^{-i\chi} \frac{1}{1-\epsilon/u-e^{-i\chi}(1-\epsilon/u')} \{(1-\epsilon/u)\left[1-\epsilon/u+e^{-i\chi}\times\right.$$

$$\left.(1+\epsilon/u')\right]^{-1} - (1-\epsilon/u')\left[1+\epsilon/u+e^{-i\chi}(1-\epsilon/u')\right]^{-1}\},$$

$$(\epsilon \ll u,u') \,. \tag{16}$$

For $\chi \neq \pi$, the expression in the curly bracket above can be shown to be of the order of ϵ. On the other hand, for $\chi = \pi$,

$$I_\epsilon(u,u',\pi) = \frac{4\pi}{uu'} \frac{1}{\epsilon/u+\epsilon/u'} = 0(\epsilon^{-1}) \tag{17}$$

This means that for small enough ϵ, $I_\epsilon(u, u', \chi)$ is sharply peaked around $\chi = \pi$. If we change the integration variable b_{13} to χ according to (11), the region near $\chi = \pi$ gives a major contribution for small ϵ. Thus, if we restrict ourselves to this region and write

$$\chi = \pi + \theta , \quad |\theta| \ll \pi , \tag{18}$$

we then have,

$$I_\epsilon(u, u', \chi) \cong \frac{4\pi}{uu'} \left(\frac{\epsilon}{u} + \frac{\epsilon}{u'}\right) \Big/ \left[\left(\frac{\epsilon}{u} + \frac{\epsilon}{u'}\right)^2 + \theta^2\right], \tag{19}$$

and the integral appearing in (5) becomes

$$\int I_\epsilon(u, u', \chi) db_{13} [\ldots]^* \cong \left(\frac{\partial b_{13}}{\partial \chi}\right)_{\chi=\pi} [\ldots]^*_{\chi=\pi} \; I_\epsilon(u, u', \chi) d\chi \tag{20}$$

As long as the condition

$$\epsilon/u + \epsilon/u' \ll 1 \tag{21}$$

is satisfied, the limits of integration over θ can be extended to $\pm\infty$ [6]. Thus we find

$$\oint I_\epsilon(u, u', \chi) d\chi = \oint I_\epsilon(u, u', \chi) d\theta = 4\pi^2/uu', \quad \left(\frac{\epsilon}{u} + \frac{\epsilon}{u'} \ll 1\right). \tag{22}$$

Since u and u' are proportional to k, the integral grows as k^{-2} for small k as long as the condition (21) holds. Therefore, the integral

$$\int_0^{k_{max}} kdk \int db_{13} I_\epsilon \left(k \frac{|\underline{p}_1 - \underline{p}_2|}{m}, \; k \frac{|\underline{p}_1^* - \underline{p}_2^*|}{m}, \chi\right) [\ldots]^* \tag{23}$$

can be estimated by using (19) and (20) and introducing the cut-off at small k given by

$$k_1 = m\epsilon \left[|\underline{p}_1 - \underline{p}_2|^{-1} + |\underline{p}_1^* - \underline{p}_2^*|^{-1} \right] . \tag{24}$$

Now taking $[\ldots]^*$ in (23) outside the integral since it is generally finite at k = 0, we find

$$\int_0^{k_{max}} dk\, k \oint d\chi I_\epsilon \left(k \frac{|\underline{p}_1 - \underline{p}_2|}{m}, k \frac{|\underline{p}_1^* - \underline{p}_2^*|}{m}, \chi\right) \cong$$

$$\frac{4\pi^2 m^2}{|\underline{p}_1 - \underline{p}_2| \, |\underline{p}_1^* - \underline{p}_2^*|} \int_{k_1}^{k_{max}} \frac{dk}{k}$$

$$\cong \frac{4\pi^2 m^2}{|\underline{p}_1 - \underline{p}_2| \, |\underline{p}_1^* - \underline{p}_2^*|} (-\ln \epsilon) \tag{25}$$

where we have retained only the leading term for small ϵ. Eq. (25) agrees with the leading term in (15a) where $v = |\underline{p}_1 - \underline{p}_2|/m$ and $v' = |\underline{p}_1^* - \underline{p}_2^*|/m$.

The fact that the diverging contribution arises from the region near $\chi = \pi$ means that those recollision processes in which the second collision (13) is very near a head-on collision are responsible for this divergence in agreement with the interpretation of other authors[7]. The divergence can also be considered as arising from the lower cut-off of the k-integral[8]. It is interesting to note that in the earlier calculation, the contributing pole occurs at $\zeta \cong -1$ for $\epsilon \ll u, u'$, which corresponds to $\chi = \pi$.

In the above calculation, alternatively, one can first perform the k-integration without difficulty (Haines et al, Ref. 7), and the divergence arises from subsequent integrations. This, however, does not mean that the divergence does not arise from the small k region, since if one introduces a cut-off at some small but finite k there would be no divergence.

We do not discuss the other triple collision processes in detail since they may be treated in a similar fashion, and have been considered by other authors[7]. It now appears established that altogether these triple collisions lead to a non-vanishing diverging contribution to the first density corrections to the transport coefficients of a two-dimensional classical gas.

We now turn to a discussion of the higher order terms appearing in the resummation of the formal density series of I (ring diagrams). So far, it has not been possible to give as detailed a discussion of the general terms as of the triple collision. Nevertheless, we can obtain some insight into the structure of the general ring term by considering the function:

$$J_{n\epsilon} \equiv \int_0^{k_{max}} kdk \oint d\phi_1 \oint d\phi_2 \cdots \oint d\phi_n$$

$$\frac{1}{\epsilon + ikv_1\cos\phi_1} \frac{1}{\epsilon + ikv_2\cos\phi_2} \cdots \frac{1}{\epsilon + ikv_n\cos\phi_n} F(\phi_1, \phi_2, \ldots \phi_n) \tag{26}$$

which appears in the sum of ring diagrams of the formal density series. In Eq. (26), the v's are certain velocities and F is a function of the ϕ's which may also depend on momenta and is essentially a product of scattering cross sections arising from the terms $VT_{ij}(0|0)$. Eq. (26) involves integrals of the form,

$$j \equiv \oint d\phi \frac{f(\phi)}{\epsilon + ikv\cos\phi} \tag{27}$$

which may be evaluated by converting them into contour integrals along the unit circle with the integration variable $z = e^{i\phi}$. That is,

$$j = \oint_c dz \frac{g(z)}{i\epsilon z - \frac{1}{2}kv(z^2+1)}, \qquad f(\phi) = g(z) . \tag{28}$$

The denominator of the integrand has a pole at $z' = i\epsilon/kv - i\sqrt{1+(\epsilon/kv)^2}$ inside the unit circle. Therefore, if the function $F(\phi_1, \phi_2, \ldots, \phi_n)$ is such that all of the g(z) have no poles inside the unit circle, we obtain

$$j = \frac{2\pi}{kv} \frac{g(z')}{\sqrt{1+(\epsilon/kv)^2}} \tag{29}$$

and hence (26) becomes

$$J_{n\epsilon} = (2\pi)^n \int_0^{k_{max}} dk\, k^{-n+1}\, G(z_1, z_2, \ldots, z_n) \prod_{j=1}^{n} v_j \sqrt{1+(\epsilon/kv_j)^2} \tag{30}$$

where

$$G(z_1, z_2, \ldots, z_n) = F(\phi_1, \phi_2, \ldots, \phi_n), \quad z_j = e^{i\phi_j} \tag{31}$$

and we substitute for z_j,

$$z_j = i\epsilon/kv_j - i\sqrt{1+(\epsilon/kv_j)^2} \;. \tag{32}$$

For small ϵ, $J_{n\epsilon}$ diverges as $\epsilon^{-n+2} \sim k_1^{-n+2}$ $(n > 2)$ where $k_1 \sim \epsilon/v$ is the cut-off wave vector. On the other hand, a similar analysis demonstrates that for a given order in the density the non-ring diagrams of category (3) of I are less divergent than the ring diagrams. Such non-ring diagrams are constructed from tho ring diagrams by drawing additional connecting lines among particles already in the ring diagrams following the rules of the binary collision expansion[3]. See Fig. 1. These lines introduce

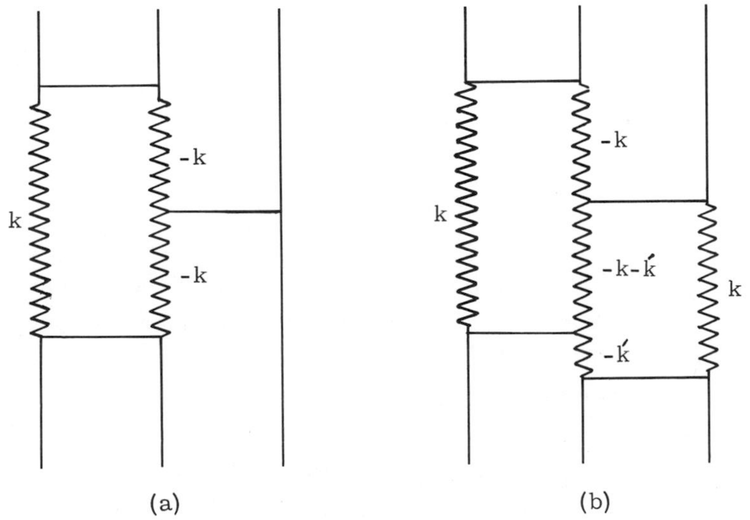

Fig. 1.

(a) A ring diagram

(b) A non-ring diagram derived from the ring diagram (a)

additional integrals over new k-vectors and the same number of new free particle propagators $[\epsilon + i\underline{k}^N \cdot \underline{p}^N/m]^{-1}$. Thus, after the integration over angles, each new k integral introduces additional factors of k in the numerator for the two-dimensional gas and reduces the degree of divergence at small k. This justifies the estimates of the divergences of the ring terms and hence the choice of the ring terms as the most divergent ones in I. For n = 2, we obtain a divergence of the form - ln ε in agreement with (25). Although the calculation given here is much simpler, the physical origin of the divergence becomes more transparent in the earlier more complex calculation which starts from Eq. (16).

In three-dimensions, a similar analysis may be made. However, for simplicity, we only consider the following integral:

$$K_{n\epsilon} = \int_0^{k_{max}} dk k^2 \int d\underline{\omega}_1 \int d\underline{\omega}_2 \cdots \int d\omega_n \frac{1}{\epsilon + i\underline{k}\cdot\underline{v}_1} \frac{1}{\epsilon + i\underline{k}\cdot\underline{v}_2} \cdots \frac{1}{\epsilon + i\underline{k}\cdot\underline{v}_n}$$

where $\underline{\omega}_j$ is the solid angle spanned by $\underline{v}_j$. This is easily integrated to yield

$$K_{n\epsilon} = \left(\frac{2\pi}{i}\right)^n \int_0^{k_{max}} dk\, k^{-n+2} \prod_{j=1}^{n} \frac{1}{v_j} \ln \frac{\epsilon + ikv_j}{\epsilon - ikv_j} . \qquad (34)$$

Since the ln factors introduce a cut-off in the integral over k at $k_1 \sim \epsilon/v$, $K_{n\epsilon}$ diverges as $\epsilon^{-n+3} \sim k_1^{-n+3}$ in agreement with I.

In the above discussion, we have ignored the k dependence of the T_{ij}, which is permissible if we are concerned only with the most divergent contributions in each order of the density. It should be remembered, however, that this k-dependence can give rise to less divergent contributions from the ring terms which may be combined with the non-ring terms to produce contributions to higher order terms in the density expansion (which may again be non-analytic).

In the foregoing, we have seen that the ring terms furnish the most divergent terms in each order in the formal density series, and in I we have shown that the resummation introduces an operator $[1 + \rho\Lambda(\underline{k}, -\underline{k})]^{-1}$ into the previously divergent triple collision term. However, the demonstration of the elimination of the divergence by this operator in I can be improved. We now study this problem again restricting ourselves to the two-dimensional gas. First, we note that in selecting the ring terms in I, we have omitted those ring diagrams with dots on the arc starting with the particle 1 due to the property of the T_{ij} given in I(3.2). Thus, adding these terms to the original ring terms of I does not change the resummed series I(3.12), in which $\Lambda(\underline{k}, -\underline{k})$ is now changed to

$$\Lambda(\underline{k}, -\underline{k}) = \Lambda_1^{(k)}(p_1; p_2) + \Lambda_d^{(k)}(p_1; p_2) + \Lambda_1^{(-k)}(p_2; p_1) + \Lambda_d^{(-k)}(p_2; p_1) \tag{35}$$

where

$$\Lambda_d^{(k)}(p_1; p_2) \equiv \int V\, T_{13}(\underline{k}, -\underline{k}, 0 \,|\, 0, -\underline{k}, \underline{k}) \mathscr{P}_{13} \left[\epsilon + i\, \frac{\underline{p}_1 - \underline{p}_2}{m} \cdot k\right]^{-1} \times \phi\,(p_3)\, d\underline{p}_3 \tag{36}$$

and the other operators in (35) are defined in I(3.14) and I(3.15)[9]. If we ignore the k-dependences of the T_{ij}, which is justified from our earlier discussion, (35) can be written as

$$\Lambda(\underline{k}, -\underline{k}) = \overline{\mathscr{L}}\,(\underline{p}_1\, \underline{p}_2)\, g(\underline{k}) \tag{37}$$

where

$$g(\underline{k}) \equiv \left[\epsilon + i\, \frac{\underline{p}_1 - \underline{p}_2}{m} \cdot \underline{k}\right]^{-1} \tag{38}$$

and

$$\overline{\mathscr{L}}\,(\underline{p}_1\, \underline{p}_2) \equiv \mathscr{L}_B(\underline{p}_1) + \mathscr{L}_B(\underline{p}_2) \tag{39}$$

where

$$\mathscr{L}_B(\underline{p}_i) \equiv \int V T_{i3}(0|0)\, \phi\,(p_3)(1 + \mathscr{P}_{i3})\, d\underline{p}_3, \qquad i = 1,2 \tag{40}$$

is the Boltzmann collision operator defined by Eqs. (3.23) and (3.25) of Kawasaki and Oppenheim, Ref. 3 (there, $\mathscr{L}_B$ is simply denoted as $\mathscr{L}$ which should not be confused with the $\mathscr{L}$ defined by I(2.18).)

Substituting this Λ into I(3.12) and transforming the resulting triple collision operator back to the form of I(3.9), the new modified triple collision operator $\tilde{t}(\underline{p}_1)$ becomes

$$\tilde{t}(\underline{p}_1) = \int V\,(0|T_{12}\,\overline{G}_o \overline{\mathcal{L}}\, G_o\, T_{12}|0)\,\phi(p_2)\,d\underline{p}_2 \tag{41}$$

where we have suppressed $\underline{p}_1, \underline{p}_2$ in $\overline{\mathcal{L}}(\underline{p}_1\underline{p}_2)$,

$$\overline{G}_o \equiv G_o(1+\rho\overline{\mathcal{L}}G_o)^{-1} = \left[\epsilon+\rho\overline{\mathcal{L}}+iL_o\right]^{-1} \tag{42}$$

and L_o is the Liouville operator for non-interacting particles.

In this form, the meaning of $\overline{G}_o$ is quite clear. It is a free particle propagator which is modified by the collision damping factor $\rho\overline{\mathcal{L}}$. (Only one G_o in (41) is changed to $\overline{G}_o$, otherwise some terms in the resummation are included more than once.) It is well-known that the Boltzmann collision operator $\mathcal{L}_B$ is positive semi-definite[10], and so is $\overline{\mathcal{L}}(\underline{p}_1\,\underline{p}_2)$. Since the operands of $\overline{\mathcal{L}}$ in the expressions for the transport coefficients do not contain the collision invariants, $\overline{\mathcal{L}}$ can be regarded as positive definite for our purpose. The effect of the $\rho\overline{\mathcal{L}}$ in (42) is to replace ϵ by ϵ plus some positive number which is proportional to ρ. In order to investigate the effect of this substitution, we use the result

$$\int_0^{k_{max}} kdk \oint\oint d\phi\, d\chi \frac{1}{\epsilon+ikv\cos\phi}\,\frac{1}{\epsilon'+ikv'\cos(\phi+\chi)}$$

$$= \frac{(2\pi)^2}{vv'}\int_0^{k_{max}} \frac{dk}{k}\,(1+(\epsilon/kv)^2)^{-1/2}\,(1+(\epsilon'/kv')^2)^{-1/2}$$

$$\cong -\frac{(2\pi)^2}{vv'}\,\ln\epsilon' \tag{43}$$

where $\epsilon' \gg \epsilon$.

Eq. (43) shows that if we take $\epsilon' = \alpha\rho\,(\alpha>0)$, $t(p_1)$ gives rise to a contribution of $\ln\rho^{-1}$ as $\epsilon \to 0+$. This makes the discussion of the elimination of divergence in I more transparent and substantiates the qualitative arguments in terms of collision damping[11].

In summary, we have analyzed the terms appearing in the

formal density expansion series of the transport coefficients, and have shown how, in the binary collision expansion scheme, the divergences arise from small k. The physical origin of these divergences is identical to that discussed by others[7]. Throughout these calculations ϵ is kept small but nonzero and previous criticism[2] of our calculation does not apply. This criticism, however, indicates that a weak coupling perturbation calculation of the transport coefficients of a classical gas may not yield the divergences[12] discussed here. We should also point out that the resummation given in I is just sufficient to eliminate the divergence appearing in the lowest order in density. In general, it will be necessary to introduce new resummations to eliminate additional divergencies. Thus, one cannot exclude the appearances, for example, of density corrections of the form $\rho^2 \ln \rho$ in the transport coefficients of a two-dimensional gas. Dorfman has raised the question as to whether the present resummation leads to a different value for the coefficient of the $\rho \ln \rho$ term in the transport coefficients than that found from the coefficient of the triple collision divergent term[11]. We cannot, of course, answer this question with certainty at this moment, since it is extremely difficult to evaluate numerically the resummed series. However, we should note that the sole effect of the resummation on the divergent term is to modify one free particle propagator and does nothing more than to provide a cut-off at a small k in the integration over k; it is unlikely that the resummation alters the coefficient of the $\rho \ln \rho$ term.

REFERENCES

1. K. Kawasaki and I. Oppenheim, Phys. Rev. 139, A1763 (1965), referred to as I hereafter.

2. J. Stecki, Phys. Letters 19, 123 (1965).

3. K. Kawasaki and I. Oppenheim, Phys. Rev. 136, A1519 (1964); 139, A649, (1965), R. W. Zwanzig, Phys. Rev. 129, 486 (1963).

4. This case was considered by Stecki, Ref. 2 and was shown to give no divergence.

5. L. K. Haynes, J. R. Dorfman and M. H. Ernst, Phys. Rev. 144, 207 (1966).

6. More exactly, use of Eq. (19) leads to

$$\oint I_\epsilon(u, u', \chi) d\chi = \int_{-\pi}^{\pi} d\theta\, I_\epsilon(u, u', \pi + \theta) \cong \frac{8\pi}{uu'} \tan^{-1}\{\pi/\epsilon(u^{-1} + u'^{-1})\} \tag{22'}$$

Or,

$$\oint I_\epsilon(kv, kv', \chi) d\chi \cong \frac{8\pi}{k^2 vv'} \tan^{-1}\{\frac{k\pi}{\epsilon}(v^{-1} + v'^{-1})^{-1}\} \tag{23'}$$

In the integration over k, the $\tan^{-1}$ factor then provides a natural cut-off at k_1 given by (24) and the leading term is the same as (25).

7. J. R. Dorfman and E. G. D. Cohen, Phys. Letters 16, 124 (1965), J. V. Sengers, Phys. Rev. Letters 15, 515 (1965) and to be published. J. Weinstock, Phys. Rev. 140, A461 (1965), E. A. Frieman and R. Goldman, Bull. Am. Phys. Soc. 10, 531 (1965).

8. In fact, the divergence appears only in the last integration. Thus, depending upon the order of performing multiple integrals, the divergence can be regarded as arising from long times (small ϵ) or from small k or from small angles.

9. We find it appropriate to change the notation of I slightly as follows: $\Lambda_1^{(k)}(p_1)$, $\Lambda_1^{(-k)}(p_2)$, $\Lambda_d^{(-k)}(p_2)$ etc. should read $\Lambda_1^{(k)}(p_1; p_2)$, $\Lambda_1^{(-k)}(p_2; p_1)$, $\Lambda_d^{(-k)}(p_2; p_1)$ etc. respectively.

10. L. Waldmann, Handbuch der Physik, edited by S. Flügge (Springer Verlag, Berlin, 1958), Vol. XII, p. 365.

11. J. R. Dorfman, Lecture at 4th Eastern Theoretical Physics Conference, State University of New York, Stony Brook (1965), M. S. Green, Physica 24, 393 (1958).

12. P. Résibois, private communication (1965).

Temperley: The "small-angle anomaly" occurs already in the neutron transport problem in an infinite slab, even though collisions between neutrons can be neglected. One cannot neglect neutrons travelling nearly parallel to the sides of the slab because they have a long path in the material. The anomaly prevents the use of a conventional treatment using eigenfunctions. The analytic situation has been investigated by Lehner and Wing in several papers (Communications on Pure and Applied Mathematics of about 1956). It turns out that a consistent eigenfunction treatment becomes possible if one makes the slab finite and takes accounts of the escape of neutrons at the edges as well as the sides of the slab. This implies a time cut-off, but the limiting process can be carried out satisfactorily. The problem being discussed is far more complicated but I wonder whether an analogous prescription might help here?

Bruckner: The analysis that Oppenheim has just presented bears a remarkable similarity to the study of the ground state energy of the Bose gas, the quantum mechanical case. The important diagrams in that case are the same as in this one, the ring diagrams. One has there the particles excited from the zero momentum state into a state of finite momenta. Again the terms are individually divergent and only if summed lead to a convergent answer. Now, there is one feature of that analysis which seems to be potentially interesting for this problem. If one looks at the analysis there one finds that the diagrams, order by order, have the same singularity for a Maxwell or Bose case. But in the case of distinguishable particles in each order the coefficients are exactly zero. There is a precise cancellation between the matrix elements of the T-operators for exactly forward scattering and the matrix elements of the operators for small angle forward scattering. These effects exactly cancel order by order and the divergence therefore is peculiar to the Bose statistics. It enters from the fact that the matrix elements of the scattering operators for small angle forward scattering and small angle forward exchange scattering, these combined, are not fully cancelled by the matrix elements for exact forward scattering. If the exchange terms are missing these matrix elements cancel each other in the limit of small momentum. So there is a characteristic difference between the state of the distinguishable and non-distinguishable case, but aside from that the diagrams have the same structure, the ring diagrams, the excitation from zero momentum states into paired states of opposite small momenta. The second point is that the problem can be solved in that case not by diagram summation, the diagram summation is rather tedious and takes some careful accounting in high order, a much simpler way of solving it is by diagonalizing exactly the hamiltonian by a simple orthogonal transformation. That transformation, of course, is equivalent to summing the ring diagrams, but the summation is hereby carried out in a very simple way. Of the precise analogy here I am not sure. If one looks at the diagrams, the ring diagrams, the characteristic of these is that in every order the same momentum transfer occurs, so one sums ring diagrams for the same momentum transfer and then finally does an integral over the momentum transfer. So one is really only dealing with one class of particles at a time, or two classes, those of zero momentum and those of finite small momentum. One solved the problem for that momentum first which is the same as summing the ring diagrams and find the energy over the momentum. The fact that this is a separable problem allows one to take that part of the hamiltonian and treat it exactly. I should think that the same techniques would hold here.

Kubo: It seems that the thing is simpler here, perhaps rather unfortunately. Managing hamiltonians, say by canonical transformation, will not be of much use.

Résibois: I would like to make one comment which, I hope, will help clarify some controversy existing in the literature about the existence of divergences in the 3- and more-particle collision operator. If we consider for definiteness the three-body collision in two dimensions, one finds terms of the type

$$C \sim \cdots \int k\,dk \, \frac{1}{kV_{12} - i\varepsilon} \langle k | T_{13} | k \rangle \frac{1}{kV_{12} - i\varepsilon} \cdots \tag{1}$$

leaving aside factors unimportant for the present discussion. If one neglects in (1) the operator character of the T-matrix (in momentum space), one finds in the small k limit

$$C_\Delta \sim \cdots \int_{-\Delta}^{+\Delta} \frac{k\,dk}{(kV_{12} - i\varepsilon)^2} \langle 0 | T_{13} | 0 \rangle \tag{2}$$

which is perfectly well defined in the limit $\varepsilon \to 0$. Similarly, if one treats the T-matrix in any finite order Born approximation, the finite number of $\partial/\partial p_1$ operators appearing in T_{13} will lead now to integrals of the type

$$C'_{\Delta} \sim \cdots \int \frac{\kappa^{n-1}\, d\kappa}{(\kappa v_{12} - i\varepsilon)^n} \cdots \qquad (n \geq 2) \tag{3}$$

which again are perfectly well defined when $\varepsilon \to 0$. However, from a geometrical phase space analysis of the three-body process, it appears clearly that the divergences come from the large angle deflections caused by T_{13}. For instance, with two fixed scattering centers and one moving particle, the diverging term comes precisely from the "head on" collisions. In this case one has to treat the full formula (1), involving the T_{13} operator, and this leads indeed to a divergent expression for $\varepsilon \to 0$, as indicated by Prof. Oppenheim. The absence of divergence found by some authors (for instance J. Stecki, Phys. Letters 1966) comes from the consideration of finite order Born approximations, which are well known to be unsuitable to describe large deflection collisions.

Lebowitz: I may raise a question related to Bruckner's statement. You can make a quantum expansion in density at any finite temperature for a hard sphere gas. Taking into account, however, spacial inhomogeneities it might not diverge.

Oppenheim: We have looked at the statistical correlations and they are of low order.

<u>Lebowitz</u>: It is still an open question.

THE DENSITY EXPANSION OF THE DIFFUSION COEFFICIENTS OF A LORENTZ GAS

J. M. J. van LEEUWEN
AND
A. WEIJLAND
University of Nijmegen
The Netherlands

With respect to the recently discovered divergencies[1] in the density expansion of transport coefficients we have studied the low density limit of the diffusion coefficient of a Lorentz gas. The Lorentz gas consists of one classically moving particle in an assembly of static centra which scatter the particle according to a hard sphere interaction with diameter σ. The distribution of scattering centra is taken as that of a canonical ensemble of hard spheres with diameter σ_s. Most of our results depend only on the reduced density $\rho = n\sigma^s$ of the scattering centra and not on the more refined details of their distribution.

The object of investigation is the diffusion coefficient D as given by the integral over the velocity auto-correlation function:

$$D = \frac{1}{s} \int_0^\infty dt < \vec{v}(0) \cdot \vec{v}(t) > \tag{1}$$

where s is the dimensionality of the system, $\vec{v}(t)$ the velocity of the moving particle and the average < > is taken over all initial positions and momenta of the moving particle as well as over the distributions of the scattering centra. The main simplication of this model is the fact that $|\vec{v}(t)| = v$ is conserved due to the special hard sphere character of the interaction.

1. The density expansion $D^{-1} = D_1\rho + D_2\rho^2 + \ldots$

The theory for the calculation of the coefficients of the expansion of D in powers of the density ρ uses the (partial) average velocity $\vec{\psi}_t(\vec{v})$ of the moving particle under the restriction that it had the velocity $\vec{v}$ at the time $t = 0$:

$$\vec{\psi}_t(\vec{v}) = \langle \delta(\vec{v}(0) - \vec{v})\ \vec{v}(t) \rangle . \tag{2}$$

One has generally in isotropic systems that $\vec{\psi}_t(\vec{v})$ is parallel to $\vec{v}$, but, due to the conservation of $|\vec{v}(t)|$ in our model, $\vec{\psi}_t(\vec{v})$ is also essentially a function of the reduced time variable $t^* = vt/\sigma$:

$$\vec{\psi}_t(\vec{v}) = \vec{v}\phi_t(v) = \vec{v}\phi(t^*) . \tag{3}$$

Because of this property the expression for D becomes:

$$D = \frac{\Gamma(\frac{s+1}{2})}{\Gamma(\frac{s+2}{2})} \left[\frac{kT}{2m}\right]^{1/2} \sigma \int_0^\infty dt^*\ \phi(t^*) . \tag{4}$$

The difficulties of a density expansion arise as long time divergencies in the time integral in (4). Therefore it is convenient to work with Laplace transforms :

$$\hat{\vec{\psi}}_z(\vec{v}) = \int_0^\infty e^{-zt}\, dt\ \vec{\psi}_t(\vec{v}) . \tag{5}$$

The value of $\hat{\phi}(0)$ gives D, but from the viewpoint of the singularities to be expected in the limit $z \rightarrow 0$, we keep the z-dependence in the expressions.

As long as z is large a density expansion for $\hat{\vec{\psi}}_z(\vec{v})$ is straightforward, being of the form:

$$\hat{\vec{\psi}}_z(\vec{v}) = \left[z^{-1} + \sum_{l=1} \rho^l M_l(z)\right] \vec{v} , \tag{6}$$

where the $M_l(z)$ are well defined collision operators (involving l scattering centra). However for $z \rightarrow 0$ they have the property[2)]

$$M_l(z)\,\vec{v} \sim z^{-l-1}\,\vec{v}\,. \tag{7}$$

Thus the expansion (6) is of no use for D.

There exist many equivalent ways[3] to solve this problem. Zwanzig proposed to consider instead of (6) the inverse relation

$$\vec{v} = \left[z + \sum_{l=1} \rho^l K_l(z)\right] \vec{\psi}_z(\vec{v}) \tag{8}$$

in which the $K_l(z)$ may be calculated successively from the $M_l(z)$ (In fact the $K_l(z)$ would result from an Husimi expansion of the streaming operator). The idea behind this inversion was the conjecture that the $K_l(0)$ would exist.

$K_1(0)$ is the well known Boltzmann collision operator for this model and equation (8) may be seen as a kind of kinetic equation.

In our model the equation (8) can be solved generally due to the relation (3) yielding:

$$\hat{\vec{\psi}}_z(\vec{v}) = \frac{\sigma\vec{v}}{v}\,\hat{\phi}(z^*) = \frac{\vec{v}\sigma}{v}\left[z^* + \gamma(z^*)\right]^{-1} \tag{9}$$

with $z^* = z\sigma/v$ and

$$\gamma(z^*) = \frac{\sigma\vec{v}}{v^3}\cdot \sum_{l=1} \rho^l K_l(z)\,\vec{v} = \sum_{l=1} \rho^l \gamma_l(z^*)\,. \tag{10}$$

If the $K_l(0)$ would be finite (10), (9) and (4) would provide the density expansion for D^{-1}. We have calculated the first few $\gamma_l(z^*)$ in two and three dimensions for $z^* \to 0$. The results are given in Table 1.

	s = 2	s = 3
l = 1	$8/3$	π
l = 2	$-1/2(8/3)^2 \ln z^*$	$\pi^2(1+4\pi^2/35)/3$ + corr.
		($r=\sigma_s/\sigma$)
		$+\pi r^3\left[8/3 - r\right]/4$ + corr.
l = 3	$0(1/z^*)$	$(\pi^3/4)\ln z^*$

$\gamma_l(z^*)$ for $z^* \to 0$ in two (s = 2) and three (s = 3) dim.

Thus only a few $\gamma_l(0)$ exist.

2. The renormalisation: $D^{-1} = D_1(\rho) + D_2(\rho) \ln \rho$

The origin of these divergencies can be seen from a phase space argument which in this model is very simple. From the various collision processes contributing to $\gamma_l(z^*)$,the one with the least number of collisions is symbolically represented in fig. 1 ($l = 3$). It consists of a collision sequence in which the moving particle collides with 1, 2, ... l and finally again with 1. For larger interseparations $R_1 \ldots R_l$ of the static centra the probability that the moving particles hits 2 after 1 decreases as $[\vec{R}_1 - \vec{R}_2]^{1-s}$. Similar factors $|R_2 - R_3|^{1-s} \ldots |\vec{R}_l - \vec{R}_1|^{1-s}$ come in from the other collisions. The total time needed for the cycle is $(|\vec{R}_1 - \vec{R}_2| + \ldots |\vec{R}_l - \vec{R}_1|)/v$. So the asymptotic part of the phase space integral becomes:

$$\phi^l_s(z) = \int d^s R_2 \ldots d^s R_l \, e^{-z[|\vec{R}_1-\vec{R}_2|+\ldots|\vec{R}_l-\vec{R}_1|]/v} \left[|\vec{R}_1 - \vec{R}_2| \ldots |\vec{R}_l - \vec{R}_1|\right]^{1-s} . \quad (11)$$

The integral (11) can be done, being a convolution, leading to:

$$\phi^l_s(z) \sim \begin{cases} z^{s-1} & l > s \\ \ln z & l = s \\ O(1) & l < s \end{cases} \qquad \begin{pmatrix} s \geqq 2 \\ l \geqq 2 \end{pmatrix}$$

Other collision processes with l static spheres and with more collisions lead to less divergent integrals.

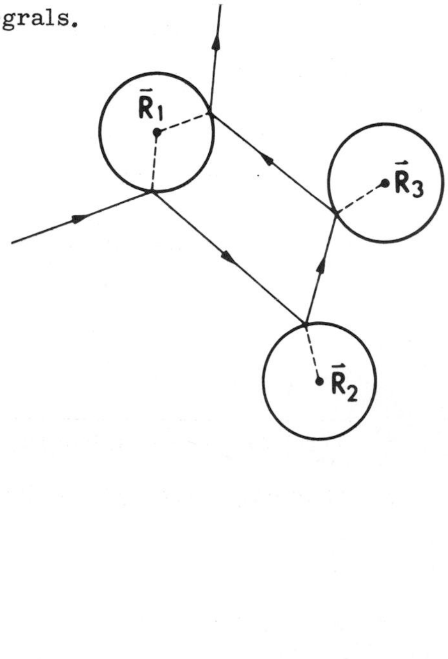

Fig. 1. A typical ring Diagram ($l = 3$).

Once the source of the divergencies is found, the inadequate representation (7) may be repaired by summing up the most divergent contributions. In lowest order this amounts to the summation of the so-called ring diagrams of which one (for l = 3) is shown in fig. 1. The contribution of the ring diagrams to $\gamma(z^*)$ is denoted by $\gamma^r(z^*)$. $\gamma^r(z^*)$ has to be computed from the solution $\vec{p}_{z\vec{k}}(v)$ of the following integral equation which describes the summation of the ring diagrams:

$$\left[z + v\rho\,\sigma^{-1}\mu_s - i\vec{k}\cdot\vec{v}\right]\vec{p}_{z\vec{k}}(\vec{v}) = \vec{b}_{\vec{k}}(\vec{v}) + \\ + \rho\,\sigma^{-2}\int_{\vec{v}\cdot\vec{\sigma}<0} d\Omega_o\,|\vec{v}\cdot\vec{\sigma}|\,\vec{p}_{z\vec{k}}(\vec{v} - 2(\vec{v}\cdot\vec{\sigma})\vec{\sigma}/\sigma^2)\,. \tag{13}$$

Here $\mu_2 = 2$ and $\mu_3 = \pi$. $\gamma^r(z^*)$ is expressed in terms of $\vec{p}_{z\vec{k}}(\vec{v})$ as following from (12) as:

$$\gamma^r(z^*) = -\frac{\rho\,\sigma^{1-s}}{v}\int\frac{d^sk}{(2\pi)^s}\,\vec{a}_{\vec{k}}(\vec{v})\cdot\left\{\vec{p}_{z\vec{k}}(\vec{v}) - \frac{\vec{b}_k(\vec{v})}{z - i\vec{k}\cdot\vec{v}}\right\}, \tag{14}$$

with $\vec{a}_k(\vec{v})$ and $\vec{b}_k(\vec{v})$ given by:

$$\begin{cases} \vec{a}_k(\vec{v}) = \sigma^{s-2}\displaystyle\int_{\vec{v}\cdot\vec{\sigma}<0} d\Omega_o\,|\vec{v}\cdot\vec{\sigma}|\left\{e^{-i\vec{k}\cdot\vec{\sigma}}\left[\vec{v} - 2(\vec{v}\cdot\vec{\sigma})\,\vec{\sigma}/\sigma^2\right] - e^{i\vec{k}\cdot\vec{\sigma}}\,\vec{v}\right\} \\ \vec{b}_k(\vec{v}) = \sigma^{s-2}\displaystyle\int_{\vec{v}\cdot\vec{\sigma}<0} d\Omega_o\,|\vec{v}\cdot\vec{\sigma}|\left[-2(\vec{v}\cdot\vec{\sigma})\,\vec{\sigma}/\sigma^2\right]e^{-i\vec{k}\cdot\vec{\sigma}}\,. \end{cases} \tag{15}$$

The low density behaviour can be extracted without difficulty for z=0 because z occurs in (12) only in combination with $v\mu_s\rho\,\sigma^{-1}$. One finds:

$$\gamma^r(0) = \begin{cases} -\frac{1}{2}\left(\frac{8}{3}\right)^2\rho^2\ln\rho + O(\rho^2) & (s=2) \\ \pi^2\left(\frac{1}{3} + \frac{4\pi^2}{105}\right)\rho^2 + \frac{\pi^3}{4}\rho^3\ln\rho + O(\rho^3) & (s=3)\,. \end{cases} \tag{16}$$

The general form of $\gamma^r(0)$ is of the type :

$$\gamma^r(0) = A(\rho) + B(\rho)\ln\rho + \ldots.. \tag{17}$$

in which $A(\rho)$ and $B(\rho)$ can be expanded in powers of ρ.

Thus we have found that the divergencies lead to a $\ln\rho$ term in this model, whereas the coefficient of the lnz divergency and the corresponding lno term are the <u>same</u>. This could have been predicted from the nature of the divergencies as indicated by the phase space argument (12). The $\ln\rho$ term appears in the expression for the inverse diffusion coefficient D^{-1}, so powers of $\ln\rho$ appear in the expansion for D.

3. The binary collision expansion and the Enskog approximation

In our calculation we made use of the binary collision expansion. The use of this method is not without danger because of the singular character of the potential and the fact that, by the introduction of hypothetical trajectories, the particle has to be considered also for a situation *inside* the spheres. This difficulty can be avoided by redefining the dynamical interaction in such a way that the particle suffers no forces when it is inside the spheres.

We have checked the convergence of the binary collision expansion by calculating the ρ^2 term in three dimension. Two types of contribution occur: the "dynamical" contributions which are independent of the detailed distribution of the static scatterers and the "statistical" which do depend on this distribution.

From the dynamical contributions, the largest is included in the ring diagrams and amounts $\pi^2(1+4\pi^2/35)/3$. The second contribution has been computed numerically giving $-(0.65 \pm 0.01)$ which is smaller by a factor 10. Thus it does not seem worthwhile to calculate yet higher terms.

From the statistical contribution the largest gives for a hard sphere distribution $\pi^2 r^3(8/3 - r)/4$ with $r = \sigma_s/\sigma$. This is precisely the density correction to order ρ^2 predicted by the Enskog theory of hard spheres. The next correction has been calculated numerically and is a very small fraction of the "Enskog" term as long as the hard sphere ratio $r = \sigma_3/\sigma$ is not to close to $r = 2$. The results are drawn in fig. 2.

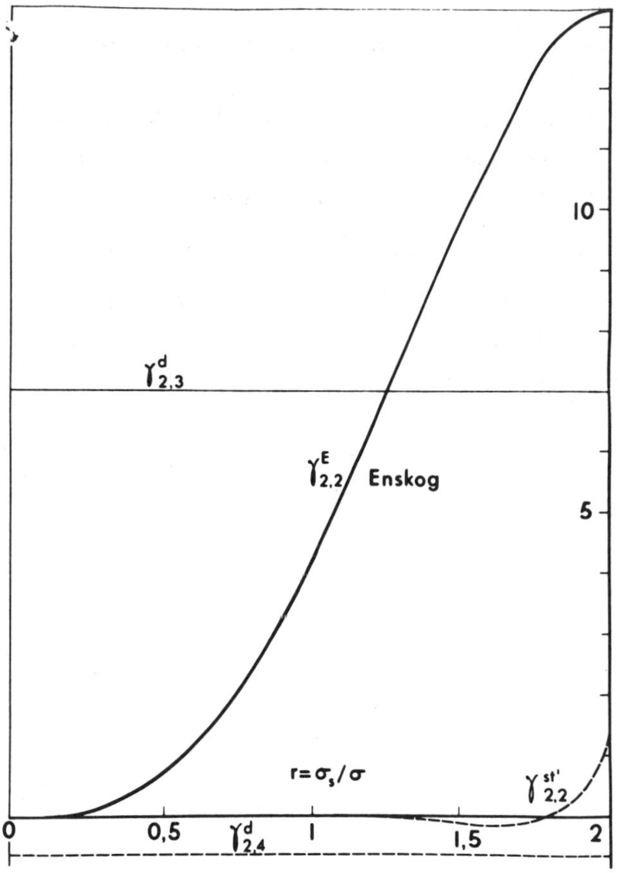

Fig. 2. The contributions to the ρ^2 term in three dimensions as a function of the hard sphere diameter ratio $r = \sigma_s/\sigma$.

The following conclusions may be drawn:

a. The convergence of the binary collision expansion is in our model rapid.

b. The Enskog theory of hard spheres predicts the influence of the distribution of the scatterers fairly well for low densities, but is by no means the main density effect.

The full details of the calculation will be published in Physica.

REFERENCES

1. J. R. Dorfman and E. G. D. Cohen, Physics Letters 16 (1965) 124.
J. V. Sengers, Phys. Rev. Letters 15 (1965) 515.
K. Kawasaki and I. Oppenheim, Phys. Rev. 139A (1965) 1763.
J. Weinstock, Phys. Rev. 140A (1965) 461.

2. M. S. Green, J. Chem. Phys. 25 (1965) 836.

3. R. Zwanzig, Phys. Rev. 129 (1963) 486.
M. H. Ernst, J. R. Dorfman and E. G. D. Cohen, Physica 31 (1965) 493.

DISCUSSION

Lebowitz: In the cases of a linear problem, say a test particle in an equilibrium background, you get a generalized kinetic eqn. The eqn. is $\frac{\partial f(t)}{\partial t} = \int_0^t \underline{B}\,(t'; \rho) f(t-t')\,dt'$ where ρ is the density. Now if $f(t-t')$ is replaced by $f(t)$ and the integral extended to infinity you get a Markoffian eqn.

$$\frac{\partial f(t)}{\partial t} = \underline{U}(\rho)\, f(t), \quad \underline{U}(\rho) = \lim_{t\to\infty} \int_0^t B(t'; \rho)\,dt'$$

In the one dimensional case which Percus and I investigated $\underline{U}$ is linear in ρ (more precisely in $\rho/(1-\rho a)$, a=diameter of hard rods), but does not coincide with Boltzmann equation. The kinetic equation with the operator $\underline{U}$ gives the correct diffusion coefficient while the linear Boltzmann equation does not (even to lowest order, it is about 16% off according to van Leeuwen and Weyland). I would like to know whether in higher dimensions: (1) the Boltzmann equation (or the linear Boltzmann equation for a test particle) always gives the correct lowest order diffusion coefficient? and (2) whether the operator $\underline{U}(\rho)$ exists?

Cohen: (To Lebowitz). In one dimension one has to be very careful because this case is somewhat pathological. F.i. contrary to in 2- and 3- dimensions, the Boltzmann equation in one dimension does not give the correct result in lowest order in the density for the transport coefficients. The answer to your second question, I do not know.

(To van Leeuwen). In the 3-dimensional case, if you simply write f_2 as $f_1 f_1$ times the (local) equilibrium radial distribution function as Enskog does, then one eliminates all divergences from the theory, but the transport properties can be obtained as a function of density within a few percent of the experimentally known values. This demonstrates that the numerical effect of the non-analytic terms in the density is small. Is this also true for the Lorentz gas, which you studied?

Van Leeuwen: The answer depends on the ratio of the two hard sphere diameters. When the static spheres are very small with respect to the moving one, there is no Enskog correction at all. However, there are still ρ^2 terms from the dynamical contribution. So in that limit the Enskog theory of hard sphere is completely wrong in predicting the density dependence. In the opposite limit the Enskog contribution is a more important part (2/3) of the whole ρ^2 term. What I want to point out is, that one has to be careful in trusting theories which arrive at the Enskog theory of hard spheres as a first approximation, because in our model (to which these derivations apply) the Enskog theory does not give the dominant part of these density corrections.

Résibois: I would like to ask Dr. van Leeuwen if he has any idea why the binary collision expansion converges so rapidly in his Lorentz gas model?

Van Leeuwen: It is basically a phase space argument. In comparing the integral for the contribution involving three and four collisions respectively, the integrands are similar, but the requirement that a fourth collision can occur, restricts the integration domain enormously, such that the result is a factor 10 smaller.

Uhlenbeck: I would like to ask the question whether for the Lorentz model there is a closed kinetic equation. I object to calling such an equation a Markoff process. The question is whether the distribution function of the moving particles is determined (irrespective of the fixed particles) when it is known at $t = 0$. If this is so, then a closed and causal kinetic description is possible. But I don't know, and I get the impression that there are conflicting opinions about this point.

Cohen: What do you mean by a kinetic equation?

Uhlenbeck: An equation which is closed and which determines the time evolution of the distribution function.

Mayer: One calls a process Markoff when one cannot calculate, and therefore uses a random process to disguise ignorance.

Van Kampen: Exactly speaking a kinetic equation never exists; so the question is - is it good enough when you try to add higher approximations to the Boltzmann equation ?

Oppenheim: The operators that appear in the convergent terms in the density expansions of the correlation function expressions of the transport coefficients are the same as those that appear in the linearized transport equations which are valid when the system is close to equilibrium. Therefore, I think, that it is reasonable to expect that the operator including the collision damped free particle propagator would appear in the appropriate linearized transport equation in second (third) order in two (three) dimensions.

Martin: That is true but I do not think that is the question asked. You have obtained an approximate expression (not analytic in the density) for the kernel that describes for all times, the approach to equilibrium of the one particle distribution function in a system in which the velocity distribution has been infinitesimally altered in a spatially uniform manner. There is no reason to believe that this kernel or any other functional of the one particle distribution function describes the relaxation of the one particle distribution function for systems which vary spatially over distances small compared to a mean free path and differ more than infinitesimally from the equilibrium distribution function. Probably, therefore, the answer is no to the question of Professor Uhlenbeck as I understand it, i.e. does there exist a time scale short compared to the hydrodynamic time scale, but long compared to some microscopic time, in which the one particle distribution function is governed by an integro-differential equation in which the initial conditions do not appear explicity (in the same sense that the conserved variables are governed by the Navier Stokes equations for hydrodynamic times) ?

The great utility of the correlation function approach is that it permits one to understand and calculate a useful physically interesting class of irreversible phenomena, without having to answer, and indeed irrespective of the answer to Prof. Uhlenbeck's interesting but difficult question. I believe that this is particularly satisfying in view of suspicion, based on the results of the past twenty years, that only a negative answer to so general a question (i. e. a counterexample) is likely to be given, in a mathematically sound fashion in the foreseeable future.

Kubo: This is not so much related to the preceeding discussion. But there is a point which I would like to comment. A Boltzmann equation or more generally a kinetic equation does not really have a stationary solution which represent an inhomogeneous non-equilibrium state because the only truely stationary solution corresponds to equilibrium. Enskog's solution is thus only asymptotic. You cannot proceed to higher order approximations in any simple way. I do not know, however, if this has anything to do with the divergence discussed here.

Ford: I believe that for the model of van Leeuwen the divergences imply that the long time behaviour still depends on the initial conditions.

Lebowitz: For the linear problem - e.g. Lorentz gas - you always have a rigorous non- Markoffian eqn.

Ford: I think you are making a mistake here in thinking that the Bogoliubov approach consists in expanding f(t-t') in powers of t'. It is not that at all.

Résibois: As far as the validity of a "reduced" description (in terms of a one particle distribution function) is concerned, it depends of how long you are willing to wait after the initial time t = 0. Indeed, for times of the order of the collision time (which itself is of the order of the relaxation time in a dense system), the kinetic equation generally involves an explicit dependence on the initial correlation, and we have thus no closed description in terms of f_1; schematically one has:

$$\partial_t f_1 (p;t) = C (f_1 (t - \tau)) + D (t; \rho_{corr.}(t=0)) \qquad (1)$$

where C is a generalized, non-Markoffian, collision operator while D depends on the initial correlations, $\rho_{corr.}(t=0)$.

For times much larger than the collision time (in the so called hydrodynamical regime for inhomogeneous situations or at the very end of the process of approach to equilibrium), (1) reduces to a closed equation for f_1:

$$\partial_t f_1 (p;t) = \tilde{C} (f_1 (p;t)) \qquad (2)$$

Yet, in an initial value problem, the simplicity of (2) is of no real help because for short times, one needs the exact equation (1). However, in many physical problems, like in the calculation of transport coefficients, one never solves an initial value problem but one uses some kind of Chapman - Enskog scheme, in which case the reduced description (2) is perfectly adequate.

Van Leeuwen: (Note added in proof). A further investigation of the model has shown that the so called ring diagrams are not the only class of most divergent contributions. However, this new class of divergencies does not affect the equality of the coefficient of the lnz divergency and the corresponding $\ln\rho$ term. Only the reputed value $\pi^3/4$ for this coefficient in 3 dim. has to be changed to $0.2\,\pi^2$.

ON THE STRUCTURE OF THE BBGKY HIERARCHY FOR A BOLTZMANN GAS

R. GOLDMAN
Institute for Fluid Dynamics
and Applied Mathematics
University of Maryland
College Park, Maryland
and
E. A. FRIEMAN
Department of Astrophysical
Sciences, Princeton University
Princeton, New Jersey

ABSTRACT

We treat the evolution in time of a spatially uniform Boltzmann gas with no initial correlations. For the case of cut-off potentials and arbitrary initial velocity distribution functions, on using the expansion parameter nr_o^3, with n = particle density and r_o = range of binary potential, we show for terms of the order $(nr_o^3)^2$ and lower that the hierarchy is formally self-closing even with the inclusion of many body effects; i.e., at a given order in (nr_o^3), with the exception of contributions linear in the single particle distribution function of the same order, the binary correlation function which determines the kinetic behavior of the single particle distribution function only depends on functions which themselves are fully determinable within a prescribed iteration procedure. The actual convergence of the various orders of the formal expansion is discussed for initially arbitrary velocity distributions and for linearizations around Maxwellian velocity distributions.

Basic equations

In terms of the correlation functions:

$$g_s(\tilde{x}_1, \ldots \tilde{x}_s, v_1 \ldots v_s, \tilde{t}), \quad s = 1, 2, \ldots,$$

the BBGKY hierarchy in the Boltzmann approximation[1] takes the form:

$$\frac{\partial g_s}{\partial t} + H_s g_s - \sum_{j=1}^{s} \sum_{i<j} \sum_{\alpha=1}^{s-1} \theta_{ij} g_\alpha(i, \ldots) g_{s-\alpha}(j, \ldots)$$

$$= \epsilon \sum_{i=1}^{s} \int \theta_{i,s+1} \left(\sum_{\alpha=1}^{s} g_\alpha(i, \ldots) g_{s+1-\alpha}(s+1, \ldots) + g_{s+1} \right) d\Omega_{s+1} . \tag{1}$$

The equations are in dimensionless units with distances in units of r_o, the range of the binary interaction and velocities in units of v_{av} the root mean square particle velocity; therefore times are in units of r_o/v_{av}, the time of a binary interaction.

Equations (1) have been obtained from the general hierarchy equations by choosing $<\phi>/mv_{av}^2 \sim 1$, with $<\phi>$ the characteristic strength of the potential, and $nr_o^3 = \epsilon$, $\epsilon << 1$. The g_s are defined in a recursive manner from the reduced distribution functions, f_s, by the relations:

$$f_1(1) = g_1(1)$$

$$f_2(1,2) = f_1(1)f_1(2) + g_2(1,2)$$

$$f_3(1,2,3) = f_1(1)f_1(2)f_1(3) + \sum_p f_1(1)g_2(2,3) + g_3(1,2,3) .$$

Expansion procedure

Our expansion procedure is a version of the many time scale procedure[2] amended to allow for additional many space scale variations. We assume

$$g_s = \sum_{m=0}^{\infty} \epsilon^m g^m(t, \epsilon t, x_1, \epsilon x_1, \ldots x_s, \epsilon x_s)$$

with t and x defined by: $t = \tilde{t}$, $x = \tilde{x}$. Thus we obtain

$$\frac{\partial}{\partial \tilde{t}} = \frac{\partial}{\partial t} + \epsilon \frac{\partial}{\partial \epsilon t} \; ; \qquad \frac{\partial}{\partial \tilde{x}} = \frac{\partial}{\partial x} + \epsilon \frac{\partial}{\partial \epsilon x}$$

and we can write

$$H_s = H_s^o + \epsilon H_s^1$$

with

$$H_s^o = \sum_{i=1}^{s} v_i \cdot \frac{\partial}{\partial x_i} - \sum_{i=1}^{s} \sum_{j=1}^{i-1} \frac{\partial \phi}{\partial x_i}(x_{ji}) \cdot \left(\frac{\partial}{\partial v_i} - \frac{\partial}{\partial v_j} \right)$$

and

$$H_s^1 = \sum_{i=1}^{s} v_i \cdot \frac{\partial}{\partial \epsilon x_i} \; ; \qquad \frac{\partial \phi}{\partial \epsilon x_i} \equiv 0 \, .$$

Neglect of the $\epsilon^n t$ and $\epsilon^n x_i$ scales ($n \geqq 2$) for spatially homogeneous distribution functions has been justified in earlier work[3].

Mutilated hierarchy

On equating the coefficient of each power of ϵ to zero in the expansion of (1) we obtain the basic hierarchy:

$$\frac{\partial g_s^m}{\partial t} + H_s^o g_s^m + \frac{\partial}{\partial \epsilon t} g_s^{m-1} + H_s^1 g_s^{m-1}$$

$$- \sum_{n=0}^{m} \sum_{j=1}^{s} \sum_{i<j} \sum_{\alpha=1}^{s-1} \phi_{ij} \, g_\alpha^n(i, \ldots) \, g_{s-\alpha}^{m-n}(j, \ldots)$$

$$= \sum_{i=1}^{s} \int \theta_{i,s+1} \left(\sum_{n=0}^{m-1} \sum_{\alpha=1}^{s} g_\alpha^n(i, \ldots) \, g_{s+1-\alpha}^{m-1-n}(s+1, \ldots) \right.$$

$$\left. + \, g_{s+1}^{m-1} \right) d\Omega_{s+1} \quad . \qquad (1')$$

For m = 0 we use the above. For m = 1 we promote terms (to be specified later) from the m = 2 equations, which itself next receives contributions from the m = 3 equation. Therefore in place of the basic hierarchy for $m \geqq 1$ we can write a mutilated hierarchy of the form

$$\frac{\partial g_s^m}{\partial t} + H_s^o g_s^m - \sum_{n=0}^{m} \sum_{j=1}^{s} \sum_{i<j} \sum_{\alpha=1}^{s-1} \theta_{ij}\, g_\alpha^n(i, \ldots)\, g_{s-\alpha}^{m-n}(j, \ldots)$$

$$+ \frac{\partial}{\partial \epsilon t} g_s^{m-1} - \sum_{i=1}^{s} \int_{|x_{i,s+1}| < r_o} \theta_{i,s+1} \left(\sum_{n=0} \sum_{\alpha=1}^{s} \right.$$

$$\left. g_\alpha^n(i, \ldots) g_{s+1-\alpha}^{m-1-n}(s+1, \ldots) + g_{s+1}^{m-1} \right) d\Omega_{s+1} - \Delta(s,m)$$

$$+ \epsilon \Delta(s, m+1) \; . \qquad (1'')$$

For m = 0 or m = 1, $\Delta(s,m) = 0$. For $m \geqq 2$ we choose:

$$\Delta(s, m) = - \frac{\partial}{\partial \epsilon t} g_s^{m-1} - H_s^1 g_s^{m-1} + \Delta'(s, m)$$

with $\Delta'(s, m)$ still to be specified.

Determination of g_s^o

On using equation (1'') for m = 0 for a time τ of order unity ($\tau \approx$ collision duration) we have for $|x_{i,\, s+1}| \leqq r_o$

$$g_{s+1}^o(t) = e^{-H_{s+1}^o \tau} \Big(\sum_{\alpha=1}^{s} g_\alpha^o(i, \ldots, t-\tau)\, g_{s+1-\alpha}^o(s+1, t-\tau) + g_{s+1}^o(t-\tau) \Big)$$

$$- \sum_{\alpha=1}^{s} g_\alpha^o(i, \ldots, t) g_{s+1-\alpha}^o(s+1, \ldots, t)$$

$$+ \delta_{10}(i, s+1; 1, \ldots, s+1, t) \qquad (2)$$

and

$$\theta_{i,\, s+1} = - H_{s+1}^o + H_s^o + v_{s+1} \cdot \frac{\partial}{\partial x_{s+1}} + \delta_{11} \; . \qquad (3)$$

If only i and s+1 interact with each other from $t-\tau$ to t, then δ_{10} and δ_{11} are zero. There are no secular contributions involving terms in δ_{10} and δ_{11}, since these are only non-zero for times of order unity.

By means of (2) and (3), the right hand side of (1'') for m=1 can be put in the form

$$R(s,0) = \Bigg(H_s^o \sum_{i=1}^{s} \int_{|x_{i,s+1}|<r_o} e^{-H_{s+1}^o \tau} - \sum_{i=1}^{s} \int_{|x_{i,s+1}|<r_o} e^{-H_{s+1}^o \tau} H_{s+1}^o + \sum_{i=1}^{s} \int_{|x_{i,s+1}|<r_o} (v_{s+1}-v_i)\cdot \frac{\partial}{\partial x_{s+1}} e^{-H_{s+1}^o \tau} + \sum_{i=1}^{s} \int_{|x_{i,s+1}|<r_o} \delta_{11}\, e^{-H_{s+1}^o \tau} \Bigg) \times \left(I_1(i, s+1, 1, \ldots s, t) + e^{H_{s+1}^o \tau} \delta_{10} \right) d\Omega_{s+1} \tag{4}$$

with

$$I_1(i, s+1, 1 \ldots s, t) \equiv \left[\sum_{\alpha=1}^{s} g_\alpha^o(i, \ldots, t-\tau)\, g_{s+1-\alpha}^o(s+1, t-\tau) + g_{s+1}^o(t-\tau) \right].$$

The terms linear in H_s^o and H_{s+1}^o (with the addition of terms of order ϵ) contribute to a total derivative with respect to time a quantity of order unity. The terms linear in $v_{s+1} - v_i$ $(\equiv v_{s+1,i})$ have a contribution which can be put in the form

$$A(s,0) + B(s,0) + C(s,0) + \delta_{12}$$

with

$$A(s,0) = -\sum_{i=1}^{s} \int_{|x_{i,s+1}|=r_o,\, x_{i,s+1}\,\|\, -v_{i,s+1}} d_3 v_{s+1}\, d\sigma_{s+1}\, |v_{s+1,i}|\, g_1^o(s+1)\, g_s^o(t)$$

$$B(s,0) = \sum_{i=1}^{s} \int_{|x_{i,s+1}| = r_o,\ x_{i,s+1} \| v_{i,s+1}} d_3 v_{s+1}\, d\sigma_{s+1} |v_{s+1,i}|\, e^{-H^o_{s+1}\tau}\, g^o_1(s+1)\, g^o_s$$

$$+ \sum_{i=1}^{s} \int_{|x_{i,s+1}| = r_o} d_3 v_{s+1}\, d\sigma_{s+1} |v_{s+1,i}|\, e^{-H^o_{s+1}\tau}\, g^o_1(i)\, g^o_s(s+1)$$

$$C(s,0) = \sum_{i=1}^{s} \int_{|x_{i,s+1}| = r_o} d_3 v_{s+1}\, d\sigma_{s+1} |v_{s+1,i}|\, e^{-H^o_{s+1}\tau}$$

$$\times \left(\sum_{\alpha=2}^{s-1} g^o_\alpha (i, \ldots)\, g^o_{s+1-\alpha}(s+1, \ldots) + g^o_{s+1} \right)$$

with $d\sigma_{s+1}$ denoting a surface element. As long as all of the s particles in the collection (1, 2, . . . , s) are further apart than a distance of order unity, $\delta_{12} = 0$. It has been shown earlier[3] for g^1_s to be bounded that one must take:

$$\left(\frac{\partial}{\partial \epsilon t} + H^1_s \right) g^o_s = A(s, 0)$$

This completes the definition of g^o_s.

<u>Determination of g^1_s in general</u>

Within the m = 2 equations of (1'') for $|x_{i,s+1}| < r_o$ we have as in the case of the m = 1 equations:

$$g^1_{s+1}(t) = e^{-H^o_{s+1}\tau} \left[\sum_{n=0}^{1} \sum_{\alpha=1}^{s} g^n_\alpha (i, \ldots)\, g^{1-n}_{s+1-\alpha}(s+1, \ldots) + g^1_{s+1}(t-\tau) \right]$$

$$- \sum_{n=0}^{1} \sum_{\alpha=1}^{s} g^n_\alpha(i, \ldots t)\, g^{1-n}_{s+1-\alpha}(s+1, \ldots)$$

$$+ \delta_{20}(i, s+1;\ 1, \ldots, s+1,\ t) \,. \qquad (5)$$

For the particles $(1, \ldots, s)$ far apart we assume that δ_{20} is small compared to the terms linear in $e^{-H^o_{s+1}\tau}$. This has been verified in some detail for s=1, 2 and 3, where one finds that δ_{20} is characteristically of order t^{-1} or x^{-1} compared to the terms linear in $e^{-H^o_{s+1}\tau}$. (Here and afterward x is taken to be the minimum interparticle separation of the s particles.)

The terms, excluding $\Delta(s, m) + \epsilon\Delta(s, m+1)$, on the right hand side of (1'') for m=2 can therefore be written:

$$\Bigg(H^o_s \sum_{i=1}^{s} \int_{|x_{i,s+1}|<r_o} e^{-H^o_{s+1}\tau} - \sum_{i=1}^{s} \int_{|x_{i,s+1}|<r_o} e^{-H^o_{s+1}\tau} H^o_{s+1}$$

$$+ \sum_{i=1}^{s} \int_{|x_{i,s+1}|<r_o} (v_{s+1} - v_i) \cdot \frac{\partial}{\partial x_{s+1}} e^{-H^o_{s+1}\tau} + \sum_{i=1}^{s} \int_{|x_{i,s+1}|<r_o} \delta_{11} e^{-H^o_{s+1}\tau} \Bigg)$$

$$\times (I_2(i, s+1, 1, \ldots, s, t) + e^{H^o_{s+1}\tau} \delta_{20}) \, d\Omega_{s+1} \tag{6}$$

with

$$I_2(i, s+1; 1, \ldots, s, t) \equiv \left[\sum_{n=0}^{1} \sum_{\alpha=1}^{s} g^n_\alpha(i, \ldots) \, g^{1-n}_{s+1-\alpha}(s+1, \ldots) + g^1_{s+1}(t-\tau) \right] \tag{7}$$

By coupling the arguments following (4) with considerations which put the integral terms in Eq. (1'') for m=1 of order t^{-1} or x^{-1} compared with g^1_s, one finds that the dominant terms in (6) are linear in

$$(v_{s+1} - v_i) \cdot \frac{\partial}{\partial x_{s+1}} e^{-H^o_{s+1}\tau} I_2 \; . \tag{8}$$

The contribution from (8) within (6) may be put in the form

$$A(s, 1) + B(s, 1) + C(s, 1) + \delta_{22}$$

with

$$A(s,1) = -\sum_{i=1}^{s} \int_{|x_{i,s+1}| = r_o,\ x_{i,s+1} || -v_{i,s+1}} d_3 v_{s+1}\, d\sigma_{s+1} |v_{s+1,i}|\, g_1^o(s+1)\, g_s^1(t)$$

$$B(s,1) = \sum_{i=1}^{s} \int_{|x_{i,s+1}| = r_o,\ x_{i,s+1} || v_{i,s+1}} d_3 v_{s+1}\, d\sigma_{s+1} |v_{s+1,i}|\, e^{-H^o_{s+1}\tau}$$

$$\times \left(g_1^o(s+1)\, g_s^1(i,t) + g_s^1(s+1,\ldots t)\, g_1^o(i)\right)$$

$$- \sum_{i=1}^{s} \int_{|x_{i,s+1}| = r_o,\ x_{i,s+1} || v_{i,s+1}} d_3 v_{s+1}\, d\sigma_{s+1} |v_{s+1,i}|\, e^{-H^o_{s+1}\tau} g_1^o(i)\, g_s^1(s+1,t)$$

$$C(s,1) = \sum_{i=1}^{s} \int_{|x_{i,s+1}| < r_o} d\Omega_{s+1}\, v_{s+1,i} \cdot \frac{\partial}{\partial x_{s+1}}\, e^{-H^o_{s+1}\tau}$$

$$\times \left[\sum_{n=0}^{1} \sum_{\alpha=2}^{s-1} g_\alpha^n(i,\ldots)\, g^{1-n}_{s+1-\alpha}(s+1,\ldots,t-\tau) + g_1^1(i,t-\tau) g_s^o \right.$$

$$\left. + g_s^o(i,\ldots,t-\tau)\, g_1^1(s+1,t-\tau) + g^1_{s+1}(s+1,t-\tau) \right] .$$

The term in δ_{22} is of order t^{-1} or x^{-1} compared to $A+B$. The term linear in $g_s^o g_1^1(s+1)$ evaluated at $x_{i,s+1} || -v_{i,s+1}$ yields a higher order correction to g_s^o which we will neglect.

We are free to "promote" the A(s,1) term to the lower order equation with $m = 1$; since it leads to exponential damping and does not result in an essentially more complicated equation to solve, we do so. Therefore we have for (1") with $m \geqq 2$, $s \geqq 2$:

$$\Delta'(s,2) = -A(s,1) + \Delta''(s,2)$$

The term in Δ'' contains terms which if they were not "promoted" would lead to divergent behavior in g_s^2. Such terms can be estimated by usage of the values obtained for g_s^1 on the omission of the term in $\epsilon\Delta(s,2)$.

For $s = 2$, B(s,1) is of order $|x_{12}|^{-1}$ for $|x_{12}| >> 1$. Consequently the contribution to g_2^2 through (1'') is logarithmic. Therefore we write

$$g_2^1 = (g_2^1)_1 + (g_2^1)_2$$

and "promote" the terms within B(2,1) linear in $(g_2^1)_1$. For $s = 3$ the contribution to g_3^2 is finite (at least as concerns x, v arguments which ultimately contribute to g_2 for $|x_{12}| < r_o$). Hence we do not "promote" B(3,1). For $s \geqq 4$ we assume that the conclusion for B(s,1) is the same as for B(s,1).

Hence the solution for g_s^1, $s \geqq 3$ is a matter of simple iteration (subject to a knowledge of g_s^1 and g_2^1).

Solution for g_2^1 in particular

For g_2^1 we have from (1''):

$$\left[\frac{\partial}{\partial t} + H_2^o + \epsilon \frac{\partial}{\partial \epsilon t} + \epsilon H_2^1 + \epsilon \sum_{i=1}^{2} \int_{|x_{i,3}| = r_o, x_{i3}||-v_{i3}} d_3 v_3 \, d\sigma_3 |v_{3i}| \, g_1^o(3)\right] g_2^1$$

$$- \theta_{12}(g_1^o g_1^1 + g_1^1 g_1^o)$$

$$= \epsilon \sum_{i=1}^{2} \int_{|x_{i3}| = r_o, x_{i3}||v_{i3}} d_3 v_3 \, d\sigma_3 |v_{3i}| \, e^{-H_3^o \tau}$$

$$\times (g_1^o(3)(g_2^1)_1 (i, \ldots, t) + (g_2^1)_1 (3, \ldots, t) \, g_1^o(i))$$

$$- \epsilon \sum_{i=1}^{2} \int_{|x_{i3}| = r_o, x_{i3}||-v_{i3}} d_3 v_3 \, d\sigma_3 |v_{3,i}| \, e^{-H_3^o \tau} \, g_1^o(i) \, (g_2^1)_1 \, (3, t)$$

$$+ B(2,0) + [R(2,0) - A(2,0) - B(2,0)] . \qquad (9)$$

We write

$$g_2^1 = (g_2^1)_\alpha + (g_2^1)_\beta + (g_2^1)_\gamma$$

$$(g_2^1)_1 = (g_2^1)_{\alpha|1} + (g_2^1)_{\beta|1}$$

$$(g_2^1)_2 = (g_2^1)_{\alpha|2} + (g_2^1)_\gamma$$

$$(g_2^1)_\alpha = (g_2^1)_{\alpha|1} + (g_2^1)_{\alpha|2}$$

$$(g_2^1)_\beta = (g_2^1)_{\beta|1} \tag{10}$$

with

$$\left[\frac{\partial}{\partial t} + H_2^o + \epsilon \frac{\partial}{\partial \epsilon t} + \epsilon\, H_2^1 + \epsilon \sum_{i=1}^{2} \int_{|x_{i,3}| = r_o,\ x_{i3}|\,|-v_{i3}} d_3\, v_3\, d\sigma_3 |\, v_{3,i}|\, g_1^o(3)\right] (g_2^1)_{\alpha|2}$$

$$- \theta_{12}(g_1^o\, g_1^1 + g_1^1\, g_1^o) = \left[R(2,0) - A(2,0) - B(2,0)\right] \tag{11}$$

$$\left[\frac{\partial}{\partial t} + H_2^o + \epsilon \frac{\partial}{\partial \epsilon t} + \epsilon\, H_2^1 + \epsilon \sum_{i-1}^{2} \int_{|x_{i,3}| = r_o,\ x_{i3}|\,|-v_i} d_3\, v_3\, d\sigma_3 |\, v_{3,i}|\, g_1^o(3)\right] (g_2^1)_{\alpha|1}$$

$$= B(2,0) \tag{12}$$

$$\left[\frac{\partial}{\partial t} + H_2^o + \epsilon \frac{\partial}{\partial \epsilon t} + \epsilon\, H_2^1 + \epsilon \sum_{i=1}^{2} \int_{|x_{i,3}| = r_o,\ x_{i3}|\,|-v_{i3}} d_3\, v_3\, d\sigma_3 |\, v_{3,i}|\, g_1^o(3)\right] (g_2^1)_{\beta|1}$$

$$= \epsilon \sum_{i=1}^{2} \int_{|x_{i3}| = r_o,\ x_{i3}|\,|v_{i3}} d_3\, v_3\, d\sigma_3 |\, v_{3,i}|\, e^{-H_3^o \tau} (g_1^o(3)\,(g_2^1)_{\alpha|1} + (g_2^1)_{\alpha|1}\, g_1^o(i))$$

$$- \epsilon \sum_{i=1}^{2} \int_{|x_{i3}| = r_o,\ x_{i3}|\,|-v_{i3}} d_3\, v_3\, d\sigma_3 |\, v_{3,i}|\, e^{-H_3^o \tau} g_1^o(i)\,(g_2^1)_{\alpha|1}(3,t)\,. \tag{13}$$

$$\left[\frac{\partial}{\partial t} + H_2^o + \epsilon\frac{\partial}{\partial \epsilon t} + \epsilon H_2^1 + \epsilon \sum_{i=1}^{2}\int_{|x_{i,3}| = r_o,\ x_{i3}||-v_{i3}} d_3 v_3\, d\sigma_3 |v_{3,i}|\, g_1^o(3)\right](g_2^1)_\gamma$$

$$= \epsilon \sum_{i=1}^{2}\int_{|x_{i3}| = r_o,\ x_{i3}||v_{i3}} d_3 v_3\, d\sigma_3 |v_{3,i}|\, e^{-H_3^o \tau} (g_1^o(3)\,(g_2^1)_\beta|_1$$

$$+ (g_2^1)_\beta|_1\, g_1^o(i)) - \epsilon \sum_{i=1}^{2}\int_{|x_{i3}| = r_o,\ x_{i3}||-v_{i3}} d_3 v_3\, d\sigma_3 |v_{3,i}|\, e^{-H_3^o \tau} g_1^o(i)\,(g_2^1)_\beta|_1(3,t)$$

(14)

The term $[R(2,0) - A(2,0) - B(2,0)]$ falls off with increasing $|x_{12}|$ more rapidly than $|x_{12}|^{-2}$. Consequently $(g_2^1)_\alpha|_2$ does not contribute to secular behavior in (g_2^2). The term $B(2,0)$ varies with increasing $|x_{12}|$ as $|x_{12}|^{-2}$. Consequently the right hand side of (13) is of the order $|x_{12}|^{-1}$ and the right hand side of (14) is of order $\epsilon \ln(\epsilon|x_{12}|)$ for $|x_{12}| \lesssim \epsilon^{-1}$, from which $(g_2^1)_\gamma$ is of order ϵ for $|x_{12}| \lesssim \epsilon^{-1}$.

For $\epsilon x >> 1$ one has that both $(g_2^1)_\beta|_1$ and $(g_2^1)_\gamma$ are of the form $\epsilon e^{-\alpha\epsilon x}$ with α positive, of order unity, and bounded from below.

Determination of g_s^2 and g_2^2 in particular

We now turn to the determination of g_s^2. The right hand side of (1'') for m = 3 can be written, analogously to (6) and (7):

$$\left[H_s^o \sum_{i=1}^{3}\int_{|x_{i,s+1}|<r_o} e^{-H_{s+1}^o \tau} - \sum_{i=1}^{s}\int_{|x_{i,s+1}|<r_o} e^{-H_{s+1}^o \tau} H_{s+1}^o\right.$$

$$\left.+ \sum_{i=1}^{3}\int_{|x_{i,s+1}|<r_o} (v_{s+1} - v_i)\cdot\frac{\partial}{\partial x_{s+1}} e^{-H_{s+1}^o \tau} \sum_{i=1}^{s}\int_{|x_{i,s+1}|<r_o} \delta_{11}\, e^{-H_{s+1}^o \tau}\right]$$

$$\times (I_3(i, 3+1, 1, \ldots, s, t) + e^{H_{s+1}^o \tau}\delta_{30})\, d\Omega_{s+1} \qquad (15)$$

with

$$I_3(i, s+1; 1, \ldots, s, t) \equiv \left[\sum_{n=0}^{2} \sum_{\alpha=1}^{s} g_\alpha^n(i, \ldots)\, g_{s+1-\alpha}^{2-n}(s+1, \ldots) \right.$$

$$\left. + \; g_{s+1}^2(t-\tau) \right]. \qquad (16)$$

One may first calculate the various $g_s^2(t-\tau)$ without the contributions $\Delta'(s,3)$ and then determine the resulting corrections from the $\Delta'(s,3)$. For $s = 3$, at least as concerns g_3^2 which contributes directly to g_2 for $|x_{12}| < r_o$, the term in $v_{3i} \cdot \frac{\partial}{\partial x_3} e^{-H_3^o \tau} g_3^2(t-\tau)$

does not contribute to g_2 in order ϵ^2 or lower. We assume that the iteration with $\Delta'(s,3)$ does not decrease the order of g_3^2, and we take the size of this term as representative of the size of other terms involving $g_3^2(t-\tau)$ within (15). Also we take the contribution from $s = 3$ to be a bound on the contributions from $s \geqq 4$, so that these too can be neglected in finding g_2 to order ϵ^2 for $|x_{12}| < r_o$.

For $\Delta'(2,3)$ we note that due to the presence of $(g_2^1)_\gamma$ one expects that one may write

$$g_2^2 = g_{2|1}^2 + g_{2|2}^2$$

with $g_{2|1}^2$ of order unity on a length scale of order the mean free path and a time scale of order the mean free time. Correspondingly we have

$$\Delta'(2,3) = \sum_{i=1}^{2} \int_{|x_{i,3}| < r_o} d\Omega_3 \, v_{3i} \cdot \frac{\partial}{\partial x_3} e^{-H_2^o(i,3)\tau} \left(g_1^o(i)\, g_{2|1}^2 + g_1^o(3)\, g_{2|1}^2 \right)$$

and

$$\frac{\partial}{\partial t} g_{2|1}^2 + H_2^o g_{2|1}^2 + \epsilon \frac{\partial}{\partial \epsilon t} g_{2|1}^2 + \epsilon H_2^1 g_{2|1}^2 - \theta_{12}\left(g_{1|1}^2(1)\, g_1^o + g_{1|1}^2(2) g_1^o\right)$$

$$- \; \epsilon \sum_{i=1}^{2} \int_{|x_{i,3}| < r_o} d\Omega_3 \, v_{3i} \cdot \frac{\partial}{\partial x_3} e^{-H_2^o(i,3)\tau} \left(g_1^o(i)\, g_{2|1}^2 + g_1^o(3)\, g_{2|1}^2 \right)$$

$$= \sum_{i=1}^{2} \int_{|x_{i3}| = r_o,\, x_{i3} || v_{i3}} d_3 v_3 \, d\sigma_3 \, |v_{3,i}| \, e^{-H_3^o \tau} (g_1^o(3) \, (g_2^1(i, \ldots, t)))_\gamma$$

$$+ g_1^o(i) \, (g_2^1(3, \ldots, t))_\gamma) - \sum_{i=1}^{2} \int_{|x_{i3}| = r_o,\, x_{i3} || -v_{i3}} d_3 v_3 \, d\sigma_3$$

$$|v_{3,i}| \, e^{-H_3^o \tau} g_1^o(i) \, (g_2^1(3, \ldots, t))_\gamma . \qquad (17)$$

For $g_{2|2}^2$ we note that the equation is of the form:

$$\left\{ \frac{\partial}{\partial t} + H_2^o + \epsilon \frac{\partial}{\partial \epsilon t} + \epsilon H_2^1 + \epsilon \sum_{i=1}^{2} \int_{|x_{i,3}| = r_o,\, x_{i3} || -v_{i3}} d_3 v_3 \, d\sigma_3 |v_{3,i}| g_1^o(3) \right\} g_{2|2}^2$$

$$- \theta_{12}(g_{1|2}^2(1) \, g_1^o + \quad g_{1|2}^2(2) \, g_1^0 \quad + g_1^1 \, g_1^1) = S(1, 2, t, \epsilon t).$$

$$(18)$$

S decreases sufficiently rapidly with increasing $|x_{12}|$ that to order unity the solution for $g_{2|2}^2$, subject to a knowledge of g_1^1 and $g_{1|2}^2$, is obtained without iteration.

Discussion of Eq. (17) and comments on the general structure

Equation (17) treats the many body effects whose existence has been previously noted by other authors[5)6)7)8)]. The behavior in Eq. (17) is not entirely unexpected since the binary correlation function at distances of order the mean free path in general is of order ϵ^2. One expects that parts of the binary correlation function in order higher than ϵ^2 will have equations whose homogenous parts are similar in form to the left hand side of (17). Since the correlation function for n bodies at distances of order the mean free path from each other is in general of order $\epsilon^{2(n-1)}$ and higher, part of the n body correlation function will satisfy an integrodifferential equation whose homogeneous terms are acted on by the operator

$$\left(\frac{\partial}{\partial t} + H_n^o + \epsilon \frac{\partial}{\partial \epsilon t} + \epsilon H_n^1 - \epsilon \sum_{i=1}^{n} \int_{|x_{i,n+1}|<r_o} d\Omega_{n+1} v_{n+1} \cdot \frac{\partial}{\partial x_{n+1}} e^{-H_n^o(i,n+1)\tau} \right.$$

$$\left. \times (1 + \epsilon(i, n+1))\, g_1^o(n+1) \right)$$

with $\epsilon(i, n+1)$ exchanging the labels i and n+1.

Form of single particle distribution function

The single particle distribution function g_1 is of the form

$$g_1 = g_1^o + \epsilon\, g_{10}^1 + \epsilon^2 \ln \epsilon\, g_{11}^1 + \epsilon^2\, g_1^2$$

with g_1^o, g_{10}^1, g_{11}^1 and g_1^2 of order unity. Its behavior for all times is given by the equations:

$$\frac{\partial g_1^o}{\partial t} = 0 \tag{19}$$

$$\frac{\partial g_1^o}{\partial \epsilon t} = \lim_{t\to\infty} \int \theta_{12}\, g_2^o\, d\Omega_2 \tag{20}$$

$$\frac{\partial g_{10}^1}{\partial t} = (1 - \lim_{t\to\infty}) \int \theta_{12}\, g_2^o\, d\Omega_2 \tag{21}$$

$$\frac{\partial g_{10}^1}{\partial \epsilon t} = \lim_{t\to\infty} \int \theta_{12} (1 - P_1 - P_2)(g_2^1)_\alpha\, d\Omega_2 \tag{22}$$

$$\frac{\partial g_{11}^1}{\partial t} = (1 - \lim_{t\to\infty}) \int \theta_{12}\, P_3 (g_2^1)_\alpha\, S(-t+\epsilon^{-1})\, d\Omega_2 \tag{23}$$

$$\frac{\partial g_{11}^1}{\partial \epsilon t} = \lim_{t\to\infty} \int \theta_{12}\, (P_1 (g_2^1)_\alpha + (1 - P_4)(g_2^1)_\beta) d\Omega_2 \tag{24}$$

$$\frac{\partial g_1^2}{\partial t} + \epsilon \frac{\partial g_1^2}{\partial \epsilon t} = (1 - \lim_{t \to \infty}) \int \theta_{12}(1 - P_1 - P_2 - P_3)(g_2^1)_\alpha \, d\Omega_2$$

$$+ (1 - \lim_{t \to \infty}) \int \theta_{12} P_3 (g_2^1)_\alpha \, S(t - 1/\epsilon) \, d\Omega_2$$

$$+ (1 - \lim_{t \to \infty}) \int \theta_{12}(P_1 (g_2^1)_\alpha + (1 - P_4)(g_2^1)_\beta) \, d\Omega_2$$

$$+ \int \theta_{12}(P_2 (g_2^1)_\alpha + P_4 (g_2^1)_\beta + (g_2^1)_\gamma + \epsilon g_2^2) \, d\Omega_2 \tag{25}$$

Here

$$S(x) = 1, \; x > 0$$

$$S(x) = 0, \; x < 0$$

and the operators P_i denote the existence of contributions from the functions following them.

Equation (20) is the Boltzmann equation. Equations (22) and (24) are linearized spatially homogeneous Boltzmann equations with known source terms. From Eq. (25) the behavior due to $g^2_{2|1}$ is given by

$$\frac{\partial g^2_{1|1}}{\partial t} = 0 \tag{26}$$

$$\frac{\partial g^2_{1|1}}{\partial \epsilon t} = \int_{|x_{12}| = r_o} v_{21} \cdot d\sigma_2 \, dv_2 \, e^{-H_2^o \tau} (g^2_{1|1}(1) \, g_1^o(2) + g^2_{1|1}(2) \, g_1^o(1) + g^2_{2|1}) \tag{27}$$

Within (27), the term in $g^2_{2|1}$ is independent of $g^2_{1|1}$. The form of (27) follows from the fact that the integral terms in (17) are of order ϵ.

Description of the asymptotic time behavior of g_1 to order ϵ^2

If the deviation of g_1^o from its asymptotic value in time approaches zero exponentially or more rapidly, then g_{10}^1, g_{11}^1 and $g_1^2 - g_{1|1}^2$ approach their asymptotic values exponentially. However, a normal mode[9)10)] analysis of (17) and (27) reveals that $g_{1|1}^2$ may in principle approach its asymptotic value algebraically as $t^{-3/2}$ for $t >> 1$.

If the deviation of g_1^o from its asymptotic value approaches zero less rapidly than exponentially, then in general one cannot even conclude that g_{10}^1 and g_1^2 approach limits.

However, provided g_{10}^1, g_{11}^1 and $g_{1|1}^2$ remain bounded one can, after a sufficiently long time, linearize (20) in the deviations of g_1^o from its asymptotic Maxwellian velocity form. Then, for cut-off Maxwellian or "harder" cut-off potentials[11)], it appears that the deviation of g_1^o from its asymptotic value decays exponentially in time and the corresponding conclusions as to g_{10}^1, g_{11}^1, $g_1^2 - g_{1|1}^2$ and $g_{1|1}^2$ follow.

Finally for the potentials just mentioned, if g_1^o has a constant small deviation from the Maxwellian velocity distribution and one linearizes in this small deviation, the contribution from those modes which yield previous $t^{-3/2}$ contribution is finite.

ACKNOWLEDGMENT

This work was supported by the National Aeronautics and Space Administration under Grant NsG 220-62 and the Air Force Office of Scientific Research of the Office of Aerospace Research under Contract AF 49(638)-1555.

REFERENCES

1. See J. E. McCune, G. Sandri, and E. A. Frieman, Third Symposium on Rarefied Gas Dynamics (Academic Press, N.Y., 1963) Vol. I, pp. 102-114, for further discussion in terms of the notion of temperature.
2. E. A. Frieman, Journal of Math. Phys. 4, 410 (1963).
3. E. A. Frieman and R. Goldman, Journal of Math. Phys. 7, 2153 (1966).
4. R. Goldman and E. A. Frieman,(submitted to Journal of Math. Phys.).
5. H. Grad, Handbook of Physics (Springer Verlag, Berlin, 1958) Vol. XII, p. 205.
6. J. R. Dorfman and E. G. D. Cohen, Phys. Letters 16, 124 (1965).
7. K. Kawasaki and I. Oppenheim, Phys. Rev. 139A, 1763 (1965).
8. J. Weinstock, Phys. Rev. 140A, 460 (1965).
9 L. Sirovich, Phys. Fluids 6, 218 (1963).
10. L. Sirovich, Phys. Fluids 6, 218 (1963).
11. H. Grad, Physics of Fluids 6, 147 (1963).

DISCUSSION

Ford: Your procedure of using the secular pertubation approach is perhaps not well enough appreciated. However, I would like to ask you, whether it does not assume that the correlation functions are independent variables? Is this so?

Goldman: Within the context of the spatially uniform Boltzmann hierarchy with the assumption of initial chaos the approach implies, for example, that the lowest order binary correlation function cannot in general be written in the simple form:

$$g_2^0 (x_{12}, v_1, v_2, t) = (e^{-H_2 t} - 1) g_1^0 (v_1, t) g_1^0 (v_2, t).$$

The correct form* for g_2^0 (t) depends on g_1^0 (t') with $t' < t$. Hence the assumption is one of a more complicated variation for the correlation functions, rather than necessarily of a variation independent of the single particle distribution function (although if this did occur, it could be accounted for).

* See reference 3.

ON PHASE-TRANSITIONS OF SIMPLE LIQUIDS

H. N. V. TEMPERLEY
Department of Applied
Mathematics, University
College, Swansea,
Great Britain

1. INTRODUCTION

I shall not be saying much about the liquid-gas transition because I have very little to add to what was said at the Conference on Critical Phenomena in Washington in 1965. Perhaps one can sum up the present position like this. If the effective range of the attractive forces between molecules were very large compared with the molecular diameter, the equation of state would be very like that obtained from the van der Waals equation plus the Maxwell construction. If this range were made finite, or if the law of fall-off with distance were fairly rapid, the critical region would be of more complicated analytic structure and the laws of variation of quantities like the compressibility, specific heat and coefficient of expansion would be changed. These conclusions apply not only to the rare gases, but to a large number of other types of assembly that present a similar statistical mechanical problem. Where comparison between theory and experiment is possible the results are encouraging. Predictions of theory are more sensitive to the number of dimensions than to the precise lattice structure; indeed it does not seem to matter much whether we work with a lattice or a continuum model in discussing this transition.

I shall return to the liquid-gas transition at the end of my talk. At this stage I shall just point out how important has been the process of cross-fertilisation of the lattice and continuum treatments.

2. THE SOLID-FLUID TRANSITION

The wheel has indeed come full circle. Recent work seems to have established quite clearly the essential correctness of the old Kirkwood-Monroe explanation of freezing, which has been revived at various times by Born and Green, (the Russian) Fisher and many others. You will remember that it runs like this: The two-molecule cistribution function satisfies an integral equation that can be written down exactly in "diagram" form (de Boer et al) but cannot be solved without some knowledge of the higher order distribution functions. Making the simplest possible closure leads effectively to either the Kirkwood or the Born-Green integral equations. It is then merely a matter of analysis or numerical work to show that the analytic form of the solutions must indeed change at a certain density, the "damped oscillations" of $g(\gamma)$ characteristic of a liquid distribution function being replaced by a solution that is partly periodic in space.

A function $g(\gamma)$ that is partly periodic in γ alone is not a precise description of the crystalline state; we should expect a function that also varies appropriately with the polar angles, but approximations at present in use are too drastic to produce such a refinement. This limitation may not be serious, as we shall see later.

For a long time the Kirkwood-Monroe theory was regarded with healthy scepticism. It had been realised that mathematically inadequate treatments may predict the wrong form of a transition, or may even predict a mathematical anomaly that should not really be there at all! It gradually became clear that the Kirkwood superposition approximation was becoming unreliable long before liquid densities were reached, and when the machine calculations of Wood and Jacobson and of Alder and Wainwright on the rigid sphere model became available in 1957, it was clear that, at liquid densities, the pressures calculated using the superposition approximation might be in error by factors of the order of three or more. Although the machine calculations confirmed that an assembly of rigid spheres would show a transition, it therefore still remained in doubt whether the Kirkwood-Monroe explanation was correct or not, a doubt that was, of course, entirely legitimate and proper.

Why do I now say that this doubt is removed? From two entirely independent lines of evidence. First of all better integral equations are now available that can be pushed into the region of liquid densities, and yet, for some liquid models anyway, remain reliable to a few per cent. (This is certainly a fact, but we have, so far, only a few hints of the precise analytic reasons for it). I have used one of these equations, the Percus-Yevick, to show that, for two simple models[(1)], the rigid sphere and the "gaussian repulsion", spatially periodic solutions do become possible at above a certain critical density. Secondly, from a study of various lattice models one could, in principle, deduce the true analytic situation for a continuum. If we assume a purely repulsive interaction between nearest neighbours on e.g. a plane square or simple cubic lattice, the statistics are practically identical with those of the antiferromagnetic problem, and we obtain a transition between a disordered and one possible type of ordered configuration. (In the latter, one sub-lattice is preferentially occupied.) We can imitate the continuum problem more closely if we take the lattice problem and extend the repulsion to more distant neighbours. If we do this our lattice divides up into more than just two sub-lattices. (In the language of graph theory, the chromatic number of the lattice increases). The number of types of configuration showing "order" (that is to say spatial periodicity in the distribution function) increases and, in the continuum limit where the lattice "grid" becomes small compared with a molecular diameter, there are infinitely many ordered configurations each of which shows a local minimum in the free energy and we have to select the most advantageous one. (We know that the free energy differences between different crystal structures can be quite small. For this reason, it may not be too serious to neglect the variations of the distribution function with angle).

Thus, we have to pick out the configuration that corresponds to the minimum free energy consistent with being mathematically and physically allowable. This is precisely the same situation that is suggested by a direct study of the integral equations for the continuum problem, which we can regard as equivalent to a lattice problem with a very large chromatic or co-ordination number. In fact, I have shown that a certain pseudo-lattice with a chromatic number of only three can be handled exactly, and that it would have a transition closely resembling that of the rigid sphere gas[(1)]. You will hear about real, as distinct from pseudo-, lattices in the next paper.

3. THE CORRECT MATHEMATICAL TOOL

Can we set up an exact treatment of the continuum model to help us follow the onset of order? (Any lattice model can, in principle, be solved as accurately as we please, by the systematic counting of configurations). I suggest that the correct approach is via the "functional differentiation" technique used by Lebowitz et al., in the derivation of integral equations. Verlet[2)] has shown that this process can be expressed in the following way. We write down the partition function for an interacting gas, with the additional assumption that the molecules are subject also to an external potential field. "Functional differentiation" then involves differentiating the partition function with respect to the amplitude of this field, afterwards putting it equal to zero.

We can obtain a theory of ordered arrangements in a continuum by applying a spatially periodic potential field which will induce a distribution of matter with similar periodicity. However, this periodicity is not fixed in advance, but we have to choose it in order to get the most favourable free energy. For a given periodicity, we may regard the amplitude of the applied field as a force variable, and the statistically conjugate variable, which we obtain in the usual way by differentiation of the appropriate partition function, will correspond to one of the order parameters possible in a lattice model. We hope that, at a high enough density, order appears at zero applied field.

This approach is suitable for generalising Mayer cluster expansions to handle the situation when an ordered configuration is appearing. We can discuss liquefaction of a gas in an analogous way. Here, what is happening is a "crowding together" of the molecules rather than the appearance of an ordered state. We deal with this by imposing a small non spatially-periodic field, like gravitation, so that the molecules have more potential energy at the top of the vessel than they have at the bottom. Thus, this technique of "functional differentiation" enables us to handle both the liquid-solid and liquid-gas transitions by a single formalism. This looks promising, but there are no concrete results to report as yet.

REFERENCES

1. Temperley. Various papers in Proc. Phys. Soc. 1964 and 1965.

2. Verlet. "The theory of Classical Fluids V". Physica 32, 304, 1966.

PHASE TRANSITIONS IN HARD-SQUARE LATTICE GASES

A. BELLEMANS
Université Libre de Bruxelles
Belgium

1. INTRODUCTION

Our aim is to discuss the thermodynamic properties of lattice gases of "hard molecules" with special emphasis on phase transitions. The assumed potential between two molecules is such that

a) the multiple occupancy of sites is forbidden,
b) the occupancy of a certain neighborhood of any occupied site is also forbidden,
c) this neighborhood has the same symmetry as the lattice itself.

We limit ourselves here to a two-dimensional square lattice and consider three different systems of molecules with exclusion neighborhoods extending up to the first, second and third neighboring sites respectively; see fig. 1. All three cases (hereafter denoted as A, B and C respectively) correspond to "hard-square" molecules and are discontinuous analogs of the two-dimensional hard disks continuum fluid which exhibits a (presumably first-order) phase transition at high density. We notice here that both cases A and C attain a perfectly ordered state at maximum density; see fig. 1. This is not exactly so for case B: all molecules must be located on parallel lines of sites but a whole line may be shifted with respect to adjacent ones; see fig. 2.

The advantage of these (somewhat less realistic) lattice gases (as opposed to hard disks) is that a wider variety of methods can be applied to them e. g.

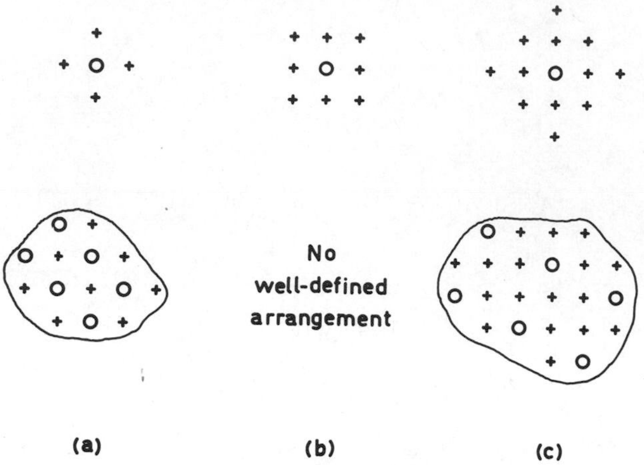

Fig. 1. Hard-square molecules on the square lattice:
Case A: first neighbors exclusion,
Case B: first and second neighbors exclusion,
Case C: first, second and third neighbors exclusion.
The exclusion cores are shown on upper part of the figure; the lower part represents the configurations of close-packing.

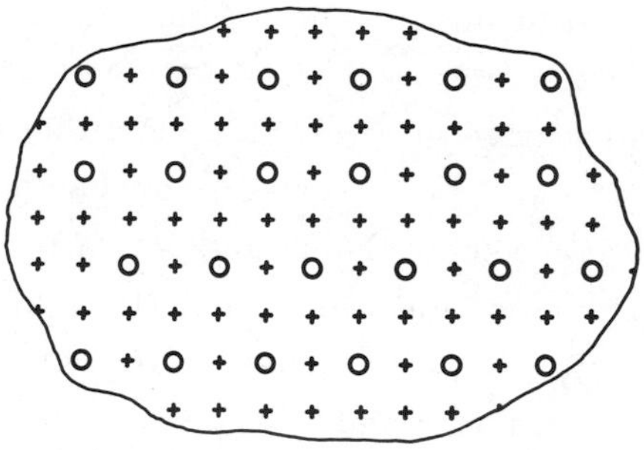

Fig. 2. Close-packing configuration of case B.

a) the matrix method of Kramers and Wannier,
b) the derivation of both low and high density series,
c) closed approximations of the Bethe type.

We shall analyze some results obtained by these methods for the three cases A, B and C. The first case has been considered by many authors[1, 2, 3] so that we merely recall their results here. Cases B and C have been treated in collaboration with Dr. Nigam[4].

2. CASE A

Runnels[2] has recently applied the matrix method to this system by considering cylindrical lattices of circumference n. As n increases a peak progressively appears in the compressibility, strongly suggesting a continuous second-order transition when $n \to \infty$; see fig. 3. This result agrees with the analysis of low and high density series by Gaunt and Fisher[3] who also concluded to the existence of a continuous transition from a disordered to an ordered phase at high density. Approximate treatments based on the Bethe method[1] or on integral equations alternatively led to a second-order transition with a finite compressibility jump or even to a first-order phase change.

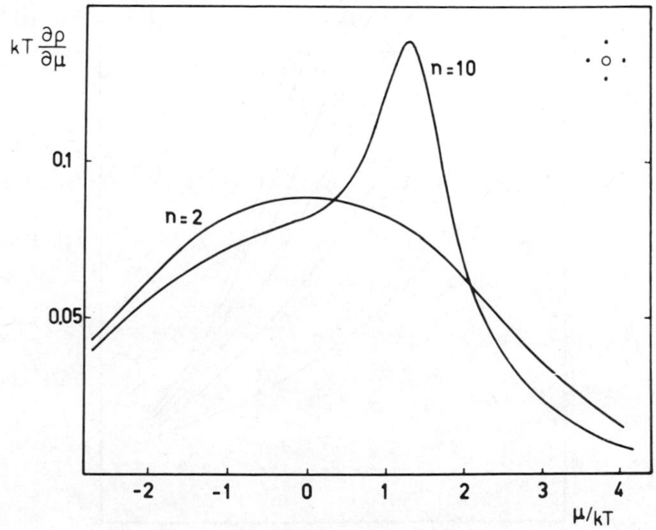

Fig. 3. Case A: plot of $kT\ \partial\rho/\partial\mu$ vs. μ/kT for n = 2 and 10 (Note that $kT\ \partial\rho/\partial\mu = kT\rho^2 K_T$ where K_T is the isothermal compressibility).

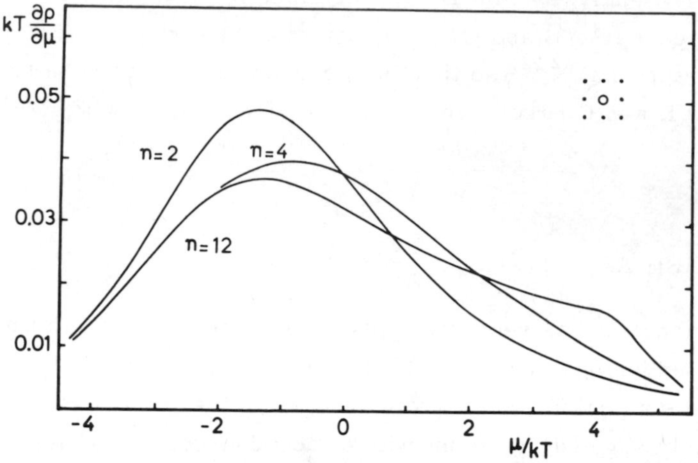

Fig. 4. Case B: plot of kT $\partial\rho/\partial\mu$ vs. μ/kT for n = 2 and 12.

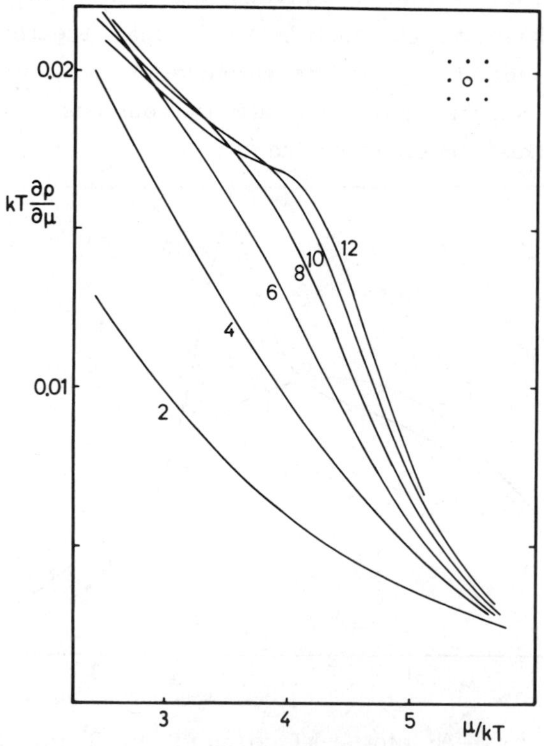

Fig. 5. Case B: enlarged portion of figure 4 around $\mu/kT = 4$, for n = 2 to 12.

3. CASE B

We applied the matrix method to this case for even values of n up to 12; see fig. 4 and 5. For $\mu/kT < 4$ the quantity $kT\ \partial\rho/\partial\mu$ (i.e. essentially the compressibility) varies regularly as n increases (μ = chemical potential, ρ = density). Nearto $\mu/kT = 4$ however, a bump or a kink seems to appear, suggesting that the system goes into an ordered state by means of a weak phase transition. One must however be extremely careful here because in the region near close-packing the analytic behavior of the thermodynamic properties of an infinite system is not straightforwardly obtained from finite ones: an (infinitely long) cylindrical lattice of circumference n gives indeed for the pressure:

$$p/kT = \frac{1}{4} \ln z + \frac{1}{16} (n+4)\, z^{-1} + O(z^{-2})$$

(z = activity) sothat the second term (as well as the following ones) diverges when $n \to \infty$. This means that long range correlations between "lattice defects" (i.e. empty sites) prevent a simple expansion of p in terms of z^{-1} at high densities. A careful rearrangement of divergent terms gives

$$p/kT = \frac{1}{4} \ln z + A\, z^{-1/2} + O(z^{-1})$$

for n infinite. It seems thus somewhat dangerous to infer the existence of a phase change from results corresponding to relatively small n values.

We now turn to density series; fig. 6 shows a ten-term low density expansion and a three-term high density expansion; no conclusions can be drawn about the existence of a phase transition because of the too small number of terms on the high density side.

Finally we considered an approximate treatment of the Bethe type based on a theorem demonstrated by Rushbrooke and Scoins[5] and previously applied to this kind of systems by Temperley[6]. In this way a second-order transition with a finite compressibility jump is obtained at $\mu/kT = 2.84$, in disagreement with the matrix method; see fig. 7.

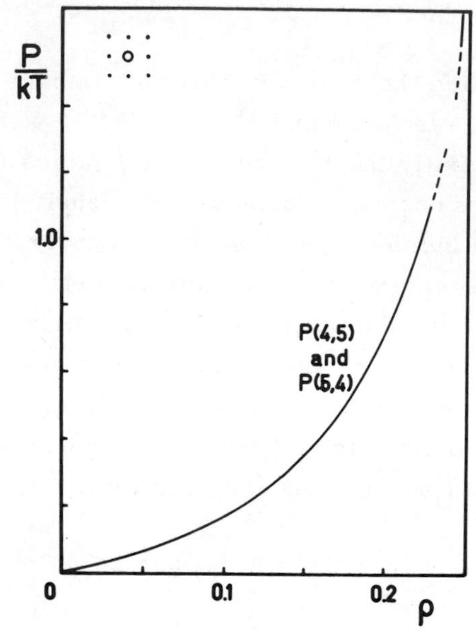

Fig. 6. Case B: pressure vs. density from low and high density series (the low density series has been fitted into Padé approximants).

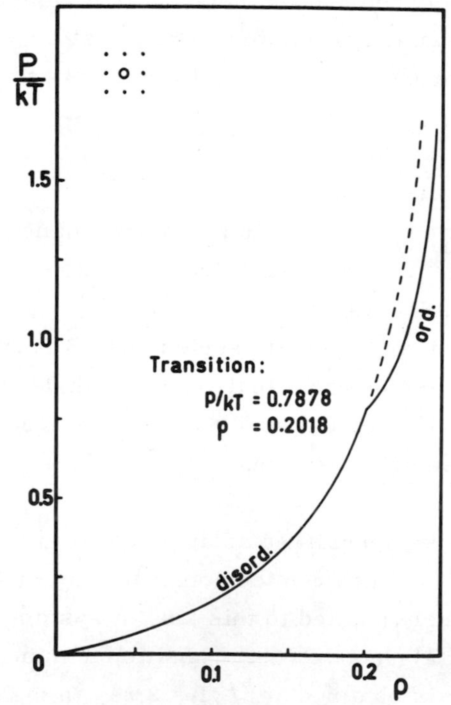

Fig. 7. Case B: approximate treatment based on the Rushbrooke-Scoins theorem, showing a second-order transition: the dotted line corresponds to a metastable disordered phase.

4. CASE C

We applied the matrix method to this case for $n = 5$ and 10 (n ought to be a multiple of 5 in order to approach the close-packing configuration of fig. 1c at high density). The sharp peak of fig. 8 appearing for $n = 10$ around $\mu/kT = 3.6$ definitely indicates that this system exhibits a phase change as $n \to \infty$; the corresponding values of p/kT and ρ are roughly 0.74 and 0.175 respectively (maximum density: $\rho = 0.20$). Although it is difficult to discuss the nature of this transition here, one will notice that the peak of fig. 8 is much steeper than that of case A and might well correspond to a first-order phase change.

Fig. 9 shows a five-term low density series and a three-term high density series for the pressure. Although it is clearly desirable to include more terms on both sides, this plot suggests a first order transition from a disordered (fluid) phase to an ordered (solid) phase.

An approximate treatment based on the Rushbrooke-Scoins theorem and retaining all molecular configurations covering five lattice sites or less leads to a first-order phase change with the following characteristics:

$$(\mu/kT)^* = 3.64\,, \qquad (p/kT)^* = 0.738\,,$$

$$\rho^*_{fluid} = 0.160\,, \qquad \rho^*_{solid} = 0.192\,, \qquad S_{fusion} = 0.78\,k\,,$$

in concordance with the position of the peak observed by the matrix method; see fig. 10.

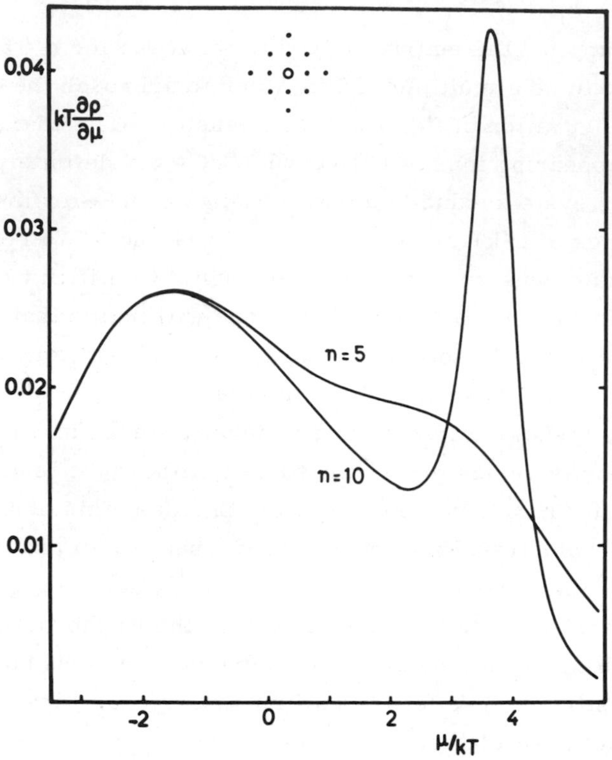

Fig. 8. Case C: plot of kT $\partial\rho/\partial\mu$ vs. μ/kT for n = 5 and 10.

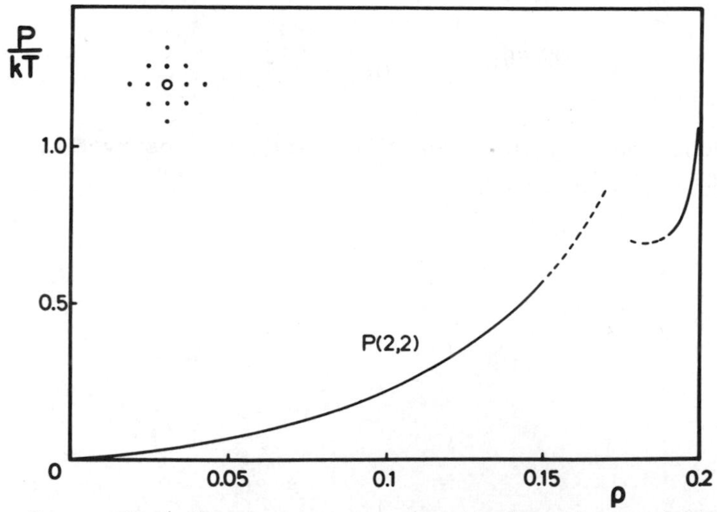

Fig. 9. Case C: pressure vs. density from low and high density series (the low density series has been fitted into a Padé approximant).

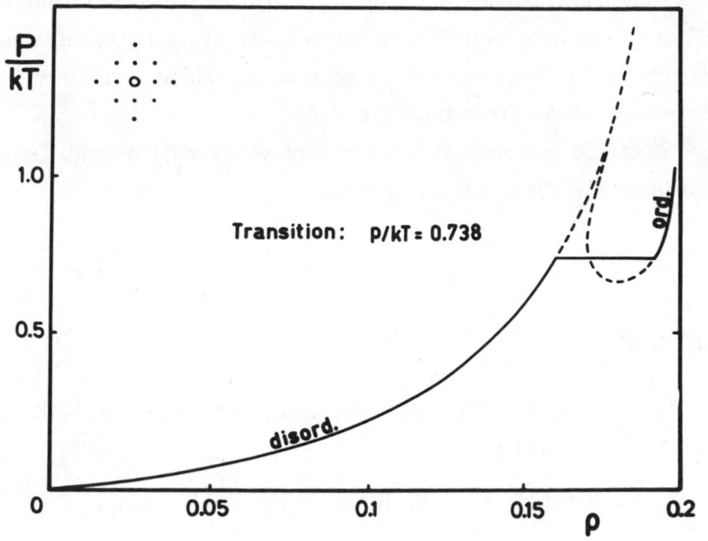

Fig. 10. Case C: approximate treatment based on the Rushbrooke-Scoins theorem, showing a first-order transition; the dotted lines correspond to metastable phases.

5. CONCLUSIONS

For the three cases discussed here one is tempted to conclude that

a) Case A goes from a disordered to an ordered phase through a second-order continuous transition.
b) Case B remains doubtful.
c) Case C goes from a disordered to an ordered phase through a first-order transition.

It seems thus that a lattice gas with moderately extended hard core already shows the same behavior as hard disks or hard spheres and could be used as a simple model for fusion. This view seems to be confirmed from Monte-Carlo calculations on the triangular lattice by Chesnut[7]: molecules with a hard core including second neighboring sites as well as first ones might well present a first-order phase change while this is not so for a core limited to first neighbors.

A detailed account of the present work will be published in the Journal of Chemical Physics.

REFERENCES

1. D. M. Burley, Proc. Phys. Soc. (London) 75, 262 (1960); 77, 451 (1961).

2. L. K. Runnels, Phys. Rev. Letters 15, 581 (1965).

3. D. A. Gaunt and M. E. Fisher, J. Chem. Phys. 43, 2840 (1965).

4. A. Bellemans and R. K. Nigam, Phys. Rev. Letters 16, 1038 (1966), (preliminary communication).

5. G. S. Rushbrooke and H. I. Scoins, Proc. Roy. Soc. (London) A230, 74 (1955).

6. H. N. V. Temperley, Proc. Phys. Soc. (London) 80, 813 (1962).

7. D. A. Chesnut, private communication.

DISCUSSION

Deltour: For the case B, the density series, it would be interesting to use not a simple Pade approximant but a two points Padè approximant.

Bellemans: I agree with this idea but the first thing to do is to increase the number of available coefficients of both series, especially on the high density side.

Temperley: In the matrix method, were you working with the highest eigenvalue? Did you find others of comparable value near?

Bellemans: We considered only the largest eigenvalue. By the way we worked on a reduced matrix (taking into account the rotational symmetry of the system) so that looking at other eigenvalues may have no sense because we do not get all of them.

Bell: A change from double degeneracy to higher degeneracy in the ground state seems to replace a second-order by a first-order transition. An example is 1:1 and 1:3 superlattices.

Bellemans: This seems indeed to be the case, or is at least strongly suggested by the approximate treatment considered here and by a pseudo-triangular lattice model previously treated by Temperley, Proc. Phys. Soc. (London) 86, 185 (1965).

Uhlenbeck: I recently received a paper by Runnel in which he treated, by the same numerical method, not only the square lattice, corresponding to case a of Dr. Bellemans, but also the triangular lattice (for which the molecules are hexagons). Originally Dr. Runnel had told me that the phase transition for the two lattices has a different nature, namely that for the triangular lattice the transition seemed first order. However, he now showed that by taking a sufficient number of rows (I think he went to more than twenty rows) the difference tends to disappear. I think this shows how cautious one most be before believing the existence of a first order Kirkwood transition.

Compagner: I wish to comment on the case of an imperfect gas subject to gravity mentioned by Prof. Temperley. I have studied a one-dimensional system of particles interacting with hardcore rectangular-well potentials in a uniform gravitational field (see Physics Letters 21, (1966) 627). The density and the pressure were obtained exactly as functions of altitude. One has to replace the usual thermodynamic limit by a continuum limit in which all particle parameters as well as the Boltzmann constant vanish with $1/N$, and which is equivalent to the thermodynamic limit if the external field is absent. Supplementing van Hove's well-known proof, one can show that a one-dimensional fluid with arbitrary interactions subject to an arbitrary but continuous external field does not show a phase transition if the corresponding field-free case does not show one.

ORIENTATIONAL CORRELATIONS IN LIQUIDS AND THE DEPOLARIZATION OF SCATTERED LIGHT*

WILLIAM A. STEELE
Department of Chemistry.
Whitmore Laboratory.
The Pennsylvania State University, University Park, Pennsylvania.

ABSTRACT

The molecular theory is presented which expresses the intensity of scattered light (for two specific experimental geometries) as a function of frequency relative to the frequency of the incident light and of the scattering wave vector. The time dependent ensemble averages of functions of molecular position and orientation which appear in the general equations are evaluated using simple models for translation and rotation in the fluid. The resulting theoretical expressions are compared with experimental data for some simple systems, and it is shown that a proper analysis of such data can yield considerable information about the nature of angle dependent correlations in fluids.

1. INTRODUCTION

At the present time, theories dealing with orientational distribution functions in dense fluids are relatively crude[1]. Very little is known about static orientational correlations in such

* This work supported in part by a grant from the Petroleum Research Fund of the American Chemical Society and in part by American Petroleum Institute (project 42).

systems; furthermore, almost all treatments of rotational motion in liquids and the time-dependent angular distribution functions which describe this motion are based on simple Brownian motion models,[2,3,4] modified to include inertial effects when the potential barriers to rotation are sufficiently small[5,6]. However, comparisons of experimental data for reasonably symmetric but non-spherical molecules with theories which have been developed for spherically symmetric systems indicates that it may not always be necessary to include these effects in approximate calculations of many macroscopic properties. Nevertheless, some macroscopic properties are essentially entirely determined by angle-dependent molecular properties: frequency-dependent dielectric constants of polar fluids, for example[7,8]. The intensity of depolarized scattered light as a function of frequency is another such property[9,10,11] In this paper, the general theory giving the relationship between the angle-dependent molecular properties of a fluid made up of optically anisotropic molecules and the intensity of this scattered light will be briefly summarized;[11] the averages which appear in general expressions will be evaluated using a rotational Brownian motion model; and the predictions of the theory will be compared with experimental data for two simple systems.[12] In order to simplify the general expressions, which are rather lengthly when written down for an arbitrary experimental geometry, the treatment given here will be limited to a simple but experimentally popular case which is that of a scattering angle of 90°, and an incident beam with its plane of polarization perpendicular to the scattering plane. The intensity of the light scattered with plane of polarization perpendicular to the scattering plane will be denoted by I_{VV}, and that with polarization plane parallel to the scattering plane, by I_{HV}. The relationship between molecular properties and the intensity of scattered light is most readily exhibited if one deals not with $I(\Delta\omega, \underset{\sim}{\mathcal{K}})$, the scattered intensity with angular frequency equal to the angular frequency of the incident beam plus $\Delta\omega$ and scattering vector of length $\mathcal{K}$, but with its Fourier transform $\tilde{I}(t, \underset{\sim}{\mathcal{K}})$ which is defined by:

$$I(\Delta\omega,\underset{\sim}{\chi}) = \frac{1}{2\pi} \int_{-\infty}^{\infty} \tilde{I}(t,\underset{\sim}{\chi})\, e^{-i\Delta\omega t}\, dt \qquad (1)$$

Since the total intensity of scattered light measured in ordinary scattering experiments is given by the integral of $I(\Delta\omega,\underset{\sim}{\chi})$ over all values of $\Delta\omega$, it is evident that this is also given by $\tilde{I}(0,\underset{\sim}{\chi})$, the zero time limit of $\tilde{I}(t,\underset{\sim}{\chi})$.

2. THEORY

It is readily shown that $I(t,\underset{\sim}{\chi})$ can be written as a sum of terms, each of which involves an ensemble average over molecular properties.[11] If it is assumed that the total scattering from unit volume of the fluid can be obtained by summing the products of the amplitudes of the electric vectors which characterize the radiation scattered by individual molecules, one can write:

$$\tilde{I}(t,\underset{\sim}{\chi}) = I_s(t,\underset{\sim}{\chi}) + I_c(t,\underset{\sim}{\chi}) \qquad (2)$$

where the self-scattering term $I_s(t,\underset{\sim}{\chi})$ is given by:

$$I_s(t,\underset{\sim}{\chi}) = \rho \left\langle e^{i\underset{\sim}{\chi}\cdot\delta\underset{\sim}{r}_{11}} X(1,t)\, X^*(1,0) \right\rangle \qquad (3)$$

and the correlation-scattering term $I_c(t,\underset{\sim}{\chi})$ is

$$I_c(t,\underset{\sim}{\chi}) = \rho \left\langle \sum_{1\neq m} e^{i\underset{\sim}{\chi}\cdot\delta\underset{\sim}{r}_{1m}} X(1,t) X^*(m,0) \right\rangle \qquad (4)$$

In these expressions, $\delta\underset{\sim}{r}_{11}$ is the displacement vector for molecule 1 in time interval t; $\delta\underset{\sim}{r}_{1m} = \underset{\sim}{r}_m(t) - \underset{\sim}{r}_1(0)$, and is thus the position of molecule m at time t relative to the position of molecule 1 at time zero; ρ is the number density of molecules in the fluid; and the $X(m,t)$ are functions of the experimental geometry and of the optical polarizability tensor of molecule m in laboratory coordinates at time t. Since this tensor is time-independent only when defined in a molecular coordinate system (for rigid molecules), it is first necessary to transform from molecular axes to the appropriate laboratory axes. When this is done, the time dependence of $X(m, t)$ is seen to be due to the fact that the elements of the transformation matrix depend upon the orientation of the molecule in these laboratory coordinates, and thus will change as the molecules rotate in the fluid.

The transformation matrix takes on a particularly useful form if the molecular polarizability tensor, which is assumed to be diagonal with elements α_x, α_y, α_z in Cartesian axes, is written in a spherical basis. One thus defines an average polarizability α_o:

$$\alpha_o = (\alpha_x + \alpha_y + \alpha_z)/3 \tag{5}$$

and two coefficients of anisotropy:

$$\alpha_1 = (\alpha_x - \alpha_y)/2 \tag{6}$$

$$\alpha_2 = \alpha_z - (\alpha_x + \alpha_y)/2 \tag{7}$$

When these polarizability elements are used, it is found that the transformation elements can be expressed in terms of the $D^J_{K,M}(\Omega_m(t))$, the representations of the three-dimensional rotation group. These functions form a complete orthonormal set in the space of the Euler angles $\alpha_m(t)$, $\beta_m(t)$, $\gamma_m(t)$ which define the orientation of molecule m at time t and (denoted by $\Omega_m(t)$) here defined to be:

$$D^J_{K,M}(\Omega) = \sqrt{\frac{2J+1}{8\pi^2}}\, e^{-iK\alpha} B^J_{K,M}(\beta)\, e^{-iM\gamma} \tag{8}$$

Definitions of the functions $B^J_{K,M}(\beta)$ are well known,[13,14] and will not be repeated here. Since the general expressions for $X(m,t)$[11] are rather lengthy when expressed in terms of these quantities, they will be given only for the specific experimental geometries of interest. In particular, $I_{VV}(t,\chi)$ is obtained when the scattering factor is:

$$[X(m,t)]_{VV} = Y\alpha_o + \sqrt{\frac{8\pi^2}{5}}\, Y \left[\sqrt{\frac{2}{3}}\,\alpha_1 \cdot \sum_{sgn} D^2_{0,\pm 2}(\Omega_m(t)) + \frac{2}{3}\alpha_2 \cdot D^2_{0,0}(\Omega_m(t))\right] \tag{9}$$

Furthermore, $I_{HV}(t, \mathcal{X})$ is obtained when

$$[X(m,t)]_{HV} = i\sqrt{\frac{8\pi^2}{5}}\, Y\, \Big[\frac{\alpha_1}{2}\sum_{sgn} D^2_{\pm 1,\pm 2}\ (\Omega_m(t))$$

$$+\frac{\alpha_2}{\sqrt{6}}\sum_{sgn} D^2_{\pm 1,0}\ (\Omega_m(t))\Big] \qquad (10)$$

In eq. 9 and 10 sgn denotes a sum of functions with positive and negative subscripts, and Y is defined by:

$$Y = E_o \mathcal{X}^2\, e^{i\tilde{\mathcal{X}}\cdot\tilde{R}}/4\pi R\epsilon \qquad (11)$$

where $\tilde{R}$ is the vector denoting the position of the scattering detector relative to the scattering volume, and ϵ is the dielectric constant and E_o is the amplitude of the incident electric vector in the fluid. Note that I_{HV} vanishes when the coefficients of anisotropy in the polarizability vanish. Thus, it is evident that the Fourier transform of measured values of $I_{HV}(\Delta\omega, \mathcal{X})$ will yield information concerning the time dependence of certain functions of molecular orientation, as well as giving a measure of the static angular correlations in the fluid. These relationships are shown most clearly if one writes the $D^J_{K,M}\ (\Omega_1(t))$ in terms of $\Omega_1(0)$, the orientation of 1 at time zero and $\delta\Omega$, its angular displacement in time t:

$$D^J_{K,M}\ (\Omega_1(t)) = \sqrt{\frac{8\pi^2}{2J+1}}\sum_R D^J_{K,R}\ (\Omega_1(0))\ D^J_{R,M}\ (\delta\Omega) \qquad (12)$$

When eq. 12 is substituted into eq. 9 or 10, the resulting expression can be substituted into eqs. 3 and 4 to give explicit equations for $\tilde{I}_{HV}(t, \mathcal{X})$ as averages over functions of molecular orientation at time zero and of angular displacement during time interval t. The averaging over orientation at time zero can readily be done for the self-scattering contribution to the intensities, since all orientations of a single molecule are equally probable at zero time. The results of averaging over $\Omega_1(0)$ can be written as:

$$[\tilde{I}_s(t,\mathcal{K})]_{VV} = \rho |Y|^2 [\alpha_o^2 \langle e^{i\underset{\sim}{\mathcal{K}} \cdot \delta \underset{\sim}{r}_{11}} \rangle + \tfrac{4}{45} F_s(t,\mathcal{K})] \tag{13}$$

$$[\tilde{I}_s(t,\mathcal{K})]_{HV} = \rho |Y|^2 \tfrac{3}{45} F_s(t,\mathcal{K}) \tag{14}$$

where

$$F_s(t,\mathcal{K}) = \sqrt{\frac{8\pi^2}{5}} \Big\langle e^{i\underset{\sim}{\mathcal{K}} \cdot \delta \underset{\sim}{r}_{11}} [3\alpha_1^2 \sum_{sgn} D^2_{\pm 2, \pm 2} (\delta\Omega) +$$

$$\sqrt{24}\, \alpha_1 \alpha_2 \sum_{sgn} (D^2_{0,\pm 2} (\delta\Omega) + D^2_{\pm 2,0} (\delta\Omega)) +$$

$$\alpha_2^2 D^2_{0,0} (\delta\Omega) \Big\rangle \tag{15}$$

The expressions for $I_o(t,\underset{\sim}{\mathcal{K}})$, when written as averages of functions of $\Omega_1(t)$ and $\Omega_2(0)$, can be simplified by writing the functions of $\Omega_1(t)$ in terms of functions of $\Omega_{12}(t)$, the angles between molecules 1 and 2 (or more precisely, the angles required to rotate molecule 2 from an orientation specified by $\Omega_2(0)$ to one specified by $\Omega_1(t)$), and $\delta\Omega^*$, the angular displacement of molecule 1 in time t when molecule 2 is known to have orientation $\Omega_2(0)$ at time zero. One has[14]

$$D^J_{K,M} (\Omega_1(t)) = \sqrt{\frac{8\pi^2}{2J+1}} \sum_R D^J_{K,R} (\Omega_2(0)) D^J_{R,M} (\Omega_{12}(t)) \tag{16}$$

and

$$D^J_{R,M} (\Omega_{12}(t)) = \sqrt{\frac{8\pi^2}{2J+1}} \sum_{R'} D^J_{R,R'} (\Omega_{12}) D^J_{R',M} (\delta\Omega^*) \tag{17}$$

where Ω_{12} denotes $\Omega_{12}(t)$ at time zero. When eqs. 16 and 17 are substituted into the expressions for $I_c(t,\underset{\sim}{\mathcal{K}})$, one can average over all values of $\Omega_2(0)$ to obtain a result which is:

$$[I_c(t,\mathcal{K})]_{VV} = \rho^2 |Y|^2 [\alpha_o^2 \langle e^{i\underset{\sim}{\mathcal{K}} \cdot \delta \underset{\sim}{r}_{12}} \rangle + \tfrac{4}{45} F_c(t,\mathcal{K})] \tag{18}$$

$$\left[I_c(t,\mathcal{K})\right]_{HV} = \rho^2 |Y|^2 \frac{3}{45} F_c(t,\mathcal{K}) \tag{19}$$

where

$$F_c(t,\mathcal{K}) = \frac{8\pi^2}{5} \Big\langle e^{i\underset{\sim}{\mathcal{K}}\cdot \delta\underset{\sim}{r}_{12}} \Big[3\alpha_1^2 \sum_{R,\,sgn} D^2_{\pm 2,R}(\Omega_{12}).$$

$$D^2_{R,\pm 2}(\delta\Omega^*) + \sqrt{24}\alpha_1\alpha_2 \sum_{R,\,sgn} (D^2_{0,R}(\Omega_{12}).$$

$$D^2_{R,\pm 2}(\delta\Omega^*) + D^2_{\pm 2,R}(\Omega_{12})\, D^2_{R,0}(\delta\Omega^*))$$

$$+ \alpha_2^2 \sum_R D^2_{0,R}(\Omega_{12})\, D^2_{R,0}(\delta\Omega^*)\Big]\Big\rangle \tag{20}$$

Eqs. 13-15 and 18-20 contain general expressions for the intensity of scattered light from a fluid made up of molecules with known polarizability. Note that the so-called Rayleigh and Brillouin scattering[15, 16] can be obtained by measuring $I_{VV} - \frac{4}{3} I_{HV}$, since

$$\left[I(t,\mathcal{K})\right]_{VV} - \frac{4}{3}\left[I(t,\mathcal{K})\right]_{HV} = \rho |Y|^2 \alpha_o^2 \cdot$$

$$\Big\langle\Big[e^{i\underset{\sim}{\mathcal{K}}\cdot \delta\underset{\sim}{r}_{11}} + \rho\, e^{i\underset{\sim}{\mathcal{K}}\cdot \delta\underset{\sim}{r}_{12}}\Big]\Big\rangle \tag{21}$$

In order to progress further with the evaluation of the ensemble averages, which appear in the general expressions, it is now necessary to introduce some specific assumptions about the nature of the translational and rotational motions in the fluid. Therefore, it will be assumed that:

1) translational and rotational motions are uncoupled, so that averages over functions of $\delta\underset{\sim}{r}_{11}$ and $\delta\underset{\sim}{r}_{12}$ can be performed separately from those over functions of $\delta\Omega$ and $\delta\Omega^*$.

2) The Landau-Placzek theory can be applied to give the requisite ensemble averages of functions of translational displacements.

3) The time dependence of $\delta\Omega^*$, which is conditioned by the

presence of molecule 2 with a fixed orientation at time zero, is the same as the time dependence of $\delta\Omega$, the unconditional orientational displacement.

4) The molecules undergo rotational Brownian motion.

Note that these approximations all have at least one common feature: they should be most nearly correct at long times. Since the frequency shifts in light scattering experiments are ordinarily quite small, the Fourier transforms which appear in the theory will be strongly dependent upon the behavior of the system at these long times. In fact, the Landau-Placzek theory, which is known to be in good agreement with experiment, has been derived[16] from the hydrodynamic equations of motion, with the additional assumption that the time dependence of the conditional displacement $\delta \underset{\sim}{r}_{12}$ is the same as that of $\delta \underset{\sim}{r}_{11}$ - an assumption which is equivalent to the second one made above. The well-known results of this theory can be written as:

$$\left\langle e^{i\underset{\sim}{\chi}\cdot\delta\underset{\sim}{r}_{12}}\right\rangle = \left\langle e^{i\underset{\sim}{\chi}\cdot\delta\underset{\sim}{r}_{11}}\right\rangle \left\langle e^{i\underset{\sim}{\chi}\cdot\underset{\sim}{r}_{12}}\right\rangle \tag{22}$$

where $\underset{\sim}{r}_{12}$ is the vector separation between molecules 1 and 2 at time zero, and

$$\left\langle e^{i\underset{\sim}{\chi}\cdot\delta\underset{\sim}{r}_{11}}\right\rangle = \frac{C_P - C_V}{C_P}\, e^{-\lambda \chi^2 t/\rho C_P} + \frac{C_V}{C_P}\, e^{-\Gamma\chi^2 t} \cos C_o \chi t \tag{23}$$

where λ, Γ, and C_o are the thermal conductivity, sound absorption coefficient, and velocity of sound in the liquid.

The time dependence of the angle-dependent terms can also be readily obtained from the solutions of the rotational diffusion equation. Although these are known even for the case where three unequal friction constants are required to characterize the reorientation about the three principal axes of the molecule;[3, 4, 5] the present treatment will be limited to a simpler case in which it is assumed that the friction constants are $\xi_x = \xi_y \neq \xi_z$. In this case, one finds that:

$$D^{J}_{K,M}(\delta\Omega) = \sqrt{\frac{2J+1}{8\pi^2}}\ \delta_{K,M}\, f_M^{\ J}(t) \qquad (24)$$

where $\delta_{K,M}$ is a Kronecker delta. The $f_M^{\ J}(t)$ which are of interest in the present problem are:

$$f_0^{\ 2}(t) = \exp\left(-\left[6\ kT/\xi_x\right] t\right) \qquad (25)$$

$$f_2^{\ 2}(t) = f_{-2}^{\ 2}(t) = \exp\left(-\left[2kT/\xi_x + 4kT/\xi_z\right] t\right) \qquad (26)$$

The line widths and splittings in spectra of scattered light can be calculated by the Fourier transforms of the time dependent functions in eqs. 23, 25, and 26; in addition, the intensities of the lines are determined by the time-independent ensemble averages in eqs. 20 and 22. The results for $I_{VV} - \frac{4}{3} I_{HV}$ are well known: one has a central line (Rayleigh scattering) with line width $\lambda \mathcal{K}^2/\rho C_P$, and two identical lines (Brillouin scattering) which are split from the central line by $C_\upsilon \mathcal{K}$ and which have widths given by $\Gamma \mathcal{K}^2$. The ratios of the intensity of the Rayleigh to the Brillouin scattering is given by $(C_P - C_V)/C_V$, and the total intensity of this scattering is proportional to $1 + \rho \left\langle \exp(i\underset{\sim}{\mathcal{K}} \cdot \underset{\sim}{r}_{12})\right\rangle$, which, for liquids not too close to their critical points, can be shown to be equal to $\rho kT \mathcal{K}_T$, where $\mathcal{K}_T$ is the isothermal compressibility of the fluid. Comparisons of this theory with experiment have recently been discussed;[17,18] in these experiments, the incident light was obtained from a He-Ne laser with a line width of $\sim .06\ cm^{-1}$, and the scattered light was analyzed with the aid of interferometers with free spectral ranges of the order of $.3\ cm^{-1}$. It is found that the broadening of the scattered Rayleigh or Brillouin lines is undectably small (as predicted) but that the Brillouin splittings and the intensity ratios agree reasonably well with Landau-Placzek theory. Some typical values for the Brillouin splittings are shown in Table I. However, when I_{HV} is measured in the course of these experiments, it is frequently found that this intensity seems to be essentially independent of frequency, and it is thus frequently described as "depolarized background scattering."[12,17] In fact, line widths for the depolarized scattering which were measured[19, 20] some time ago using other techniques indicate that these lines are too broad to be resolved by the interferometers used in the recent experiments. Values of these line widths are also shown in Table I for some relatively simple liquids. As an example, the case of liquid benzene will be considered further. Because of the six-fold symmetry axis perpendicular to the plane of the benzene molecule, only one coefficient of optical anisotropy is non-zero; furthermore, the assumption that $\xi_x = \xi_y$ should be valid for benzene if one takes the molecular z axis to be perpendicular to the plane of the molecule. In such systems, the general expressions for $F_s(t, \mathcal{K})$ and $F_c(t, \mathcal{K})$ can be considerably simplified, particularly if the assumptions listed above are invoked. The resulting expression which gives the width of depolarized scattered light can be written:

$$\left[I(t,\mathcal{K})\right]_{HV} = \left[I(0,\mathcal{K})\right]_{HV} \left\langle e^{i\underset{\sim}{\mathcal{K}}\cdot \delta\underset{\sim}{r}_{11}} \right\rangle e^{-\left[6kT/\xi_x\right]t} \tag{27}$$

However, the change of $\left\langle \exp\left(i\underset{\sim}{\mathcal{K}}\cdot \delta\underset{\sim}{r}_{11}\right)\right\rangle$ due to translational displacements is quite small compared to the decay of $\exp\left[(-6kT/\xi_x)t\right]$ which is due to rotational motion. Although this statement is evidently not applicable to all fluids, it is clearly true in the case of benzene, as may be seen by comparing the width of the depolarized scattered light (6,0 cm^{-1}) with that of the light scattered by translational fluctuations (.32 cm^{-1}). In fact, a line width of 6,0 cm^{-1} implies that $\xi_x/6kT = 1.9 \cdot 10^{-12}$ sec. for benzene at room temperature. In contrast, the depolarized scattered light from ethylene glycol at room temperature[12] shows a distinctly different behavior. When observed using a He-Ne laser and an interferometer, the usual depolarized background is found, which indicates that at least one rotational motion is present with relaxation time which is too short to give an observable line shape with the interferometer; in addition to this, the depolarized spectrum contains a narrow line which is centered on the incident frequency and which is broadened by $\sim$ .02 cm. This broadening corresponds to a rotational relaxation time of $\sim 1.6 \cdot 10^{-10}$ sec. Note that the microscopic dielectric relaxation time[21] (corrected for internal field effects) is $\sim 3 \cdot 10^{-11}$ sec.; if the Brownian motion model is applicable, this should give rise to a relaxation time for depolarized light scattered due to dipolar reorientation which is $3(3 \cdot 10^{-11})$ or $\sim 10^{-10}$ sec. It is thus reasonable to suppose that the narrow line in the scattered light is due to reorientation of the molecular dipole moment, and that the broad line is due to more rapid rotational motions which probably do not involve appreciable dipolar reorientation.

Table I

Experimental data for liquids at 20°C., $\mathcal{K} \cong 10^5$ cm^{-1}.

Substance	Brillouin splitting[17] (cm^{-1})	Rotational relaxation times[20] (sec. 10^{12})	Rotational broadenings (cm^{-1})
Benzene	.16	1.8	6.0
Carbon disulfide	.15	1.9	5.6
Toluene	.15	4.0	2.6

Finally, the total intensity for a system in which $\alpha_1 = 0$ is given by

$$[I(0,\mathcal{K})]_{VV} = \rho\, |Y|^2 \{\alpha_o^{\,2}\, \rho k T\, \mathcal{K}_T + \frac{4}{45}\, F(0,\mathcal{K})\} \quad (28)$$

$$[I(0,\mathcal{K})]_{HV} = \rho\, |Y|^2\, \frac{3}{45}\, F(0,\mathcal{K}) \quad (29)$$

Now $F(0,\mathcal{K})$ is nearly independent of $\mathcal{K}$ for systems where $\underset{\sim}{\mathcal{K}} \cdot \underset{\sim}{r}_{12} \ll 1$ for values of $\underset{\sim}{r}_{12}$ which correspond to appreciable correlation between molecules 1 and 2. In this case, one can write

$$\lim_{\mathcal{K} \to 0} F(0,\mathcal{K}) = \alpha_2^{\,2} \{1 + \rho \left\langle \sqrt{\frac{8\pi^2}{5}}\, D^2_{0,0}\, (\Omega_{12}) \right\rangle \} \quad (30)$$

If the optical constants of the molecule are known, it is thus possible to obtain an experimental measurement of $3/2 \cos^2 \theta_{12} - 1/2$ by evaluating:

$$\frac{[I(0,\chi)]_{HV}}{[I(0,\chi)]_{VV} - \frac{4}{3}[I(0,\chi)]_{HV}} = \frac{\alpha_2^{\,2}\{1+\rho\langle \frac{3}{2}\cos^2\theta_{12} - \frac{1}{2}\rangle\}}{15\,\alpha_o^{\,2}\,\rho\,kT\,\chi_T} \tag{31}$$

If both α_1 and α_2 are not zero, the theoretical equations for the intensity of depolarized light become much more complicated. However, some simplifications can be made if the system is characterized by a few well-separated rotational relaxation times which produce a spectrum of scattered light made up of distinctly different contributions, since the total intensities associated with the various relaxation times can then be calculated separately. In this way, the degree of angular correlation associated with each relaxation mechanism can be estimated.

3. DISCUSSION

Although the explicit results obtained in this paper are based on rather crude models for translational and rotational motion in the fluid, it is actually possible to refine the calculations considerably by modifying the Brownian motion models to include inertial effects, or the effects of the acceleration due to the fixed position of another molecule. However, at the present time, it does not appear that sufficient experimental detail is available to require such refinements in the theory. For example, the expressions given here all predict Lorentzian line shapes, but it is known that one obtains a Gaussian line if inertial effects are predominant.[22] However, no quantitative measurements of line shapes have yet been published, even for the depolarized lines which are broad enough to have easily measurable shapes. The best experiments of this type are Raman scattering spectra for simple liquids[23, 24] which do appear to indicate that inertial effects can be quite important in the rotation of simple molecules in fluids.[6]

Although the theory given here also shows how the integrated intensity of depolarized scattered light is related to the static angular correlations, it is not clear that it can be compared to experiment without including corrections for depolarization due to internal field effects,[25, 26] for changes in the optical polarizability tensor as the density of the fluid changes, or for scattering which is a non-linear function of the intensity of the incident beam.[10, 26]

It is hoped that the importance of these effects can be minimized by calculating intensity ratios rather than absolute intensities, but further theoretical work must be done to justify this procedure.

REFERENCES

1. W. A. Steele, J. Chem. Phys. 39, 3197 (1963).
2. F. Perrin, J. Phys. Radium 7, 1 (1936).
3. L. D. Favro, Phys. Rev. 119, 53 (1960).
4. K. A. Valiev and M. M. Zaripov, Sov. Phys. JETP 15, 353 (1962).
5. W. A. Steele, J. Chem. Phys. 38, 2411 (1963).
6. R. G. Gordon, J. Chem. Phys. 43, 1307 (1965).
7. H. Fröhlich, "Theory of Dielectrics" (Oxford University Press, London, 1949).
8. W. A. Steele, J. Chem. Phys. 43, 2598 (1965).
9. H. Benoit and W. H. Stockmayer, J. Phys. Radium 17, 21 (1956).
10. S. Kielich, Acta. Phys. Polon. 19, 149 (1960).
11. R. Pecora and W. A. Steele, J. Chem. Phys. 42, 1872 (1965).
12. D. H. Rank, A. Hollinger and D. P. Eastman, J. Opt. Soc. Am., 56, 1057 (1966).
13. M. E. Rose, "Elementary Theory of Angular Momentum" (John Wiley and Sons, New York, 1957) Chap. IV.
14. A. R. Edmonds, "Angular Momentum in Quantum Mechanics" (Princeton Univ. Press, Princeton, N. J., 1957) Chap. 4.
15. L. Landau and S. Lifshitz, "Electrodynamics of Continuous Media" (Addison-Wesley Publishing Co., Inc., Reading, Mass., 1960).
16. R. D. Mountain, Rev. Mod. Phys. 38, 206 (1966).
17. H. Z. Cummins and R. W. Gammon, J. Chem. Phys. 44, 2785 (1966).
18. D. H. Rank, E. M. Kiess, U. Fink and T. A. Wiggins, J. Opt. Soc. Am., 55, 925 (1965).

19. M. F. Vuks and A. K. Atakhodzhaev, Optika i Spectroskopiya 5, 51 (1958).

20. M. F. Vuks and A. K. Atakhodzhaev, Sov. Phys. (Doklady) 1, 496 (1956).

21. F. Buckley and A. A. Maryott, National Bureau of Standards Circular 589 (U. S. Gov. Printing Office, 1958) p. 26.

22. R. Kubo, in "Fluctuations, Relaxation and Resonance in Magnetic Systems," Ed. D. Ter Haar (Oliver and Boyd, Ltd., Edingburgh, 1962).

23. M. F. Vuks and V. L. Litvinov, Doklady Akad. Nauk. SSSR 105, 696 (1955).

24. A. V. Rakov, Optics and Spectroscopy 7, 128 (1959).

25. M. Fixman, J. Chem. Phys. 23, 2074 (1955).

26. R. Zwanzig, J. Am. Chem. Soc. 86, 3489 (1964).

Anon.: Did you consider any internal field effects in the Einstein theory of light scattering? In the isotropic case it only makes a difference in the constant factor independent of k, κ, or ω.

Steele: I haven't really considered the internal field effects in detail. They are pretty well lumped into this factor Y which I haven't really specified, and as long as one is taking ratios of various intensities scattered by different mechanisms, the internal field effects at least in part cancel out. This is why this interpretation of Landau-Placzek theory in terms of ratios of the intensities of the two lines, works pretty well. The ratios of the intensities are given in terms of the heat capacity differences and this seems to agree with experiments, even though one can't predict absolute values of the intensity of the scattered light too well because of lack of knowledge of internal field effects. The same sort of analysis can be done for the rotational contributions to the depolarized scattered intensity.

VELOCITY AUTOCORRELATION FUNCTION IN LIQUID ARGON: A HINDERED-TRANSLATOR MODEL *)

V. ARDENTE
Joint Nuclear Research Centre, Euratom, Ispra
and
G. F. NARDELLI
Istituto di Fisica, Università di Milano
and
L. REATTO **)
Applicazioni Ricerche Scientifiche, Milano

ABSTRACT

A model is proposed for the interpretation of computer experiments on liquid dynamics in terms of an ensemble average. The dynamical unit entering the model is a hindered translator, and the computer-experiment data on the correlated pair distribution function $g(r, \mu; \tau)$ as well as the interatomic potential $\varphi(r)$ are used as input data for the evaluation of the potential-energy function $U(r, \mu; \tau)$. Dissipation processes are taken into account in the weak-collision hypothesis through suitable relaxation times. The velocity autocorrelation function and its Fourier spectrum are evaluated on the assumption that no transitions between vibrational and translational states occur during the time the dynamical correlation persists. The velocity autocorrelation function is

*) Work supported by the Euratom-A.R.S. Milano contract N. 196 - 65 - 4 ISP-I.

**) Present address: Laboratory of Atomic and Solid State Physics, Cornell University, Ithaca, New York.

found to be a weighted superposition of a vibrational and a translational term; the statistical weights are shown to be related to the vibrational frequencies and to the height of the barrier against translations. A preliminary estimate of the Fourier transform of the vibrational and translational components is presented and compared with Rahman's "rattling" and "slipping" components. A qualitative agreement is found. It is shown that a precise evaluation of the energy barrier on the basis of $g(r, \mu; \tau)$, when compared with the experimental activation energy for self-diffusion, can allow some predictions on the existence of a free-volume mechanism in self-diffusion.

1. INTRODUCTION

In recent times the correlated motion of atoms in a classical monoatomic liquid has begun to be investigated by means of computer experiments[1, 2]. The main result of these investigations concerns the manner in which the motion of an individual particle is related to the configuration of the surrounding particles. This correlation was evaluated by the quoted authors in terms of a distribution $g(r, \mu; \tau)$, which, in addition to the dependence on the distance r, contains through the quantity $\mu = \cos\theta$ the angular correlation between the "displacement direction in time τ" of a given particle and the position of a neighbouring particle. Rahman was able to calculate on a computer, using the method of molecular dynamics,the velocity autocorrelation function $\langle \vec{v}(t) \cdot \vec{v}(0) \rangle$ and its spectrum $f(\omega)$. These were found to have characteristics related to the local fluctuation in the distribution of the neighbouring particles.

In order to give some insight on the molecular dynamics in liquids, the present authors recently proposed a model[3] in which every particle is thought to behave as a damped hindered translator. The starting point of that model was the idea that in a liquid which exhibits a well-defined activation energy Q for self-diffusion, every particle carries out translations only when it overcomes a potential energy barrier of height U_o equal to Q. In this way vibrational and translational components were included in the dynamics of an individual particle and it was possible to evaluate the weight with which these two components contribute to the velocity autocorrelation function.

The result of the last Rahman experiment seems to indicate that (i), in the range r = 3.29 - 3.75 Å, $g(r, \mu; z)$ exhibits a marked decrease of the nearer neighbors along "the displacement direction", and (ii) the structure of the velocity autocorrelation function for liquid Argon can be "resolved", i.e. the velocity autocorrelation function can be separated into the sum of a vibrational and a translational component.

Rahman's experiment consists in simulating on a computer the dynamics of a large number of interacting particles at given density and temperature, and in following them during their dynamical evolution in time. In order to exhibit the role that the local fluctuation plays in self-diffusion, Rahman introduces the direction of displacement of a particle in time τ, i.e. $\vec{r}(\tau) - \vec{r}(0)$, and the distribution function $g(r, \mu; \tau)$; then he splits the velocity autocorrelation function into longitudinal $< v_L(t)\ v_L(0) >$ and transverse $< \vec{v}_T(t) \cdot \vec{v}_T(0) >$ components with respect to this direction. The value of τ which makes the longitudinal component to have gas-like behaviour, enables Rahman to give a picture of the local fluctuation in the distribution of the neighbouring particles, through the evaluation of $g(r, \mu; \tau)$. In doing this, Rahman implicitly assumes that this value of τ represents, essentially, the duration of the local fluctuation. To evaluate the velocity autocorrelation function Rahman follows the trajectory of a given particle and then takes the average over a large number of equivalent trajectories. It should then be possible to find a correspondence between the result of a computer experiment and the result of an ensemble average.

In the present paper we try to give an interpretation to Rahman's result on the velocity autocorrelation function in terms of an ensemble average. As dynamical unit we use the hindered translator we have mentioned above.

2. THE DYNAMICAL UNIT

The dynamical unit we are considering here consists of a particle (hereafter called test particle) in a potential well $U(r, \mu; z)$. We use Rahman's distribution $g(r, \mu; \tau)$ and the interatomic potential $\varphi(r)$ as input data in order to define the potential function in our dynamical unit. We have

$$U(r, \mu; \tau) \equiv \int dr' \varphi(|\vec{r}' - \vec{r}|) g(r', \mu'; \tau). \qquad (1)$$

The displacement direction in time τ is the direction which makes $< v_L(t)\, v_L(0) >$ as close as possible to a gas-like velocity autocorrelation function; then it seems to be a natural assumption to identify $U(r), \mu; \tau)$ as the average potential energy which is felt by the test particle on the time-scale of the local fluctuation which is involved in the diffusion process.

The quoted behaviour of $g(r, \mu; \tau)$ suggests that, along the displacement direction, $U(r, \mu = 1; \tau)$ could be a flat function of r, or, alternatively, it could display a saddle point. On the basis of Rahman's data it is difficult to decide about the actual situation. Here we adopt the second point of view. This is equivalent to assume that

$$U_o = U(r_o, \mu = 1; \tau),$$

is the saddle-point energy.
The position r_o of the saddle point along the displacement direction in time τ, has to be determined by looking for the saddle point of the potential-energy function as given by (1).

Keeping in mind the definition of $g(r, \mu; \tau)$ and assuming that r_o is very close to the absolute value of the displacement in time τ, say $|\vec{r}(\tau) - \vec{r}(0)|$, of the test particle, $U(r, \mu; \tau)$ is seen to include a sort of "memory" of all the dynamical events which make the test particle able to overcome in a time τ the potential - energy barrier U_o.

Dissipation processes are included in our dynamical unit by considering the neighbouring particles as a loss mechanism.

We assume that a coordinate-axis transformation which brings the z-axis to be aligned with the displacement direction in time τ makes the equation of motion of our dynamical unit to be separable. Then, following Rahman, we split the velocity autocorrelation function as

$$<\vec{v}(t) \cdot \vec{v}(0)> = <v^2> \{R_\tau(t) + S_\tau(t)\} , \tag{2}$$

where

$$<v^2> S_\tau(t) = <v_\zeta(t)\, v_\zeta(0)> , \tag{3}$$

and

$$<v^2> R_\tau(t) = <v_\xi(t)\, v_\xi(0) + v_\eta(t)\, v_\eta(0)> . \tag{4}$$

ζ is the coordinate along the displacement direction in time τ and ξ and η two coordinates in transverse direction.

The energy $E = U_o$ splits the phase space of the test particle in two regions, i.e.: $0 \leq E_\zeta < U_o$ (hereafter denoted by I) and $U_o < E_\zeta$ (hereafter denoted by II); E_ζ denotes the energy associated with the motion along the displacement direction in time τ.

In order to make the evaluation of the velocity autocorrelation function easier, we introduce some more simplifying assumptions. First of all we split $<v_\zeta(t)\, v_\zeta(0)>$ as

$$<v_\zeta(t)\, v_\zeta(0)>^{I} + <v_\zeta(t)\, v_\zeta(0)>^{II} = <v^2> \left\{ S_\tau^{I}(t) + S_\tau^{II}(t) \right\} , \tag{5}$$

where the superscript I or II indicates the region in which the ensemble average has been performed.

Next, we assume that a phase-space trajectory which starts at time $t = 0$ in a given energy region remains in the same region during the time the dynamical correlation with the neighbouring particles persists.

Finally, we approximate by harmonic oscillations with frequencies ω_T and ω_L, respectively, the motion in (ξ, η) - directions and in ζ - direction, if $E_\zeta < U_o$ (region I). Following Rahman, we represent the motion along the ζ coordinate in region II by a translator or by a harmonic oscillator with frequency ω_L, depending on whether we are considering motion in forward or backward directions.

These approximations enable us to write the "rattling" part of the velocity autocorrelation function as

$$R_{\tau}(t) + S_{\tau}^{I}(t) + S_{\tau}^{II,-}(t) =$$

$$= (2/3)\ \exp\left[-|t|/2\tau_R\right]\left[\cos\omega_R t - (1/2\omega_R\tau_R)\sin\omega_R|t|\right]$$

$$+ (1/3)\ (F_{I,\zeta} + \frac{1}{2}F_{II,\zeta})\ \exp\left[-|t|/2\tau'_R\right]\left[\cos\omega'_R t\right.$$

$$\left. - (1/2\omega'_R\tau'_R)\sin\omega'_R|t|\right], \qquad (6)$$

and the "slipping" part as

$$S_{\tau}^{II,+}(t) = (1/6)\ F_{II,\zeta}\ \exp\left[-|t|/2\tau_s\right]. \qquad (7)$$

A superscript + or - has been added to $S_{\tau}^{II}(t)$ in order to distinguish between motions in forward or backward directions. In writing expressions (6) and (7) it has been assumed that the loss mechanism for our dynamical unit can be simulated by the stochastic model considered by Wang and Uhlenbeck[4]. It is well known that the use of a stochastic model prevents the velocity autocorrelation function from representing the true dynamical correlation at very short times. However, keeping in mind that the physical picture on which our model is based is adequate only for times not too much smaller than the vibrational period, the use of the stochastic model considered by Wang and Uhlenbeck seems to be consistent with the approximation inherent to the model itself. ω_R and ω'_R are the frequencies for the transverse and longitudinal "rattling" motion, respectively; τ_R and τ'_R the corresponding relaxation times; τ_s the relaxation time for the "slipping" motion.

$$F_{I,\zeta} = \langle v_\zeta^2\rangle^I/\langle v_\zeta^2\rangle \text{ and } F_{II,\zeta} = \langle v_\zeta^2\rangle^{II}/\langle v_\zeta^2\rangle$$

are, respectively, the statistical weights associated with the regions I and II in the onedimensional phase space.

From the Einstein-Stokes relation, τ_s is seen to be

$$\tau_s = \frac{MD}{F_{II,\zeta}\, k_B T}, \qquad (8)$$

where D is the self-diffusion coefficient. K_B is the Boltzmann constant, T the absolute temperature, and M the particle mass.

It has been shown in a previous paper[3] that ω_R and ω'_R can be written as

$$\omega_R = \omega_T(1 + \delta_T) , \quad (9a)$$

and

$$\omega'_R = \omega_L(1 + \delta_L) , \quad (9b)$$

where δ is the dimensionless frequency shift due to dissipation.

From expression (1) ω_T^2 and ω_L^2 are seen to be

$$\omega_T^2 = (\pi/M) \int_0^\infty dr\, r^2 \int_{-1}^{+1} d\mu\, (1 - \mu^2) \left[\varphi''(r) - \frac{1}{r}\varphi'(r)\right] g(r, \mu; \tau)$$

$$+ (4\pi/M) \int_0^\infty dr\, r\varphi'(r)\, g(r) , \quad (10a)$$

and

$$\omega_L^2 = (2\pi/M) \int_0^\infty dr\, r^2 \int_{-1}^{+1} d\mu\, \mu^2 \left[\varphi''(r) - \frac{1}{r}\varphi'(r)\right] g(r, \mu; \tau)$$

$$+ (4\pi/M) \int_0^\infty dr\, r\varphi'(r)\, g(r) . \quad (10b)$$

In expressions (10a) and (10b) g(r) is the usual radial distribution function.

The expression for τ_R was given in a previous paper[3]; it reads

$$\frac{1}{\tau_R} = \left[2\omega_T B_2 + \gamma + (n\omega_T/2\pi) \exp\left[-U_o/k_B T\right]\right] , \quad (11)$$

where $B_2 = \langle\alpha^2\rangle^{1/2} / 2M\omega_T^2$; $\langle\alpha^2\rangle$ measures the coupling constant for the relaxation process and is given by

$$\langle\alpha^2\rangle = \frac{1}{3} \sum_{x,y} \int d\vec{r}\, g(r) \frac{\partial^2}{\partial x\, \partial y} \varphi(r) \frac{\partial^2}{\partial x\, \partial y} \varphi(r) ; \quad (12)$$

n denotes the nearest-neighbour coordination number; γ is the hard - collision probability per unit time. An expression analogous to (11) holds for τ'_R .

3. NUMERICAL RESULTS AND DISCUSSION

Let us comment briefly on the physical ideas underlying our model. The evaluation of the velocity autocorrelation function is here approached by looking at the dynamical evolution of a test particle, rather than at the equation for the autocorrelation function itself[5, 6].

Our aim in doing this is to see how much a suitable choice of the potential function makes the one-particle dynamics able to predict the time behaviour of the velocity autocorrelation function. The essential point is the choice of the potential function; it seems to us that the potential $U(r, \mu; \tau)$ we have considered here enables us to include in the potential itself a sort of memory of the effects that, at the advanced time τ , the local fluctuations of the surrounding cage have on the test particle.

With the aim of testing the reliability of our model for the interpretation of the results of computer experiments on liquids, we have performed a preliminary estimate of the velocity autocorrelation function in liquid Argon as well as of its "rattling" and "slipping" components, as given respectively by expressions (2), (6), and (7). Since Rahman's data on $g(r, \mu; \tau)$ reported up to now are too poor to be employed in numerical calculations, we adopted the following assumptions: (i) U_o, the saddle-point energy, corresponds to the activation energy Q for self-diffusion, and (ii) the frequency ω_o, as deduced from Rahman's g(r), represents a good estimate of an average vibrational frequency[3]. On the assumption that no free-volume mechanism operates in Argon self-diffusion, it seems to be quite natural to put $U_o = Q$. On the contrary the second assumption needs to be improved on the basis of expressions (10a) and (10b).

For the values of the other quantities entering expressions (6), (7), and (11) reference is made to our previous paper. D was choosen equal to the value obtained by Rahman.

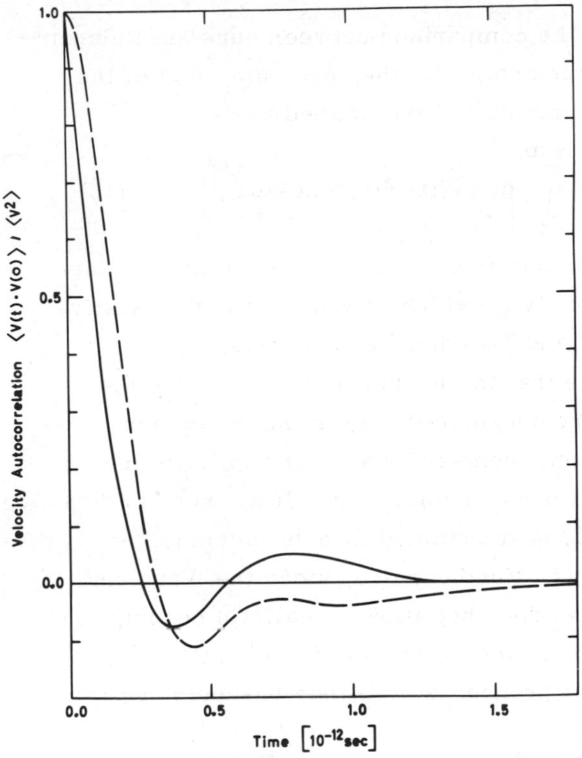

Fig. 1. Ensemble-average velocity autocorrelation function (continuous line) showing the comparison with the Rahman computer experiment for liquid Argon.

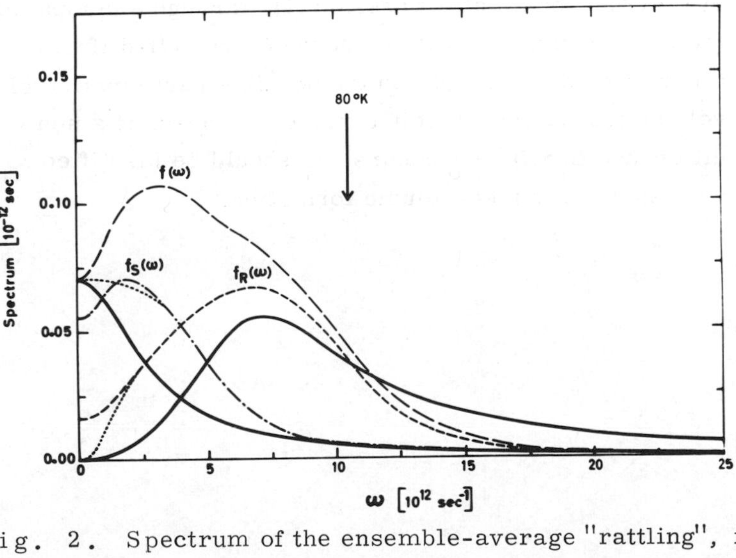

Fig. 2. Spectrum of the ensemble-average "rattling", $f_R(\omega)$, and "slipping", $f_S(\omega)$, components (continuous lines), showing the comparison with Rahman's results. The arrow shows the value of the Debye temperature for solid Argon near its melting point.

Figures 1 and 2 show the comparison between ours and Rahman's results. The Fourier transform, i. e. the spectrum, $f(\omega)$ of the velocity autocorrelation function is here defined as

$$f(\omega) = \pi^{-1} \langle v^2 \rangle^{-1} \int_{-\infty}^{+\infty} dt \, \langle \vec{v}(t) \cdot \vec{v}(0) \rangle \cos \omega t \, , \qquad (13)$$

so that it is normalized to unit area from $\omega = 0$ to ∞. A qualitative agreement is found for $\langle \vec{v}(t) \cdot \vec{v}(0) \rangle$ as well as for the relative intensity of the "rattling" and "slipping" components.

It is worthwhile to note that in the present approach the effects of hard collisions are considered only in the relaxation time τ_R, but hard collisions themselves are not explicitly included in the time evolution of our dynamical unit. If we were to do so, one of the effects we would have obtained is a broadening of the "slipping" component. Furthermore, since the Wang and Uhlenbeck stochastic model does not allow a realistic description at short times, our result for the spectrum of the "rattling" component exhibits a more pronounced tail than it should really have.

As a final remark, it seems to us that a precise evaluation of U_o on the basis of expression (1), through a comparison with the experimental activation energy Q for self-diffusion, should allow to shed some light on the possible participation of a free-volume mechanism in self-diffusion. Indeed, if a non-vanishing difference $\Delta = Q - U_o$ occurs, it should be identified with energy for free-volume formation.

REFERENCES

1. A. Rahman, Phys. Rev. 136, A 405 (1964);
A. Rahman, Proceedings of the Topical Meeting of the American Nuclear Society, S. Diego, Calif., February 1966, (M.I.T. Press) Vol. I, p. 123.
A. Rahman, J. Chem. Phys. 45, 2585 (1966).

2. A. Paskin and A. Rahman, Phys. Rev. Letters, 16, 300 (1966).

3. V. Ardente, G. F. Nardelli, and L. Reatto, Proceedings of the Topical Meeting of the American Nuclear Society, S. Diego, Calif., February 1966, (M.I.T. Press) Vol. I, p. 73.
V. Ardente, G. F. Nardelli, and L. Reatto, Phys. Rev. 148, 124 (1966).

4. M. C. Wang and G. E. Uhlenbeck, Rev. Mod. Phys. 17, 323 (1945); see also S. Chandrasekhar, ibid., 15, 1 (1943).

5. Stuart A. Rice, "Some Comments on the Usefulness of the Concept of Coherence Time in the Statistical Theory of Liquids" (this Conference).

6. Bruce J. Berne, Jean Pierre Boon, and Stuart A. Rice, J. Chem. Phys. 45, 1086 (1966).

Rice: In my opinion this calculation gives a completely erroneous interpretation of the motion of an atom in a liquid. Zwanzig derived an exact result for the time dependence of the autocorrelation function. This equation has the property that the autocorrelation function is, in a certain sence, a functional of itself (Résibois and de Leener).
Equations of this type have oscillatory solutions. Indeed, the oscillatory behaviour has nothing to do with harmonic oscillators.

Ardente: It is well known that the method of working out an equation for the autocorrelation function is, in principle, more powerful than the method of looking at the single-particle dynamics. However, two kinds of arguments seem to be applicable to the first method. The first concerns the reliability of the approximations one needs to introduce, in order to make the exact Zwanzig integro differential equation a practical tool for the evaluation of the velocity autocorrelation function. The second one concerns the relation which must exist between the time behaviour of the kernèl of this equation and the actual physical situation in liquids. For what concerns the first argument, it seems to me that no consensus of opinion has been reached till now about a general reliability of a simple exponential behaviour of the kernel.
As regards the second one, in my opinion, it is still an open question, and it seems to me quite hard to draw definite conclusion about the physical meaning of the solutions of the equation you have mentioned.

In conclusion, I do not see, a priori, any inconsistency between our model and the results that one can obtain on the basis of Zwanzig's equation.

Rice: Be that as it may, I believe your model is seriously incorrect.

Ardente: Do you have evidence ?

Rice: What would you accept as evidence? There is no evidence for the existance of harmonic oscillators in a liquid (neglecting sound waves). Studies of transport phemonena are also not in agreement with activated state models, significant structure models, etc., at least in the case of Argon. The distribution of mean free paths in a hard sphere liquid shows no preference for jumps - only gas like motion. I expect this is true for Argon also. Finally, better agreement than you obtain with the Rahman experiments is obtained from the equation mentioned above and a memory ansatz (see my paper).

Ardente: On this point I have quite a different opinion. The recent results of Rahman on $g(r, \mu; \tau)$ seem to indicate that the potential energy which is felt by a particle during its motion in liquid Argon really exhibits a well defined minimum and a saddle point. Although Rahman's results might not admit a unique interpretation, our model represents the first attempt to give a physical interpretation of such results.

NON MARKOVIAN EFFECTS AND EVOLUTION OF ENTROPY IN SPIN SYSTEMS

J. PHILIPPOT AND
D. WALGRAEF. Faculté
des Sciences, Université
Libre de Bruxelles, Belgique.

Nuclear paramagnetic relaxation in solids is especially interesting for the study of irreversible processes. The experimental techniques offer many possibilities for preparing non equilibrium situations and analyzing the approach to equilibrium in all its details.

The Hamiltonian of a lattice of interacting spins placed in a constant (and large) external field has the form

$$H = H_z + \Sigma_{s=o,\pm 1,\pm 2} V_s \tag{1}$$

where H_z is the Zeeman energy and where the dipole-dipole interaction has been splitted in several terms V_s characterized by their commutation relations with the total angular momentum

$$[S_z, V_s] = s\hbar\, V_s \tag{2}$$

These relations show that V_o commutes with the Zeeman energy. We shall therefore work in the representation where H_z and V_o are diagonal. The V_s terms induce transitions between states whose Zeeman energies differ by $s\hbar\omega_o$ (ω_o being the Larmor frequency).

A characteristic time of such a system is given by ω_1^{-1}, the inverse of the Larmor frequency in the local field, i.e. the field originating from the neighbouring spins. ω_1^{-1} is for a crystal like Ca F_2 of the order of 10^{-5} sec. This time is very long on the molecular scale. This is the reason why it is possible to observe phenomena which are not described by a Pauli equation which is only valid for times much longer than ω_1^{-1}. One has to use either the fundamental equation of motion for the density matrix

$$i\hbar \frac{\partial \rho}{\partial t} = [H, \rho] \tag{3}$$

or the non Markovian master equation of the form

$$\frac{\partial \rho^d}{\partial t} = \int_0^t K(t-z)\, \rho^d(z)\, dz + D \tag{4}$$

where ρ^d is the diagonal part of the density matrix and where D is the destruction term in Prigogine and Résibois's formalism[1). This terms takes the presence of initial correlations into account.

A recent experiment of Strombotne and Hahn[2) offers a beautiful example of such phenomena. These authors studied how a system of nuclear spins in internal equilibrium and thus represented by a density matrix of the form

$$\rho(t=0) = \frac{\exp(-\beta\, \Sigma_s V_s)}{\mathrm{Tr}\left[\exp(-\beta\, \Sigma_s V_s)\right]} \cong \frac{1-\beta\, \Sigma_s V_s}{\mathrm{Tr}\, 1} \tag{5}$$

(with $\hbar\omega_1 \ll kT$

responds when a large external field is suddenly switched on. They found that the macroscopic magnetization is built up in an oscillatory way at the expense of the non secular dipole-dipole energy. This process is thus essentially described by the destruction term. The calculations are most easily performed using for ρ an expansion in orthogonal operators of the form

$$\rho(t) = \left[1 + \alpha(t)\, H_z + \beta(t)\, V_o + \Sigma_{s \neq o}\, \gamma_s(t)\, V_s + \ldots\right] (\mathrm{Tr}\, 1)^{-1} \tag{6}$$

In a large external field, the evolution towards equilibrium occurs in the three steps:

a) the macroscopic magnetization is built up, the oscillations are damped in a time of the order of ω_1^{-1}, α becomes nearly equal to γ.

b) In a time of the order $\omega_1^{-1} \left(\frac{\omega_o}{\omega_1}\right)^2$ the dipole-dipole system comes to internal equilibrium.

c) α, β, γ become equal, this is the Zeeman - dipole-dipole relaxation.

As time increases, the density matrix ρ, if one starts from an initial state (5) will involve more and more orthogonal operators expressing correlations between a large number of spins. However, if the system is ergodic, the asymptotic solution should be only a function of the total Hamiltonian. We therefore expect that starting from (5) new operators will appear for short times but disappear asymptotically. If we restrict ourselves to the first order in the perturbation V_s, we can show that these operators vanish for times of the order of the relaxation time of the dipole-dipole system. To first order in ω_1/ω_o, the solution is

$$\rho(t) = \left[1 + \alpha(t) H_z + \beta(t) V_o + \Sigma_s \gamma_s(t) V_s + \Sigma_s \varphi_s(t) A_s\right] (\mathrm{Tr}\ 1)^{-1} \tag{7}$$

with

$$A_s = e^{-iV_o \frac{t}{\hbar}} V_s e^{+iV_o \frac{t}{\hbar}} - V_s \frac{\mathrm{Tr}\{V_{-s} e^{-iV_o \frac{t}{\hbar}} V_s e^{iV_o \frac{t}{\hbar}}\}}{\mathrm{Tr}(V_s V_{-s})}$$

The operator A_s has a more complicated physical meaning. The second term ensures the orthogonality with the V_s operators. This expression of A_s is found from the formal solution of ρ in the interaction representation. Expressions for the coefficients $\alpha, \beta, \gamma_s, \varphi_s$, valid for times of the order of ω_1^{-1} are easily written[3]. The corresponding canonical entropy is

$$\mathrm{Tr}\,\rho \ln \rho = Nk \ln(2I+1) - \frac{k}{2}\left[\alpha^2(t)\,\frac{\mathrm{Tr}\,H_z^2}{\mathrm{Tr}\,1} + \dots\right] \tag{8}$$

and it is constant as it should be. In this first step of the evolution we thus observe the irreversible behaviour of the magnetization while we verify at the same time that the canonical entropy remains constant.

To analyse the behaviour of the system for longer times, we follow a recent work of Prigogine, Henin and George[4] on anharmonic oscillators and we split $\gamma_s(t)$ and $\varphi_s(t)$ in a first part $\gamma_s^1(t)$, $\varphi_s^1(t)$ depending on $\gamma_s(0)$, i.e. on the initial correlations and in a second part $\gamma_s^{(2)}(t), \varphi_s^{(2)}(t)$

$$\gamma_s(t) = \gamma_s^1(t) + \gamma_s^{(2)}(t)$$

$$\varphi_s(t) = \varphi_s^{(1)}(t) + \varphi_s^{(2)}(t) \tag{9}$$

depending on $\alpha(0)$ or on ρ^d. This separation induces a corresponding one for the canonical entropy.

$$S_{can} = S^I + S^{II} + S^{III} \tag{10}$$

S^I depends on the initial correlations, S^{II} is a functional of $\rho^d(t)$ and t and S^{III} is a functional of $\rho^d(t)$ alone. S^I vanishes after a time of the order of ω_1^{-1}. In the second phase of the evolution, the dipole-dipole system goes to equilibrium in a time of the order of $\omega_1^{-1}(\frac{\omega_o}{\omega_1})^2$ and $\varphi_s(t)$ and S^{II} vanish.

According to Prigogine, Henin and George, we may define the thermodynamical entropy as that part of the canonical entropy which is a functional of $\rho^d(t)$ as well at equilibrium as out equilibrium.

This part is equal to

$$S_{th} = \mathrm{Tr}\,\rho^d \ln \rho^d - \frac{k}{2} \sum_{s\neq 0} \gamma_s^{(2)}(t)\, \gamma_{-s}^{(2)}(t)\, \mathrm{Tr}\, V_s V_{-s} \tag{11}$$

Using this definition, one finds that the thermodynamical entropy is also, for $t > \omega_1^{-1}$, that part of the canonical entropy which is related to simple macroscopic observables. We think that the expansion in orthogonal operators shows clearly how irreversibility is related to a projection of ρ on a particular subspace.

REFERENCES

1. Résibois, P., Physica 29, (1963), 721.
2. Strombotne, R. L. and Hahn, E. L., Phys. Rev. 133, A 1616 (1964).
3. Philippot, J. and Walgraef, D., Physica 32, (1966).
4. I. Prigogine and F. Henin., Physics Letters 20, 255, (1966).

DISCUSSION

Snider: How did you eliminate the quadratic terms in V_s from your entropy expression?

Philippot: The expression (8) for the canonical entropy is valid in the neighborhood of the uniformity in the Hilbert space. There are as many quadratic terms as orthogonal operators in the expression (7) for ρ.

Snider: You said this was constant.

Philippot: Yes, the canonical entropy is constant as a consequence of the equations of motion (3).

Kubo: What is the criterion to find which part of the canonical entropy is to be identified with the thermodynamic entropy?

Philippot: The three terms S^I, S^{II} and S^{III} are characterized by their time dependence. S^I and S^{II} vanish for times of the order of the relaxation time. S^{III} is a functional of $\rho^d(t)$.

Kubo: Does the canonical entropy change in time?

Philippot: By compensation the total entropy is constant.

Sewell: Am I correct in thinking that the macroscopic entropy will not monotonically increase with time?

Philippot: Yes, the two definitions are equivalent only for times longer than the oscillation time ω_l^{-1}.

KINETIC EQUATION , QUASIPARTICLES AND ENTROPY

I. PRIGOGINE
and
F. HENIN
Faculté des Sciences
Université Libre de Bruxelles
Belgique.

SUMMARY.

Starting with the general evolution equation we have derived for the energy (or velocity) distribution function, we first define what may be called the "Post Boltzmannian approximation" of statistical physics. In this kinetic equation the finite duration of the collisions is taken into account in an asymptotic way.

A transformation theory of the kinetic equation is presented in § 2. It is shown that, by means of a suitable transformation of ρ_0 (the velocity distribution function in classical mechanics or the diagonal elements of the von Neumann density matrix in quantum mechanics), the kinetic equation can be brought into a form such that the collision operator is hermitian to all orders in the coupling constant. Therefore in the whole range of validity of the Post-Boltzmannian approximation, the approach to equilibrium is monotonous (for times larger than the collision time).

In § 3, a new general transformation theory of interest for large dissipative systems is presented. The main feature of this theory is that these transformations involve only the diagonal elements of the density matrix. The effect of the off-diagonal elements is absorbed in a new definition of the observables. The transformation laws are such that all average values remain invariant exactly as for usual unitary transformations.

Our basic problem is then to find a transformation to a representation in which both equilibrium and non equilibrium properties take a specially simple form, formally identical to that for weakly coupled or dilute systems. For this reason, we call such a representation the "Boltzmann representation".

In § 4. we give the explicit form of the transformation leading to the Boltzmann representation for anharmonic lattices. The physical meaning of the contributions to the kinetic equation becomes then quite simple.

A large part of the higher order terms can be added to the lowest order, Boltzmann type, contribution; this involves only a change in the definition of the energy (or frequency) and of the interactions. Once this is done the remaining terms represent genuine many body collisions whose physical meaning is clear.

In this way, we obtain a new approach to renormalization theory. While in all existing approaches to the renormalization and quasiparticles problem the existence of dissipative processes appears as the crucial difficulty, our approach is specifically conceived to deal with dissipative systems.

Once the "Boltzmann representation" is found, the $\mathcal{H}$- theorem is automatically secured. By going back to the usual representation we may discuss the microscopic meaning of entropy for strongly coupled systems. This is done in § 5. Perhaps one of the most unexpected aspects of this work is that we are now in a position to discuss the difference between the Boltzmann and the Gibbs statistical definitions of entropy.

In the Boltzmann representation of the density matrix, there exists a one to one correspondence between occupation numbers and diagonal elements of the density matrix. To each set $\{N\}$ of occupation numbers corresponds one and only one diagonal element. This leads to a new definition of "physical particles" and excitations which generalizes the usual concepts of field theory and of the Landau theory of the Fermi liquid because it permits to include in the definition of the excitations the effects of the finite life time and of dissipative processes.

1. - THE POST-BOLTZMANNIAN APPROXIMATION.

Let us start with the evolution equation we derived[1] for the energy (or velocity) distribution function, valid both in the classical and the quantum cases:

$$\frac{\partial \rho_o}{\partial t} = \int_0^t d\tau \, G(t-\tau)\, \rho_o(\tau) + D(t; \rho_k(o)) \qquad (1.1.)$$

In this equation G(t) is a generalized collision operator defined formally in terms of all irreducible vacuum of correlations to vacuum of correlations transitions. A fundamental role is played by the Laplace transform $\psi(z)$ of G(t),

$$\psi(z) = \langle 0 | \, \delta L \sum_{n=1}^{\infty} \left(\frac{1}{z - L_o} \delta L \right)^n | \, 0 \rangle_{irr} \qquad (1.2.)$$

where the index "irr" means that only terms such that all intermediate states are different from the vacuum of correlations ($|0\rangle$) must be taken into account. The quantity

$$L = L_o + \lambda \delta L \qquad (1.3.)$$

is the Liouville operator corresponding to a hamiltonian of the form

$$H = H_o + \lambda V \qquad (1.4.)$$

(for more details see [1])

The finite duration of the collision is expressed through the non-instantaneous character of equation (1.1). The second term in the r. h. s. of (1. 1) expresses the influence of initial correlations.

Equation (1. 1.) is exact and may be introduced every time a statistical description in terms of distribution functions appears as necessary or useful. However its very generality makes its use difficult.

Let us introduce the following three approximations into (1. 1).

1) we may neglect the effect of initial correlations;
2) we retain the effects of the finite duration of the collision only in an asymptotic way;
3) we retain only the lowest order contributions in terms of a suitable perturbation parameter.

Then equation (1. 1.) reduces to the "kinetic equation"

$$i \frac{\partial \rho_o}{\partial t} = \psi(0)\, \rho_o \qquad (1.\ 5.)$$

where $\psi(0)$ is the analytic continuation of $\psi(z)$ for $z \rightarrow +0$. According to the choice of the parameter, (1. 5.) reduces to one of the well known classes of transport equations (e. g. Fokker-Planck, Boltzmann, Balescu-Lenard...) The reduction of (1. 1) to (1. 5.) is possible if there exist two widely separated time scales t_{coll} and t_{rel} where t_{coll} is a time characterising the duration of the collision process and t_{rel} the relaxation time of the process. If moreover we consider the limit

$$\frac{t_{coll}}{t_{rel}} \longrightarrow 0 \qquad (1.\ 6.)$$

equation (1. 5.) is recovered. We may say that (1. 5.) corresponds to the Boltzmann approximation of statistical physics.

We shall be concerned here with a more general situation in which the third of the approximations we have mentioned is not used. We shall indeed consider situations such that

$$t_{rel} > t_{coll} \qquad (1.\ 7.\ )$$

but where the ratio of t_{coll} to t_{rel} is considered as a finite non vanishing quantity

$$\frac{t_{coll}}{t_{rel}} = \text{finite} < 1 \qquad (1.\ 8.\ )$$

Expanding in (1. 1.) $\rho_o(\tau)$ around $\rho_o(t)$ one may easily obtain [1)2)3)]

$$i \frac{\partial \rho_o}{\partial_t} = \Omega \psi(0)\ \rho_o(t) \qquad (1.\ 9.\ )$$

where Ω is a functional of $\psi(z)$ and its derivatives in respect to z, for $z \longrightarrow +0$. For example the first terms are

$$\Omega = 1 + \psi'(0) + \frac{1}{2}\psi''(0)\psi(0) + [\psi'(0)]^2 + \cdots \qquad (1.\ 10)$$

with

$$\psi'(0) = \left(\frac{d\psi}{dz}\right)_{z \to +o} \qquad (1.\ 11)\ \text{etc.}\ldots$$

The basic difference between (1. 5.) and (1. 9.) is that in (1. 9.) the finite duration of the collisions is taken into account through the operator Ω . The transition from equation (1. 1) to equation (1. 9.) is only possible if the relaxation process corresponds to the longest relevant time scale in the system. If this is not so, the singularities of ψ (z) in the lower half plane have to be taken into account explicitly (see in this connection a theorem due to Lagrange [4]).

Therefore there are certainly important problems involving many degrees of freedom which cannot be described through (1. 9.); examples are gravitational interactions for which the inequality (1. 7.) is not satisfied [5] and spin relaxation through a Heisenberg hamiltonian (see [6]) for which there does even not exist a double time scale.

Such "non-Boltzmannian" situations are explicitly excluded from our discussion. Even in this limited frame there are basic questions which remain unsolved : what are the general features of the approach to equilibrium ?
It may be shown that $i\,\psi(0)$ is a hermitian operator [7][8] (more generally $i\,\psi^{(n)}(0)$, where n is the order of derivation in respect to z , is hermitian for n even and antihermitian for n odd). Therefore in the Boltzmann approximation all relaxation times (the eigenvalues of the operator $i\,\psi(0)$) are real. We have a monotonous approach to equilibrium.

However in the Post-Boltzmannian approximation (1. 9.) we deal with the operator $\Omega\,\psi$ which contains non symmetrized products of non-commuting hermitian operators such as

$$\psi'(0) \cdot i\psi(0) \qquad (1.12.)$$

Therefore we can no more conclude a priori that the approach to equilibrium will be monotonous.

Closely related to this question is the statistical definition of entropy. In the frame of the Boltzmann approximation (1. 5.) the $\mathcal{H}$ -quantity as defined by Boltzmann *)

$$\mathcal{H}_B = \int d_p \, \rho_o(p) \log \rho_o(p) \qquad (1.13.)$$

leads directly to the $\mathcal{H}$ -theorem:

$$\frac{d\mathcal{H}_B}{dt} \leqq 0 \qquad (1.14.)$$

Does there exists in the Post-Boltzmannian approximation a functional which would exhibit a behavior similar to that of the Boltzmann $\mathcal{H}$ -quantity ?

Besides these very general questions there are others of a more technical nature. To apply (1. 9.) we have to understand its structure as precisely as possible. Now a detailed analysis as performed by Mangeney[9)] for charged particles interacting with an electromagnetic field, and by Résibois[10)] for the classical and quantum three body contributions to the transport equations has shown the occurrence of a bewildering variety of terms whose physical interpretation is not simple.

---

*) We use here the definition of $\mathcal{H}$ appropriate to a classical gas. Similar definitions exist of course for classical solids as well as for quantum systems.

To deal with these problems we shall now develop a transformation theory of the kinetic equation which, we expect, may play in statistical theory the same central role as unitary transformations in classical or quantum physics.

2. - TRANSFORMATION THEORY OF THE KINETIC EQUATION.

Let us start with the integral representation of the solution of equation (1. 1)

$$\rho_o(t) = -\frac{1}{2\pi i}\int_C dz\, e^{-izt}\left(-\frac{1}{z}\right)\sum_{n=0}^{\infty}\left(\frac{\psi(z)}{-z}\right)^n \rho_o\,(t=0) \quad (2.\ 1)$$

To simplify the notations we have assumed that at t = 0 all correlations are vanishing. The definition of the Laplace transform of the collision operator has been given in (1. 2).

The contour C in (2. 1) is in the upper half plane of the complex variable z above all singularities of the integrand. The Post-Boltzmannian approximation (1. 9) corresponds precisely to the situation in which all singularities of the integrand except the pole at z = 0 are neglected. We then obtain from (2. 1) after some simple manipulations

$$\rho_o(t) = e^{it\Omega\psi(0)}\, A\, \rho_o(0) \quad (2.\ 2)$$

where

$$A = \sum_{n=0}^{\infty}\frac{1}{n!}\left(\frac{d^n\psi^n(z)}{dz^n}\right)_{z\to+0} \quad (2.\ 3)$$

Of course (2. 2) satisfies the kinetic equation (1. 9) but the important feature is that in (2. 2) appears also the operator A which, exactly as Ω , is a well defined functional of ψ
For example, the first terms are according to (2. 3)

$$A = 1 + \psi'(0) + \frac{1}{2}\left[\psi''(0)\psi(0) + \psi(0)\psi''(0)\right] + \left[\psi'(0)\right]^2 + \cdots \tag{2, 4}$$

For t $\longrightarrow$ 0, formula (2. 2.) reduces to

$$\rho_0(t) \underset{t\to 0}{\longrightarrow} A\,\rho_0(0) \tag{2. 5. }$$

The operator A corresponds therefore to a short time correction (on the scale of the relaxation time) which has to be applied to the initial distribution ρ_0 (t = 0) because in equation (2. 2.) short time transients (corresponding e. g. to the poles of $\psi(z)$ in the lower half plane of z) have been neglected. As a consequence we have to redefine our initial condition.

It should also be noticed that $\Omega\psi$ and A are non-commuting operators. Therefore, the order in which they appear in (2. 2) is crucial.

The basic observation is now that the integral representation (2. 2) for $\rho_0(t)$ may be written in the symmetric form

$$\rho_0(t) = \chi\, e^{-it\varphi}\chi\, \rho_0(0) \tag{2. 6. }$$

Through identification with (2. 2) we see that

$$\chi\,\chi = A \tag{2. 7}$$

$$\varphi = \chi^{-1} \Omega \psi \chi \tag{2.8}$$

The characteristic feature of (2. 6) is that the operator χ "acts" both at t = 0 and at t while in (2. 2) A acted only on the distribution function at t= 0.

When A and $\Omega\psi$ are represented as expansions in powers of λ, the expressions (2. 7)-(2. 8) may be used to obtain similar expansions for χ and φ. The first terms are

$$\chi = 1 + \frac{\lambda^2}{2} \psi'(0) + \cdots \tag{2.9}$$

$$\varphi = \lambda^2 \psi_2(0) + \lambda^4 \{\psi_4(0) + \frac{1}{2} [\psi_2'(0), \psi_2(0)]_+ + \cdots \tag{2.10}$$

where $[\ ,\ ]_+$ is an anticommutator; ψ_2 is the part of ψ which is proportional to λ^2, ψ_4 to λ^4; as before $\psi'(0)$ is the derivative of ψ taken at z = + 0.

General recursion formulae have been given by Cl. George[7]. Let us now introduce the new distribution function

$$\tilde{\rho}_0(t) = \chi^{-1} \rho_0(t) \tag{2.11}$$

We see immediately from (2. 6) that it satisfies the kinetic equation

$$i \frac{\partial \tilde{\rho}_0}{\partial t} = \varphi \tilde{\rho}_0 \tag{2.12}$$

The most remarkable feature of the operator $i\varphi$ is that it is hermitian (We may verify this here easily on the first orders (for the general proof see[7]). As we have already noticed in §1, $i\psi^{(n)}(0)$ is a hermitian operator when the order n of derivation in respect to z is even, and antihermitian when n is odd. We also noticed that $\Omega\psi$ has no well defined hermiticity character. But as shown by (2. 10), $i\varphi$ contains only symmetrized expressions such as the anticommutator and is therefore hermitian exactly as $i\psi(0)$. Similarly, relation (2. 7) together with (2. 3) permits to prove that the operator χ is hermitian to all orders in λ To order λ^2 this is in agreement with (2. 9) as $\psi_2'(0)$ is also an hermitian operator.

There remains a degree of freedom open in the transformation (2. 11) . Indeed we may introduce an operator corresponding to an arbitrary unitary transformation χ'' and write (2. 6.) as

$$\rho_o(t) = \chi\chi'' e^{-it[\chi''^{-1}\varphi\chi'']} (\chi\chi'')^{-1} \qquad (2.13)$$

If we introduce

$$\tilde{\rho}_o^1(t) = (\chi\chi'')^{-1} \rho_o(t) \qquad (2.14)$$

and

$$\varphi' = \chi''^{-1}\varphi\chi'' \qquad (2.15)$$

we easily derive the kinetic equation

$$i \frac{\partial \tilde{\rho}_o(t)}{\partial t} = \varphi' \, \tilde{\rho}^1_o \, (t) \qquad (2.16)$$

We see therefore that there exists in the Post-Boltzmannian approximation an infinite number of kinetic equations with hermitian collision operators $i\varphi'$ differing only through an unitary transformation.

We may now give an answer to the first question we asked in § 1. Indeed, the collision operator $i\Omega\psi$ is related through the similitude transformation (2. 8) (or 2. 15) to the hermitian operator $i\varphi$. Therefore the eigenvalues of $i\Omega\psi$ are also real. The approach to equilibrium is monotonous in the whole range of validity of the Post-Boltzmannian approximation.
Oscillations may persist only for times of the order of the duration of the collision. Inversely for situations in which oscillations are likely to occur over the whole relaxation time because of strong coupling (see e. g. [13) 14)]) the expression (1. 10) is no more convergent and the Post-Boltzmannian approximation no more valid.

The fact that in the Post-Boltzmannian approximation oscillations are excluded indicates of course that only <u>real</u> transitions appear in the collision operator.

Let us now conclude this section with a brief discussion of correlations. Any given correlation may be split into two parts

$$\rho_\nu(t) = \rho'_\nu(t) + \rho''_\nu(t) \qquad (2.17)$$

The evolution of the first part is given by an equation similar to the kinetic equation for $\rho_0(t)$, which describes the scattering of the free correlations. This part vanishes for $t \to \infty$

The second part corresponds to the creation of correlations from $\rho_0(t)$. It is given by :

$$\rho''_\nu(t) = \int_0^t d\tau \, C_\nu(\tau) \, \rho_0(t-\tau) \qquad (2.18)$$

where the "creation fragment" is the Laplace transform of the operator

$$C_\nu(z) = \langle \nu | \sum_{n=1}^{\infty} \left(\frac{1}{z - L_0} \delta L\right)^n | 0 \rangle_{irr} \qquad (2.19)$$

The index "irr" again means that no intermediate state is identical to the vacuum of correlations.

Again , expanding $\rho_0(t-\tau)$ around $\rho_0(t)$, we may obtain $\rho''_\nu(t)$ in terms of the distribution function $\rho_0(t)$ at the same time. This corresponds exactly to the Post-Boltzmannian approximation (1. 9) in which we also have expressed $\partial \rho_0 / \partial t$ in terms of ρ_0 taken at the same time.

3. - THE BOLTZMANN REPRESENTATION.

Let us begin by two preliminary remarks : the operators considered in § 2 act on functions of canonical momenta such as for example action variables J, or in second quantization occupation numbers N. The hermiticity of the operator χ defined through (2. 7) implies that for two functions $f_i(J)$, $f_j(J)$,

$$\int dJ\, f_i^*(J)\, \chi\, f_j(J) = \left[\int dJ\, f_j(J)\, \chi\, f_i^*(J) \right]^* \qquad (3.1.)$$

Similarly

$$\sum_N f_i^*(N)\, \chi\, f_j(N) = \left[\sum_N f_j(N)\, \chi\, f_i^*(N) \right]^* \qquad (3.2)$$

Let us also recall the basic property of unitary transformations both in classical or quantum mechanics: they leave invariant the average ensemble value $\langle A \rangle$ associated to an observable A.

In classical statistical mechanics this average value is defined through

$$< A > = \int dJ\, d\alpha\, A(J, \alpha)\, \rho(J, \alpha) \qquad (3.3)$$

(the variables α , J are the usual action-angle variables) or in quantum mechanics through

$$< A > = \mathrm{Tr}\, A\rho \qquad (3.4)$$

We only consider observables which are sums of terms, each of which involves only a finite number of degrees of freedom *)

At the present time, such a restriction does not seem to imply a restriction of a physical nature.

Now for such variables we may adopt an asymptotic point of view. Indeed using a Fourier expansion in angle variables we may also write (3. 3.)

$$< A > = \sum_{\nu} \int dJ\, A_{\nu}(J)\, \rho_{-\nu}(J) \qquad (3.5)$$

The "off-diagonal" elements ρ_{ν} , $\nu \neq 0$ are now replaced by (2. 7). After times large in respect to t_{coll}, $\rho_{\nu}'(t)$ may be neglected and ρ_{ν} may be expressed as a functional of ρ_0 alone using (2. 8) and (2. 9).

This corresponds to the suppression of memory effects and is consistent with the use of the Post-Boltzmannian approximation in which the contribution $\mathfrak{D}$ in (1. 1) was also neglected.

---

*) For example, for anharmonic solids interacting through three phonon processes, each term in the hamiltonian involves only three degrees of freedom. Similarly in the well known Lee model of field theory (see e. g. 16) 17)). There, one considers interactions between the fermions V, N and the boson θ , such that

$$V \rightleftarrows N + \theta$$

Each term in the potential energy contains a product of three creation or destruction operators and involves therefore only three degrees of freedom of the system.

Now the operators involved in the creation fragment (2. 9) may be transformed by partial integration till (3. 5) takes the form

$$< A > = \int dJ \mathcal{A}(J)\, \rho_o(J) \tag{3.6}$$

or using occupation numbers

$$< A > = \sum_N \mathcal{A}(N)\, \rho_o(N) \tag{3.7}$$

where ρ_o (N) corresponds to the diagonal elements of the density matrix.

A detailed example may be found in our paper[15] (page 1878). To the Hamiltonian $H_o + \lambda V$ corresponds now the single expression $\mathcal{H}$ (N) such that

$$< H > = \sum_N \mathcal{H}(N)\, \rho_o(N) \tag{3.8}$$

We may now consider simultaneous transformations of ρ_o and of the observables $\mathcal{A}$ such that the average values $\langle A \rangle$ remain invariant. It is sufficient to subject both ρ_o and $\mathcal{A}$ to the operations

$$\begin{cases} P_o(N) = \mu\, \rho_o(N) \\ A_p(N) = (\mu^{-1})^+ \mathcal{A}(N) \end{cases} \tag{3.9}$$

where μ is an arbitrary operator in N-space. Note that these operations are performed only on the diagonal elements of the density matrix. We go in this way from ρ_o, $\mathcal{A}$ to P_o and $\mathcal{A}_p$.

We shall call such transformations: ρ_0 - transformations. Such transformations exist, only in large systems in which the information contained in the memory terms ρ'_ν may be neglected.

We may now formulate our basic problem as follows: does there exist a ρ_0 - transformation which leads from the initial representation to a representation in which we have both at equilibrium and out of equilibrium

$$\left\{\begin{array}{lll} \langle H \rangle = \sum_N \mathcal{H}_P (N)\, P_o & \text{(a)} & \\ S = -k \sum_N P_o \log P_o & \text{(b)} & \\ 1 = \sum_N P_o & \text{(c)} & (3.10) \end{array}\right.$$

While conditions (a) and (c) are automatically satisfied in the ρ_0-transformation, the basic new requirement as expressed by condition (3.10, b) is that the entropy takes in this representation a form identical to that corresponding to the Boltzmann $\mathcal{H}$ quantity (1.13). All the effects of the interactions are therefore included in the definition of the operator which leads to the new representation as well as in the kinetic operator. For this reason we suggest to call this representation the "Boltzmann representation". Exactly as in the Landau theory of the Fermi liquid, the effective hamiltonian $\mathcal{H}_P (N)$ is now a complicated function of N (and no longer a simple linear function as in the case of a perfect gas).

We have now shown that till order λ^6 in the coupling constant (and therefore hopefully to all orders!) such a representation exists. These results will be briefly summarized in § 4.

At the present stage, we want to discuss first what the existence of such a representation implies.

As a simple example, let us again consider the Lee model (see footnote, p. 436). We first consider a single physical V particle. Let us use the representation corresponding to the unperturbed hamiltonian H_o. In this representation the state corresponding to a single V particle is expressed as a superposition of states corresponding either to a single bare V particle or to an N particle together with a θ particle. In other terms a situation corresponding to a single physical V particle will be described by a set of diagonal elements of the density matrix. (as well as by non diagonal elements). In this representation it is clear that condition (3. 10, b) cannot be satisfied. The application of the Boltzmann formula would give a finite (non vanishing) entropy for a state represented by a single wave function.

We know of course how to calculate the entropy even in this representation. We have to use the canonical Gibbs expression for the entropy

$$S_{can} = -k \operatorname{Tr} (\rho \log \rho) \qquad (3.\ 11).$$

which involves both diagonal and off-diagonal elements of the density matrix.

For equilibrium problems there is no difficulty associated with the use of (3. 11) but for the proof of an $\mathcal{H}$ -theorem, the definition (3. 11) is not suitable as we shall see in more detail in § 5.

In the case of a single stable V particle we know what to do: we have to use the solution of the Schrödinger equation corresponding to the complete Hamiltonian and involving the physical mass. The density matrix then takes the well known form corresponding to a pure state with a single non-vanishing diagonal element (see e. g. [18]).

We see now clearly what the basic property of the Boltzmann-representation is : in this representation, there is a one-to-one correspondence between the occupation numbers of physical particles and the diagonal elements. To each ensemble $\{N\}$ corresponds a single diagonal element $\rho_0(\{N\})$.

A non vanishing value of the entropy is therefore associated to a superposition of states involving different values of the $\{N\}$. The value of the entropy corresponds to the existence of a "mixture" of quantum states. To a single quantum state corresponds a single non vanishing diagonal element of the density matrix and a zero entropy.

However, there is an essential point to keep in mind: In the case of a single stable V particle we may use the Schrödinger equation to obtain the suitable density matrix. But this is no more so, neither in the case of an arbitrary number of particles nor if the V particles are unstable.

Let us consider this latter case: the usual method due originally to Peierls[19] (see also Levy[16]) is to define the mass and life time of an unstable particle through the real and imaginary parts of a complex pole appearing in the "second Riemann sheet" of the analytic continuation of the propagator. This is of course also the method used in Green's function formalism and in the Landau theory of the Fermi liquid (see e. g. [12]).

In this method the unstable particle or the excitation is represented by a wave packet. The corresponding density matrix would have a set of diagonal elements and we are not in the Boltzmannian representation as defined by (3. 10). A very important exception is of course the case of excitations near the Fermi surface, the life time of which is sufficiently long to neglect the spread in energy. Then we come to the Landau quasi-particle theory for which (3. 10) is applicable. But our specific purpose here is to discuss the possibility of a theory which would include dissipative processes and for which the spread of energy would have to be considered as finite.

What means then a quantum mechanical "state" ? How can we separate virtual and real transitions ? As emphasized by Heitler already some years ago (see [11]) , this is a basic problem quite different from the usual S-matrix problems. We can no more here first "dress" the particles and then make them interact.

Virtual and real processes occur together.

What we propose is to discuss these problems in the frame of the density matrix formalism taking advantage of the existence of the $\mathcal{S}_c$ -transformations for large dissipative systems.

We can indeed immediately give a criterion for the existence of the Boltzmannian representation (3. 10) : at equilibrium, the maximization of S leads to

$$P_0 \sim \exp\left[- \frac{\mathcal{H}_P(N)}{kT} \right] \qquad (3.12)$$

Now to each $\mathcal{S}_c$ -transformation (3. 9) corresponds a different form of the collision operator φ (see 2. 8) and the equilibrium distribution (3. 12) has to be an eigenfunction of the collision operator corresponding to an eigenvalue zero

$$\varphi = \exp\left[- \frac{\mathcal{H}_P (N)}{k T} \right] = 0 \qquad (3.\ 13)$$

Both φ and $\mathcal{H}_p$ are functionals of the $\mathcal{S}_c$ -transformation one considers and the consistency condition (3. 13) implies a test for the existence of the Boltzmann representation.

Inversely (3. 13) may be used to construct the explicit form of the $\mathcal{S}_o$ -transformation leading to the Boltzmann representation. In § 4, we shall show how this is realized, using the operators χ and χ'' considered in § 2.

4. - ANHARMONIC OSCILLATORS - RELATION WITH RENORMALIZATION THEORY.

We shall now apply the general considerations of §2, 3. to anharmonic solids interacting through three phonon processes. As this problem is discussed in full detail in two recent papers[15], we only outline the calculations.

The hamiltonian of this system may be written:

$$H = \hbar \sum_k \omega_k (a_k^+ a_k + \frac{1}{2})$$

$$+ (\frac{h}{2})^{\frac{3}{2}} \lambda \sum_{\{k\}} \sum_{\{\epsilon = \pm 1\}} V_{\{k\epsilon\}} (\omega_k \omega_{k'} \omega_{k''})^{-\frac{1}{2}} a_k^{\epsilon} a_{k'}^{\epsilon'} a_{k''}^{\epsilon''} \qquad (4.\ 1)$$

where a_k^+ and a_k are the creation and destruction operators for phonons and where we restrict ourselves to the cubic anharmonic term. With this hamiltonian, the evolution equation for weakly ooupled systems, where the operators ψ and φ coincide (see (2.10)), has the form

$$\frac{\partial \rho_o(t)}{\partial t} = - i \lambda^2 \varphi_2 \rho_o(t) \tag{4. 2}$$

with

$$- i\varphi_2 = - 2\pi \sum_1 \sum_{\epsilon_1} \delta(\epsilon_1 \omega_1) < \overline{\epsilon}_1 \epsilon_1 > \left[1 - \exp(-\epsilon_1 \frac{\partial}{\partial N_1}) \right] \tag{4. 3}$$

where "1" corresponds to a set of 3 phonons k, k', k'' and where the following abbreviations are used:

$$\epsilon_1\omega_1 = \epsilon\omega_k + \epsilon'\omega_{k'} + \epsilon''\omega_{k''}$$

$$\epsilon_1 \frac{\partial}{\partial N_1} = \epsilon \frac{\partial}{\partial N_R} + \epsilon' \frac{\partial}{\partial N_{R'}} + \epsilon'' \frac{\partial}{\partial N_{k''}}$$

$$< \overline{\epsilon}_1 \epsilon_1 > = < \{N\} \mid V \mid \{N\}' , N_{k'} - \epsilon , N_{k'} - \epsilon' , N_{k''} - \epsilon'' > \times$$

$$\times < \{N\}', N_k - \epsilon, N_{k'} - \epsilon', N_{k''} - \epsilon'' \mid V \mid \{N\} > \tag{4. 4}$$

The operator (4. 3) describes scattering between 3 phonons, with energy conservation.

There exists no special difficulty to write the fourth order kinetic equation explicity (see(1. 9);(1. 10)).

$$i \frac{\partial o_o}{\partial t} = \Omega \psi(0) \rho_o$$

$$= (1 + \lambda^2 \psi'_2(0))(\lambda^2 \psi_2(0) + \lambda^4 \psi_4(0)) \rho_o \tag{4. 5}$$

which now includes correlations involving four phonons (four phonon "collisions"). But as we mentioned already in § 1 we obtain a large number of contributions whose physical interpretation is not simple. We now perform a $\mathcal{S}_0$ -transformation using the operator χ defined in (2. 9). As the result (for all calculations see[15]), we obtain the kinetic equation

$$i \frac{\partial \tilde{\rho}_0}{\partial t} = (\lambda^2 \psi_2 + \lambda^4 \varphi_4) \tilde{\rho}_0 \tag{4. 6}$$

In agreement with the general theory given in § 2, the new collision operator $i(\varphi_2 + \varphi_4)$ is hermitian.

Moreover the fourth order contribution φ_4 has now a simple physical meaning. It contains two types of terms

a) contributions which may be added to φ_2 to form a new three phonon collision operator which differs from (4. 3) only through a redefinition of the energy (or frequency) and of the interaction;

b) a genuine four phonon collision operator $\tilde{\varphi}_4$ which conserves the energy of the four phonons involved;

As the result (4. 6) may also be written as

$$i \frac{\partial \tilde{\rho}_0}{\partial t} = (\tilde{\varphi}_2 + \tilde{\varphi}_4) \tilde{\rho}_0 \tag{4. 7}$$

where $\tilde{\varphi}_2$ is a renormalized three phonon collision operator. We see that the hermitian operator χ which was introduced in § 2 to obtain the hermitian form of the kinetic equation leads automatically to a renormalized theory *). In this approximation no use of the unitary operator χ'' is made.

The distribution function $\tilde{\rho}_0$ may therefore also be called a "dressed" or "quasiparticle" distribution function. The Hamiltonian $\mathcal{H}_{\tilde{\rho}}$ corresponding to the distribution function $\tilde{\rho}$ can be easily calculated using (3. 9). One obtains to order λ^2 (see [15] page 1879), as could be expected, a quadratic form in the occupation numbers:

$$\mathcal{H}_{\tilde{\rho}} = \sum_k \hbar\omega_k (N_k + \frac{1}{2}) + \frac{\lambda^2}{2} \hbar \sum_{kk'} g_{kk'} (N_k + \frac{1}{2})(N_{k'} + \frac{1}{2}) + \frac{\lambda^2}{2} \hbar g \tag{4. 8}$$

where $g_{kk'}$ and g are quantities independent of the occupation numbers which are defined in our original paper. It has also been shown [15] (p. 1883) that the self consistency condition (3. 13) is satisfied. We obtain the equilibrium distribution

$$\tilde{\rho}_{equ} \sim \exp\left[-\frac{\mathcal{H}_{\tilde{\rho}}}{hT}\right] \tag{4. 9}$$

which is an eigenfunction corresponding to a zero eigenvalue of the collision operator (4. 7).

---

*) In fact, in our previous work on this problem, we started with the idea of renormalization and the Landau picture of quasiparticles to introduce a new distribution function and an hermitian collision operator (see 15) 21) and specially the paper by Résibois (20)). It should also be noticed that the idea of renormalization as used here is quite different from that which appears in field theory. There one proceeds with a renormalization of the phase of the wave function (see e. g. 17)). As we deal here with the kinetic equation involving the diagonal elements of the density matrix, we are concerned with renormalization of the "modulus". Both procedures may be shown to be equivalent only to lowest order in λ (see for more details a paper by one of us (F. H.)21).

The ρ_0 -transformation performed with the hermitian operator χ has therefore brought us to the Boltzmann representation (3. 10).

All this can be extended to order λ^6 . But there the transformation χ is not sufficient. We have also to use the unitary χ'' operator (2. 14) to obtain a ρ_0 -transformation which leads us from the initial bare particle representation to the Boltzmann representation.

We cannot go here into more details; these will be given in a paper in preparation. We want only to make the following observation: Already to order λ^4 the Hamiltonian corresponding to the Boltzmann representation mixes "virtual" and "real" processes (that is, it contains both principal parts and δ -functions). That is of course a very essential feature. It is precisely because our approach includes dissipative procesces that it can go beyond the important results obtained by Landau for a Fermi liquid.

Already to order λ^4 in the operators χ, χ'', the construction of the Boltzmann representation involves more than the consideration of the self energy as is done in the Landau theory or the Green's function approach. However, in the limit of non dissipative situations, the usual results are of course recovered.

The most characteristic feature of the hamiltonian (4. 1) is the occurrence of products of three creation and destruction operators. For this reason, all this can be trivially extended to the Lee model and other field theoretical models.

But we cannot go into more details here as we wish to devote the last section of this report to a discussion of the entropy concept.

5. - ENTROPY.

We may immediately expect that the existence of the Boltzmann representation (3. 10) implies the validity of the $\mathcal{H}$ -theorem (1. 14) exactly as for the weakly coupled case. This has been explicitly verified for the case of anharmonic oscillators till order λ^4 (see [15) 7)]). If in agreement with (3. 10) we define the Boltzmann $\mathcal{H}$ - quantity as

$$\mathcal{H}_B = \sum_N \tilde{\rho}_o (N) \log \tilde{\rho}_o (N) \qquad (5.1)$$

we have verified using (4. 7) (or the corresponding kinetic equation valid till order λ^6) that we recover at equilibrium the correct expression of entropy (as calculated from partition functions) and that during the approach to equilibrium the basic inequality (1. 14) is satisfied. Both fundamental requirements necessary for the definition of entropy are therefore satisfied. The extension of Boltzmann's $\mathcal{H}$ -theorem to the "Post-Boltzmannian" approximation seems to us an important step in the statistical justification of the Second Law of Thermodynamics.

To appreciate this point we would like to make the following comments: Since Boltzmann's work, it is clear that the existence of a large number of interacting degrees of freedom is a necessary requirement for the validity of the Second Law . But is this also a sufficient requirement ?

In other words, is it possible to give a proof of the $\mathcal{H}$-theorem which would introduce no specific dynamical assumptions (as to the form of the Hamiltonian) but be based only on arguments taken from the theory of probability , "information" theory and so on?

Inspite of repeated claims in the literature (see e. g. [22]), no proof has ever been published, to our best knowledge. It is true that interesting non-dynamical inequalities have been obtained (such as the so called "Klein inequality", see Tolman [18]) but no proof of a continuous increase of entropy of the type postulated in phenomenological thermodynamics has been produced (see also the excellent discussions by Pauli and Yvon [23]).

When one considers typical non Boltzmannian situations such as in the case of gravitational forces where an asymptotic collision operator can even not be defined (see [5]) one is really led to doubt the possibility of some extension of the $\mathcal{H}$ -theorem which would not involve specific dynamical assumptions. Therefore the existence of a proof involving at least the Post-Boltzmannian situation is already in our opinion an important advance.

Let us now go back to (5. 1) (or to (3. 10, b)) and retransform the entropy into the ρ_0 - representation using (2. 11). For example in the case of a system of classical anharmonic oscillators, we obtain for the entropy correct to order λ^2

$$- \frac{S}{k} = \int d J \rho_o \log \rho_o +$$

$$+ \frac{\lambda^2}{2} \int d J \frac{1}{\rho_o} \sum_1 \sum_{\epsilon_1} \mathcal{P} \left(\frac{1}{\epsilon_1 \omega_1} \right) \frac{\partial}{\partial \epsilon_1 \omega_1} \frac{| V_{\{k\epsilon\}} |^2}{\omega_k \omega_{k'} \omega_{k''}} \times$$

$$\times J_k J_{k'} J_{k''} \left(\left[\epsilon_1 \frac{\partial}{\partial J_1} \right] \rho_o \right)^2 \qquad (5. 2)$$

where the J's are action variables and where the notations are defined in (4. 4.).

The interest of this expression is that we have here a model for the entropy of a strongly coupled system in which the effect of correlations is retained.

As could be expected, at equilibrium the contribution of the correlations to the entropy is negative. The correlations order the system. The simple disorder interpretation of entropy is only valid in the Boltzmannian representation. The expression (5. 2) has even not the usual logarithmic form !

Let us now consider the relation of (5. 2) with the Gibbs definition (3. 11) (we use as canonical variables the action and angle variables J, α):

$$S_{can} = - k \int dJ \, d\alpha \, \rho \log \rho \tag{5. 3}$$

The entropy (5. 2) has an "irreversible" behavior while the canonical entropy (5. 3) involving the complete density in phase space (and not only ρ_o) is a constant. Let us write the canonical entropy as a sum of two terms:

$$S_{can} = S_{kin} + S_{corr} \tag{5. 4}$$

where S_{kin} is the Boltzmann entropy

$$S_{kin} = - k \int dJ \, \rho_o \log \rho_o \tag{5. 5}$$

We have then to ask what is the mechanism by which the correlations (which for a weakly coupled system play a negligible role at equilibrium) can compensate the systematic variation of the kinetic part out of equilibrium ? In order to understand this, we have computed the correlation part of the canonical entropy up to order λ^2 . For an anharmonic solid, we have:

$$S_{corr} = - k \int d J \frac{1}{\rho_o} \sum_{\{k\}} | \rho_{\{k\}} |^2 \tag{5. 6}$$

where $\rho_{\{k\}}$ represents a 3-phonon correlation . The very important feature is that this quantity is a non-linear functional of the correlations. As we have seen, the correlations may be split into 2 parts: ρ' and ρ'' (see (2. 15)). To this corresponds a splitting in the entropy:

$$S_{corr} = S^I \left[\rho'_{\{k\}} , \rho''_{\{k\}} \right] + S^{II} \left[\rho''_{\{k\}} \right] \tag{5. 7}$$

J. Philippot [24] has discussed at this conference a problem where the first term, which depends on the initial correlations plays a role. However, here we shall be interested in the asymptotic evolution when this term vanishes. The second term is given by (5. 6) with $\rho_{\{k\}}$ replaced by $\rho''_{\{k\}}$; great care has to be exerted in the asymptotic evaluation of such quantities. Using (2. 18) and (2. 19) we obtain an integral over a product of propagators. This expression has then to be reduced to a succession of Cauchy integrals (see [15]). In this way it can be shown that up to order λ^2, S^{II} consists of two completely different types of contributions:

1) a contribution of order $\lambda^2 t$ which depends explicitely on time but vanishes identically if ρ_0 corresponds to equilibrium;

2) a contribution which depends on time only through ρ_0 and which is identical to the λ^2 contribution in (5. 2.).

The existence of these two types of contributions comes from the non linear form of (5. 6) in terms of the correlations $\rho_{\{k\}}$.

The first class of terms came to us as a surprise. But, after some thought, it is clear that such terms have to exist: they have to be present out of equilibrium to compensate similar $\lambda^2 t$ terms which arise in the kinetic term (5. 5) as the result of the effect of collisions. In other words , they have to be present to insure precisely the constancy of the canonical entropy.

The existence of these two different types of contributions has also been verified by Nicolis [25] for weakly coupled gases interacting through a gaussian potential, for which all calculations can be explicitly performed.

All this leads to the following conclusions:

a) we see that the role of correlations in the canonical entropy (5. 3) out of equilibrium is completely different from what it is at equilibrium. At equilibrium we have only "normal" λ^2 (and higher orders in λ) contributions while out of equilibrium we have also contributions which are much larger as they involve explicitly the time t . This has been qualitatively verified by machine calculations on hard discs by Bellemans and Orban [26];

b) we see now the precise relation between the Boltzmann and the Gibbs definitions of entropy (at least in the frame of the Post-Boltzmannian approximation): the abnormal terms which in the Gibbs definition depend explicitly on time have to be subtracted to obtain the Boltzmann definition showing the expected monotonous behavior in time.

In other words the Gibbs definition of entropy while valid at equilibrium cannot be continued out of equilibrium. First the " abnormal terms", whose role is to compensate the collisional effect on the kinetic part , have to be subtracted.

In this way one of the oldest difficulties of statistical mechanics seems to find a simple and clear solution.

6. - CONCLUSION.

This report is devoted to the study of situations such as described by the kinetic equation (1. 9) for which the Boltzmann kinetic equation (1. 5) may be considered as a first approximation. The precise domain of validity of this "Post Boltzmannian" approximation has to be investigated carefully in each specific case. Here we have been concerned with the discussion of some general properties implied by this approxi mation. We have developed a transformation theory of the kinetic equation (§ 2) and emphasized the existence of a new class of transformations (§ 3) in such systems. Using such a transformation we may construct a rep resentation we called the Boltzmann representation in which both equilibrium and non-equilibrium properties have a most simple form.

The existence of such a representation has some similarity with results of Balian and de Dominicis [27)]. Their work is however limited to equilibrium and a detailed comparison has not been done.

There is an amusing analogy between the type of approach used in this paper and the well known Hamilton-Jacobi integration method in mechanics. Once appropriate cyclic variables are found, the integration problem is trivial. Similarly once the appropriate ρ_0- transformation is found, we may set up our "Boltzmannian representation".

The success of this method will ultimately depend on the effective possibilities to construct such ρ_0-transformations. As the explicit form of the energy in the Boltzmann representation leads ultimately to a new definition of excitations or quasi-particles which extends the usual definitions to unstable particles and dissipative situations, this seems to us a most important problem of modern statistical physics.

In a paper which is now prepared for publication, we shall discuss in more detail than it was possible here the application to specific problems such as the Lee model and discuss in detail the differences with the usual theory.

ACKNOWLEDGEMENTS.

We want to mention that most results described in this paper have been obtained in collaboration with Dr. Cl. George.

We would also like to thank the members of our group for their help in discussing various aspects of the problems described in this report. Our special thank is due to A. Bellemans, F. Mayné, G. Nicolis and P. Résibois.

Support of the Air Force under grant EOAR 64-52, monitored by the European Office, Office of Aerospace Research, is gratefully acknowledged.

A preliminary version of this report was written during the stay of one of us (I. P) at General Motor's Technical Center, Warren, Michigan. He wants to thank Dr. R. Herman and the whole group of Theoretical Physics for their interest and hospitality.

REFERENCES.

I.- I. Prigogine, Non Equilibrium Statistical Mechanics, Interscience, New-York, (1962).
R. Balescu, Statistical Mechanics of Charged Particles, Interscience, New-York (1963).
P. Résibois, in "Many Particle Physics", E. Meeron Ed., Gordon and Breach (to be published)

2. - I. Prigogine and P. Résibois, Physica, 27, 629 (1961).

3. - Cl. George, Physica, 30, 1513 (1964).

4. - See e. g. E. T. Whittaker and G. N. Watson, Modern Analysis, Cambridge, London (1953).

5. - I. Prigogine, Nature, 209, 602 (1966)
I. Prigogine and G. Severne, Physica, 32, 1376 (1966).

6. - P. Résibois and M. De Leener, Phys. Rev., 152, 305 (1966)

7. - Cl. George and I. Prigogine, Physica (to appear, 1967).

8. - I. Prigogine, Introduction to Non-Equilibrium Statistical Physics, Notes International School on Non-Linear Physics and Mathematics, Munich, 1966 (to appear, Springer 1967).

9. - A. Mangeney, Physica, 30, 461 (1964).

10. - P. Résibois, Physica, 29, 721 (1963); Physica, 31, 645 (1965)

11. - W. Heitler, The Quantum Theory of Radiation, 3rd edition, Oxford Clarendon Press (1954).

12. - P. Nozières, le Problème à N corps, Dunod, Paris (1963).

13. - K. Haubold, Physica, 28, 834 (1962).

14. - L. van Hove and E. Verboven, Physica, 27, 418 (1961).

15. - F. Henin, I. Prigogine, Cl. George and F. Mayné, Physica 32, 1828 (1966).
I. Prigogine, F. Henin and Cl. George, Physica, 32, 1873 (1966).

16. - M. Lévy, Nuovo Cimento, 13, 115, (1959); Nuovo Cimento, 14, 612 (1959).

17. - S. Schweber, An introduction to Relativistic Quantum Field Theory, Row, Peterson and Co, New-York (1961).

18. - R. Tolman, The Principles of Statistical Mechanics, Oxford, London (1938).

19. - R. E. Peierls, Proc. of the 1954 Glasgow Conf. London, Pergamon Press, p. 296.

20. - P. Résibois, Phys. Rev. 138, B281 (1965)
M. Watabe and R. Dagonnier, Phys. Rev., 143, 110 (1966).

21. - F. Henin (to be published).

22. - E. Jaynes, Amer. J. Phys. 33, 391, 1965.

23. - There exist many excellent discussions in which the problem is clearly stated. We cannot quote them all here but we want at least to mention the excellent discussions by W. Pauli, Nuovo Cimento, Statistical Mechanics Conf. Florence (1959); J. Yvon, l'Entropie, Dunod, Paris (1965).

24. - See the report of J. Philippot at this meeting.

25. - G. Nicolis, J. Chem. Phys. (to appear, 1967).

26. - A. Bellemans and J. Orban (private communication (1966))

27. - C. de Dominicis, Suppl. to Physica, 26, 94, (1960)

Van Kampen: There are two kinds of operators: one kind for the dressing of particles and one kind for the dynamics. How unique is this separation?

Henin: There exists in our theory only a single operator which appears as the kernel in the general non Markovian evolution equation. However, when we neglect memory effects and retain the effects of the finite duration of the collisions in an asymptotic form, the solution of this equation may, as we have seen in our report, be written as:

$$\rho_o(t) = e^{-it\Omega\psi} A \rho_o(0) \tag{1}$$

where $\Omega\psi$ and A are both well defined functionals of the operator ψ. One could indeed say that A is an operator for the dressing of the particles and $\Omega\psi$ for the dynamics. This separation is indeed not unique. This is precisely the reason why we have studied the alternative for of (1):

$$\rho_o(t) = \chi e^{-it\phi} \chi \rho_o(0) \tag{2}$$

Now, χ is the operator for dressing and ϕ for the dynamics.

The form (1) leads to a kinetic equation for $\rho_o(t)$ which is independent of A. We believe that this equation can be considered as the equation for the bare distribution function. Indeed, even the renormalization effects (self-energy, charge renormalization) which appear in the usual field theory are still entirely contained in $\Omega\psi$.

On the contrary (2) leads as we have seen to a kinetic equation for

$$\tilde{\rho}_o = \chi^{-1} \rho_o \tag{3}$$

This is an equation for dressed particles. Indeed, at least to order λ^4, all terms conserve the renormalized energies of the particles which participate in the collision processes which they describe. All other terms (which do not conserve energy and correspond broadly speaking to virtual processes) are in the dressing. This is precisely the form we wanted to obtain. To order λ^4, there seems to be no other ordering of the integral representation (1) which leads to this result.

Van Kampen: In your framework it may be unique, but how are you forced to take some terms as dressed terms that do not contribute to irreversible behaviour?

Henin: At order λ^4, the structure of each contribution to $\Omega\psi$ is such that each term has a simple physical meaning; accordingly, the splitting between contributions to the dynamics (with conservation of the energies of all the particles involved in the process) and contributions to the dressing (which do not conserve the energy of all the particles involved) is quite obvious.

Résibois: There is no reason to believe the separation to be unique in the mathematical sense, however, there is a clear physical interpretation in this case.

Penrose: In statistical mechanics, we observe bare particles. I think, for instance, of the classical statistical mechanics of a gas whose atoms can emit light. By observing the thermal broadening of spectral lines we can, in principle, measure the velocity of the bare particles.

Henin: In order to avoid misunderstanding, it is necessary perhaps to distinguish (as it is done in the text of the lecture) between renormalization effects as considered in field theory from specific statistical mechanical effects. The former are linear in the occupation numbers while the latter depend in a non-linear (i. e. quadratic) way on the number of particles. With respect to this second type of effects, it is perfectly true, as Prof. Penrose says, that we observe bare particles.

However, the introduction of renormalization concepts in statistical mechanics has much interest. We may mention the following reasons:

1) The introduction of quasi-particles may lead to much simpler equations. The classical example is of course Landau's theory of normal Fermi liquids, recently generalized to finite temperatures including dissipative effects by Résibois (P. Résibois, Phys. Rev. 138, B281 (1965); M. Watabe and R. Dagonnier, Phys. Rev. 143, 110 (1966)).

2) The kinetic method includes as a special case the field theoretical renormalizations. This alternative approach is of great interest for unstable particles, resonances ... for which the usual

approach is far from giving unambiguous or simple results (see the interesting work by Heitler and Arnous, mentioned in our paper, as well as M. Levy, Nuovo Cimento 13, 1687 (1959)).

Martin: In connection with the question of Penrose, I would like to point out that one can measure quantities akin to the renormalized frequencies which have been discussed. Two examples are the natural frequency measured in the self diffusion spectrum of liquids and the natural frequencies observed in solids by neutron or Brillouin scattering. This definition of the renormalized quasi-particle frequency as the maximum in a measured or measurable frequency spectrum is physical and unique in a classical system.

On the other hand in connection with van Kampen's question I would like to point out that the kind of analysis discussed by Mrs. Henin for a kinetic equation has been carried out for the equilibrium properties and equilibrium correlation functions to all orders by Balian and De Dominicis. They also found that it was useful to define a mathematical construct, a quasi-particle energy which, I believe, corresponds with that discussed by Mrs. Henin, but that this quantity differed, to order λ^4, from the kind of quantity I defined experimentally. There is no doubt about the measureability of the quasi-particle energy I described; whether the convenient but unobservable quasi-particle energy of Balian and De Dominicis (and Mrs. Henin) is unique is unclear but its domain of universality appears to encompass at least Paris and Bruxelles.

Henin: The universality of the definition of the quasi-particle energy is less restrictive than your comment implies. Our methods, although aimed at treating relaxation in the kinetic stage also lead in equilibrium, exactly to the type of renormalization introduced recently by T. H. K. Barron (see Proc. Conf. on Lattice Dynamics, Copenhagen (1963), ed. by R. F. Wallis, Pergamon Press 1965, p. 247). Barron has shown that the equilibrium properties of an anharmonic lattice may be represented in terms of quasiphonons with appropriate shifts in frequencies. Our conclusion concerning equilibrium co incides with his. Moreover, a difficulty in his presentation (there seemed to be two types of shifts necessary, see the remarks by A. A. Maradudin at the Copenhagen Conference 1963, p. 724) is easily resolved in our method (see our paper in Physica, 32 1828 (1966).
Finally, we would like to mention that, at low temperatures where dissipative processes become negligible, our definition of quasiparticles coincides with that obtained by the Landau theory. The "measurability problem" is then the same.

Kubo: A question about anharmonic oscillators. At finite temperatures the long waves correspond to adiabatic conditions and the shorter waves to isothermal conditions. This is a sort of quasiparticle effect or dressing effect. May I ask how this renormalization comes out of your formalism?

Henin: Professor Kubo's question is very interesting and would deserve a more detailed study. For phonons, the renormalization depends on the occupation numbers of all the phonons present in the system. The question is then: what occupation numbers should be used? For equilibrium, there is of course no problem. However, out of equilibrium, there may be indeed many circumstances in which adiabatic occupation numbers should be used for long waves and isothermal for short waves.

Martin: In connection with Kubo's question, I would like to remark that the specific problem about which he has asked is studied in detail in a paper in Phys. Rev. 142, 475 (1966), by P. C. Kwok and myself. In order to get the adiabatic effects which come about as a result of many collisions it is necessary to carry out a more complicated perturbation theory than the ones covered in the examples discussed this morning.

THERMODYNAMICALLY-EQUIVALENT HAMILTONIAN METHOD IN NONEQUILIBRIUM STATISTICAL MECHANICS *)

M. D. GIRARDEAU
Institute of Theoretical Science and Department of Physics, University of Oregon, Eugene, Oregon.

ABSTRACT

The equilibrium statistical mechanics of the Bardeen-Cooper-Schrieffer model of superconductivity, as well as that of a wide class of similar models, can be evaluated exactly by the "thermodynamically-equivalent Hamiltonian" method of Bogoliubov, Zubarev, Tserkovnikov, and Wentzel. It has been pointed out by Wentzel that this method can be extended to certain nonequilibrium situations. It is shown here that the method allows an exact evaluation of the nonequilibrium statistical mechanics of the following situations: (a) temporal evolution of the statistical expectation value of an observable $O(\underset{\sim}{r})$ whose initial deviation from equilibrium is <u>spatially localized</u>, but <u>not necessarily small</u>; (b) temporal evolution of the statistical expectation value of an observable O due to a perturbation V which is <u>spatially localized</u>, but <u>not necessarily small</u>.

Long ago an elegant method of exact evaluation of the equilibrium thermodynamics of the Bardeen-Cooper-Schrieffer model of superconductivity[1)] was devised by Bogoliubov, Zubarev, and

*) Supported in part by the National Science Foundation under grants GP4367 and GP6087.

Tserkovnikov[2]. Their method was extended by Wentzel[3] to a wide class of model Hamiltonians, of the general structure

$$H = \sum_{k\lambda}(E_{k\lambda} b_{k\lambda} + E_{k\lambda}^* b_{k\lambda}^\dagger) + \Omega^{-1} \sum_{k\lambda, k'\lambda'} J_{k\lambda, k'\lambda'} b_{k\lambda}^\dagger b_{k'\lambda'} .$$

Here Ω is the volume of the system, k refers to linear momentum, each $b_{k\lambda}$ is bilinear in Fermi or Bose operators, and λ takes on a finite (volume-independent) set of values. It is assumed that $E_{K\lambda}$ and $J_{k\lambda, k'\lambda'}$ are volume-independent, and that

$$[b_{k\lambda}, b_{k'\lambda'}^\dagger] = 0 \quad \text{unless} \quad k' \in \mathcal{S}_k$$

where, for each k, $\mathcal{S}_k$ is a finite (volume-independent) set of k'-vectors. E.g., $\mathcal{S}_k = \{k, -k\}$ for the BCS model Hamiltonian.

The basis of the BZT-Wentzel method is an exact linearization of the interaction terms with the aid of the identity

$$b_{k\lambda}^\dagger b_{k'\lambda'} = (b_{k\lambda}^\dagger - \eta_{k\lambda}^*)(b_{k'\lambda'} - \eta_{k'\lambda'})$$
$$+ (\eta_{k\lambda}^* b_{k'\lambda'} + \eta_{k'\lambda'} b_{k\lambda}^\dagger) - \eta_{k\lambda}^* \eta_{k'\lambda'}$$

where the η_k are c-number parameters to be determined. In this way H is separated into a zero-order Hamiltonian H_o incorporating some of the interaction, plus a residual interaction H':

$$H = H_o + H' ,$$

$$H_o = \text{const.} + \sum_{k\lambda} (G_{k\lambda} b_{k\lambda} + G_{k\lambda}^* b_{k\lambda}^\dagger) ,$$

$$H' = \Omega^{-1} \sum_{k\lambda, k'\lambda'} J_{k\lambda, k'\lambda'} (b_{k\lambda}^\dagger - \eta_{k\lambda}^*)(b_{k'\lambda'} - \eta_{k'\lambda'}) ,$$

$$G_{k\lambda} = E_{k\lambda} + \Omega^{-1} \sum_{k'\lambda'} \eta_{k'\lambda'}^* J_{k'\lambda', k\lambda} .$$

Since H_o is only quadratic in Fermi or Bose operators, it can be diagonalized by a linear canonical transformation to quasiparticle annihilation and creation operators; then H' is to be interpreted as the quasiparticle-interaction Hamiltonian.

It is clear that the effects of H' can be minimized by appropriate choice of the parameters $\eta_{k\lambda}$; what BZT and Wentzel noticed is that with the optimal choice, H' is completely negligible as far as the equilibrium thermodynamics is concerned. This is no miracle, since the optimal choice of $\eta_{k\lambda}$ is found to be the thermal average of $b_{k\lambda}$ in the equilibrium ensemble of H_o. With this choice, H' becomes quadratic in fluctuations of the $b_{k\lambda}$ about their mean values, and it is plausible that these fluctuations become negligible in the limit of an infinite system. The details of the proof involve statistical-mechanical perturbation theory, with the quasiparticle-interaction Hamiltonian H' as the perturbation.

The exact thermodynamic equivalence of H_o and H does not extend to arbitrary nonequilibrium situations. Nevertheless, since the quasiparticle-interaction Hamiltonian is completely negligible in equilibrium, a continuity argument shows that its effects must be small near equilibrium. This was first pointed out by Wentzel[4)], who showed that the quasiparticle interactions could be ignored in a first-order calculation of the momentum transferred to the system by a weak force center dragged through the system with constant velocity. I shall consider the slightly different problem of the time evolution of the statistical expectation value of a position-dependent observable due to an initial spatially-localized deviation from equilibrium, in the absence of any external driving force. It will be shown that in evaluating this time evolution, all effects of H' are negligible in the thermodynamic limit. This result will be found to hold to all orders in H' and to all orders in the departure from equilibrium.

Suppose that at time t = 0 not only the mean energy, but also the statistical expectation values of certain other observables F_j, are known. It has been shown by Jaynes[5)] that the initial density matrix consistent with this known initial data but maximally noncommital with respect to all other observables is

$$\rho(0) = \frac{\exp(-\beta H - \Sigma_j \lambda_j F_j)}{\mathrm{Tr}\exp(-\beta H - \Sigma_j \lambda_j F_j)}$$

where the Lagrange multipliers λ_j and β are determined by the known initial statistical expectation values of H and the F_j. Assuming H time-independent, the statistical expectation value of any observable O at any later time will be

$$\langle O(t)\rangle = \mathrm{Tr}\left[O(t)\ \rho(0)\right]$$

where O(t) is the Heisenberg operator

$$O(t) = e^{itH}\, O\, e^{-itH} .$$

In case the only initial data consists of the statistical expectation values of the Hamiltonian and of a position-dependent operator $O(\underset{\sim}{r}) = O(\underset{\sim}{r}, 0)$ at all positions $\underset{\sim}{r}$, this becomes

$$\langle O(\underset{\sim}{r}, t)\rangle = \frac{\mathrm{Tr}\,\{O(\underset{\sim}{r}, t)\ \exp\left[-\beta H - \int d^3r'\,\lambda_o(\underset{\sim}{r}')\,O(\underset{\sim}{r}')\right]\}}{\mathrm{Tr}\,\exp\left[-\beta H - \int d^3r'\,\lambda_o(\underset{\sim}{r}')\,O(\underset{\sim}{r}')\right]} .$$

In order to formalize the evaluation of such expectation values, it is convenient to define a nonequilibrium partition function Ξ and thermodynamic potential W:

$$\Xi \equiv e^{-\beta W} = \mathrm{Tr}\,\exp\left[-\beta H - \int_{-\infty}^{\infty} dt \int d^3r\,\lambda(\underset{\sim}{r}, t)\ O(\underset{\sim}{r}, t)\right] .$$

Then the statistical expectation value can be expressed as a functional derivative:

$$\langle O(\underset{\sim}{r}, t)\rangle = \left[\delta(\beta W)/\delta\lambda(\underset{\sim}{r}, t)\right]_{\lambda(\underset{\sim}{r}, t)\,=\,\lambda_o(\underset{\sim}{r})\,\delta(t)}$$

where the subscript means that $\lambda(\underset{\sim}{r}, t)$ is to be set equal to $\lambda_o(\underset{\sim}{r})\,\delta(t)$ after the differentiation. The multipliers β and $\lambda_o(\underset{\sim}{r})$ are determined from the known initial data:

$$\left[\partial(\beta W)/\partial\beta\right]_{\lambda(\underset{\sim}{r}, t)\,=\,\lambda_o(\underset{\sim}{r})\,\delta(t)} = \langle H(0)\rangle ,$$

$$\left[\delta(\beta W)/\delta\lambda(\underset{\sim}{r}, 0)\right]_{\lambda(\underset{\sim}{r}, t)\,=\,\lambda_o(\underset{\sim}{r})\,\delta(t)} = \langle O(\underset{\sim}{r}, 0)\rangle .$$

Statistical-mechanical perturbation theory yields an expansion of the partition function in powers of λ_o. Substituting this expansion into the expression for the statistical expectation value and evaluating the functional derivatives, one finds

$$\langle O(\underset{\sim}{r}, t)\rangle = \langle O(\underset{\sim}{r}, 0)\rangle_{eq} + \int K(\underset{\sim}{r}, t; \underset{\sim}{r}_o, 0)\lambda_o(\underset{\sim}{r}_o)\, d^3r_o + O(\lambda_o^2)$$

where the linear transport kernel K is defined as

$$K(\underset{\sim}{r}, t; \underset{\sim}{r}_o, 0) = \langle O(\underset{\sim}{r}, 0)\rangle_{eq} \langle O(\underset{\sim}{r}_o, 0)\rangle_{eq}$$

$$- \frac{1}{2}\int_0^1 ds \left[\langle O(\underset{\sim}{r}_o, 0)\, O(\underset{\sim}{r}, t + i\beta s)\rangle_{eq} + \langle O(\underset{\sim}{r}, t - i\beta s)\, O(\underset{\sim}{r}_o, 0)\rangle_{eq}\right]$$

and the angular brackets denote thermal-equilibrium averages:

$$\langle O\rangle_{eq} = \frac{\mathrm{Tr}\,(O\, e^{-\beta H})}{\mathrm{Tr}\, e^{-\beta H}} \quad .$$

The second term in K, which is the only term in case the mean value of $O(\underset{\sim}{r})$ happens to vanish in equilibrium, is a space-time correlation function of a type already familiar in the theory of transport[6]. Since the average of O approaches its equilibrium value as $\lambda_o \to 0$, the terms denoted by $O(\lambda_o^2)$ are of second and higher orders in the departure from equilibrium. In the approximation of linear transport, the function λ_o is to be determined by inversion of the integral transform

$$\int K(\underset{\sim}{r}, 0; \underset{\sim}{r}_o, 0)\lambda_o(\underset{\sim}{r}_o)\, d^3r_o = \langle O(\underset{\sim}{r}, 0)\rangle - \langle O(\underset{\sim}{r}, 0)\rangle_{eq} \quad .$$

Then one can determine $\langle O(\underset{\sim}{r}, t)\rangle$ at all later times by integration.

This approach is only useful if the initial deviation from equilibrium is <u>spatially localized</u>, i. e. of finite (volume-independent) range. Only in that case will λ_o be of finite range. If the deviation from equilibrium were appreciable throughout the volume of the system, then the same would be true of $\lambda_o(\underset{\sim}{r}_o)$. Then the integral over $\underset{\sim}{r}_o$ would be proportional to the volume, the term $O(\lambda_o^2)$ proportional to the square of the volume, etc. In such a case the expansion of the partition function would first have to be converted into a linked-cluster expansion for the thermodynamic potential before meaningful results could be obtained. Since the BZT-Wentzel proof involves an expansion of the partition function rather than a linked-cluster expansion of the thermodynamic potential, we shall not consider nonlocalized deviations from equilibrium here.

The thermodynamically-equivalent Hamiltonian method can be extended to localized linear transport theory by showing that if the Hamiltonian is of the type previously considered (typified by the BCS model Hamiltonian), then the contribution of the quasiparticle-interaction Hamiltonian to the transport kernel is negligible in the thermodynamic limit. This can be shown by an extension of the original BZT-Wentzel equilibrium proof[2)3)]. Consider first the term $\langle O(\underset{\sim}{r}, 0)\rangle_{eq} \langle O(\underset{\sim}{r}_o, 0)\rangle_{eq}$ in K, in which H' enters only through $e^{-\beta \tilde{H}}$; the proof for this term is essentially the same as the equilibrium proof. Using the expansion of $e^{-\beta H}$ in powers of H', one finds

$$\langle O(\underset{\sim}{r}, 0)\rangle_{eq} = \frac{\sum_{j=0}^{\infty} (-i)^j \int_0^{-i\beta} dt_1 \ldots \int_0^{t_{j-1}} dt_j \langle H'^{(o)}(t_1) \ldots H'^{(o)}(t_j) O^{(o)}(\underset{\sim}{r}, 0)\rangle_o}{\sum_{j=0}^{\infty} (-i)^j \int_0^{-i\beta} dt_1 \ldots \int_0^{t_{j-1}} dt_j \langle H'^{(o)}(t_1) \ldots H'^{(o)}(t_j)\rangle_o}$$

where $\langle\ \rangle_o$ denotes an equilibrium average with H_o rather than the full Hamiltonian, and the superscript zero denotes a Heisenberg operator propagated with H_o:

$$O^{(o)}(t) = e^{itH_o}\, O\, e^{-itH_o} \quad .$$

The j=0 term in the numerator is $\langle O^{(o)}(\underset{\sim}{r}, 0)\rangle_o$, and that in the denominator is unity.

To proceed it is necessary to make some definite assumption concerning the structure of the observable O. For the present it will be assumed to be a single-particle operator:

$$O(\underset{\sim}{r}) = \Omega^{-1} \Sigma_{kk'} O_{kk'}(\underset{\sim}{r})\, a_k^{\dagger} a_{k'} \quad .$$

The matrix elements $O_{kk'}(\underset{\sim}{r})$ are assumed volume-independent, and a and $a^\dagger$ are fermion or boson annihilation and creation operators.

Since H_o is bilinear in the a and $a^\dagger$ operators, one can apply the thermodynamic Wick's theorem (more properly, Matsubara's theorem) to decompose the averages into sums of products of contractions, each such contraction being the average of an operator bilinear in the a and $a^\dagger$ operators. It is convenient to consider separately the terms in which $O^{(o)}$ is self-contracted and those in which the two a and $a^\dagger$ operators in $O^{(o)}$ are contracted with a and $a^\dagger$ operators in $H'^{(o)}$ factors. Then each average separates into two terms:

$$\langle H'^{(o)}(t_1)\ldots H'^{(o)}(t_j)\, O^{(o)}(\underset{\sim}{r}, 0)\rangle_o$$

$$= \langle H'^{(o)}(t_1)\ldots H'^{(o)}(t_j)\rangle_o \langle O^{(o)}(\underset{\sim}{r}, 0)\rangle_o$$

$$+ \langle H'^{(o)}(t_1)\ldots H'^{(o)}(t_j)\, O^{(o)}(r, 0)\rangle_o' ,$$

where the prime on $\langle\ \rangle_o'$ implies omission of all terms in which $O^{(o)}$ is self-contracted, since these are contained in the explicit factor $\langle O^{(o)}(\underset{\sim}{r}, 0)\rangle_o$ in the first term.

The operators $H'^{(o)}$ are bilinear in the fluctuations $b_{k\lambda} - \eta_{k\lambda}$ and $b_{k\lambda}^\dagger - \eta_{k\lambda}^*$. It follows from the linearity of the transformation from the a, $a^\dagger$ representation to the quasiparticle representation that

$$\langle b_{k\lambda}^{(o)}(t)\rangle_o = \langle b_{k\lambda}^{(o)}(0)\rangle_o = \langle b_{k\lambda}\rangle_o = \eta_{k\lambda} .$$

Substitution of the explicit expressions for H' and $O(\underset{\sim}{r})$ then shows that

$$\langle H'^{(o)}(t_1)\ldots H'^{(o)}(t_j)\, O^{(o)}(\underset{\sim}{r}, 0)\rangle_o'$$

$$= \Omega^{-(j+1)} \sum_{kk'} \sum_{k_1\lambda_1\ldots k_j\lambda_j} \sum_{k_1'\lambda_1'\ldots k_j'\lambda_j'} [\quad]$$

$$\times \langle b_{k_1\lambda_1}^{\dagger(o)}(t_1) b_{k_1'\lambda_1'}^{(o)}(t_1)\ldots b_{k_j\lambda_j}^{\dagger(o)}(t_j) b_{k_j'\lambda_j'}^{(o)}(t_j) a_k^\dagger a_{k'}\rangle_o''$$

where the square bracket denotes volume-independent factors and the double prime on the angular bracket implies omission of all terms in which either the operator $a_k^{\dagger} a_{k'}$ or any of the $b^{(o)}$ or $b^{\dagger(o)}$ operators is self-contracted, the latter terms having been cancelled by the $\eta_{k\lambda}$ and $\eta_{k\lambda}{}^*$ factors. Because of the absence of self-contractions, the expression $\langle\ \rangle_o{}''$ vanishes unless not more than j of the 2j+2 vectors $k_1 \ldots k_j$, $k_1' \ldots k_j'$, kk' are independent; this is the analog of the crucial step in the BZT-Wentzel equilibrium proof. Conversion of k-sums to integrals then leads to only j factors of the volume. Because of the prefactor $\Omega^{-(j+1)}$, it follows that

$$\langle H'^{(o)}(t_1) \ldots H'^{(o)}(t_j)\, O^{(\dot{o})}(\underset{\sim}{r}, 0)\rangle_o{}' = O(\Omega^{-1}) ,$$

$$\langle H'^{(o)}(t_1) \ldots H'^{(o)}(t_j)\, O^{(o)}(\underset{\sim}{r}, 0)\rangle_o$$
$$= \langle H'^{(o)}(t_1) \ldots H'^{(o)}(t_j)\rangle_o \langle O^{(o)}(\underset{\sim}{r}, 0)\rangle_o + O(\Omega^{-1}) .$$

Thus the numerator of the expression for $\langle O(\underset{\sim}{r}, 0)\rangle_{eq}$ differs from the denominator only by the factor $\langle O^{(o)}(\underset{\sim}{r}, 0)\rangle_o$ apart from negligible terms of $O(\Omega^{-1})$, so that

$$\langle O(\underset{\sim}{r}, 0)\rangle_{eq} = \langle O^{(o)}(\underset{\sim}{r}, 0)\rangle_o + O(\Omega^{-1}) .$$

It follows that in the thermodynamic limit $\Omega \rightarrow \infty$, no error is made in evaluating the term $\langle O(\underset{\sim}{r}, 0)\rangle_{eq} \langle O(\underset{\sim}{r}_o, 0)\rangle_{eq}$ in the transport kernel if one replaces H by H_o.

The proof for the more complicated correlation-function terms in K can be constructed by analogy. One has to expand not only the operator $e^{-\beta(H_o+H')}$, but also the operators $e^{\mp it(H_o+H')}$ occurring in the evaluation of Heisenberg operators. Although the details of the proof are more complicated, one arrives at a similar conclusion:

$$\langle O(\underset{\sim}{r}, 0)\, O(\underset{\sim}{r}', t)\rangle_{eq} = \langle O^{(o)}(\underset{\sim}{r}, 0)\, O^{(o)}(\underset{\sim}{r}', t)\rangle_o + O(\Omega^{-1}) .$$

Thus H_o is a "thermodynamically-equivalent" Hamiltonian not only in thermal equilibrium, but also for linear transport involving spatially-localized deviations from equilibrium.

This result can be generalized to nonlinear transport by considering the higher-order terms in the expansion of the thermodynamic potential; these involve triple, quadruple, ... correlation functions of the operators $O(\underset{\sim}{r}, t)$ evaluated in thermal equilibrium. A straightforward extension of the previous reasoning shows, again, that only errors of $O(\Omega^{-1})$ are made if H is replaced by H_0 in the evaluation of these. The previous restriction to single-particle observables is also easily removed. The final conclusion is that in evaluating the time evolution $\langle O(\underset{\sim}{r}, t)\rangle$ in cases where the initial deviation from equilibrium is spatially localized and the Hamiltonian is of the previously-described generalized BCS form, one makes no error in the thermodynamic limit if the full Hamiltonian is replaced by the thermodynamically-equivalent Hamiltonian H_0:

$$\langle O(\underset{\sim}{r}, t)\rangle = \frac{\mathrm{Tr}\{O(\underset{\sim}{r}, t)\exp[-\beta H - \int d^3r'\lambda_0(\underset{\sim}{r}')\,O(\underset{\sim}{r}')]\}}{\mathrm{Tr}\exp[-\beta H - \int d^3r'\lambda_0(\underset{\sim}{r}')\,O(\underset{\sim}{r}')]}$$

$$= \frac{\mathrm{Tr}\{O^{(0)}(\underset{\sim}{r}, t)\exp[-\beta H_0 - \int d^3\underset{\sim}{r}'\lambda_0(\underset{\sim}{r}')\,O(\underset{\sim}{r}')]\}}{\mathrm{Tr}\exp[-\beta H_0 - \int d^3r'\lambda_0(\underset{\sim}{r}')\,O(\underset{\sim}{r}')]} + O(\Omega^{-1}) .$$

The analysis has so far been restricted to cases in which the time evolution $\langle O(t)\rangle$ is due not to any external field absent in thermal equilibrium, but instead is a result of the noncommutativity of the observable O with H together with an initial localized deviation from equilibrium. An equally interesting case is that in which the time evolution is due to some perturbation not contained in H. By analysis similar to that previously employed, one can show that the quasiparticle-interaction Hamiltonian H' again has negligible effect on the evolution of observables similar to those previously considered provided that the perturbation is spatially localized. However, the perturbation need not be everywhere small.

In summary: it has been shown that the BZT-Wentzel method of the "thermodynamically-equivalent Hamiltonian" can be extended to problems of nonequilibrium statistical mechanics involving spatially-localized deviations from equilibrium; large local deviations do not invalidate the formalism. A detailed account of the analysis can be found elsewhere[7].

REFERENCES

1. J. Bardeen, L. N. Cooper, and J. R. Schrieffer, Phys. Rev. **108**, 1175 (1957).
2. N. N. Bogoliubov, D. N. Zubarev, and Yu. A. Tserkovnikov, Dokl. Akad. Nauk SSSR **117**, 788 (1957); English translation in Soviet Phys.-Doklady **2**, 535 (1957).
3. G. Wentzel, Phys. Rev. **120**, 1572 (1960).
4. G. Wentzel, "Quasi-Particles and Transport Phenomena", in *Werner Heisenberg und die Physik unserer Zeit* (Verlag Friedr. Vieweg und Sohn, Braunschweig).
5. E. T. Jaynes, Phys. Rev. **106**, 620 (1957); Phys. Rev. **108**, 171 (1957); "Information Theory and Statistical Mechanics", in 1962 Brandeis Lectures, Vol. 3 (W. A. Benjamin, Inc., New York, 1963). Also unpublished work of E. T. Jaynes presented in an informal seminar at the University of Oregon.
6. See, e.g., R. Zwanzig, in *Annual Reviews of Physical Chemistry* (Annual Reviews, Inc., Palo Alto, 1965), Vol. 16, pp. 67 ff.
7. M. D. Girardeau, J. Math. Phys. (to be published in March 1967).

DISCUSSION

Singh: Apart from the case of a superconductor, does one know any example where the thermodynamically equivalent Hamiltonian has proved useful?

Girardeau: Yes, there is a solvable Boson model which is similar and contains more terms than in the Bogolubov Hamiltonian. A lower ground state energy is found. Also, there is a ferromagnetism model.

Singh: So far as the Bose system is concerned, the thermodynamically equivalent Hamiltonian taken in its entirety gives unrealistic results such as an energy gap in the spectrum and a first order Bose-Einstein transition. I should also like to point out that the use of the thermodynamically equivalent Hamiltonian in this case is equivalent to using the first order diagrams in the pertubation expansion of the self energy parts of the one-particle temperature Green's functions. The latter approach makes it clear that results calculated with the thermodynamically equivalent Hamiltonian beyond the first order in the interaction have no physical meaning.

Girardeau: That depends on what you calculate. It does give a lower free energy.

Sewell: The fact that the model Hamiltonian may adequately reproduce the equilibrium properties of the original many-fermion

Hamiltonian does not ensure that it will also yield the correct non-equilibrium properties.

Girardeau: Is there an obvious reason why it should be worse in the non-equilibrium case?

Sewell: Yes, take the BCS theory for example. The reduced BCS Hamiltonian lacks the part of the original Fröhlich Hamiltonian that governs real electron-phonon scattering processes. These processes play a vital role in dissipative properties of the system, though not in equilibrium properties.

Girardeau: I am aware of the physical unreality of such model Hamiltonians but exact calculations with simplified models are often informative.

Sewell: I agree that model calculations may be instructive. I merely want to emphasise that two Hamiltonians which lead to similar equilibrium properties might lead to entirely different dissipative properties.

SOME COMMENTS ON THE USEFULNESS OF THE CONCEPT OF COHERENCE TIME IN THE STATISTICAL THEORY OF LIQUIDS

STUART A. RICE*)
Dept. of Chemistry and Institute for The Study of Metals, University of Chicago, Chicago, Illinois, 60637.

ABSTRACT

The possibility that a liquid may be described as a system in which the lifetime of dynamical correlations is very short is examined. Conditions under which the Rice-Allnatt equation is recovered are cited. Also, a simple theory of the autocorrelation function and of transport coefficients is developed in terms of a memory function.

It is appropriate that this talk follows a talk by R. W. Zwanzig, since it is through the study of his work[1)], and the related work of Fano[2)], that we were led to make the analysis to be presented. In particular, the projection operator formalism and the memory function were introduced by Zwanzig[1)], while the role of a dynamical coherence time in defining a suitable expansion parameter for strongly interacting systems was studied by Fano[2)] using techniques introduced by Zwanzig. The work to be presented this morning is connected, in my mind, by the concept of dynamical coherence time, of which more will be said later. Despite the connection cited, the analyses naturally fall into two classes, and these are discussed separately. The work in section I was done in collatoration with Dr. Norman Hurt[3)]. The work in sections II and III was done in collaboration with Prof. Bruce Berne and Dr. Jean-Pierre Boon[4)].

*) During 1965-66: National Science Foundation Senior Postdocteral Fellow and Visiting Professor, Université Libre de Bruxelles.

I. A REINTERPRETATION OF THE KINETIC EQUATION FOR A SIMPLE LIQUID

The theory of transport phenomena in dense fluids has developed slowly during the past 20 years[5]. During this same period there has also been developed an extensive and general theory of irreversible processes[6]. However, the special problems associated with the high density and strong intermolecular interactions in a typical liquid have, as of this date, prevented the use of the general theory for the description of dissipative processes in liquids. In the absence of a general theory which is applicable, the analysis of linear, steady state, transport phenomena in a liquid has usually been based on the hypothesis, due to Kirkwood[7], that in describing a dynamical system of many particles it is possible to find a time interval such that there is a (possibly complex) dynamical event in that time interval which is independent of similar prior events. As used by Rice and co-workers[5], this hypothesis states that if the intermolecular potential is represented as the superposition of a rigid-core interaction (or other very rapidly varying, very short range, repulsive interaction) and a relatively weak and longer ranged interaction, then the fundamental dynamical event consists of a strongly repulsive encounter followed by a quasi-Brownian motion of the molecule, pair of molecules, ..., in the fluctuating force field due to the remaining molecules in the system. It is asserted that because the destruction of dynamical correlations by the quasi-Brownian motion is efficient, successive strongly repulsive encounters are statistically independent. One consequence of this assumption is that the kinetic equations assume a form in which the effects of the strongly repulsive short range portion and the weak long range portion of the potential appear as separate scattering cross sections. Of course, the full potential determines the statistical geometry and other properties of the liquid, and the distribution function is a functional of the full intermolecular interaction despite the additivity of scattering processes in the kinetic equation.

The Rice-Allnatt equations represent, of course, only an approximate theory of transport phenomena in liquids. It has been shown, however, that:

a) In the steady state limit, the cluster expansion of the kinetic equation obtained using time smoothing is identical with that obtained from the theories of Green, Bogolubov and Prigogine[8, 9, 10, 11].

b) In the weak coupling limit, the Fokker-Planck like equation obtained by use of the time smoothing hypothesis is identical with that obtained by Prigogine using other methods[12].

c) In the limit that the interactions are of the rigid core type, the Enskog equation is recovered.

d) In the low density limit, the separation of cross sections in the kinetic equation is valid[13].

Today, I wish to describe an analysis which supplements the results cited. Specifically, using a formal expansion scheme based on the work of Zwanzig and Fano, the time smoothing hypothesis takes a natural form related to the lifetime of dynamical coherence in the liquid. Using this expansion it is possible to:

a) Show that the Rice-Alnatt kinetic equations represent a correct description of the stationary state behaviour of a liquid in the limit of short coherence time.

b) Define sufficient conditions which permit the description of dissipative phenomena in terms of the additive effects of the short range and long range interactions (albeit with the distribution function still a functional of the full intermolecular interaction).

c) Establish a connection between the time smoothing hypothesis and a formal perturbation theory.

It is convenient to digress momentarily and explore, in a qualitative fashion, how the motion of coherence time can be related to the formal properties of the Liouville operator. We shall not, in this qualitative argument, explore the relationship between the dynamical coherence time and the details of the molecular dynamics. Rather, it is our intention to motivate the search for, and use of, a formalism which exploits the properties of the dynamical coherence time of a many body system.

It is, of course, just a restatement of what is well known, to note that a subsystem, in interaction with a large reservoir, quickly dissipates the effects of a disturbance if the interactions between the subsystem and reservoir and within the reservoir are such that the disturbance propagates away as fast or faster than the disturbance is built up in the subsystem. What is less obvious is how important the history of the evolution of the disturbance is to the instantaneous rate of dissipation, i.e. whether the rate of dissipation should be Markoffian or non-Markoffian. In general, a Markoffian description will be valid only if it is possible to neglect effects created within the lifetime of the dynamical correlations. More explicitly, the Liouville equation

$$\frac{\partial}{\partial t} f^{(N)} = i\, L^{(N)}\, f^{(N)} \tag{1}$$

$$L^{(N)} = i \sum_j \left[\frac{\tilde{P}_j}{m} \cdot \nabla_j + \tilde{F}_j \cdot \nabla_{P_j} \right] \tag{2}$$

has the solution

$$\begin{aligned} f^{(N)}(t) &= e^{i(t-t')L^{(N)}}\, f^{(N)}(t') \\ &= G^{(N)}(t,t')\, f^{(N)}(t'), \end{aligned} \tag{3}$$

and it is clear that $G^{(N)}(t,t')$ has the group property

$$G^{(N)}(t,t'') = G^{(N)}(t,t')\, G^{(N)}(t',t''), \tag{4}$$

which defines a Markov process. In the case of the full N body system, the Markov process is trivial in the sense that the transition probability for the motion of the phase point is a delta function with argument determined by the N-body dynamics. However, the transition probability describing the motion of a phase point in a subspace, for example the point Γ_2 in the phase space of a pair of molecules, is not determined solely by the two body dynamics and is not a Markov process. If, however, the quantity

$$G^{(n)} = \int d\Gamma_{N-n}\, G^{(N)} , \qquad (5)$$

(which is obtained by expanding the exponential operator $G^{(N)}$ in its defining power series and integrating term by term with a suitable test function) can be written in the form

$$G^{(n)}(t-t'') \simeq \left[G^{(n)}(\tau)\right]^m , \qquad (6)$$

then the projection $G^{(n)}$ defines an approximately Markoffian process. Now, Eq. (6) will only be valid, if at all, provided that τ_c, the lifetime of the dynamical correlations built up in the time interval t-t'', satisfies the inequality $\tau \gg \tau_c$, where $t-t'' = m\tau$. It is just because τ_c is finite that Eq. (6) can only represent an approximately Markoffian process. It is clear that the correlations neglected when Eq. (6) is adopted are those built up in the interval τ_c just prior to t''. Whether or not their neglect introduces negligible error depends on the phenomenon under discussion.

The preceding observation can be formalized and quantified. We start with the exact equations[5)]

$$\left[\frac{\partial}{\partial t} + \frac{\underset{\sim}{p}_1}{m}\cdot\nabla_1\right]\bar{f}^{(1)} = \Omega_H + \Omega_S , \qquad (7)$$

$$\Omega_H = -\frac{1}{\tau}\int_0^\tau\!\!\int \underset{\sim}{F}{}_{12}^{(H)}\cdot\nabla_{p_1} f^{(2)}(\Gamma_2, t+s)\,d\Gamma_1(2)\,ds , \qquad (8)$$

$$\Omega_S = -\frac{1}{\tau}\int_0^\tau\!\!\int \underset{\sim}{F}{}_{12}^{(S)}\cdot\nabla_{p_1} f^{(2)}(\Gamma_2, t+s)\,d\Gamma_1(2)\,ds , \qquad (9)$$

$$\bar{f}^{(n)}(t) = \frac{1}{\tau}\int_0^\tau f^{(n)}(t+s)\,ds , \qquad (10)$$

where $\underset{\sim}{F}_{12}^{(H)}$ and $\underset{\sim}{F}_{12}^{(S)}$ are the hard and soft components of the intermolecular force corresponding to a representation of the intermolecular pair potential as the superposition of a short ranged repulsion and a longer ranged, weaker, interaction. As usual, $d\Gamma_1(2)$ is the differential element of volume in the phase space of molecule 2. To determine the properties of the pair distribution function, $f^{(2)}(t+s)$, we introduce the Laplace transform of the N body distribution function. Let

$$f^{(N)}(\omega) = i \int_0^{\infty} e^{i\omega t} f^{(N)}(t)dt , \qquad (11)$$

$$f^{(N)}(t) = \frac{1}{2\pi i} \int_{-\infty+i\epsilon}^{\infty+i\epsilon} e^{-i\omega t} \tilde{f}^{(N)}(\omega)d\omega , \qquad (12)$$

with $\mathrm{Im}\omega > 0$. The use of the formal solution of the Liouville equation, Eq. (3), in Eq. (11), leads to

$$\tilde{f}^{(N)}(\omega) = \frac{1}{\omega - L^{(N)}} f^{(N)}(0) . \qquad (13)$$

To evaluate the time dependence of the pair distribution function, we imagine a pair of molecules to be in interaction with an N-2 molecule reservoir. The liouville operator is then written in the form

$$L^{(N)} = L^{(2)} + L^{(N-2)} + \delta L = L_0^{(N)} + \delta L , \qquad (14)$$

where

$$L^{(2)} = \frac{\underset{\sim}{p}_1}{m} \cdot \nabla_1 + \frac{\underset{\sim}{p}_2}{m} \cdot \nabla_2 + \underset{\sim}{F}_{12} \cdot (\nabla_{p_1} - \nabla_{p_2}) ,$$

$$L^{(N-2)} = \sum_{j=3}^{N} \left[\underset{\sim}{F}_{1j} \cdot \nabla_{p_1} + \underset{\sim}{F}_{2j} \cdot \nabla_{p_2}\right] + \sum_{j=s}^{N} \left[\frac{\underset{\sim}{p}_j}{m} \cdot \nabla_j + \underset{\sim}{F}_j \cdot \nabla_{p_j}\right] ,$$

$$\delta L = \sum_{j=3}^{N} \left[\underset{\sim}{F}_{1j} \cdot \nabla_{p_1} + \underset{\sim}{F}_{2j} \cdot \nabla_{p_2}\right] . \qquad (15)$$

This subdivision of the Liouville operator corresponds to examining the motion of a pair of particles, described by $L^{(2)}$, coupled by the interaction operator δL to a reservoir of N-2 molecules which move in the fixed field of the subset of the two molecules. The Liouville operator for this reservoir is $L^{(N-2)}$. Using the projection operator

$$P_n = f^{(N-n)}(0) \int d\Gamma_{N-n} \tag{16}$$

and the normalization condition

$$\int f^{(n)} \, d\Gamma_n = 1 , \tag{17}$$

it is possible to show that

$$\tilde{f}^{(2)}(\omega) = \left[f^{(N-2)}(0)\right]^{-1} P_2\left[(\omega - L^{(N)})^{-1} f^{(N)}(0)\right] \tag{18}$$

The function $f^{(2)}(\omega)$ may also be represented in terms of the interaction operator δL. To do so we use the operator identity

$$(\omega - L_0^{(N)} - \delta L)^{-1} = (\omega - L_0^{(N)})^{-1}\left[1 + M(\omega)(\omega - L_0^{(N)})^{-1}\right], \tag{19}$$

$$M(\omega) = \delta L + \delta L(\omega - L_0^{(N)} - \delta L)^{-1} \delta L$$

$$= \delta L \sum_{n=0}^{\infty} \left[(\omega - L_0^{(N)})^{-1} \delta L\right]^n . \tag{20}$$

Since Eq. (18) involves $f^{(N)}(0)$, it is now necessary to examine the correlations in the initial state. Let

$$(1 - C_n) = P_n^* = f^{(N-n)*}(0) \int d\Gamma_{N-n} , \tag{21}$$

where $f^{(N-n)*}(0)$ is the (N-n) molecule distribution function conditioned on the configurational distribution of the subset n, i.e. in the field of n fixed molecules. Then

$$C_n f^{(N)} = f^{(N)}(t) - f^{(N-n)*}(0)\, f^{(n)}(t) \tag{22}$$

represents the residual dynamical correlations in the momentum space which are introduced by the initial conditions. In the theory of Prigogine and coworkers these are the terms described by the destruction fragment[6)]. For the study of steady state transport phenomena we take

$$C_n f^{(N)}(0) = 0 \;, \tag{23}$$

which is equivalent to the statement that initial dynamical correlations have negligible influence on the dynamical event on the time scale of the total dynamical event. We regard (23) as a boundary condition which specifies the state of the system at t=0. The neglect of initial dynamical correlations is equivalent to supposing that in the initial state the N-2 molecule distribution is in a stationary state with respect to the field generated by the fixed pair of molecules. In more formal terms,

$$L^{(N-2)} f^{(N-2)*}(0) = 0 \tag{24}$$

because $L^{(N-2)}$ contains the force field of the fixed molecules.

The substitution of Eqs. (19) and (20) into (18), together with the condition (23) and the relation

$$\int d\Gamma_{N-2}\, L_o^{(N)} = L^{(2)} \int d\Gamma_{N-2} \tag{25}$$

leads to

$$\tilde{f}^{(2)}(\omega) = \frac{1}{\omega - L^{(2)}} \int d\Gamma_{N-2} \left[1 + M(\omega)(\omega - L_0^{(N)})^{-1}\right] f^{(N-2)*}(0) \times f^{(2)}(0) \tag{26}$$

$$= \frac{1}{\omega - L^{(2)}} \left[1 + \langle M(\omega)\rangle (\omega - L_0^{(N)})^{-1}\right] f^{(2)}(0) \;, \tag{27}$$

where

$$<M(\omega)> = \int d\Gamma_{N-2}\, f^{(N-2)*}(0)\, M(\omega)\ . \tag{28}$$

A more convenient form of (27) is

$$\tilde{f}^{(2)}(\omega) = \frac{1}{\omega - L^{(2)} - <M_c(\omega)>}\, f^{(2)}(0) \tag{29}$$

where

$$<M_c(\omega)> = <M(\omega)> \sum_{n=0}^{\infty} \left[(\omega - L_0^{(N)})^{-1} <M(\omega)>\right]^n . \tag{30}$$

The inversion of Eq. (29) provides an explicit representation of the time dependence of the pair function, $f^{(2)}(t)$, subject to the boundary conditions cited. Given $f^{(2)}(t+s)$, Eqs. (8) and (9) may be used to obtain a kinetic equation. Of course, it is not in practice possible to invert (29), but sufficient information can be obtained by examining the limiting behaviour of $\tilde{f}^{(2)}(\omega)$ for $\omega \to \infty$, and for $<M_c(\omega)>$ small.

Consider first the case of a rigid core interaction. Since the duration of a rigid core encounter is infinitesimally small, the limit $\omega \to \infty$ should isolate the behaviour of $\tilde{f}^{(2)}(\omega)$ under quasi-binary collisions. Indeed

$$\lim_{\omega \to \infty} <M_c(\omega)> = <\delta L>\ , \tag{31}$$

$$\lim_{\omega \to \infty} \tilde{f}^{(2)}(\omega) = \frac{1}{\omega - L^{(2)} - <\delta L>}\, f^{(2)}(0)\ , \tag{32}$$

describes a binary encounter in the averaged field of the surroundings. Further, when $<M(\omega)>$ is small,

$$<M_c(\omega)> = <\delta L> + <\delta L\,(\omega - L_0^{(N)})^{-1}\, \delta L> + \ldots\ , \tag{33}$$

and it may be shown that in this limit the evolution of $f^{(2)}$ is described by the weak coupling master equation. We thus recover the Rice-Allnatt kinetic equation[5], in which the time evolution of $f^{(2)}$ is determined by the sum of the scattering caused by quasi-binary encounters and a quasi-Brownian motion.

We must now justify, in some sense, limiting the representation of $\tilde{f}^{(2)}(\omega)$ to only the two terms of Eqs. (31) and (33). If the spectrum of $\tilde{f}^{(2)}(\omega)$ is such that there is little (or no) overlap between the frequency domains characteristic of the hard core collisions and the quasi-Brownian motion, the transform for each part may be obtained by extrapolating $\tilde{f}^{(2)}(\omega)$ without fear that interference will occur, and the total scattering is just the sum of the effects of the separate scattering events. The term $\langle M(\omega) \rangle$ depends on the ratio of the interaction time to the time between interactions, $\delta L(\omega - L_0^{(N)})^{-1}$. This ratio will be small relative to unity when the frequency of molecular fluctuations is large compared with the frequency of hard core collisions. Then, dynamical correlations accumulate coherently only over a single memory period,

$$\tau_c \approx \left[(\omega - L_0^{(N)})\right]^{-1}_{\text{eff}} \tag{34}$$

We have not been able to <u>prove</u> that $\delta L(\omega - L_0^{(N)})^{-1}$ is small, but a model calculation by Rice and Allnatt shows that for liquid Ar, for the relaxation of a perturbation to the momentum distribution function, this ratio is about 1/20. These considerations constitute nothing more than a plausibility argument, but the results are suggestive and do support the contention that the Rice-Allnatt equations are a valid description of steady state transport phenomena in simple liquids.

It should now be clear that the time smoothing hypothesis is well founded within the framework of a formal perturbation theory, but that the pertinent expansion parameter is not either the reduced density, $\rho\sigma^3$, or the reduced interaction strength, ϵ/kT, but rather τ_c/τ. The reason that the relevant expansion parameter is the ratio of the correlation time to the time between dynamical events arises from the fact that, in the limit that the Liouville operator has a continuous spectrum, it is not pertinent to enquire into the relative magnitudes of the interaction strength and the separation of the eigenvalues of the Liouville operator. What is relevant is that the effective value of the resonance denominator is determined by the rapidity with which correlations are damped, i. e. the rate at which the surrounding medium carries away the dynamical coherence. Then, because interaction effects can accumulate only over a short time, the effective interaction remains weak. The hypothesis of time smoothing now appears as a natural procedure which is justified by the nature of the perturbation expansion. Indeed, the very statement of the time smoothing hypothesis is related to the existence of a short memory time.

II. THE CALCULATION OF AUTOCORRELATION FUNCTIONS OF DYNAMICAL VARIABLES

It is now well known that the linear transport coefficients can be obtained from an autocorrelation function representation. In this representation, the role of the dynamical memory is particularly clearly displayed. For example, in the simple case that the momentum autocorrelation function decays as $\exp(-t/\tau_c)$, the relaxation time τ_c determines the diffusion coefficient.

The reader should note that a Markoffian kinetic equation leads to the same transport coefficients as obtained from the autocorrelation function representation, because of the implicit long time integration involved in the use of asymptotic cross sections in the kinetic equation. Thus, for the computation of linear transport coefficients from a kinetic equation, it is not necessary to examine the dynamical behavior of the system at short times. On the other hand, consideration of the structure of the autocorrelation function of a dynamical variable requires just such an examination of the dynamics. We shall see that in our formulation of the problem the calculation of the time dependence of the autocorrelation function for short times cannot be carried out using only asymptotic (and Markoffian) considerations.

It is worthwhile to rephrase the considerations of the last section and to probe a little more deeply into the way that the property expressed in Eq. (6) is used to obtain both a kinetic equation and an autocorrelation function representation[14)]. Consider the following derivation of the singlet kinetic equation for a dilute gas. As before, the starting point is the formal representation of the time dependence of the singlet distribution function in terms of the propagator exp $(itL^{(N)})$ acting on the N-body distribution function at t = 0, and an integration over the phases of N-1 molecules. Also as before, the system of N molecules may be thought of as a subsystem of one molecule and a reservoir of N-1 molecules, to which corresponds a decomposition of $L^{(N)}$ into operators for the subsystem, the reservoir, and their complete interaction. If the interaction operator is regarded as a perturbation, and the formal representation of the singlet function expanded in a perturbation series with use of the initial condition that the full distribution function can be written as the product $f^{(1)}(0)\ f^{(N-1)}(0)$, then the resulting expansion may be converted to a kinetic equation as follows. The structure of the perturbation series involves multiple time integrations over products of the interaction representation of the perturbation operator. Consider some small time interval τ, with τ chosen so that $\tau \gg \tau_c$, but also small enough that the terms in the perturbation series involving more than two time integrations are small and may be neglected. Provided that $\tau \gg \tau_c$ as assumed, the time dependence of the singlet distribution function at long times may be generated from the truncated perturbation expansion by replacing the actual N-body distribution function generated from the initial state with the product function $f^{(1)}(\tau)\ f^{(N-1)}(0)$. When this condition is entered into the integrand of the perturbation expansion, and the procedure repeated chainwise, the resultant $f^{(1)}(t)$ is the same as the function that would be obtained from the integration of a differential equation on a time mesh of size τ. Thus, the variations of f(t) obtained satisfy a kinetic equation where the interval τ is treated formally as a differential. The reader should note that the repeated use of the product function at intervals of length τ is very close to the philosophy of time smoothing, where a dynamical event occurring in an interval τ is taken to be independent of prior dynamical events[5].

How do short time correlations appear in the representation of dissipative processes? When $\tau >> \tau_c$, it is to be expected that the coherence imposed by the molecular dynamics is lost because of propagation of the disturbance away from the source (the dynamical event studied) by the coupling with the surrounding molecules. Then, the average of the products of operators in the perturbation expansion described in the last paragraph is expected to approach a product of the averages of the operators. By introduction of cumulants representing the difference between an average of several operators and the product of the averages taken all possible ways, it may be shown that the perturbation expansion may be expressed in terms of the autocorrelation function of the cumulants. But, by definition, if $t >> \tau_c$ the cumulants vanish, and therefore in this representation the effects of short time correlations in the molecular dynamics are displayed.

Since both representations discussed can be obtained from perturbation theory, their connection is easily established in the same formalism. The key point is that the cumulants vanish rapidly as t increases, so that integrals over the cumulants rapidly approach their asymptotic values and are not sensitive to the precise value of the upper limit of integration. Under these circumstances, the neglect of third and higher order cumulant terms leads to a kinetic equation in which the entire effect of the dissipative interaction enters through integrals over the pair cumulant function. Thus, even though the dissipation appears through the structure of the pair cumulant, an asymptotic limit must be used to obtain a kinetic equation. A much more general and incisive analysis of the relationship between kinetic equations and the autocorrelation function representation has been given by Resibois[15]. The preceding simple arguments suffice to introduce the points of interest to us.

It is indeed a remarkable result in many ways, that a Markoffian kinetic equation leads to the same linear transport coefficients as does the autocorrelation function representation of the transport coefficients. Because of the role played by the coherence time in defining both the autocorrelation function of a dynamical variable and the corresponding kinetic equation, we are encouraged to pose the following question: Given a formal, but useable, definition of dynamical memory, what do simple physical arguments about the nature of the dynamical memory imply about the autocorrelation function? We now seek to answer this question.

We seek an equation which describes the time evolution of the normalized autocorrelation function, $\Psi(t)$, of the phase function $U(\Gamma_N)$. $\Psi(t)$ is defined by

$$\Psi(t) = Z_N^{-1} \int d\Gamma_N\, U(\Gamma_N) \exp(itL^{(N)})\, U(\Gamma_N)\, e^{-H^{(N)}/kT}, \quad (35)$$

where Z_N is the canonical partition function for the N molecule system, and $L^{(N)}$, $H^{(N)}$, are the corresponding Liouville operator, and Hamiltonian function, respectively. The phase function $U(\Gamma_N)$ is assumed to have the following properties:

$$\langle U \rangle = 0\,, \qquad \langle U^2 \rangle = 1\,, \quad (36)$$

where the bracket defines an average in the canonical ensemble,

$$\langle \alpha \rangle \doteq Z_N^{-1} \int d\Gamma_N\, \alpha\, e^{-H^{(N)}/kT}. \quad (37)$$

If $\Psi(t)$ is differentiated twice with respect to t,

$$\frac{d^2\Psi(t)}{dt^2} = Z_N^{-1} \int d\Gamma_N\, U(\Gamma_N)\, iL^{(N)} \exp(itL^{(N)}) \times \left[iL^{(N)}\, U(\Gamma_N)\right] e^{-H^{(N)}/kT}, \quad (38)$$

and the right-hand side of this equation integrated by parts, it is found that

$$\frac{d^2\Psi(t)}{dt^2} = -Z_N^{-1}\int d\Gamma_N \left[iL^{(N)}\, U(\Gamma_N)\right] \times$$

$$\times \exp(itL^{(N)}) \left[iL^{(N)}\, U(\Gamma_N)\right] e^{-H^{(N)}/kT} \tag{39}$$

$$= -< \Phi(\Gamma_N) \exp(itL^{(N)})\, \Phi(\Gamma_N) >,$$

where $\Phi(\Gamma_N) = iL^{(N)}\, U(\Gamma_N)$.

The time evolution of the phase function $U(\Gamma_N)$ is described by the relation

$$\frac{d}{dt} U(\Gamma_N) = iL^{(N)}\, U(\Gamma_N) , \tag{40}$$

whereupon

$$\Phi(\Gamma_N) = \frac{d}{dt} U(\Gamma_N) = \dot{U}(\Gamma_N) . \tag{41}$$

Now, the operator $\exp(itL^{(N)})$ is the unitary time displacement operator which, when applied to an arbitrary phase function, displaces it in time according to the canonical equations of motion. Thus, Eq. (39) can be rewritten, using the previous notation, in the form

$$\frac{d^2\Psi(t)}{dt^2} = -< \dot{U}(0)\, \dot{U}(t) > . \tag{42}$$

Eq. (42) is to be solved subject to the initial conditions

$$\Psi(0) = 1 \quad \text{and} \quad \dot{\Psi}(0) = < U(0)\, \dot{U}(0) > = 0. \tag{43}$$

The first of Eqs. (43) is merely the second condition in Eq. (36), whereas the second of Eqs. (43) follows from considerations of parity.

Denoting by $\tilde{\Psi}(s)$ the Laplace transform of $\Psi(t)$ with respect to t, with s the Laplace variable,

$$\tilde{\psi}(s) = \int_0^\infty e^{-st}\psi(t)\,dt\,, \tag{44}$$

and by $<\widetilde{\dot{\phi}\,\dot{\phi}}(s)>$ the Laplace transform of the autocorrelation function $<\dot{\phi}(0)\,\dot{\phi}(t)>$, the Laplace transform of Eq. (42) is

$$s^2\,\tilde{\psi}(s) - s = -<\widetilde{\dot{U}\,\dot{U}}(s)> \;. \tag{45}$$

The identity

$$\left[s\,\tilde{\psi}(s) - 1\right]\,s\,\tilde{\psi}(s) = (s^2\,\tilde{\psi}(s) - s)\,\tilde{\psi}(s) \tag{46}$$

can be rearranged in the following way. Unity is added to and subtracted from the factor on the extreme left,

$$\left[s\,\tilde{\psi}(s) + 1 - 1\right]\,\left[s\,\tilde{\psi}(s) - 1\right] = (s^2\,\tilde{\psi}(s) - s)\,\tilde{\psi}(s)\,, \tag{47}$$

whereupon, for $s \neq 0$, this may be rewritten as

$$\left[\frac{1}{s}\,(s^2\,\tilde{\psi}(s) - s) + 1\right]\,\left[s\,\tilde{\psi}(s) - 1\right] = (s^2\,\tilde{\psi}(s) - s)\,\tilde{\psi}(s). \tag{48}$$

Eq. (45) is now substituted into Eq. (48) to yield

$$\left[1 - \frac{1}{s}\,<\widetilde{\dot{U}\,\dot{U}}(s)>\right]\,\left[s\,\tilde{\psi}(s) - 1\right] = -<\widetilde{\dot{U}\,\dot{U}}(s)>\psi(s). \tag{49}$$

For values of s such that $1 - \frac{1}{s}<\widetilde{\dot{U}\,\dot{U}}(s)> \neq 0$, Eq. (49) can be written in the form

$$s\,\tilde{\psi}(s) - 1 = -\left[1 - \frac{1}{s}<\widetilde{\dot{U}\,\dot{U}}(s)>\right]^{-1}<\widetilde{\dot{U}\,\dot{U}}(s)>\tilde{\psi}(s)\,, \tag{50}$$

and by inversion,

$$\frac{d\psi(t)}{dt} = -\int_0^t d\tau\;K(\tau)\,\psi(t-\tau)\,, \tag{51}$$

where

$$\tilde{K}(s) = \left[1 - \frac{1}{s} < \widetilde{\dot{U}\,\dot{U}(s)} > \right]^{-1} < \widetilde{\dot{U}\,\dot{U}(s)} > . \tag{52}$$

Consider, now, the function $<\widetilde{\dot{U}\,\dot{U}(s)}>$. This function may be written in terms of the resolvent operator $(s - iL^{(N)})^{-1}$ i.e.

$$<\widetilde{\dot{U}\,\dot{U}(s)}> = \int_0^\infty dt\, e^{-st} <\dot{U}\, e^{itL^{(N)}}\, \dot{U}> \tag{53}$$

$$= <\dot{U} \frac{1}{s - iL^{(N)}} \dot{U}> .$$

We now define a projection operator P acting on a well-behaved function of the phase Γ_N, $G(\Gamma_N)$, as follows:

$$PG(\Gamma_N) = U(\Gamma_N)\, f_{eq.}^{(N)} \int d\Gamma'_N\, U(\Gamma'_N)\, G(\Gamma'_N) , \tag{54}$$

where

$$f_{eq.}^{(N)} = Z_N^{-1}\, e^{-H^{(N)}/kT} . \tag{55}$$

Noting that, for the operators A and B, there exists the identity

$$A^{-1} = B^{-1} + A^{-1}(B - A)\, B^{-1} , \tag{56}$$

we find that

$$<\widetilde{\dot{U}\,\dot{U}(s)}> = <\dot{U} \frac{1}{s - i(1 - P)L^{(N)}} \dot{U}> +$$

$$<U \frac{1}{s - iL^{(N)}}\, iPL^{(N)} \frac{1}{s - i(1 - P)L^{(N)}} \dot{U}>. \tag{57}$$

Now, exploiting the definition of P in Eq. (54)

$$iPL^{(N)} \frac{1}{s - i(1 - P)L^{(N)}} \dot{U}\, f_{eq.}^{(N)}$$

$$= U\, f_{eq.}^{(N)} <U\, i\, L^{(N)} \frac{1}{s - i(1 - P)\, L^{(N)}} \dot{U}> . \tag{58}$$

In the bracket on the extreme right-hand side of Eq. (58), we integrate by parts and use Eq. (40) to obtain

$$iPL^{(N)} \frac{1}{s - i(1 - P)\, L^{(N)}} \dot{U}\, f^{(N)}_{eq.}$$

$$= - U\, f^{(N)}_{eq.} < \dot{U} \frac{1}{s - i(1 - P)\, L^{(N)}} \dot{U} > . \tag{59}$$

Thus, from Eqs. (57) and (59), we find

$$< \widetilde{\dot{U}\, \dot{U}}(s) > = < \dot{U} \frac{1}{s - i(1 - P) L^{(N)}} \dot{U} > - < \dot{U} \frac{1}{s - iL^{(N)}} U > \times$$

$$\times < \dot{U} \frac{1}{s - i(1 - P)\, L^{(N)}} \dot{U} > . \tag{60}$$

It is easily recognized that

$$< \dot{U} \frac{1}{s - i\, L^{(N)}} U > = \frac{1}{s} < \dot{U} \frac{1}{s - i\, L^{(N)}} \dot{U} > . \tag{61}$$

When Eq. (61) is substituted into Eq. (60), we find that

$$< \widetilde{\dot{U}\, \dot{U}}(s) > = \left[1 - \frac{1}{s} < \dot{U} \frac{1}{s - iL^{(N)}} \dot{U} > \right] < \dot{U} \frac{1}{s - i(1 - P)\, L^{(N)}} \dot{U} > . \tag{62}$$

Eq. (62) is now substituted into Eq. (52) to yield

$$\tilde{K}(s) = < \dot{U} \frac{1}{s - i(1 - P)\, L^{(N)}} \dot{U} > , \tag{63}$$

which, by inverse transformation, becomes

$$K(t) = < \dot{U} \exp\left[it(1 - P)\, L^{(N)} \right] \dot{U} > . \tag{64}$$

From the structure of Eq. (64) it is clear that the kernel K(t) is related to the memory, or dynamical coherence time, of the system, an interpretation which will be exploited later in this talk.

If one is interested in autocorrelation functions of vector quantities such as $\psi_\alpha(t)$ defined by

$$\psi_\alpha(t) = \langle \underset{\sim}{\alpha}(0) \cdot \underset{\sim}{\alpha}(t) \rangle , \tag{65}$$

the analysis necessary can be carried through with only one minor change: the projection operator in this case must be defined by its action on an arbitrary well-behaved vector point function of the phase Γ_N, say $\underset{\sim}{G}(\Gamma_N)$.

$$P\, \underset{\sim}{G}(\Gamma_N) = \underset{\sim}{\alpha}\, f^{(N)}_{eq.} \int d\Gamma'_N\, \underset{\sim}{\alpha}(\Gamma'_N) \cdot \underset{\sim}{G}(\Gamma'_N) . \tag{66}$$

These modifications are easily introduced into the preceding analysis.

Using a projection operator formalism, Zwanzig[1)] has derived an equation describing the time evolution of autocorrelation functions. The equation obtained from this very elegant formalism is identical with Eq. (51), with $K(\tau)$ defined by Eq. (64). By a different procedure we have obtained Eq. (51) with $\tilde{K}(s)$ defined by Eq. (52). By exploitation of Zwanzig's projection operator, Eq. (54), it was possible to demonstrate the identity of our equations with his. We feel that the form of $\tilde{K}(s)$ presented in Eq. (52) will be useful in generating new approximations.

To make use of the analysis outlined, we seek a representation of $K(\tau)$ since, once this function is known, the autocorrelation function is determined by solution of Eq. (51) with the boundary conditions $\psi(0) = 1$ and $\dot{\psi}(0) = 0$. We will in this lecture consider only the case of the normalized velocity autocorrelation function

$$\psi_v(t) = \langle \underset{\sim}{v}_1 \cdot e^{itL^{(N)}} \underset{\sim}{v}_1 \rangle / \langle v_1^2 \rangle , \tag{67}$$

which is connected to Eq. (35) by setting $\underset{\sim}{U} = \underset{\sim}{v}_1(\langle v_1^2 \rangle)^{-1/2}$ and with the requisite projection operator

$$P\,\underset{\sim}{G}(\Gamma_N) = \underset{\sim}{v}_1\, f^{(N)}_{eq.} \int d\Gamma'_N\, \underset{\sim}{v}_1 \cdot \underset{\sim}{G}(\Gamma'_N)\,. \qquad (68)$$

Then since

$$i\,L^{(N)}\, \underset{\sim}{v}_1 = \underset{\sim}{F}_1 / m\,, \qquad (69)$$

the kernel function becomes

$$\tilde{K}(s) = \left[1 - \frac{1}{s} \frac{\langle \underset{\sim}{F}_1 \cdot \tilde{\underset{\sim}{F}}_1(s) \rangle}{m^2 \langle v_1^2 \rangle} \right]^{-1} \frac{\langle \underset{\sim}{F}_1 \cdot \tilde{\underset{\sim}{F}}_1(s) \rangle}{m^2 \langle v_1^2 \rangle}\,, \qquad (70)$$

where $\underset{\sim}{F}_1$ is the force on molecule one. The value of $\tilde{K}(0)$ is easily determined from the Einstein relation for the diffusion coefficient. For,

$$\begin{aligned} D &= \frac{kT}{m} \int_0^\infty dt\, \psi(t) \\ &= \frac{kT}{m} \lim_{s \to 0} \int_0^\infty e^{-st}\, \psi(t)\, dt \qquad (71) \\ &= \frac{kT}{n}\, \tilde{\psi}(0)\,, \end{aligned}$$

whereupon, using the Laplace transform of Eq. (51),

$$s\tilde{\psi}(s) = 1 - \tilde{K}(s)\, \tilde{\psi}(s)\,, \qquad (72)$$

it is seen that

$$D = \frac{kT}{m} \left[\tilde{K}(0) \right]^{-1} = \frac{kT}{m\beta}\,. \qquad (73)$$

Thus $\tilde{K}(0)$ is just the translational friction coefficient. Note that the friction coefficient $\beta = \zeta/m$, in terms of the friction coefficient often used in other papers[5)]. A relationship involving K(0) and $(\partial^2\psi/\partial t^2)_{t=0}$ is easily obtained when it is noticed that

$$K(0) = \langle (iL^{(N)} U)^2 \rangle = \frac{\langle F_1^2 \rangle}{m^2 \langle v_1^2 \rangle}, \tag{74}$$

and

$$\frac{\partial^2 \psi(t)}{\partial t^2} = - \frac{\langle \underset{\sim}{F}_1 \cdot \underset{\sim}{F}_1(t) \rangle}{m^2 \langle v_1^2 \rangle}. \tag{75}$$

Finally, it can be shown that the memory function must be even in the time, and have zero derivative at $t = 0$.

The exact relations given above are insufficient to uniquely determine the form of the kernel function, and we propose to proceed by introducing a two parameter trial function, $K(\alpha, \gamma)$, with the parameters determined by use of Eqs. (73) and (75). It is now necessary to consider the functional form for the trial kernel.

Consider the case of the dilute gas. The probability that a molecule will travel a distance R without **undergoing** collision is proportional to $\exp(-R/\lambda_f)$, where λ_f is the mean free path. This form indicates that the sequence of collisions experienced by a molecule forms a Poisson process, and since each collision causes partial loss of the persistence of momentum, the memory of the initial momentum decays as $\exp(-t/\tau_c)$, where τ_c is the mean time between collisions.

Consider now the case of a dense fluid. Each molecule may be imagined to be surrounded by a cage of other atoms. The cage is, of course, not stationary, and in response to fluctuations in the surrounding medium undergoes quasi-random alterations as a function of time. A molecule moving away from the center of its cage interacts with the moving wall molecules. Although a strongly repulsive encounter with the wall molecules is likely to almost reverse the central particle momentum, the fact that the cage is fluctuating suggests that the sequence of interactions leading to loss of memory of the initial momentum of the particle can be approximated as a Poisson process. In the Rice-Allnatt theory, successive strongly repulsive binary encounters are taken to be independent, and the present argument suggests that the soft interactions leading to dissipation of momentum are sufficiently close to forming a Poisson process that a reasonable first approximation to the memory function is the exponential decay $\exp(-\alpha t)$. Clearly, this form has the proper regression property, but is inexact since it has finite slope at $t = 0$. It is important to emphasize that a simple exponential memory function is consistent with the velocity autocorrelation function having negative regions, as will be shown shortly. We emphasize this point in advance of demonstration so as to clearly differentiate the time dependence of the memory function from the time dependence of the corresponding autocorrelation function. One last point: If the time sequence of interactions is a Gaussian Markov process, then the correlation function is, rigorously, exponentially decaying[16]. In addition, it may be shown that the exponential memory function is derivable from linear regression theory[17].

With the preceding arguments as motivation, we adapt the two parameter trial kernel

$$K(\alpha, \gamma; t) = \gamma e^{-\alpha |t|} , \tag{76}$$

where $|t|$ is required by the parity of $K(t)$. However, in all that follows we shall only consider the positive time axis, and the modulus bars on t will therefore be dropped. The degree to which (76) is an adequate approximation to the true memory function can only be tested <u>a posteriori.</u>

To obtain the autocorrelation function, $K(\alpha, \gamma; t)$ as defined in Eq. (76) is Laplace transformed and the result is substituted into Eq. (72) to give

$$\tilde{\Psi}(s) = \frac{\alpha + s}{(s - s_+)(s - s_-)} \tag{77}$$

$$s_{\pm} = -\frac{\alpha}{2} \left[1 \mp \left(1 - \frac{4\gamma}{\alpha^2}\right)^{1/2} \right] . \tag{78}$$

Eq. (77) is inverted to yield

$$\psi(t) = \frac{1}{s_+ - s_-} \left(s_+ e^{s_- t} - s_- e^{s_+ t} \right) . \tag{79}$$

This result may be tested against the "experimental" data of Rahman[18], after numerical evaluation of α and γ. These parameters are determined, as indicated above: substitution of the Laplace transform of Eq. (76) into (73) yields

$$\beta = \lim_{s \to 0} \frac{\gamma}{s+\alpha} = \frac{\gamma}{\alpha}, \tag{80}$$

and from Eqs. (75), (78) and (79) it is found that

$$\gamma = \frac{<F_1^2>}{m^2 <v_1^2>} = \frac{<F_1^2>}{3m\,k\,T} = \frac{<\nabla_1^2 V>}{3\,m} . \tag{81}$$

How accurate is (79) as a description of a real N body system? Rahman, using a large digital computer, has solved the equations of motion for 864 atoms in a cubical box with periodic boundary conditions. The state of the system was chosen to correspond to liquid Ar at $T = 94.4\,^{\circ}K$ and $\rho_m = 1.374$ gm cm^{-3}. The interaction between the atoms was described by the known Ar-Ar Lennard-Jones potential[16]. From the solutions obtained, Rahman has calculated the velocity autocorrelation function, the power spectrum, the pair correlation function, the mean square displacement of an atom as a function of time, and the diffusion coefficient. All of these will be of use in our considerations.

Using Rahman's data, it is found that $<\nabla_1^2 V> = 11.0 \times 10^3$ ergs cm^{-2}. To check the integration over the radial distribution function, we note that for very short times the time derivative of the autocorrelation function is, from Eq. (79),

$$\frac{d\psi}{dt} = - s_+ s_- t = - \alpha\beta t \quad ; \qquad s_+ t \ll 1, \quad s_- t \ll 1 \tag{82}$$

Thus, the value of $d\psi/dt$ for t small also provides a measure of $<\nabla_1^2 V>$ (see Eqs. (80) and (81)). From the data presented by Rahman we find that $<\nabla_1^2 V> = 11.0 \times 10^3$ ergs cm^{-2}, in perfect agreement with the determination by direct integration. Using

$D = 2.43 \times 10^{-5}$ cm^2 sec^{-1}, as computed, and the value of $\langle \nabla_1^2 V \rangle$ quoted, it is found that $\alpha = 8.06 \times 10^{12}$ sec^{-1} and $\alpha\beta = 6.5 \times 10^{25}$ sec^{-2}. With these values of α and β, the roots $s_\pm$ are complex, and

$$\psi(t) = e^{-4.03\, t/\tau_o} \left[\cos(7.03 \frac{t}{\tau_o}) + 0.33 \sin(7.03 \frac{t}{\tau_o})\right] ,$$

$$\tau_o = 10^{-12} \text{ sec} . \tag{83}$$

In Figure 1 are plotted the theoretical autocorrelation function, Eq. (83), along with the Markoffian approximation ($\psi^M(t) = e^{-\beta t}$) and the "experimental" data of Rahman. As can be seen, the qualitative features of the autocorrelation function are reproduced, but the theoretical function oscillates with somewhat larger amplitude than does the observed autocorrelation function. Indeed, the agreement between the two functions is quite good up to $(t/\tau_o) \cong 0.3 - 0.4$, and it is very important to note that the theoretical function correctly predicts a negative region for $\psi(t)$, despite the very simple form of the trial memory function.

A somewhat different test of the theory proposed herein can be made by comparing the theoretical and observed normalized power spectra, defined by

$$G(\omega) = \beta \int_0^\infty dt\, \psi(t) \cos(\omega t) . \tag{84}$$

It is easily seen that

$$G(0) = 1 ,$$

and for our memory ansatz

$$G(\omega) = \beta \operatorname{Re} \int_0^\infty dt\, e^{-i\omega t} \psi(t)$$

$$= \frac{\alpha^2\beta^2}{\alpha^2\beta^2 + \alpha^2(1 - \frac{2\beta}{\alpha})\omega^2 + \omega^4} . \tag{85}$$

With the values of the parameters already cited, we find

$$G(\omega) = \frac{0.420}{0.420 - 6.5 \times 10^{-27}\omega^2 + 10^{-52}\omega^4} \quad . \tag{86}$$

In Figure 2 are plotted the theoretical power spectrum, Eq. (86), along with the Markoffian approximation ($G^M(\omega) = \frac{\beta^2}{\omega^2 + \beta^2}$) and the "experimental" data of Rahman. Again, the agreement between theory and experiment is quite good, especially in the matching of the peak in $G(\omega)$, which reaches a value of about 1.4.

It might be thought that a memory function which has zero slope at $t = 0$ would be a better approximation in describing $\psi(t)$ near $t = 0$. A form which has this property, and for which all calculations can be performed analytically, is

$$K(t) = \gamma(1 + \alpha t)\, e^{-\alpha t} \tag{87}$$

However, in the limit $t \to \infty$, (87) decays as $t \exp(-\alpha t)$, in disagreement with the requirements of the theory of linear regression. We shall see that this asymptotic discrepancy has important consequences. Using methods entirely analogous to those already described it is possible to show that

$$\psi(t) = \frac{e^{-10.7467\, t/\tau_o}}{11.7771} \quad 1.08879\, e^{-10.9801\, t/\tau_o}$$
$$+ \; e^{5.49007\, t/\tau_o} \quad 9.62776 \sin(8.29268 \frac{t}{\tau_o}$$
$$+ \; 10.6883 \cos(8.29268 \frac{t}{\tau_o})$$

(88)

$$G(\omega) = (1 + A\omega^2 + B\omega^4 + C\omega^6)^{-1}$$
$$A = -\, 0.673453 \times 10^{-26}$$
$$B = +\, 0.888569 \times 10^{-52}$$
$$C = +\, 0.227966 \times 10^{-78} \tag{89}$$

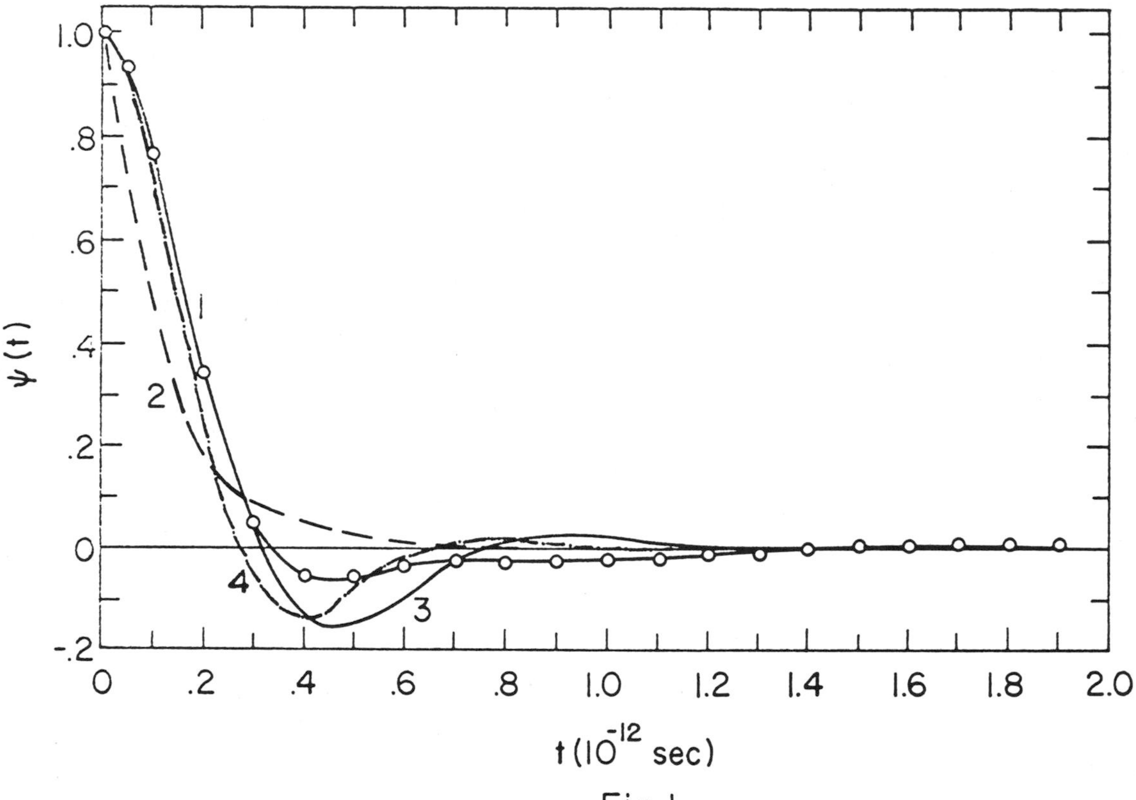

Fig. 1

(1) o o o o o o o Rahman's data

(2) - - - - - - - - Markoffian approximation

(3) ———————— $K(t) = \gamma \exp(-\alpha t)$

(4) —·—·—·—·— $K(t) = \gamma(1 + \alpha t) \exp(-\alpha t)$

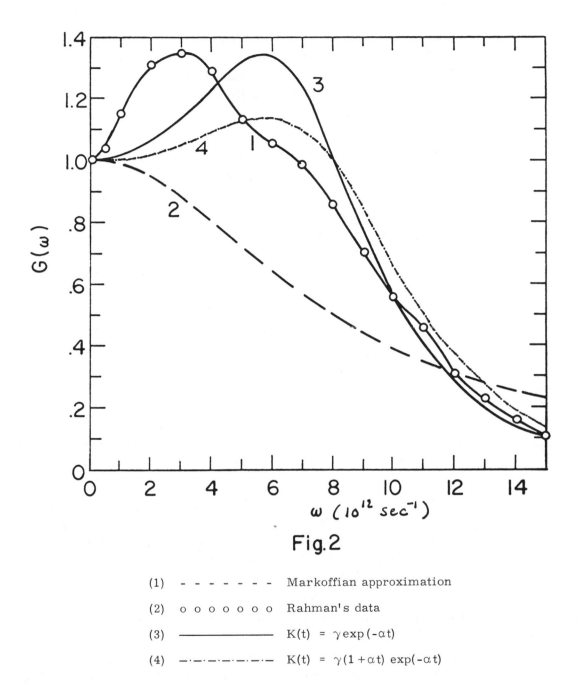

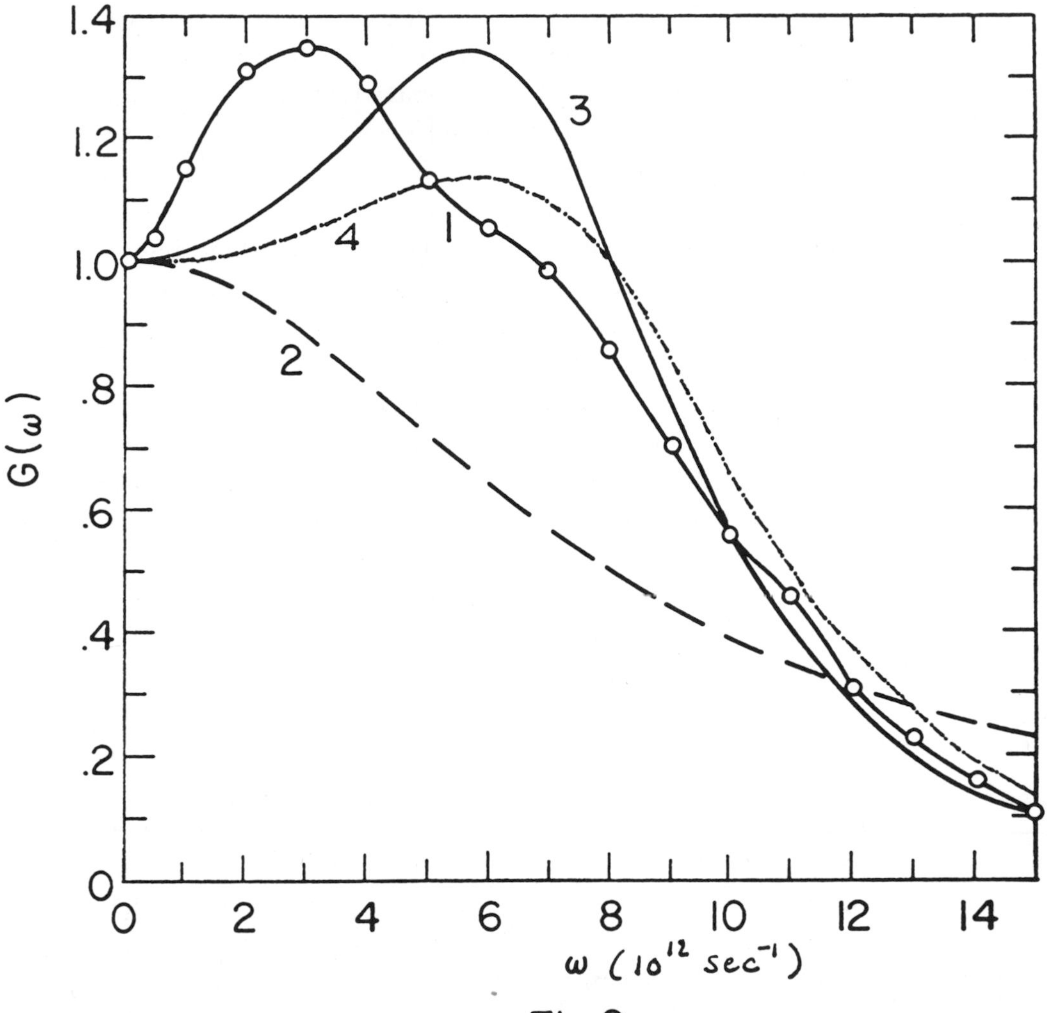

Fig.2

(1) - - - - - - - - Markoffian approximation

(2) o o o o o o o o Rahman's data

(3) ——————— $K(t) = \gamma \exp(-\alpha t)$

(4) —·—·—·—·—·— $K(t) = \gamma(1 + \alpha t) \exp(-\alpha t)$

As can be seen in Figs. 1 and 2, (87) leads to poorer agreement with experiment. In particular, the slower decay of K(t) as $t \to \infty$ implies a smaller rate of dissipation, and hence a decrease in the amplitude of the power spectrum. It appears that, as a first approximation, the exponentially decaying memory is very useful, and that the long time behaviour is of crucial importance in the representation.

Putting aside the justification for the ansatz used, it is important to note that many subtle characteristics of the autocorrelation functions of dynamical variables are simultaneously consistent with one simple form for the memory function. This observation suggests that the form of the memory function is a more general characteristic of the dynamics of the system than are other representations of dynamical coherence. Indeed, it is possible to reformulate the representation of linear transport coefficients to take advantage of this particular feature of the memory function analysis.

The general characteristics of the time dependence of the autocorrelation function can be elucidated by examining two limiting cases. Consider first the high density limit. Since $\alpha\beta$ is proportional to the mean square force acting on a molecule, which increases as the density increases, while β also increases as the density increases, $(4\beta/\alpha)$ increases as the density increases. Referring to Eq. (78), it is seen that the roots are complex when $(4\beta/\alpha) > 1$, whereupon the autocorrelation function displays a negative region which is more pronounced the higher the density. In the low density limit both β and α tend to zero in a fashion such that β/α tends to zero. Referring again to Eq. (78), it is seen that the time dependence of the autocorrelation function is now a simple exponential decay. Both of these limits are in agreement with the available data.

It is interesting to examine the momentum autocorrelation function in the high density limit from still another point of view. If the negative region of the momentum autocorrelation function is interpreted as indicating that, on the average, a displacement of a molecule towards its near neighbors is followed by a displacement back towards the original position, the exponential memory ansatz can be tested for internal consistency with a simple model. Let the average distance a molecule with given initial velocity travels before its momentum is reversed by interaction with a near neigbor be $<\Delta \underset{\sim}{R}_1>^1$. Now, the average velocity of a molecule at time t, given that the initial velocity is $\underset{\sim}{v}_1(0)$, is approximately $\underset{\sim}{v}_1(0)\psi(t)$. The average displacement is then

$$<\Delta \underset{\sim}{R}_1(t)>^1 = \int_0^t <\underset{\sim}{v}_1(t')> dt' = \int_0^t \underset{\sim}{v}_1(0)\psi(t')dt' . \qquad (90)$$

We seek the value of $<\Delta \underset{\sim}{R}_1(t)>^1$ corresponding to a turning point in the motion, i.e., when $<\underset{\sim}{v}_1(t)> = 0$. Such a turning point occurs at the time t_0 defined by

$$\psi(t_0) = 0 , \qquad (91)$$

or

$$<\Delta \underset{\sim}{R}_1(t_0)>^1 = \int_0^{t_0} \underset{\sim}{v}_1(0)\psi(t')dt' . \qquad (92)$$

For the case that $\underset{\sim}{v}_1(0)$ is equal to the root mean square velocity, corresponding to the most probable initial velocity, it is found that $<\Delta \underset{\sim}{R}_1>^1$ has the value 0.25 Å, corresponding to an average internuclear separation of 3.67 Å. Since the negative region of the autocorrelation function is interpreted as arising from the (near) reversal of momentum resulting from the first interaction experienced by a molecule on leaving the centrosymmetric position at the center of a shell of near neighbors, the average internuclear separation for interaction ought to be equal to the equilibrium average internuclear separation. From the computed radial distribution function of Rahman[18)], this latter distance is 3.67 Å, demonstrating both the internal consistency of this physical interpretation, and the accuracy of the exponential memory ansatz with respect to reproduction of the first zero of $\psi(t)$.

Finally, we note that Mori[19] has presented a continued fraction representation of time correlation functions. Mori's formalism differs from, but is closely related to, the general analysis of this paper. Indeed, Mori finds that if the continued fraction is truncated by assuming that the Laplace transform of the autocorrelation function of the nth order random force is independent of the Laplace variable (see Mori's paper for the definitions of these terms) then the momentum autocorrelation function is identical with that deduced herein. Also, the differential equation for the linear momentum autocorrelation function, deduced with the use of the exponential memory ansatz, is the same as the differential equation for the momentum autocorrelation function deduced by Gray[20] from a model. The analysis proposed herein is considerably more general than that of Gray, since the general integro-differential equation for the autocorrelation function is exact, and therefore consistent with many possible kinetic equations. Nevertheless, the deduction of the same autocorrelation function from three very different points of view suggests that the features displayed are rather general characteristics of the liquid phase, and not anomalies of the approximations used.

III. SOME OTHER APPLICATIONS

I wish to close with a few comments about other applications of the ideas discussed in this paper. Clearly, the use of a memory time representation for the time dependence of the autocorrelation function may be used to generate new approximations. As of this date we have only preliminary results, but even these are of interest.

Consider, for example, the calculation of transport coefficients at non-zero frequency. We write for a general coefficient

$$\sigma(\omega) = \lim_{\epsilon \to 0} \int_0^\infty dt\, e^{-i\omega t}\, e^{-\epsilon t}\, \psi(t)\,. \tag{93}$$

Let $s = \epsilon + i\omega$ be the complex Laplace variable, and

$$\left[\sigma(s)\right]^{-1} = \int_0^{\infty} dt\, e^{-st} <\dot{U}(0)\ \dot{U}(t)> \tag{94}$$

so that, in the limit of zero frequency

$$\left[\sigma(0)\right]^{-1} = \lim_{s\to 0} \left[\tilde{\Psi}(s)\right]^{-1}$$

$$= \lim_{s\to 0} \tilde{K}(s) \tag{95}$$

while at high frequency it is found that[21)]

$$\tilde{K}(\omega) = \frac{1}{i\omega} <\dot{U}(0)\ \dot{U}(0)> + \frac{1}{(i\omega)^2} <\dot{U}(0)\, i\, L^{(N)}\, \dot{U}(0)> + \ldots \tag{96}$$

Our procedure generates a high frequency expansion of the inverse transport coefficient, in contrast to that of Zwanzig and Mountain[22)] which gives

$$\sigma(\omega) = \frac{1}{i\omega} <U(0)\ U(0)> + \frac{1}{(i\omega)^2} <U(0)\ \dot{U}(0)> + \ldots \tag{97}$$

A second application is to generalize the linear trajectory method[23)] of calculating transport coefficients, and to compute corrections to that approximation. We suppose the potential to consist of a rigid core plus a softer, longer ranged interaction. The principal point in the analysis is to use the hard sphere distribution function as a metric, and to expand the interaction with the hard sphere system as reference point. To do so, we introduce a formal range parameter, measuring the ratio of the rigid core diameter to the range (core finite) of the soft potential, and a strength parameter for the soft potential. It is then found that

$$\tilde{K}(s) = \frac{\mu^2\, \tilde{F}_H(s) + \lambda^2 \sum_{n=0} \lambda^n\, \tilde{F}_s^{(n)}(s)}{1 - \frac{\mu^2}{s}\, \tilde{F}_H(s) - \frac{\lambda^2}{s} \sum_{n=0} \lambda^n\, \tilde{F}_s^{(n)}(s)}\,. \tag{98}$$

Eq. (98) leads to the correct hard core friction coefficient and to the linear trajectory approximation to the soft friction coefficient, when expanded in μ^2 and λ, respectively. The first correction to the linear trajectory approximation is obtained by keeping the two first terms in λ. It is found that[24)]

$$\tilde{K}_s^{(1)}(s) = \int_0^\infty dt\, e^{-st} \int_0^t d\tau \int_0^\tau d\tau'\, F_s^{(0)}(\tau')\, F_s^{(0)}(\tau - \tau'), \tag{99}$$

which leads to

$$\zeta_{LT}^{(1)} = \frac{\rho^2}{9m} \left(\frac{1}{2\pi}\right)^6 \int_0^{\tau_0} \int_0^t d\tau \int_0^\tau d\tau'\, I(\tau'), \tag{100}$$

$$I(\tau') = \int d\underset{\sim}{k}\, k^2\, e^{-\frac{k^2 \tau'^2}{2m\beta}}\, \tilde{V}_k\, \tilde{G}_k \int d\underset{\sim}{k}'\, \underset{\sim}{k}'^2\, e^{-\frac{k'^2(\tau - \tau')^2}{2m\beta}}\, \tilde{V}'_k\, \tilde{G}_{k'},$$

where V_k and G_k are the Fourier transforms of the soft part of the potential, and of the pair correlation function minus unity, respectively. The important qualitative point in the argument is that the hard sphere distribution function is very like the fully coupled distribution function, so that expansion about the hard sphere system is much better than expansion about a non-interacting state.

It is clear that in this formalism the linear trajectory approximation to all of the usual transport coefficients may be calculated.

ACKNOWLEDGEMENTS

This research was supported by the Directorate of Chemical Sciences, AFOSR.

REFERENCES

1. R. W, Zwanzig, J. Chem. Phys. 33, 1338 (1960). Also in Lectures in Theoretical Physics, ed. by W. E. Brittin, John Wiley and Sons, New York, 1961, Vol. 3. Phys. Rev. 124, 983 (1961).
2. U. Fano, in Lectures on The Many Body Problem, ed. by E. R. Caianello, Academic Press, New York, 1964, Vol. 2.
3. N. Hurt and S. A. Rice, J. Chem. Phys. 44, 2155 (1966).
4. B. J. Berne, J. P. Boon and S. A. Rice, J. Chem. Phys. 45, 1086 (1966), and also unpublished work.
5. See for example, S. A. Rice and P. Gray, The Statistical Mechanics of Simple Liquids, John Wiley and Sons, New York, 1965.
6. See for example, I. Prigogine, Non-Equilibrium Statistical Mechanics, John Wiley and Sons, New York, 1962.
7. J. G. Kirkwood, J. Chem. Phys. 14, 180 (1946).
8. S. A. Rice, J. G. Kirkwood and R. A. Harris, Physica 27, 717 (1961).
9. M. S. Green, J. Chem. Phys. 25, 836 (1956).
10. N. N. Bogolubov, in Studies in Statistical Mechanics, ed. by J. de Boer and G. E. Uhlenbeck, North Holland Publ. Co., Amsterdam, 1962, Vol. 1.
11. P. Resibois, J. Math. Phys. 4, 166 (1963). Phys. Lett. (Netherlands) 9, 139 (1964).
12. K. Hiroike, P. Gray and S. A. Rice, J. Chem. Phys. 42, 3134 (1965).
13. N. Hurt and S. A. Rice, J. Chem. Phys , 42, 4061 (1965).
14. U. Fano, Rev. Mod. Phys. 29, 74 (1957).
15. P. Resibois, in N. Particle Physics, ed. by E. Meeron, Gordon and Breach, (probably never will appear in print).

16. M. S. Bartlett, Stochastic Processes, Cambridge Univ. Press, London, 1955.

17. S. R. De Groot and P. Mazur, Non-Equilibrium Thermodynamics, North Holland Publ. Co., Amsterdam, 1962.

18. A. Rahman, Phys. Rev. 136 A405, (1964).

19. H. Mori, Prog. Theor. Phys. 34, 399 (1965)

20. P. Gray, Mol. Phys. 7, 235 (1964).

21. The key step is the recognition that

$$\tilde{\phi}(\omega) = \lim_{\epsilon \to 0} \int_0^\infty dt\, e^{-i\omega t} e^{-\epsilon t} < \dot{U}(0)\, \dot{U}(t) >$$

$$= < \dot{U}(0) \frac{1}{i\omega - iL^{(N)}} \dot{U}(0) >$$

which can be written

$$\tilde{\phi}(\omega) = \frac{1}{i\omega} \tilde{\Phi}(\omega) .$$

Then

$$\frac{1}{\sigma(\omega)} = \frac{i\omega}{1 + \frac{\tilde{\Phi}(\omega)}{\omega^2}}$$

since

$$s\tilde{\psi}(s) - 1 = -\frac{1}{s}\tilde{\phi}(s) = -\tilde{K}(s)\,\tilde{\psi}(s)$$

$$\tilde{K}(s) = \frac{\tilde{\phi}(s)}{1 - \frac{1}{s}\tilde{\phi}(s)}$$

$$\sigma(s) = \frac{1}{s^2}(s - \tilde{\phi}(s))$$

$$\phi(t) = < \dot{U}(0)\, \dot{U}(t) >$$

and

$$\sigma(\omega) = \lim_{\epsilon \to 0} \sigma(s) = \frac{1}{\omega^2}\left[\frac{\tilde{\Phi}(\omega)}{i\omega} - i\omega\right] .$$

For the high frequency expansion use is made of the limit

$$\lim_{\omega \to \infty} \sigma(\omega) \to 0 \; .$$

22. R. W. Zwanzig and R. Mountain, J. Chem. Phys. 44, 2777 (1966).

23. E. Helfand, Phys. Fluids, 4, 1 (1961).

24. Explicitly, one finds

$$\frac{\tilde{K}_s(s)}{\lambda^2} = \left[\tilde{F}_s^{(0)}(s) + \lambda F_s^{(1)}(s)\right]\left[1 + \lambda^2 \frac{\tilde{F}_s^{(0)}(s)}{s}\right]$$

or

$$\tilde{K}_s(s) = \left\langle \nabla V^s \frac{1}{s - iL_0} \nabla V^s \right\rangle + \frac{1}{s}\left[\left\langle \nabla V^s \frac{1}{s - iL_0} \nabla V^s \right\rangle_0\right]^2 + O(\lambda),$$

where λ has been absorbed into the potential, and the subscript zero indicates an average over the hard core fluid. In this equation L_0 is the propagator for free motion between hard core collisions. To terms of order λ, the average may now be converted to an average over the full potential.

DISCUSSION

Lebowitz: Was it an exponentially decaying curve from the beginning?

Rice: There are two curves represented: The one, the Markoffian approximation, decays exponentially. The other, from the exponential memory, goes as a coefficient times a sine plus a coefficient times a cosine, all multiplied by an exponentially decaying function.

Lebowitz: A gaussian autocorrelation function, Kirkwood's old idea, seems to fit Verlet's calculation for short times.

Rice: Yes, but a gaussian autocorrelation function does not go negative even though the fitted area gives a good diffusion coefficient. The gaussian autocorrelation function makes a serious dynamical error in that it omits the recoil part completely.

Stecki: Does it make a big difference if you replace the upper limit in the time integration by infinity?

Rice: Yes, if you make the Markoffian approximation, one never gets an autocorrelation function that goes negative - a terrible thing to do.

FLUCTUATIONS AND CORRELATIONS IN SUPERFLUID HELIUM*

PAUL C. MARTIN
Harvard University,
Cambridge, Mass. and
Centre des Etudes Nucleaires,
Saclay

Within the past decade, considerable progress has been made in the understanding of superfluids and superconductors. The central feature of this understanding is the occurrence of a bose condensate in the sense of Onsager and Penrose[1)], and in the development of techniques and ideas which permit quantitative investigation of it. The far reaching implications of such a condensation -- Josephson interference effects, quantisations of flux and vorticity -- have only gradually been appreciated and exhibited. Some, like the Richards-Anderson[2)] a.c. Josephson experiment, are only qualitatively understood. It is in this area, which was not at all envisaged by the older semi-phonomenological theories, that the most active, exciting and original research has recently taken place. There has, however, also been some advance in the understanding of a quantitative evolution of the more classical phenomena associated with homogeneous superfluids and described by the Landau-Khalatnikov theory[3)]. It is this less dramatic, more statistical mechanical aspect of superfluid behavior that I wish to review today.

Just as the most convenient quantity for discussing the behavior of magnetic systems is the function which describes space-time magnetic correlations, the fundamental quantity in the superfluid is the one particle density matrix.

*) Supported in part by the U. S. Office of Scientific Research and the National Science Foundation.

$$\rho(\underline{r}, \underline{r}') = \Sigma \omega_\alpha \int d\underline{r}_2 d\underline{r}_3 .. \psi_\alpha^*(\underline{r}, \underline{r}_2, \underline{r}_3 ..) \psi_\alpha(\underline{r}', \underline{r}_2, \underline{r}_3 ...)$$

or in second quantized notation

$$< \psi^+(\underline{r}) \psi(\underline{r}') > = < N > \rho(\underline{r}, \underline{r}') = | < \psi^+(\underline{r}) \psi(\underline{r}') > | \, e^{-i\varphi(\underline{r}, \underline{r}')}$$

and its time dependent generalization

$$< \psi^+(\underline{r}t) \psi(\underline{r}'t') >$$

As with magnetic ordering, condensation is defined mathematically by the condition that

$$| < \psi^+(\underline{r}) \psi(\underline{r}') > | \nrightarrow 0$$

when first

$$V \to \infty, \quad N/V \text{ fixed}$$

and then

$$|\underline{r} - \underline{r}'| \to \infty$$

It is supposed that condensation occurs in helium in equilibrium. It is further supposed that in equilibrium the reduced density matrix may be taken to be translationally invariant so that

$$< \psi^+(\underline{r}) \psi(\underline{r}') > = \int d^3\underline{p} \, n(\underline{p}) \, e^{i\underline{p}(\underline{r} - \underline{r}')/\hbar}$$

Condensation is then characterized by the existence of a term $n_{p_s} \neq 0$ in

$$n(\underline{p}) = n_{\underline{p}_s} \delta(\underline{p} - \underline{p}_s) + n'(\underline{p})$$

where $n_{\underline{p}_s}/n \equiv$ condensate fraction and $1 - (n_{ps}/n) \equiv$ depletion[4]. Even with strong interactions these assumptions are borne out in perturbation theory. It is also consistent to assume that there are stationary states in which p_s, the momentum of the condensed mode, differs from the mean momentum per particle. Such states, at least in perturbation theory, are metastable current carrying superfluid states.

Let us first consider the truly equilibrium state in which the momentum vanishes and $p_s = 0$. In the condensed ideal Bose gas, for small p

$$n(\underline{p}) = n_o(T)\left[\delta(\underline{p}) + \frac{2k_B Tm}{h^3 p^2 n_o(T)}\right]$$

In the condensed interacting Bose gas when p is small and $T \neq 0$ this formula[5, 6] is only slightly altered:

$$n(\underline{p}) = n_o(T)\left[\delta(\underline{p}) + \frac{k_B Tm}{h^3 p^2 n_s(T)}\right] \qquad (1)$$

The quantity $n_s(T)$ is the two fluid parameter, the superfluid density. The quantity $n_s(T)$ is easy to measure; the quantity $n_o(T)$ which differs from it, has until now proven unmeasureable. It is the quantity $n_o(T)$ which plays a role parallel to the square of the spontaneous magnetization $M^2(T)$ in a magnetically ordered system.

The outlined formula is the central formula of our discussion; it is important and interesting in several respects. At low temperatures, and for weakly interacting systems it shows that the effect of the interactions is not qualitatively important, but that it is discontinuous. The qualitative similarity between the ideal and interacting gas implies that in the two dimensional system as in the two dimensional ideal gas, the fluctuations of the condensate are infinite, and there is no condensation; the non-uniformity (a factor of one half discrepancy near $T = 0$ in $n'(p)$) reflects the fact that it is only phase and not amplitude fluctuations that upset the condensation once there is an interparticle potential[7)]. This difficulty with phase fluctuations in superfluids and superconductors has been pointed out recently by several people[8-10)]. It may be pursued to deduce that the phase coherence dies down with distance algebraically in two dimensions and exponentially in one. The formula (1) has also been used by Josephson[11] to note that if $n_o(T) \sim (T_c - T)^{2\beta}$, $n'(p) \sim p^{-2+\eta}$ at T_c, and $n'(p) \sim [p^2 + (T_c - T)^{2\nu'}]^{-1+\eta/2}$ when $p^2 \ll T_c - T$, then $n_s(T)$ behaves like $(T_c - T)^{2\beta - \eta\nu'}$. If one also accepts the scaling-law hypotheses of Widom[12] and Kadanoff[13], this implies that $n_s(T) \sim (T_c - T)^{2/3-\alpha'}$ where α' is the specific heat singularity. A table contrasting n_o and n_s, at $T = 0$ and near T_c will therefore have the following entries.

		Perfect Bose Gas	Slightly Imperfect Bose Gas	Helium
$T \cong 0$	$1 - \frac{n_o}{n}$	$O(T^{3/2})$	$O(T^2) + \frac{[h(nv)^3]^{1/2}}{3\pi^2}$	$\sim g + O(T^2)$ estimated not measured
	$1 - \frac{n_s}{n}$	$O(T^{5/2})$	$O(T^4)$	$\sim \frac{2\pi^2}{45}\left(\frac{k_B T}{\hbar c}\right)^4 \frac{\hbar}{mnc}$ proven measured
$T \cong T_c$	$\frac{n_o}{n}$	$\sim T_c - T$	$(T_c - T)^{2\beta}$ eff. field theory $\beta = \frac{1}{2}$	$(T_c - T)^{2\beta}$ not estimated not measured
	$\frac{n_s}{n}$	$\sim (T_c - T)^0$	$(T_c - T)^{2\beta - \eta\nu'}$	$(T_c - T)^{2/3}$ estimated by scaling law measured

Estimates of n_o/n at $T = 0$ have been made by Onsager and Penrose and subsequently by McMillan[14] and Parry[15]. Chester and Reatto[16] have recently pointed out that these estimates are probably somewhat too high. Specifically, they have observed that to obtain a wave function which reproduces the central outlined formula and the correct long wavelength correlation function it is necessary to include zero point phonon motion in the wave function. They estimate that these long wavelength fluctuations, omitted from earlier trial functions, may reduce n_o by a factor of two. It is to be hoped and expected that it will not seriously modify in other respects the calculation of McMillan which gives quite satisfactory low temperature thermodynamic properties for solid and liquid helium.

To derive the central formula for n(p), and more generally to deduce the form of the time dependent correlation function analogous to the dynamic non-local response of the magnetic system

$$\chi''(\frac{p}{\hbar},\omega) = \frac{1}{2}\int_{-\infty}^{\infty} dt\, e^{i\omega t}\int d\underline{r}\, e^{-i\underline{p}\cdot\underline{r}/\hbar} < [\nabla\psi^{+}(\underline{r},t),\nabla\psi(0,0)] > \frac{\hbar}{n_o m^2}$$

one proves and then employs the two fluid model for the condensed system. In particular, the formula quoted for n(p) follows from the formula for $\chi''(\frac{p}{\hbar},\omega)$ by means of the fluctuation-dissipation theorem

$$\frac{p^2}{m^2 n_o} h^3 n(\underline{p}) = \int\frac{d\omega}{\pi}\chi''(\frac{p}{\hbar},\omega)\,\hbar\,[\exp(\frac{\hbar\omega}{k_B T}) - 1]^{-1}$$

and the conservation law which tells us that as $p \to 0$, $\chi''(\frac{p}{\hbar},\omega) \to 0$ when $\omega \neq 0$ so that

$$\frac{h^3 n(p)}{k_B T}\,\frac{p^2}{m^2 n_o} = \int\frac{d\omega}{\pi}\,\frac{\chi''(\frac{p}{\hbar},\omega)}{\omega} = \frac{1}{m n_s}$$

The last identity is a consequence of the two fluid model. More generally, the two fluid model implies[6)] that for small k, the even

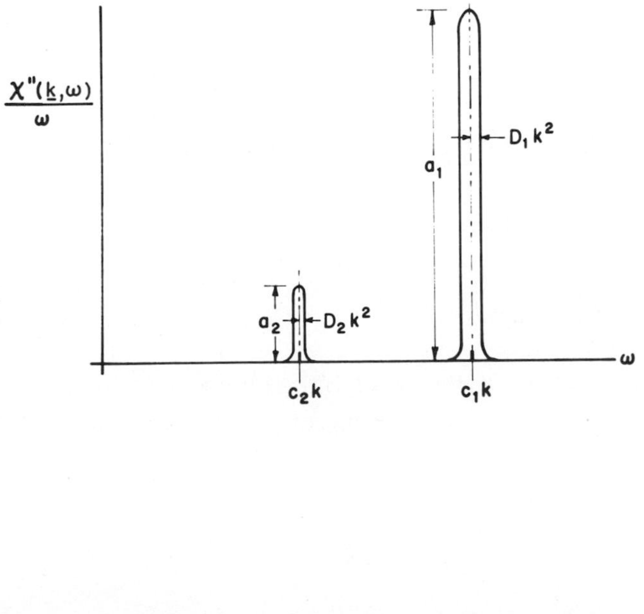

Fig. 1.

real function of the frequency $\chi''(\underline{k},\omega)$ looks as shown in Fig. 1. In this figure attenuation rates for first and second sound, and a_1 and a_2 are

$$a_1 = \frac{\pi}{2mn_s}\left(\frac{A - c_2^2}{c_1^2 - c_2^2}\right) \qquad a_2 = \frac{\pi}{2mn_s}\left(\frac{A - c_1^2}{c_2^2 - c_1^2}\right)$$

$$A = \frac{n_s}{mn}\left[\left(\frac{dp}{dn}\right)_s - \frac{2Ts}{nC_v}\left(\frac{dp}{dT}\right)_n + \frac{Ts^2m}{C_v}\right]$$

and s is the entropy for unit mass. At low temperature $a_1 \cong \pi/2mn$ and $a_2 \cong O((\frac{k_B T}{\hbar c})^4 \frac{\hbar}{mnc})$ c is the sound velocity. The full expressions for $\chi''(\omega)/\omega$ are complicated; another simple aspect of it is the "Kubo formula" which relates the bulk viscosity of Khalatnikov, ξ_3, to the correlation function

$$\lim_{\omega\to 0}\ \lim_{k\to 0} \frac{\omega\chi''(\underline{k},\omega)}{k^2} = \xi_3$$

As in the case of the ordinary bulk viscosity, the derivation of the more prevalent but equivalent time integral expression for ξ_3, requires subtraction of a time independent term, A.

We have stated that the two fluid model has been derived for helium. By that we mean that we have shown[6] that in the hydrodynamic limit in addition to the laws of mass conservation

$$\frac{\partial\rho}{\partial t} + \nabla\cdot\underline{g} = 0$$

momentum conservation

$$\frac{\partial \underline{g}}{\partial t} + \nabla\cdot\underline{\underline{T}} = 0$$

energy conservation

$$\frac{\partial\epsilon}{\partial t} + \nabla\cdot\underline{j}^{\epsilon} = 0$$

there exists a velocity, $v_s(rt)$, which is defined on a local but macroscopic scale and which is (a) irrotational and (b) conserved so that

$$\frac{\partial \underline{v}_s}{\partial t} + \nabla \tilde{\mu} = 0$$

In terms of the conserved quantities, $\rho_s \equiv mn_s$, $\rho_n \equiv mn_n$ and v_n are defined by $\rho = \rho_s + \rho_n$, $\underline{g} = \rho_s \underline{v}_s + \beta_n \underline{v}_n$ and $\left(\frac{\delta \epsilon}{\delta \underline{g}}\right)_{\rho, s, \underline{v}_s} = \underline{v}_n$ in the frame in which v_s vanishes. We have then proven that

$$\text{(c)}\quad \tilde{\mu} = \mu + \frac{1}{2} v_s^2 + \left[-S_3\, \underline{\nabla} \cdot \rho_s (\underline{v}_s - \underline{v}_n) - S_4 \underline{\nabla} \cdot v_n \right]$$

$$\text{(d)}\quad T_{ij} = p\delta_{ij} + \rho_s v_{s_i} v_{s_j} + \rho_n v_{n_i} v_{n_j} + \Big[-\delta_{ij}\, S_1\, \nabla \cdot \rho_s (\underline{v}_s - \underline{v}_n)$$

$$- \delta_{ij}\, S_2\, \underline{\nabla} \cdot \underline{v}_n - \eta (\nabla_i v_{n_j} + \nabla_j v_{n_i} - \frac{2}{3} \delta_{ij} \underline{\nabla} \cdot \underline{v}_n) \Big]$$

$$\text{(e)}\quad \underline{j}^{\epsilon} = (\mu + \frac{1}{2} v_s^2) \underline{g} + T\rho s \underline{v}_n + \rho_n \underline{v}_n \underline{v}_n \cdot (\underline{v}_n - \underline{v}_s) + \left[-\varkappa \underline{\nabla} T \right]$$

where the bracketed terms contain the dissipative effects to lowest order in the gradients. It is claimed by Khalatnikov[17)] that these equations follow purely from Galilean invariance; we have not been able to deduce them in that matter. It has also been suggested[18)] that they are ill defined. While there can be no doubt that the microscopic theory contains other information, we do not understand where there is ambiguity. The quantities ϵ, $\underline{g}$, ρ, $\underline{j}^{\epsilon}$, T_{ij}, are all unambiguous and measureable and they more than determine ρ_s, ρ_n, $\underline{v}_s$ and $\underline{v}_n$ in the homogeneous or almost homogeneous system. That these relations are consistent with one another and with the identification of $m\underline{v}_s/\hbar$ as the gradient of the condensate seems to us a clearly posed question whose answer requires the microscopic theory, although it clearly does not exhaust the consequences of the microscopic theory.

In particular, we have derived (a) - (e) using Khalatnikov's definitions for $\underline{v}_n$, ρ_s and ρ_n to order v_s^2, on the basis of an identification of the superfluid velocity operator

$$\underline{v}_s = \underline{\nabla} \frac{\hbar}{2mi\sqrt{n_o}} \left(\psi(\underline{r}) - \psi^{\dagger}(\underline{r}) \right)$$

The identification implies that in the uniform system $\underline{p}_s = m\underline{v}_s$. To derive (a) - (e) and the expressions for the dissipation coefficients it is particularly convenient to use an ensemble of the form

$$\mathrm{Tr}\ \exp\left\{-\beta\int d\underline{r}\left[h(\underline{r}) - \underline{g}(\underline{r})\cdot\underline{\gamma} - n(\underline{r})m\nu - \underline{p}_s(\underline{r})\cdot\underline{\lambda}\right]\right\}$$

where h, $\underline{g}$, n and $\underline{p}_s$ are operators for the energy, momentum, and number densities and the superfluid momentum, and where the usual definitions of ρ_s, ρ_n, and v_n imply that $\underline{\gamma} = \underline{v}_n$, $\nu = \mu + \frac{1}{2}(\underline{v}_n - \underline{v}_s)^2 - \frac{1}{2}v_n^2$ and $\underline{\lambda} = n_s(\underline{v}_s - \underline{v}_n)$. With this ensemble one easily deduces for the dissipative coefficients

$$\varkappa T = \lim_{\omega\to 0}\ \lim_{k\to 0}\ \frac{\omega\chi''_{\epsilon\epsilon}(\underline{k},\omega)}{k^2}$$

$$\eta\left(\delta_{ij} - \frac{k_ik_j}{k^2}\right) + \left(S_2 + \frac{4}{3}\eta\right)\frac{k_ik_j}{k^2} = \lim_{\omega\to 0}\ \lim_{k\to 0}\ \frac{\omega\chi''_{g_i\,g_j}(\underline{k},\omega)}{k^2}$$

$$S_4\ \frac{k_ik_j}{k^2}) = S_1\ \frac{k_ik_j}{k^2} = \lim_{\omega\to 0}\ \lim_{k\to 0}\ \frac{\omega\chi''_{v_{s_i}g_j}(\underline{k},\omega)}{k^2}$$

Where the functions χ'' are, as usual[19)], Fourier transforms of the equilibrium ensemble average of the commutators of the subscript operators.

The two fluid model characterizes the system when $\omega\tau \ll 1$ where τ is a characteristic collision time which approaches ∞ as $T \to 0$. Consequently at all frequencies when T = 0, and at most interesting frequencies when $T \neq 0$, the two fluid hydrodynamic picture is not sufficient. For this reason it is not apparent that when T = 0, the elementary excitations need be phonons with the compressional sound velocity. Nevertheless this fact has been proven to all order in perturbation theory by Gavoret and Nozières[20)]. Their proof may be greatly simplified[6)].

One has at T = 0

$$\chi''(\underline{k},\omega) \sim \frac{\pi ck}{2nm}\left[\delta(\omega - ck) - \delta(\omega + ck)\right]$$

which implies that at T = 0, formula (1) is replaced by

$$n(\underline{p}) \sim n_o \left[\delta(\underline{p}) + \frac{1}{2} \frac{mc}{h^2 np} \right]$$

which has a weaker singularity - the zero point fluctuations are less singular by a factor of 1/2 cp/kT, than the thermal fluctuations, which occur in the formula emphasized earlier.

A variational form[21)] of the perturbation theory may also be employed to prove other rigorous statements outside of the two fluid region. For example it has been shown that to lowest order in the temperature, to all orders of perturbation theory, both the specific heat[22)], and the superfluid density[23)] are rigorously given by the Landau expressions

$$mnc_v = \frac{2\pi^2}{15} \left(\frac{k_B T}{\hbar c} \right)^3 k_B \qquad mn_n = \frac{2\pi^2}{45} \left(\frac{k_B T}{\hbar c} \right)^4 \frac{\hbar}{c}$$

It has been shown that in the phonon region, when $\omega\tau >> 1$, the phonon attenuation[24)] will behave as ωT^4 and, at low temperatures the dominant term in the velocity shift[25)] will be of the form $T^4 \log T$. The most recent experiments[26)] appear to bear this out (in contrast with earlier experiments). At higher temperatures where the rotons are dominant, microscopic calculations of phonon velocity and attenuation have recently been performed[27)] which improve upon the qualitatively satisfactory phenomenological calculations of Landau and Khalatnikov. Only qualitative calculations have been performed of the small but observable temperature dependent shift and width of the roton minimum. There are suggestions[28)] that these properties have little to do with superfluidity itself and are common to all the noble fluids, although they become increasingly more difficult to calculate with increasing temperature and effective coupling.

All in all, however, the thermodynamic and transport properties of homogeneous superfluid helium, (except in the neighbourhood of the λ-line) seem to be relatively well understood from a microscopic point of view; at least we would be happy if the other simple liquids were understood equally well.

REFERENCES

1. O. Penrose and L. Onsager, Phys. Rev. 104, 576 (1956).
2. P. L. Richards and P. W. Anderson, Phys. Rev. Letters 14, 540 (1965).
3. L. D. Landau and I. M. Khalatnikov, Zh. Eksperim. i teor. Fiz. 19, 637 (1949).
   I. M. Khalatnikov, Zh. Eksperim i teor. Fiz. 20, 243 (1950).
4. $N_p = Vn(\rho)d^3\rho$ is the number with momentum p with a discrete normalization and
   $V n \rho_s = N\rho_s$ is the number with momentum p_s, a macroscopic number of order N, with discrete normalization, when there is condensation.
5. N. N. Bogolubov, Quasi-averages in Prob. of Stat. Mech. Dubna Preprint (1962.
6. P. C. Hohenberg and P. C. Martin, Ann. Phys. (N. Y.) 34, 291 (1965).
7. P. C. Martin, Jour. Math. Phys. 4, 298 (1963). The same factor of two occurs in the discussion of noise in a laser. See, for example, W. E. Lamb, Phys. Rev. 134, A1429 (1964).
8. R. Ferrell, Phys. Rev. Letters 14, 330 (1964).
9. T. M. Rice, Phys. Rev. 140, A1889 (1965).
10. J. W. Kane and L. P. Kadanoff (Private communication). B. I. Halperin and the author have come to similar conclusions independently.
11. B. D. Josephson, Phys. Letters 21, 608 (1966); J. R. Clow and J. D. Reppy, Phys. Rev. Letters 16, 887 (1966).
12. B. Widom, J. Chem. Phys. 43, 3892 (1965).
13. L. P. Kadanoff, Phys. 2, 263 (1966).
14. W. Mc. Millan, Phys. Rev. 138, 442 (1965).
15. Private communication.

16. L. Reatto and G. V. Chester, Phys. Letters 22, 276 (1966).

17. See for example, Theory of Superfluidity, I. M. Khalatnikov, Benjamin, N.Y. 1965.

18. P. W. Anderson, Quantum Fluids, Brewer, North Holland, Amsterdam, 1965, p. 146.

19. L. P. Kadanoff and P. C. Martin, Ann. Phys. (N.Y.) 24, 419 (1963).

20. J. Gavoret and P. Nozières, Ann. Phys. (N.Y.) 28, 349 (1964).

21. C. de Dominicis and P. C. Martin, J. Math. Phys. 5, 14, 31 (1964).

22. W. Götze and H. Wagner, Phys. 31, 475 (1965).

23. K. Kehr, Physics (to be published).

24. K. Kawasaki and H. Mori, Prog. of Theor. Phys. 28, 784 (1962).
A. Leggett and D. ter Haar, Phys. Rev. 139, A 779 (1965).
Kwok, Martin and Miller, Solid State Communications 3, 190 (1965).
Pethick and ter Haar, (to be published).

25. W. M. Whitney and C. E. Chase, Phys. Rev. Letters 9, 293 (1962).
I. Khalatnikov and A. Andreyev, JETP 17, 1389 (1963).

26. Abraham, Eckstein, Ketterson, and Vignos, Phys. Rev. Letters 16, 1039 (1966).

27. I. M. Khalatnikov and D. M. Chernikova, JETP 50, 411 (1966).

28. A. D. B. Woods, Phys. Rev. Letters 14, 355 (1965).
J. T. Cocking and P. A. Egelstaff, Phys. Letters 16, 20 (1965).

Girardeau: It is known from the work of Penrose and Onsager and of Yang that if a system exhibits Bose-Einstein condensation into some single-particle state, then the single-particle density matrix exhibits off-diagonal long-range order. This is the fact to which you referred. However, it is known that the converse is not true. It is possible for a system to exhibit off-diagonal long-range order in the absence of Bose-Einstein condensation into any single-particle state. In such a case, there is Bose-Einstein condensation of a generalized "smeared" kind which can be precisely defined. I think it is an open question, both experimentally and from the standpoint of exact theory, whether the Bose-Einstein condensation in liquid Helium (if there is any) is of the simple kind usually assumed or of the generalized form. It might be that in the latter case, the relationships you have discussed might still be valid, but with n_o reinterpreted as the number of particles which are condensed in the generalized sense.

Martin: Since no one has found how to measure n_o, the question is certainly experimentally unsettled. I see no reason to doubt the condensation assumption on the basis of theoretical work to this point, but I suppose remnants of the above discussion might survive a smeared out condensation.

Mattuck: Your argument for the Bose gas indicates that one cannot have a superfluid in 1 or 2 dimensions. First of all, does this argument hold for a superconductor, when you consider that

Cooper pairs do not really obey Bose statistics but rather mixed statistics? Second, does the argument hold for other phase transitions in one and two dimensions, such as, for example, the ferromagnetic transition?

Martin: The argument is a heuristic one which states that there can be no long range order in a one or two dimensional system in which the order parameter has a continuous symmetry (and therefore low lying collective modes). I believe, therefore, it applies in superconductors and Heisenberg (but not Ising) ferromagnets. It does not say there is no phase transition of a more subtle type, in which the order parameter vanishes.

Lieb: I should like to make two points about the value of n_o. Firstly, for the one-dimensional hardcore gas one can compute n_o/n using the same type of trial function as used by Penrose and Onsager and one obtains a non-zero result as in three-dimensions. But, as first shown by T. D. Schultz, n_o/n is actually zero for the exact ground state wave function. Secondly, Chester's calculation, which you mentioned, uses a long range type of trial function in order to make S(k) vanish as $k \to 0$. While it may be true that this type of function does not cause n_o/n to vanish in three dimensions, it should be pointed out that Chester's results are very sensitive to boundary conditions; it seems to be essential to use periodic boundary conditions. $\psi = 0$ boundary conditions give drastically different results.

Martin: The result quoted in the abstract is derivable by several methods. I see no reason to doubt it even if your statement that Chester's wave function is sensitive to boundary conditions is correct. Furthermore, these arguments agree with your other statement— the absence of a phase transition in one dimension. Nevertheless effective field theory is approximately correct for many purposes in three dimensions where there is an order parameter even though it is always incorrect for the reasons we have stated in one dimension. Hence I do not believe that Schultz's calculation casts any serious doubt on the Onsager and Penrose estimate.

THE PAIR DISTRIBUTION FUNCTION OF A HARD SPHERE BOSE GAS AT LOW TEMPERATURE *)

A. ISIHARA
Department of Physics,
State University of New York
at Buffalo

ABSTRACT

Using the binary kernel method developed by Lee and Yang[1] and applying the method which Yee and the present author developed recently the pair distribution function of a hard sphere Bose gas[4] is evaluated at low temperature. Diagrams characteristic of Bose statistics and in first order in the hard sphere diameter are analyzed in detail. The errors in the results of Colin and Peretti[8] are corrected. A new method to treat chain diagrams appropriate to Bose statistics is presented. Two sets of diagrams are found important in the sense that they are the generalization of the first order and Boltzmann chain diagrams. The problem is reduced to solve eigen value problems of the integral equations associated with the diagrams. The solutions naturally contain various special cases. Both short and large distance behaviors of the pair distribution function are investigated. Discussions on recent theoretical works of Luban[10], Lieb[11] as well as experimental data on liquid helium[13] are given.

---

*) This work was supported by the National Science Foundation.

1. INTRODUCTION

In recent years there has been a surge of interest in the study of a hard sphere Bose gas, and the ground state energy and the thermodynamic properties have been studied[1]. As we shall discuss a little later the pair distribution function has also been evaluated by several investigators, but most of the theories have been developed for the lowest temperature[2][3][10][11]. Therefore, we shall try in this paper to evaluate the pair distribution function of a hard sphere Bose gas at low temperature as a natural extension of the previous theories. For this purpose we shall apply the general theory and extend the binary kernel theory which Yee and the present author developed before[4]. (Hereafter this work will be referred to as paper I.)

The motivation of this work is related to the study of liquid helium, but apart from this interesting liquid it is important to develop a quantum statistical many body theory for a system of a hard sphere gas which is characterized by the singular potential.

Concerning the pair distribution functions of quantum mechanical many body systems, a general theory has been developed by Fujita, Isihara and Montroll[5]. This theory extended the formalism by Montroll and Ward[6] for the grand partition functions and gave a cluster expansion development for the pair distribution functions. As an example, the theory was applied to an electron gas at high and low temperatures in chain diagram approximation[5], and to a hard sphere gas at zero temperature by Fujita and Hirota[7]. Here, the latter authors used the pseudopotential introduced by Lee and Yang[1].

Namely, together with Huang, Lee and Yang solved the Schrodinger eigen value problem by replacing the hard sphere potential by an approximate pseudopotential. They thus evaluated the ground state energy and the pair distribution function[2], but they had to subtract a divergent term from the expression for the ground state energy. On the other hand, no such a step was taken for the pair distribution function where the same wave function was used as for the ground state energy.

We shall omit the discussion of these theories concerning the pair distribution function as it is given in paper I. Instead, we comment on the recent theory by Colin and Peretti[8]. In this work they used the binary collision method as in our previous paper and considered essentially the two groups of toron diagrams which are first order in the binary kernel. On the other hand, Fujita and Hirota treated chain diagrams connected by the approximate pseudopotential. In paper I we considered a more general type of chain diagrams linked together by binary kernels. The diagrams considered by these authors are higher order in the characteristic interaction parameter a, the hard sphere diameter, but the diagrams yield results which are first order in a.

A question arises as to what kind of diagrams one should take into consideration in order to obtain good first order results. One can say that at large distances chain diagrams are important and at short distances first order diagrams, especially those of lower order in the number of exchanges. As a matter of fact, the direct binary interaction of two representative particles 1 and 2 is always important at short distances.

In this respect it must be pointed out that chain diagrams start with the first order diagrams. Therefore, the above statement concerning the contributions of various diagrams actually means that at large distances, namely at low energy, the collective motion of particles is important and such a motion can be reproduced by considering chain diagrams.

We shall show in this paper that the first order contributions come from two types of diagram. The first type, called A, is for the diagrams which involve the two representative particles 1 and 2 in the same toron which is connected with a linear array of unnamed torons. Due to the exchanges of particles the diagrams of type A look different from tick-tack-toe diagrams considered in I but they belong to the same family. The second type of diagram, called B, is obtained by connecting a toron involving the particle 1 with another toron including 2 by a linear chain of torons. Of course there are hybrid diagrams between these two types, but the above two types A and B have distinctive features which we may discuss separately.

In the simplest case, the diagrams which are first order in the hard sphere diameter reduce to what Colin and Peretti considered. Also, if we replace all the torons by single particles we obtain the chain diagrams corresponding to Boltzmann statistics. Unfortunately, Colin and Peretti developed their theory only for the first order diagrams so that the theory in the present form is not applicable to the general A and B type diagrams. Moreover, their results contain mistakes arising from erroneous combinatorial factors and do not satisfy the correct normalization. Actually, Colin arrived at later similar but different results by using the Bogolieubov type approach[9].

In the next section we shall give a brief account of our basic method. In section III we consider the zero order diagrams. In section IV the contributions from the first order diagrams will be treated, and comparison of our results with those of Colin and Peretti will be given. In section V we examine these results by evaluating the cluster expansion for the equation of state. In section VI we shall present a general method which is applicable to all chain diagrams including those corresponding to Boltzmann statistics. Section VII gives low temperature results obtained from the formulas in section VI. Finally section VIII gives concluding remarks.

2. GENERAL FORMULAE

In this section we shall introduce briefly the basic steps and notations which we are going to use. For convenience we shall adopt units such that $\hbar = 1$ and $2m = 1$, where m is the particle mass. Also we shall use $\beta = 1/kT$ and z for the absolute activity.

We are interested in the density matrix for an N-particle system, its matrix element being given by

$$\langle \underline{r}'^N | W_N | \underline{r}^N \rangle = \sum_k \psi_k(\underline{r}'^N) \exp(-\beta H_N) \psi_k^*(\underline{r}^N) \ . \qquad (2.1)$$

In terms of the density matrix the reduced distribution function for n particles is expressed as follows

$$\rho_N^{(n)}(\underline{r}^n) = \frac{1}{(N-n)!}\,\frac{1}{Z_N}\int <\underline{r}^N|\exp(-\beta H_N)|\,\underline{r}^N> d\underline{r}_{n+1}\,d\underline{r}_{n+2}\cdots d\underline{r}_N \tag{2.2}$$

where H_N is the Hamiltonian and Z_N, the partition function, is given by

$$Z_N = \frac{1}{N!}\int <\underline{r}^N|\,\exp(-\beta H_N)\,|\,\underline{r}^N>\,d\underline{r}^N \tag{2.3}$$

In many body theories it is convenient to evaluate the distribution function in the grand ensemble. This is defined by

$$\rho^{(n)}(\underline{r}^n) = \frac{1}{\Xi}\sum_{N\geqq n}\rho_N^{(n)}\,z^N\,Z_N$$

$$= \frac{1}{\Xi}\sum_{N\geqq n}\frac{z^N}{(N-n)!}\int <\underline{r}^N|\,W_N\,|\,\underline{r}^N> d\underline{r}_{n+1}\cdots d\underline{r}_N \tag{2.4}$$

where the grand partition function is

$$\Xi = \sum_N z^N\,Z_N \tag{2.5}$$

In paper I we have expressed the reduced distribution functions in a cluster series. In particular,

$$\rho^{(2)}(\underline{r}_1,\underline{r}_2) = \rho^{(1)}(\underline{r}_1)\rho^{(1)}(\underline{r}_2) + \sum_{n\geqq 2}\frac{z^n}{(n-2)!}$$

$$\times\int <\underline{r}_1,\underline{r}_2,\ldots,\underline{r}_n\,|\,U_n|\,\underline{r}_1,\underline{r}_2,\ldots,\underline{r}_n> d\underline{r}_3\cdots d\underline{r}_n \tag{2.6}$$

where $\rho^{(1)}$ is the singlet distribution function and the U_n are the Uhlenbeck U functions.

It is convenient to express these U functions in momentum space. If we introduce

$$<\underline{k}_1, \underline{k}_2, \ldots \underline{k}_n | \underline{r}_1, \underline{r}_2 \ldots \underline{r}_n> = \frac{1}{(2\pi)^{3n/2}} \exp(-i \sum_s^n \underline{k}_s \cdot \underline{r}_s) \tag{2.7}$$

the transformation is expressed as follows:

$$<\underline{r}'_1, \underline{r}'_2, \ldots \underline{r}'_n | U_n | \underline{r}_1, \underline{r}_2, \ldots \underline{r}_n> = \frac{1}{(2\pi)^{3n}} \sum_{k, k'} \exp i \sum_s (\underline{k}'_s \cdot \underline{r}'_s - \underline{k}_s \cdot \underline{r}_s)$$

$$\times <\underline{k}'_1, \underline{k}'_2, \ldots, \underline{k}'_n | U_n | \underline{k}_1, \underline{k}_2, \ldots \underline{k}_n> \tag{2.8}$$

Accordingly, the right hand side integral of Eq. (2.6) is transformed as follows:

$$\frac{1}{(2\pi)^6} \sum_{n=2}^{\infty} \frac{z^n}{(n-2)!} \int \exp\left[i(\underline{k}'_1 - \underline{k}_1) \cdot \underline{r}_1 + i(\underline{k}'_2 - \underline{k}_2) \cdot \underline{r}_2\right]$$

$$\times <\underline{k}'_1, \underline{k}'_2 | U_n | \underline{k}_1, \underline{k}_2> d\underline{k}'_1 \, d\underline{k}'_2 \, d\underline{k}_1 \, d\underline{k}_2 \tag{2.9}$$

where

$$U_n(\underline{k}'_1, \underline{k}'_2; \underline{k}_1, \underline{k}_2) = \int <\underline{k}'_1, \underline{k}'_2, \underline{k}_3, \ldots \underline{k}_n | U_n | \underline{k}_1, \underline{k}_2, \ldots \underline{k}_n>$$

$$\times d\underline{k}_3 \, d\underline{k}_4 \ldots d\underline{k}_n = u_n(\underline{k}'_1, \underline{k}'_2; \underline{k}_1, \underline{k}_2) \delta(\underline{k}'_1 + \underline{k}'_2 - \underline{k}_1 - \underline{k}_2). \tag{2.10}$$

It is convenient to introduce the center of mass momenta K, K' and relative momenta $\underline{k}$, $\underline{k}'$ as follows:

$$\underline{k}_1 = \frac{1}{2} \underline{K} + \underline{k}, \qquad \underline{k}_2 = \frac{1}{2} \underline{K} - \underline{k};$$

$$\underline{k}'_1 = \frac{1}{2} \underline{K}' + \underline{k}', \qquad \underline{k}'_2 = \frac{1}{2} \underline{K}' - \underline{k}'. \tag{2.11}$$

For homogeneous and isotropic systems we can assume that $\rho^{(2)}$ is a function of the relative distance $r = |\underline{r}_2 - \underline{r}_1|$. Thus

$$\rho^{(2)}(r) = [\rho^{(1)}]^2 + (8\pi^3)^{-2} \sum_{n=2}^{\infty} \int \frac{z^n}{(n-2)!} u_n(\underline{k}', \underline{k}) \exp i (\underline{k}' - \underline{k}) \cdot \underline{r} \, d\underline{k} \, d\underline{k}' \tag{2.12}$$

Further simplification is possible if we introduce the new variables

$$\underline{k} = \frac{1}{2}\underline{Q} + \underline{q}$$
$$\underline{k}' = \frac{1}{2}\underline{Q} - \underline{q} \qquad (2.13)$$

and integrate Eq. (2.12) over $\underline{Q}$. We arrive at

$$\rho^{(2)}(r) = \left[\rho^{(1)}\right]^2 + (8\pi^3)^{-2}\int \exp(2i\underline{q}\cdot\underline{r})N(\underline{q})d\underline{q} \qquad (2.14)$$

where

$$N(\underline{q}) = \sum_{n=2}^{\infty} \frac{z^n}{(n-2)!} u_n(\underline{q})$$

$$U_n(\underline{r}) = (8\pi^3)^{-2}\int u_n(\underline{q}) \exp 2i\underline{q}\cdot\underline{r}\, d\underline{q} \qquad (2.15)$$

Equations (2.14) and (2.15) are basic to our calculations of the pair distribution functions. As indicated in these equations we shall evaluate first the distribution functions in momentum space and then transform the results into coordinate space.

The U functions in the classical case may be expanded in powers of the binary kernel B, the first few terms being given by

$$U_2^{cl}(\beta) = \int_0^{\beta} d\beta'\, w(\beta-\beta'; 1)w(\beta-\beta'; 2)B(\beta'; 1, 2)$$

$$U_3^{cl}(\beta; 1, 2, 3) = \int_0^{\beta} d\beta'\int_0^{\beta'} d\beta'' w(\beta-\beta''; 1)w(\beta-\beta'; 2)w(\beta-\beta'; 3)$$
$$\times\, B(\beta'-\beta''; 2, 3)B(\beta''; 1, 2)w(\beta''; 3)$$
$$+ \int_0^{\beta} d\beta'\int_0^{\beta'} d\beta'' w(\beta-\beta'; 1)w(\beta-\beta'; 2)w(\beta-\beta''; 3)$$
$$\times\, B(\beta'-\beta''; 1, 2)B(\beta''; 2, 3)w(\beta''; 1) + \ldots \qquad (2.16)$$

Here $w(\beta, i) = \exp(\beta\nabla_i^2)$ is the free particle density matrix.

The binary kernel has been expanded in powers of the hard sphere diameter. We shall retain our calculations to first order in the diameter $\underline{a}$ and use

$$B(\beta) = -a\pi^{-2}\delta(\underline{k}_1' + \underline{k}_2' - \underline{k}_1 - \underline{k}_2) \times \exp - \beta\,(k_1^2 + k_2^2) \tag{2.17}$$

Using this and the transformations (2.11) and (2.13) we obtain

$$u_2^{cl}(\underline{q}) = -\left(\frac{2\pi}{\beta}\right)^3 a\pi^{-2} \int_0^\beta K^{cl}(\underline{q};\beta-\beta')K^{cl}(\underline{q};\beta')d\beta' \tag{2.18}$$

where

$$K^{cl}(\underline{q};|x-y|) = \exp\{-4|x-y|\,q^2 + 4|x-y|^2 q^2\} \tag{2.19}$$

$u_3^{cl}(q)$ can be expressed by a product of three K^{cl} functions. In general $u_n^{cl}(q)$ can be shown to have the form

$$u_n^{cl}(q) = (n-2)!\,(-a\pi^{-2})^{n-1}\left(\frac{2\pi}{\beta}\right)^3\left(\frac{\pi}{\beta}\right)^{3(n-2)/2} \times \int_0^\beta d\beta_1 \int_0^\beta d\beta_2 \dots \int_0^\beta d\beta_{n-1} K^{cl}(\underline{q},|\beta-\beta_1|)K^{cl}(\underline{q},|\beta_1-\beta_2|)\dots \times K^{cl}(\underline{q},\beta_{n-1}) \tag{2.20}$$

The integrals in these expressions may be evaluated by using a faltung process. We shall discuss the details of calculation later in section VI where we shall consider a more general type of kernels. Equations (2.18) and (2.20) correspond to Boltzmann statistics. Generalization to quantum mechanical cases will be made by introducing exchanges of particles, as we shall discuss in the rest of this article.

3. ZEROTH ORDER DIAGRAMS

In this section we shall consider non-interacting Bose particles in zeroth order. Fig. 1 illustrates the zero order diagram which includes the two representative particles 1 and 2. The corresponding matrix element is given by

$$U_n^o(\underline{k}_1, \underline{k}_2; \underline{k}_1', \underline{k}_2') = \exp\left[-\beta\{(n_1-1)k_2^2 + k_1'^2 + (n_2-1)k_1^2 + k_2'^2\}\right]$$

$$\times\ \delta(\underline{k}_1 - \underline{k}_2')\,\delta(\underline{k}_2 - \underline{k}_1') \qquad (3.1)$$

$$n = n_1 + n_2$$

Here the integer n_1 represents the number of particles between 1 and 2 and n_2 that between 2 and 1.

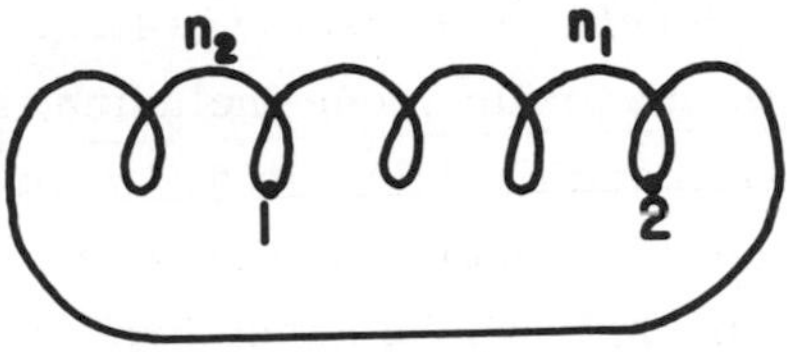

Fig. 1. Zero order diagrams.

Upon transforming the momenta in the right hand side twice in accordance with Eqs. (2.11) and (2.13) we obtain

$$u_n^o(\underline{q}) = 8\left(\frac{\pi}{\beta}\right)^{3/2}(n_1+n_2)^{-3/2}\exp\left[-4\beta(n_1+n_2)^{-1}n_1 n_2 q^2\right] \qquad (3.2)$$

Thus, we find

$$u_n^o(r) = (2\pi)^{-6}\int \exp(-2i\,\underline{q}\cdot\underline{r})\ u_n(\underline{q})\ d\underline{q}$$

$$= (4\pi\beta n_1)^{-3/2}(4\pi\beta n_2)^{-3/2}\exp\left[-\frac{r^2}{4\beta n_1} - \frac{r^2}{4\beta n_2}\right] \qquad (3.3)$$

Multiplying this result by a combinatorial factor (n-2)! and using Eq. (2.6) we arrive at

$$\rho_o^{(2)}(r) = n^2 + \left[g_{3/2}(z, r)\right]^2 \tag{3.4}$$

$$q_s(z, r) = \sum_{n=1}^{\infty} \frac{z^n}{n^o} \exp\left(-\frac{r^2}{4\beta n}\right) \tag{3.5}$$

where $\lambda = (4\pi\beta)^{1/2}$ is the thermal wave length and n is the number density. This result agrees with that obtained by London, Uhlenbeck, Placzek and others[10)5)].

4. FIRST ORDER DIAGRAMS

As Colin and Peretti discussed, the first order diagrams may be classified into two groups, one including the particles 1 and 2 in the same toron and the other in different torons. We shall present in section VI a general method which is applicable to all chain diagrams including those considered in this section. But for comparison with Colin and Peretti's work we shall give in this section discussions and explicit results for the first order diagrams.

Figure 2 illustrates a toron of order $n_1 + n_2 + n_3 + 2 = n - n_4$ including 1 and 2 which is interacting with an unnamed toron of order n_4.

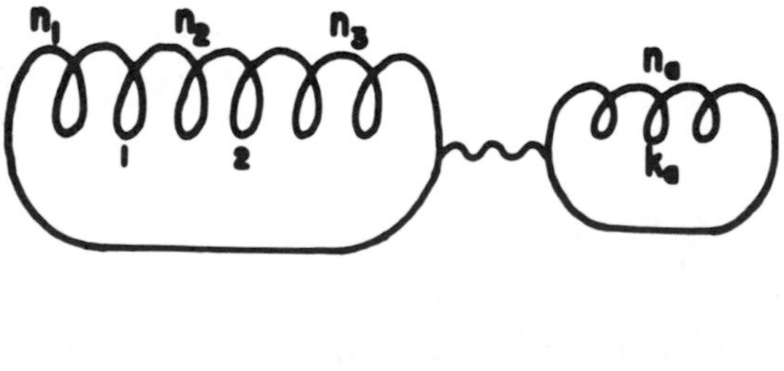

Fig. 2. First order diagram (Type A).

Corresponding to this type we have

$$U_n^{(a)}(\underline{k}_1', \underline{k}_2'; \underline{k}_1, \underline{k}_2) = -\frac{a}{\pi^2}\int \exp\{-\beta n_1 k_1'^2 - \beta k_1^2$$

$$- \beta n_2 k_2'^2 - \beta n_3 k_2^2 - (\beta-\beta_1)k_1'^2 - \beta_1 k_2^2 - \beta n_4 k_a^2\}$$

$$\times \delta(\underline{k}_1' - \underline{k}_2)\,\delta(\underline{k}_2' - \underline{k}_1)\, d\underline{k}_a \tag{4.1}$$

Changing the momentum variables and integrating over all the momentum variables but q we obtain

$$u_n^{(a)}(q) = -\frac{\beta a}{\pi^2}\left(\frac{4\pi}{\beta s}\right)^{3/2}\left(\frac{\pi}{\beta n_a}\right)^{3/2} \exp\{-4\beta q^2(n_2+1)(1 - \frac{n_2+1}{s})\} \tag{4.2}$$

where $s = n_1 + n_2 + n_3 + 2$.

This type of diagram is accompanied by conjugate diagrams which are obtained by letting the separated n_4 toron and $(n_1 + n_2 + n_3 + 2)$- toron form a single toron. This can be done by introducing an exchange between the two. Their relation is illustrated in Fig. 3 for a simple case.

Fig. 3. Conjugate diagrams.

There are other factors to be considered. The number of ways of distributing $n-2 = n_1 + n_2 + n_3 + n_4$ particles as specified in Fig. 2 is (n-2)! Besides, the two particles 1 and 2 may be exchanged to produce a new set of diagrams of the same category.

Considering all these weight factors and expressing Eq. (4.2) in coordinate space and using the grand ensemble we find

$$N^{(a)}(r) = \sum_n \frac{z^n}{(n-2)!} u_n^{(a)}(r)$$

$$= - \frac{8a}{\lambda^7} g_{3/2}(z)\, g_{3/2}(z, r)\, g_{1/2}(z, r) \quad (4.3)$$

The second type B diagrams illustrated in Fig. 4 can be treated in a similar way. We specify the two torons by giving n_1 and n_2 integers for the numbers of particles between the particle 1 and the binary kernel, and n_3 and n_4 for the second toron.

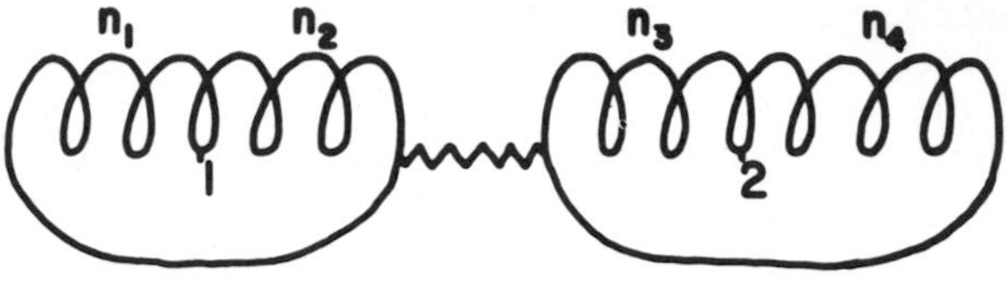

Fig. 4. First order diagram (Type B).

We find

$$u_n^{(b)}(q) = \beta(-a\pi^{-2})\left(\frac{2\pi}{\beta}\right)^3 (n_1+n_2+1)^{-3/2}(n_3+n_4+1)^{-3/2}$$

$$\times \int_0^1 \exp(-4\beta q^2 D)\, dx \quad (4.4)$$

where

$$D = \{n_1 n_3(n_2+n_4+2) + (n_2+1)(n_4+1)(n_1+n_3)$$

$$- 2x(n_1 n_3 - (n_2+1)(n_4+1)) + nx^2\}(n_1+n_2+1)^{-1}(n_3+n_4+1)^{-1}$$

$$(4.5)$$

This quantity D looks complicated but as we shall see later it can be rewritten in a more systematic form. We can show that D is positive and evaluate the Fourier inverse transformation of Eq. (4.4).

The appropriate weight factor for this case is 2(n-2)!. The

factor 2 is due to conjugate diagrams. All diagrams are counted automatically when we sum over all n_i's.
We find

$$\sum_n \frac{z^2 u_2^{(b)}(r)}{(n-2)!} = - \frac{32a}{\lambda^7} \sum_{n_i} \int_0^1 dx \frac{\exp(-r^2/\beta x)}{x^{3/2}}$$

$$\times \frac{z^n}{\{(n_1+n_2+1)(n_3+n_4+1)\}^{3/2}} \tag{4.6}$$

where x is a function of n_i defined by (A2) in the Appendix. The right hand side integral over x can be modified as discussed in the Appendix. As a result we end up with

$$\sum_1 \frac{z^n u_n^{(b)}(r)}{(n-2)!} = - \frac{8a}{\lambda^7} \frac{\lambda^{1/2}}{r} \eta(r) \tag{4.7}$$

Here λ is the de Broglie wavelength and $\eta(r)$ is defined by

$$\eta(r) = \frac{1}{\pi^{1/2}} \sum z^{n_1+n_2+n_3+n_4+2} P(n_1, n_2, n_3, n_4)$$

$$\times \exp\left[- \frac{r^2}{4\beta} \{(n_1+n_4+1)^{-1} + (n_2+n_3+1)^{-1}\}\right] \tag{4.8}$$

and

$$P(n_1, n_2, n_3, n_4) = (n_1+n_2+1)^{-1}(n_3+n_4+1)^{-1}$$

$$\times (n_1+n_4+1)^{-1/2}(n_2+n_3+1)^{-1/2} \int_0^{\xi(+)} \exp(-\xi^2)\, d\xi \tag{4.9}$$

The upper domain $\xi(+)$ is given by

$$\xi(+) = \frac{r}{\beta^{1/2}} f(n_1, n_2, n_3, n_4) ;$$

$$f(n_1, n_2, n_3, n_4) = \tag{4.10}$$

$$= \frac{(n_1+1)(n_3+1) - n_2 n_4}{\left[(n_1+n_4+1)(n_2+n_3+1)\{n_2 n_4(n_1+n_3+2)+(n_1+1)(n_3+1)(n_2+n_4)\}\right]^{1/2}}$$

ξ is a dimensionless variable. (Note that $\beta^{1/2}$ is proportional to the de Broglie thermal wavelength.)

The two expressions (4.3) and (4.7) may now be added. We arrive at the following result for the pair distribution function

$$\rho^{(2)}(r) = \rho_o^{(2)}(r) - 8a\,\lambda^{-7}F(r)$$

$$F(r) = g_{3/2}(z)\,g_{3/2}(z,r)\,g_{1/2}(z,r) + \frac{\lambda^{1/2}}{r}\eta(r) \qquad (4.11)$$

where the g functions are defined in Eq. (3.5).

It is interesting to observe in Eq. (4.11) that the second and the third terms diminish exponentially at large distances while the latter term contains $1/r$. However, in Eq. (4.9) the ξ integration yields an additional r dependence. As a result it can easily be seen that there is no singularity at $r = 0$. Namely, the term $1/r$ came from the use of our choice of a new variable and is fictitious. In the intermediate distances, the behavior of the pair distribution function is complex and requires a numerical calculation of the integral.

It is to be remarked that the above results are different from the corresponding expressions reported by Colin and Peretti. First, Eq. (4.11) differs from their expression by a factor 2. This is due to their overlooking the exchange between the particles 1 and 2. Later Colin obtained by Bogolieubov method the correct second term. (The third term was not obtained in this work.)

Second, our third term

$$-\frac{8a}{r}\lambda^{-6}\eta(r)$$

is to be compared with their

$$-\frac{8a}{r}\lambda^{-6}\left[g_{3/2}(z,r)\right]^2$$

Apparently this difference is due to their momentum space integrations. They used U_2 instead of B and were obliged to take a principal value of a certain integral in the intermediate stage.

(See Equation C (6) of their paper.) Note that the error integral appeared in $\eta(r)$ reduces to a constant value $\pi^{1/2}/2$ for $n_2 = n_4 = 0$. In this case we have precisely their simpler result:

$$\eta(r) = \sum_{n_1, n_3} \frac{z^{n_1+n_3}}{(n_1 n_3)^{3/2}} \exp\{- \frac{r^2}{4\beta n_1} - \frac{r^2}{4\beta n_3}\}$$

$$= \left[g_{3/2}(z, r)\right]^2 \tag{4.12}$$

Thus, we have shown that the result (6.16) of Colin and Peretti is correct only in this limit. It is interesting to observe that we have the same situation in the limit $r \to \infty$. In the next Section further confirmations of our result will be made.

5. THE CLUSTER EXPANSION OF THE EQUATION OF STATE

The pair distribution function defined in the grand ensemble satisfies the normalization:

$$V \int \rho^{(2)}(r)\, d\underline{r} = \langle N(N-1) \rangle \tag{5.1}$$

It is then natural to subtract $\langle N \rangle^2$ from both sides to obtain

$$V \int \rho^{(2)}(r)\, d\underline{r} - \langle N \rangle^2 = V \sum_s s(s-1)\, z^s\, b_s \tag{5.2}$$

where the b_s are the cluster integrals.

Equation (5.2) may be used to check the normalization of our expression (4.11). One can easily find

$$\sum_s \int \frac{z^s}{(s-2)!}\, u_s^{(a)}(r)\, d\underline{r} = -8a\,\lambda^{-7} g_{3/2}(z) \int g_{3/2}(z, r)\, g_{1/2}(z, r)\, d\underline{r}$$

$$= - \frac{4a}{\lambda} \frac{1}{\lambda^3} g_{3/2}(z)(g_{-1/2}(z) - g_{1/2}(z)) \tag{5.3}$$

This can of course be obtained from Eq. (4.2). For this purpose one may use the following equality of which the author was informed by T. Y. Wu.

$$\sum_{n_2} z^{n_1+n_2+n_3+2}/(n_1+n_2+n_3+2)^{3/2} = \sum_s z^s/s^{3/2}$$

$$\times \text{ (No. of ways of distributing } s-2 \text{ into three numbers.)}$$

$$= \frac{1}{2} \sum_s \frac{z^s}{s^{3/2}} s(s-1) = \frac{1}{2} (g_{-1/2}(z) - g_{1/2}(z))$$

One can also show

$$\sum_n \int \frac{z^n u_n^{(b)}(r)}{(n-2)!} d\underline{r} = - \frac{4a}{\lambda} \frac{1}{\lambda^3} g_{1/2}^2(z) \tag{5.4}$$

Using Eqs. (5.3) and (5.4) one arrives at

$$\lambda^3 \sum_s s(s-1) z^s b_s = g_{1/2}(z) - g_{3/2}(z)$$

$$- \frac{4a}{\lambda} \{g_{1/2}^2(z) + g_{3/2}(z)\, g_{-1/2}(z) - g_{3/2}(z)\, g_{1/2}(z)\} \tag{5.5}$$

Namely, we end up with the equation of state

$$\lambda^3 \sum_s b_s z^s = g_{5/2}(z) - \frac{2a}{\lambda} [g_{3/2}(z)]^2 \tag{5.6}$$

This is exactly what Lee and Yang reported in their paper III. Thus, we may consider that our result is correct to first order in the hard sphere diameter a.

6. CHAIN DIAGRAMS

In paper I we have considered chain diagrams and shown that they are important at low temperature. Actually, we have proved that these correspond to the collective excitation of particles and give rise to a phonon spectrum important in explaining the properties of liquid helium.

It is noticed that these chain diagrams do not involve exchange interactions of particles and correspond to Boltzmann statistics. This is because in paper I we were concerned with a Bose gas at the lowest temperature. In order to extend the theory to a finite temperature it becomes necessary to take exchange collisions of particles into consideration.

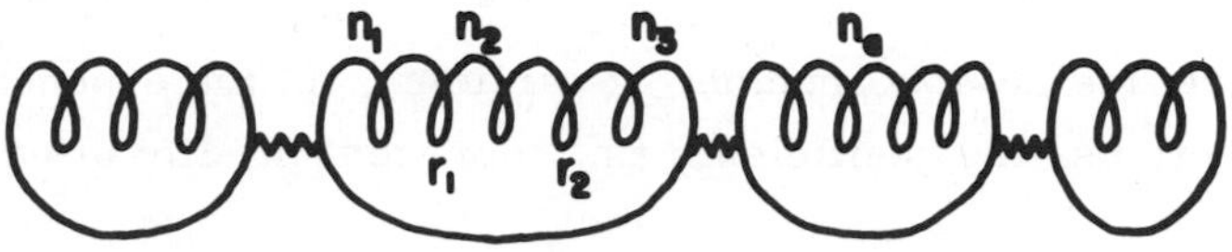

(a)

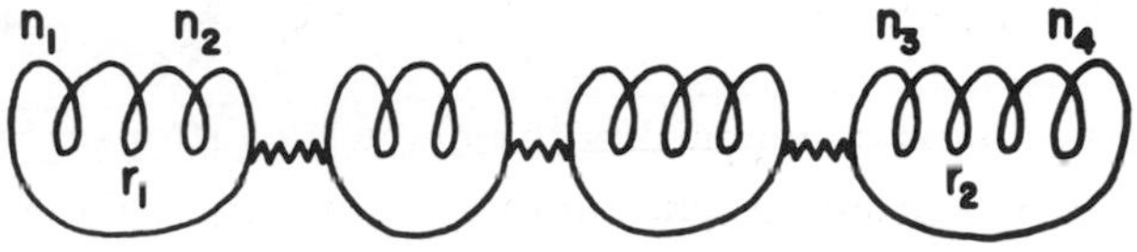

(b)

Fig. 5. Quantum Statistical Chain Diagrams

Many new diagrams are introduced through the exchanges. We find it important to treat the toron-chain diagrams such as shown in Fig. 5. Fig. 5(a) represents a $(n_1 + n_2 + 2)$ toron which always includes the particles 1 and 2 and is connected to a linear array of unnamed torons by binary kernels. Fig. 5(b) is for a linear chain of unnamed torons spanned by the two named torons at the ends. Of course, these two types could be combined to form hybrid diagrams, but it is convenient to treat them separately.

As one can easily see, these two types reduce to the Boltzmann chain and tick-tack-toe diagrams such as were considered in paper I and the first order diagrams considered by Colin and Peretti.

We shall first consider the integral associated with Fig. 5(a):

$$u_n^{(a)}(\underline{k}_1', \underline{k}_2'; \underline{k}_1, \underline{k}_2) = \int \prod_a \left(-\frac{a\beta}{\pi^2}\right) \exp(-n_a \beta k_a^2)\, d\underline{k}_a$$

$$\times\, \delta(\underline{k}_2' - \underline{k}_1)\, \delta(\underline{k}_1' - \underline{k}_2)$$

$$\times \exp(-\beta n_1 k_1'^2 - \beta k_1^2 - \beta n_2 k_2'^2 - \beta n_3 k_2^2 - (\beta - \beta_1) k_1'^2 - \beta_1 k_2^2)$$

$$(6.1)$$

Here n is the total number of particles. In the exponential functions, the coefficients βn_i represent the life of each propagation.

In order to obtain $u_n(q)$ we introduce a transformation:

$$\underline{k}_1 = \frac{1}{2}\underline{K}_1 + \underline{q}, \qquad \underline{k}_1' = \frac{1}{2}\underline{K}_1 - \underline{q}$$

$$\underline{k}_2 = \frac{1}{2}\underline{K}_2 + \underline{q}', \qquad \underline{k}_2' = \frac{1}{2}\underline{K}_2 - \underline{q}' \qquad (6.2)$$

Note that this transformation is somewhat different from that introduced in Section 2. The motivation of introducing this transformation is the same as before but this is simpler. The integrations of Eq. (6.1) over the set of variables k_a are trivial. Its integrations over $\underline{K}_1$, $\underline{K}_2$ and $\underline{q}'$ are also easy because of the δ functions. Thus, we end up with

$$u_n^{(a)}(\underline{q}) = \prod_a \left\{\left(\frac{\pi}{\beta n_a}\right)^{3/2}\left(-\frac{\beta a}{\pi^2}\right)\right\}\left(\frac{4\pi}{\beta(n_1+n_2+n_3+2)}\right)^{3/2}$$

$$\times \exp\left\{-4\beta q^2(n_2+1)\left(1 - \frac{n_2+1}{n_1+n_2+n_3+2}\right)\right\} \qquad (6.3)$$

In terms of $u_n^{(a)}(\underline{q})$ we can write $u_n^{(a)}(r)$ as follows:

$$u_n^{(a)}(r) = \frac{1}{(8\pi^3)^2}\int u_n^{(a)}(\underline{q}) \exp 2i\,\underline{q}\cdot\underline{r}\, d\underline{q} \qquad (6.4)$$

This corresponds to Eq. (2.15).

This type of diagram has a weight factor 4(n-2)!. Here the factor 4 takes conjugate diagrams and exchange diagrams into consideration. (n-2)! is for permutations of unnamed particles.

The function $N^{(a)}(q)$ defined by Eq. (2.15) may be expressed in the grand ensemble as follows

$$\sum_n \frac{z^n}{(n-2)!} u_n^{(a)}(r) = \frac{4}{\lambda^6} g_{3/2}(z,r) g_{1/2}(z,r) \prod_a \left(-\frac{2a}{\lambda}\right) g_{3/2}(z) \tag{6.5}$$

This reduces precisely to Eq. (4.3) if there is just one unnamed toron a.

The treatment of type B chain diagrams is slightly more complicated and interesting. Here the two named (n_1+n_2+1) and (n_3+n_4+1) torons are connected by a series of unnamed torons n_a, n_b, etc. which have respectively (n_a-1) complete free turns, (n_b-1) turns, etc. Correspondingly, we evaluate the $U_n^{(b)}$ function as follows:

$$U_n^{(b)}(\underline{k}_1', \underline{k}_2'; \underline{k}_1\, \underline{k}_2) = \int \cdots \int d\beta_1\, d\beta_a\, d\beta_b \cdots d\beta_2\, d\underline{k}_a\, d\underline{k}_a' \cdots d\underline{k}_t\, d\underline{k}_t'$$

$$\times \exp\{-(n_1+1)\beta k_1'^2 - n_2\beta k_1^2 - \beta_1(k_1^2 - k_1'^2)\}$$

$$\times \left(-\frac{a}{\pi^2}\right)\exp\{-(n_a\beta+\beta_a-\beta_1)k_a'^2 - (\beta-(\beta_a-\beta_1)k_a^2)\}\, \delta(\underline{k}_a+\underline{k}_b'-\underline{k}_a'-\underline{k}_b)$$

$$\times \left(-\frac{a}{\pi^2}\right)\exp\{-(n_b\beta+\beta_b-\beta_a)k_b'^2 - (\beta-(\beta_b-\beta_a)k_b^2)\}\, \delta(\underline{k}_b+\underline{k}_c'-\underline{k}_b'-\underline{k}_c)$$

$$\cdots\cdots\cdots\cdots\cdots\cdots$$

$$\times\left(\left(-\frac{a}{\pi^2}\right)\exp\{-(n_3+1)\beta k_2'^2 - n_4\beta k_2^2 - \beta_2(k_2^2-k_2'^2)\}\right\}\delta(\underline{k}_t+\underline{k}_2'-\underline{k}_t'-\underline{k}_2) \tag{6.6}$$

After making the coordinate transformations given by Eq. (6.2) and integrating over all the momenta but q we obtain factors such as $\left(\frac{\pi}{(n_a+1)\beta}\right)^{3/2}$, $\left(\frac{4\pi}{(n_1+n_2+1)\beta}\right)^{3/2}$ etc. and 2^{-3} from a δ function. In addition we introduce a factor 2 to take conjugate diagrams into consideration. Thus, we end up with

$$\sum_n \frac{z^n}{(1n-2)!} u_n^{(b)}(q) = \sum_{n_i} z^n \int \left(\frac{4\pi}{(n_1+n_2+1)\beta} \right)^{3/2} K_{n_1+n_2+1}(g; n_2 + \frac{\beta_1}{\beta})$$

$$\times 2(\frac{1}{2^3}) \prod_a (-\frac{a}{(n_a+1)\beta})^{3/2} K_{n_a+1} \{g; n_a + \frac{\beta_a - \beta_1}{\beta}\}$$

$$\times \left(\frac{4\pi}{(n_3+n_4+1)\beta} \right)^{3/2} K_{n_3+n_4+1} (g; n_3 + \frac{\beta_2}{\beta}) d\beta_1 \, d\beta_a \ldots d\beta_2 \tag{6.7}$$

where $g = 4\beta q^2$.

The β-integrations are time ordered. However, we must take all the diagrams arising from interchanges of β's. It is then appropriate to introduce an integral equation

$$\lambda_p \Psi_p(x) = \int_0^1 K(g; |x - y|) \Psi_p(y) \, dy \tag{6.8}$$

with the kernel function

$$K_n(g; |x - y|) = \exp\{-g|x - y| + g \frac{|x - y|^2}{n}\} \tag{6.9}$$

so that we have the expansion

$$K_n(g; |x - y|) = \sum_p \lambda_p(g; n) \Psi_p(x) \Psi_p^*(y) \tag{6.10}$$

We also introduce the following kernels suitable to the grand ensemble:

$$H(g; \beta_1) = \sum_{n_1, n_2} \left[\frac{4\pi}{(n_1+n_2+1)\beta} \right]^{3/2} z^{n_1+n_2+1} \exp\{-g(n_2+\frac{\beta_1}{\beta})(1 - \frac{n_2+\beta_1/\beta}{n_1+n_2+1})\} \tag{6.11}$$

$$L(g; \beta_2 - \beta_1) = \sum_{n_a} \left[\frac{\pi}{(n_a+1)\beta} \right]^{3/2} z^{n_a+1} \exp\{-g(1 - \frac{\beta_2 - \beta_1}{\beta})(1 - \frac{1-(\beta_2-\beta_1)/\beta}{n_a+1})\} \tag{6.12}$$

We can then express $H(g; \beta_1)$ and $L(g; \beta_2 - \beta_1)$ as follows:

$$H(g; \beta_1) = \sum_s \Lambda_s(g)\psi_s(\beta_1)$$
$$L(g; \beta_2 - \beta_1) = \sum_t \Gamma_t(g, n_a + 1)\psi_t(\beta_2)\psi_t^*(\beta_1) \tag{6.13}$$

Here the eigen values Λ_s and Γ_t may be induced by the eigen values of the integral equation (6.10) as follows:

$$\Lambda_s(g) = \sum_{n_1 n_2} \left[\frac{4\pi}{(n_1+n_2+1)\beta}\right]^{3/2} z^{n_1+n_2+1} \lambda_s(g; n_1, n_2)$$
$$\Gamma_s(g) = \sum_{n_a} \left[\frac{\pi}{(n_a+1)\beta}\right]^{3/2} z^{n_a+1} \lambda_s(g; n_a) \tag{6.14}$$

where

$$g = 4\beta q^2 \tag{6.15}$$

We thus arrive at

$$N^{(b)}(q) = -\frac{\beta a}{4\pi^2} \sum_s \frac{\Lambda_s^2}{1 + (a\pi^{-2})\beta\Gamma_s} \tag{6.16}$$

Correspondingly, in coordinate space we have the contributions

$$\sum_n \frac{z^n}{(n-2)!} u_n^{(b)}(r) = (8\pi^3)^{-2} \int N^{(b)}(q) \exp 2i\underline{q}\cdot\underline{r}\, d\underline{q} \tag{6.17}$$

The function $N^{(b)}(q)$ has the dimension of n because $\beta^{1/2}$ is of the dimension of length, and Λ_s and Γ_s are of the dimension of λ^{-3}, where λ is the de Broglie thermal wavelength $(4\pi\beta)^{1/2}$.

Our formula (6.16) is general for all chain diagrams. Since it is rather abstract it may be interesting and worthwhile to use the formula for special cases. As will be discussed in the next section, some caution is needed in certain cases.

7. THE LOW TEMPERATURE RESULTS

We shall start our consideration of Eq. (6.16) with the eigen value problem of Eq. (6.8). The eigen functions may be assumed to be periodic in the domain (0, 1). Then one finds the following approximate eigen value

$$\lambda_s(g; n_1, n_2) = \int_{n_2}^{n_2+1} \exp(-g x + g x^2/n) \cos s x \, dx$$
$$= \frac{g}{g^2+s^2} \{1 + \frac{2g}{n(q^2+s^2)^2} (g^2 - 3s^2)\} \exp(-gn_2) \qquad (7.1)$$

where

$$s = 2\pi m \qquad (7.2)$$

As one can see, this eigen value is asymptotically correct in the limit $\beta \to \infty$. We note that an improved result can be obtained for the case $n = 1$ by splitting the domain of integration into one-half. As a result we get

$$\lambda_s(g) = \frac{2g}{g^2+s^2} \{ 1 + \frac{2g}{(g^2+s^2)^2} (g^2 - 3s^2 \} \qquad (7.3)$$

Note a factor 2 difference between Eq. (7.1) and (7.3). Therefore, it is suitable to write the summation in Eq. (6.14) as follows:

$$\sum_{n_1, n_2} \frac{z^{n_1+n_2+1}}{(n_1+n_2+1)^{3/2}} \lambda_s (g; n_1, n_2)$$
$$= z\lambda_s(g) + \sum_{\substack{n_1, n_2 \\ n_1+n_2 = n = 1}} \frac{z^{n+1}}{(n+1)^{3/2}} \lambda_s(g; n_1, n_2) \qquad (7.4)$$
$$= \frac{1}{2} z\lambda_s^{(a)}(1 + \frac{g_{3/2}(z)}{z}) + \frac{1}{2} z\lambda_s^{(b)}(1 + \frac{g_{5/2}(z)}{z})$$

where

$$\lambda_s^{(a)} = \frac{2g}{g^2+s^2} \quad ; \quad \lambda_s^{(b)} = \frac{4g^2}{(g^2+s^2)^3}(g^2 - 3s^2) \qquad (7.5)$$

Introducing Eq. (7.4) in Eq. (6.14) we obtain

$$\Lambda_s(g) = \left(\frac{4\pi}{\beta}\right)^{3/2} \frac{z}{2}\left(1 + \frac{g_{3/2}(z)}{z}\right) \quad \lambda_s^{(a)}\left\{1 + \frac{\lambda_s^{(b)}}{\lambda_s^{(a)}} \frac{1+g_{5/2}(z)/z}{1+g_{3/2}(z)/z}\right\} \qquad (7.6)$$

Similarly

$$\Gamma_s(g) = \left(\frac{\pi}{\beta}\right)^{3/2} \frac{z}{2}\left(1 + \frac{g_{3/2}(z)}{z}\right) \quad \lambda_s^{(a)}\left\{1 + \frac{\lambda_s^{(b)}}{\lambda_s^{(a)}} \frac{1+g_{5/2}(z)/z}{1+g_{3/2}(z)/z}\right\}$$

The inclusion of the eigen values $\lambda_s^{(b)}$ is possible and interesting, but it is rather complicated. Therefore, in what follows we shall simplify our calculation by limiting our considerations to $\lambda_s^{(a)}$.

$\Lambda_s(g)$ varies as $g_{1/2}(z)$. As z approaches 1 this function diverges. This corresponds to the complication arising from the Bose-Einstein condensation. In order to circumvent this difficulty Lee and Yang suggested the use of Boltzmann statistics which is supposed to be correct at absolute zero. It is remarked that in order to derive results for a Boltzmann gas from our formula we must replace $g_{3/2}/z$ by 1 and remove a factor 2 from Eq. (6.16). The factor 2 is due to the exchanges involved in Bose statistics, and is a discontinuous factor. At the same time Λ_s and Γ_s must be replaced by $(4\pi/\beta)^{3/2}\, z\lambda_s$ and $(\pi/\beta)^{3/2}\, z\lambda$ respectively.

At low temperatures one may replace the summation over s by integration as follows:

$$\sum_s \rightarrow \frac{\lambda^2}{2\pi^2} \int dx \qquad (7.7)$$

where $x = 2\pi^2 m/\lambda^2$. We also note that the number density n is given by

$$n = g_{3/2} / \lambda^3 \tag{7.8}$$

The absolute activity z may be replaced by $n\lambda^3$.

Using all these informations we end up with

$$N^{(b)}(q) = -\frac{8a\pi z^2}{\beta^2\lambda^2}\left(1 + \frac{g_{3/2}(z)}{z}\right)^2 \times \int_{-\infty}^{\infty} q^4(q^4+x^2)^{-1}\left[q^4+x^2+\gamma q^2\right]^{-1} dx \tag{7.9}$$

$$\gamma = 4\pi a n \tag{7.10}$$

We shall now derive from this expression results which are valid at the lowest temperature. Following the remarks which we just made with respect to taking this limit and integrating Eq. (7.9) we obtain

$$N^{(b)}(q) = -\frac{256\pi^4 a n^2}{\gamma}\left[1 - \left(1 + \frac{\gamma}{q^2}\right)^{-1/2}\right] \tag{7.11}$$

The Fourier transform of N(q) into coordinate space is not difficult. One way of doing this is to use the modified Bessel and Struve functions I_ν and $\mathbb{L}$ as follows:

$$R\int \left\{1 - \frac{q}{(q^2+r^2)^{1/2}}\right\} \exp 2i\,\underline{q}\cdot\underline{r}\, d\underline{q}$$

$$= \frac{2\pi\gamma}{r}\int\left\{\frac{1}{(q^2+\gamma)} - \frac{1}{(q^2+\gamma)^{1/2}+q}\right\} \sin 2qr\, dq$$

$$= \frac{\pi^2\gamma}{r}\left\{I_o(\varkappa) - \mathbb{L}_o(\varkappa) - \frac{I_1(\varkappa) - \mathbb{L}_1(\varkappa)}{\varkappa}\right\} \tag{7.12}$$

where

$$\varkappa = 2\gamma^{1/2} r \tag{7.13}$$

It is remarked that

$$I_\nu(\varkappa) - L_\nu(\varkappa) = \sum_{j=o}^{\infty} \frac{(-)^j(\varkappa/2)^{j+\nu}}{\Gamma(\frac{j}{2}+1)\Gamma(\frac{j}{2}+\nu+1)} \tag{7.14}$$

We thus end up with

$$\rho^{(2)}(r) = n^2 \{1 - \frac{4a}{r} (I_o(\varkappa) - \mathbb{L}_o(\varkappa) - \frac{(I_1(\varkappa) - \mathbb{L}_1(\varkappa))}{\varkappa})\} \quad (7.15)$$

with $\varkappa$ defined by Eq. (7.13). Similar transcendental functions appear in the result obtained by Lieb by an intuitive method[11]. However, his expression is only approximately true. It gives D(r)-1 at short distances one-half and at large distances twice as large as our expression. However, it must be remarked that his definition of distribution functions is unique. They correspond to ψ rather than $\psi\psi^*$. Therefore, one must not make a direct comparison. Actually, the above comment is valid only when his two body distribution function is considered as the pair distribution function.

Another way of evaluating the Fourier transformation is to use the relation

$$1 - \frac{q}{(q^2+\gamma)^{1/2}} = \gamma^{1/2} \int_o^\infty e^{-q\varkappa} J_1(\gamma^{1/2}\varkappa) d\varkappa \quad (7.16)$$

Then

$$I = R \int (1 - \frac{q}{(q^2+\gamma)^{1/2}}) \exp 2i\, q \cdot r\, dq$$

$$= \frac{2\pi\gamma^{1/2}}{r^2} \int_o^\infty \frac{y\, J_1(2\,\gamma^{1/2}\, r\, y)}{(1+y^2)^2} dy \quad (7.17)$$

For small r we can take the first term in the series expansion of the Bessel function J_1 with the result

$$I = \frac{\pi^2\gamma}{2r} \quad (7.18)$$

This gives

$$\rho^{(2)}(r) = n^2 (1 - \frac{2a}{r}) \quad (7.19)$$

$$a < r \leqq 4(\pi a\, n)^{1/2}$$

It is not appropriate to conclude from this form that $\rho^{(2)}(r)$ does not vanish at $r = a$. As we have shown in paper I, if we take the second order term into consideration we obtain

$$\rho^{(2)}(r) = n^2 (1 - \frac{a}{r})^2 \tag{7.20}$$

in agreement with Luban[12].

At large distances we obtain

$$\begin{aligned} I &= \frac{8\pi}{(2r)^4} \gamma^{-1/2} \int_0^\infty y\, J_1(y)\, dy \\ &= \frac{\pi}{2r^4} \gamma^{-1/2} \end{aligned} \tag{7.21}$$

Thus, we find

$$\rho^{(2)} = n^2 \{1 - (4\pi^{5/2} a^{1/2} n^{3/2})^{-1} r^{-4}\} \tag{7.22}$$

The r^{-4} dependence appearing in this expression is important because it leads to the phonon spectrum. Conversely, if the structure factor $S(k)$ is phonon-like:

$$S(k) = \frac{k}{c} \tag{7.23}$$

the correlation function $g(r)$ defined by

$$\begin{aligned} g(r) &= \frac{\rho^{(2)}}{n^2} - 1 \\ &= \frac{1}{2\pi^2 nr} \int_0^\infty dk\, \{S(k) - 1\}\, k \sin kr \end{aligned} \tag{7.24}$$

should approach[13]

$$g(r) = - \frac{1}{\pi^2 n c r^4} \tag{7.25}$$

Thus, the sound velocity in a hard sphere gas is

$$c = 4(\pi\ a\ n)^{1/2} \tag{7.26}$$

which is in standard units $(\hbar/m)(4\pi an)^{1/2}$. This coincides with the result obtained by T. T. Wu[3].

As we have pointed out before, first order diagrams are important at short distances. One can of course use Eq. (6.3) or Eq. (6.16) for this case. As a matter of fact, for $n_1 = n_2 = 0$ one gets

$$u_2(q) = -\frac{2a}{\pi^2}\left(\frac{2\pi}{\beta}\right)^3 \int_0^\beta d\beta_1 K^{cl}(q;\beta-\beta_1)K^{cl}(q;\beta_1) \tag{7.27}$$

which agrees with Eq. (4.2) of this paper. The factor 2 is due to the exchange effect and does not appear in the case of Boltzmann statistics.

Also from Eq. (6.16) one finds for first order diagrams

$$N^{(b)}(q) = -\frac{\beta a}{4\pi^2}\sum_{\varepsilon}\Lambda_s^2$$

$$= -\frac{\beta a}{4\pi^2}\left(\frac{4\pi}{\beta}\right)^3 \sum_{n_i} \frac{z^{n_1+n_2+n_3+n_4+2}}{(n_1+n_2+1)^{3/2}(n_3+n_4+1)^{3/2}}$$

$$\times \int \exp\left[-g\left\{(n_2+x)\left(1-\frac{n_2+x}{n_1+n_2+1}\right)+(n_3+x)\left(1-\frac{n_3+x}{n_3+n_4+1}\right)\right\}\right] dx \tag{7.28}$$

This is an elegant form of Eq. (4.4). Of course, the same weight factor 2 has to be removed for comparison as in the above consideration of u_2 because Eq. (4.4) does not include conjugate diagrams.

In Eq. (7.28) $g_{3/2}(z)$ was replaced by z. At low temperature $g_{3/2}(z)$ is large. Thus, one sees the important role of the type B diagrams.

8. DISCUSSION

The distribution function of liquid helium has been determined by neutron[14] and X ray[15] diffraction methods, especially near the λ -transition point. It has been discovered that with increasing liquid density the principal maximum moves to larger angles and increases in height. For the nearest distance of approach of two atoms the value 2.27 ± 0.08 A has been reported. The spatial order has been found smaller below the λ point than above, and inelastic scattering measurements have shown that the atomic motions are more ordered below the transition[14)]. Nevertheless, these experiments reported no abrupt change in the form of the distribution function at the λ point.

From our theoretical results, especially from Eq. (4.11), we see that the distribution is determined mainly by a dimensionless variable (r/λ). This result can perhaps be checked rather easily by experiments. Thus, lowering the temperature should correspond to increasing the distance, and vice versa. At a given temperature, if we decrease the distance r all g functions increase. In particular, $g_{1/2}(z, r)$ increases most rapidly until it diverges at $r = 0$. Thus $\rho^{(2)}(r)$ is surpressed by the contribution from the first order diagrams*).

The temperature change results in a similar situation. We notice $\exp(-r^2/4\beta n) \rightarrow 1$ as $n \rightarrow \infty$. Thus the divergence in $g_{1/2}(z, r)$ takes place as z approaches 1, near the condensation point. The pair distribution function then shows a sharp drop.

Nevertheless, it must be remarked that we have used an approximate binary kernel. The short distance behavior of the pair distribution function is determined by $u_2(r)$. This function vanishes for $r = a$ if we take into consideration the terms up to the second order in a. This indicates the necessity of investigating higher order terms in a. We shall then be able to say more about the effects of condensation, and this will be our next task[16)].

---

*) Similar result has been reported for a Lennard-Jones gas (in the density independent part of the exchange correlation.) S. Y. Larsen, K. Wille and J. E. Kilpatrick, J. Chem. Phys. 44, 213 (1966).

APPENDIX

The variable ξ appearing in Eq. (4.6) is defined by

$$\frac{\xi}{r} = \frac{\beta + 2cx}{\beta^{1/2}(B^2+4AC)^{1/2}\chi^{1/2}} \qquad \text{(A1)}$$

where $$x = A - Bx - Cx^2$$

$$B^2 + 4AC = \frac{4^3(n_1+n_4+1)(n_2+n_3+1)}{(n_1+n_2+1)(n_3+n_4+1)} \qquad \text{(A2)}$$

$$A = \frac{4\{n_1 n_3(n_2+n_4+2) + (n_2+1)(n_4+1)(n_1+n_3)\}}{(n_1+n_2+1)(n_3+n_4+1)}$$

$$B = -\frac{8\{(n_2+1)(n_4+1) - n_1 n_3\}}{(n_1+n_2+1)(n_3+n_4+1)}$$

$$C = \frac{4n}{(n_1+n_2+1)(n_3+n_4+1)} \quad ; \quad n = n_1+n_2+n_3+n_4+2 \qquad \text{(A3)}$$

One can then have

$$\int \frac{\exp(-r^2/\beta\chi)}{\chi^{3/2}}\, dx = \frac{1}{(B^2+4AC)^{1/2}} \int_{\xi(-)}^{\xi(+)} \exp(-r^2/\beta\chi)\, \frac{d\xi}{r} \qquad \text{(A4)}$$

where

$$\frac{1}{\beta\chi} = \frac{\xi^2}{r^2} + \frac{4C}{\beta(B^2+4AC)} \qquad \text{(A5)}$$

and

$$\frac{4C}{B^2+4AC} = \frac{1}{4}\left\{\frac{1}{n_1+n_4+1} + \frac{1}{n_2+n_3+1}\right\} \qquad \text{(A6)}$$

The upper and lower limits (+), (-) are

$$\xi(+) = \frac{r}{\beta^{1/2}} f(n_1, n_2, n_3, n_4)$$

$$-\xi(-) = \frac{r}{\beta^{1/2}} f(n_2, n_1, n_4, n_3) \qquad \text{(A7)}$$

$f(n_1, n_2, n_3, n_4) =$

$$= \frac{(n_1+1)(n_3+1) - n_2 n_4}{\left[(n_1+n_4+1)(n_3+n_2+1)\{n_2 n_4(n_1+n_3+2)+(n_1+1)(n_3+1)(n_2+n_4)\}\right]^{1/2}}$$

It is remarked that we can split the integral over ξ as follows:

$$\int_{\xi(-)}^{\xi(+)} = \int_{\xi(-)}^{o} + \int_{o}^{\xi(+)}$$

The two integrals give the same contribution to $\rho^{(2)}(r)$ because the results are summed over all the integers and since $-\xi(-)$ has the same dependence on these integers as $\xi(+)$. It is then natural to introduce the P function.

REFERENCES

1. K. A. Brueckner and K. Sawada, Phys. Rev. 106, 117, 1128 (1957).

T. D. Lee and C. N. Yang, Phys. Rev. 113, 1165 (1959); 116, 25 (1959); 117, 22 (1960).

K. Huang and C. N. Yang, Phys. Rev. 105, 767 (1957).

K. Huang, C. N. Yang and J. Luttinger, Phys. Rev. 105, 776 (1957).

C. De Dominicis and P. C. Martin, Phys. Rev. 105, 1417 (1957).

S. T. Beliaev, J. Exptl. Theoret. Phys. U.S.S.R. 34, 417 (1958); Soviet Physics JETP 7, 289 (1958).

N. M. Hugenholtz and D. Pines, Phys. Rev. 116, 489 (1959).

2. T. D. Lee, K. Huang and C. N. Yang, Phys. Rev. 106, 1135 (1957).

3. Tai Tsun Wu, Phys. Rev. 115, 1390 (1959).

4. A. Isihara and Daniel D. H. Yee, Phys. Rev. 136, A618 (1964). Physica 30, 2123 (1964).

5. S. Fujita, A. Isihara and E. W. Montroll, Bull. Classe Sci. Acad. Roy. Belg. 44, 1018 (1958).

6. E. W. Montroll and J. C. Ward, Phys. Fluids 1, 55 (1958).

7. S. Fujita and R. Hirota, Phys. Rev. 118, 6 (1960).

8. L. Colin and J. Peretti, J. Math. Phys. 1, 97 (1960).

9. L. Colin, J. Math. Phys. 1, 87 (1960).

10. G. E. Uhlenbeck and E. Beth, Physica 3, 729 (1936); F. London, J. Chem. Phys. 11, 203 (1943); G. Placzek, Proc. Second Berkley Symposium on Math. Stat. and Prob. 581 (1950).

11. Elliott Lieb, Phys. Rev. 130, 2518 (1963).

12. Marshall Luban, Phys. Rev. A138, 1028 (1963); A139, 1033 (1963).

13. J. E. Enderby, T. Gaskell and N. H. March, Proc. Phys. Soc. 85, 217 (1965).

14. D. G. Henshaw, Phys. Rev. 100, 994 (1955).
D. G. Henshaw, Phys. Rev. 119, 9, 14 (1960).

15. Louis Goldstein and James Reekie, Phys. Rev. 98, 857 (1955); Louis Goldstein, Phys. Rev. 100, 981 (1955).

C. F. A. Beaumont and J. Reekie, Proc. Roy. Soc. (London) A228, 363 (1959).

W. L. Gordon, C. H. Shaw, and J. G. Daunt, Phys. Rev. 96, 1444 (1959); J. Phys. Chem. 1444 (1959).

D. G. Henshaw, Phys. Rev. 111, 1470 (1958).

16. The condensation precludes the direct application quantum field theoretical methods. Investigations along this line have been made by

P. C. Martin, J. Math. Phys. 4, 208 (1963):
C. De Dominicis and P. C. Martin, J. Math. Phys. 5, 14, 31 (1964).

Also studies of a vortex in the condensate of a dilute Bose gas have been reported:

E. P. Gross, Nuovo Cimento 20, 454 (1961).

L. P. Pitaevskii, Soviet Physics - JETP 13, 451 (1961).

A. L. Fetter, Phys. Rev. A138, A629, 709 (1965).

Note added in proof.

At the discussion, after this paper was submitted, the author was informed by Dr. J. Mayer about the following important and related work on a Bose gas with the Lennard-Jones potential:

S. Baldursson, J. E. Mayer and H. Aroeste,
J. Chem. Phys. 31, 814 (1959).

Mayer: Have you seen the paper in the Journal of Chemical Physics about seven years ago by Steingrimur Baldursson, now in Reykjavik? His work is very similar, but he used an imaginary classical two particle distribution function for a Helium like potential instead of the hard sphere function.

Larsen: I should like to thank Professor Isihara very much, as he cut his own speech in order to make it possible for me to say a few words about my work. Let me begin by stating that together with Kay Witte and John Kilpatrick I have calculated numerically, without approximations, at low temperatures (such as 2°K) the density independent part of the quantum mechanical pair correlations function of a gas having the mass of He^4 and subject to Lennard Jones forces. The parameters which we used have the values determined by de Boer in his study of the 2nd virial coefficient.

With Witte I have also calculated the density independent quantum mechanical pair correlation function for a gas of hard spheres and this over a wider range of temperature than was used in the L. J. case.

In both cases the correlation function is separated into 2 parts. The first represents the answer that one obtains for a Boltzmann gas and the second yields the effects due to non-classical statistics. This is a procedure borrowed from the work of Lee and Yang.

In so far as the L. J. Boltzmann calculation I will only stress that the peak of the correlation function is enormously smaller than the peak that the classical correlation function has at these temperatures, and that one obtains remarkable agreement with the results of the experimental work of Enshaw. As in the classical case the independence from the density implies that there are no wiggles beyond the main peak.

For hard spheres the Boltzmann correlation function looks as Johows. We find that as the temperature increases the correlation function looks more and more classical, as we would expect. The accuracy of the calculation is of the order of 7 significant figures.

Turning our attention now to the exchange correlation function, namely the part arising from the departure from classical statistics, we find that its outstanding feature - both for the L. J. - and the H. S. - cases - is that as the temperature increases it decreases, very quickly, vastly smaller than the free particle exchange. This very rapid disappearance of the effect of exchange is due to the presence of the core of repulsion forces which ensures that no exchange takes place at small distances and then, as the temperature rises, depresses the exchange correlation function far below the free particle result.

This point is also understood by Fosdick and Jordan who have recently made numerical path integral calculation of the density independent L. J. pair correlation function for He^4 and by Elliott Lieb who has considered the exchange term for H. S. at high temperature.

ERGODICITY OF BOLTZMANN'S GAS MODEL

Ja. G. SINAI
Department of Mathematics
Moscow State University

I. INTRODUCTION

The problem of ergodicity is as follows: under what conditions do time averages coincide with phase averages in a dynamical system? But the sense of ergodic theory as applied to the problems of statistical mechanics is much wider. It includes the explanations of the character of mixing and the phenomena of irreversibility, the sense of Boltzmann's "Stosszahlansatz", the sphere of action of the kinetic equation and so on. There is some doubt whether this program can be fulfilled on the basis of classical mechanics of hamiltonian systems[1]. There are also some papers where the authors explain why the ergodicity in its rigorous sense is unneccessary for the substantiation of thermodynamics[2].

Perhaps these objections have a real foundation. But as far as we know there exists at present no consistent theory deducing the main laws of thermodynamics and not basing itself on some additional hypotheses.

In this paper we shall speak about the mathematically rigorous proof of ergodicity for a system of hard spheres with elastic collisions contained in a box. The proof gives something more: it shows that the system of spheres has very good properties of mixing (belongs to the class of socalled K-systems, see below). These mixing properties are indeed caused by the collisions. The collisions are not used directly however, they are used for the construction of the family of special submanifolds which guarantee the properties of mixing.

The idea of constructing such submanifolds and an understanding of their role in the process of mixing did not appear all of a sudden. In 1958 there was a paper of A. N. Kolmogorov[3] who introduced the new concept of entropy*) and of K-system into ergodic theory. The connection of these notions with Shannon's information theory will be seen presently. Later in a number of papers entropy and K-systems were used for the investigation of some examples of classical dynamical systems, in particular of geodesic flows on manifolds of negative curvature. The system with elastic collisions is very similar to the systems which appear in connection with motion due to inertia in spaces of negative curvature. The elastic collisions play the dispersive role of negative curvature. This is the reason that the technique of these papers[4-8] can be applied to Boltzmann's model[9]. Here it is necessary to point out the pioneer work of N. S. Krylov who apparently was the first to notice the deep analogy between the system of spheres with elastic collisions and the geodesic flows on manifolds of negative curvature.

Without doubt the use of the entropy and of K-systems is not limited to the above-mentioned system of solid spheres. The role of these concepts needs further investigation.

II. ENTROPY AND K-SYSTEMS

The entropy of a classical dynamical system is connected with the process of observation of the given system. Let us denote the phase space by M, an invariant phase volume by μ and a one-parameter group of shifts along the trajectories by $\{S_t\}$. Let us assume that somebody observes our system so fixing the position of the moving point with a certain accuracy. Mathematically this means that there is given a partition of phase space into cells C_1, $C_2, \ldots, C_n$ and also a certain number τ. For the trajectory of

*) Here and throughout the whole paper entropy has the sense specific for ergodic theory and different from that commonly accepted in thermodynamics.

any point $\omega \in M$ we can write

$$\ldots S_{-\tau}\omega \in C_{i_{-1}}, \quad \omega \in C_{i_o}, \quad S_{\tau}\omega \in C_{i_1}, \quad S_{2\tau}\omega \in C_{i_2} \ldots \qquad (I)$$

The sequence.... $C_{-i_{-1}}$, C_{i_o}, C_{i_1} ... is the result of the observation of the trajectory of the point ω lasting from $-\infty$ until $+\infty$. If $C_1, C_2, \ldots C_n$ are the cells of fixed diameter δ and if $\tau = \delta$ then for two points the coincidence $C'_{i_o} = C''_{i_o}$, $C'_{i_1} = C''_{i_1}$ ... $C'_{i_k} = C''_{i_k}$ means that the distance between the moving points $S_t\omega'$, $S_t\omega''$ is not more than 2δ for all t, $0 \leqq t \leqq k\tau$. It is unknown a priori whether for any set of cells $C_{i_o}, \ldots C_{i_k}$ there exists at least one point ω for which

$$\omega \in C_{i_o}, \quad S_t\omega \in C_{i_1}, \ldots S_{k\tau}\omega \in C_{i_k} \qquad (2)$$

We are interested in cases when the number of admissible sets $C_{i_o} \ldots C_{i_k}$ is large. It is clear that for this it is necessary that the set of segments of trajectories of length t is possibly larger. It is natural to expect the latter property for unstable systems: the more unstable is the system, the larger is the set of trajectory-segments of given length.

The intersection (2) is equivalent to the intersection $\omega \in C_{i_o} \cap \ldots \cap S_{-k} C_{i_k}$. It follows that for any k the phase space M can be decomposed into small cells of type $C_{i_o} \cap S_{\tau} C_{i_1} \cap \ldots \cap S_{k\tau} C_{i_k}$. It appears that for almost any point ω there exists the limit:

$$\lim_{k \to \infty} \left[- \frac{\log \mu \left[C_{i_o} \cap S_{\tau} C_{i_1} \ldots \cap S_{\tau k} C_{i_k} \right]}{k\tau} \right]$$

For an ergodic system this limit does not depend on the point ω; for a non-ergodic system this limit can be different for different ergodic components.

Let us assume that the system $\{S_t\}$ is ergodic. Denoting the limit by h we come to the conclusion that for large $t = k\tau$ the main part of phase space M is decomposed on $2^{k\tau h}$ cells of approximately the same volume (we use logarithms to the base 2 following the usage of information theory). Using the language of the information theory we can say that to define a segment of a trajectory of length t with an accuracy of 2δ it is necessary that the amount of information be equal to $\frac{t}{\delta} \cdot h$.

The number h that is obtained depends both on the system $\{s_t\}$ and on the choice of cells $C_1, C_2, \dots C_n$. However for all known examples h does not depend on the C_i if these C_i are sufficiently small. But this last assertion is not a mathematical theorem, therefore we must proceed as follows. Let us construct a sequence of partitions $\{C_i^{(s)}\}$ where the (S+i)-th partition is a subpartition of the preceding partition. Let us take the corresponding numbers h_s. It can be shown that $h_s \leqq h_{s+1}$ and that the limit $\lim_{s \to \infty} h_s = h$ does not depend on the choice of the sequence of partitions if the maximum diameter of the cells $C_i^{(s)}$ tends to zero as $s \to \infty$. The number h is called the entropy of the dynamical system $\{S_t\}$.

It is clear from the definition of h that $0 \leqq h \leqq \infty$. The value $h = \infty$ occurs in typical examples of the dynamical systems arising from the theory of probabilities. The theorem of A. G. Kushnirenko [10] asserts that h is always finite for dynamical systems defined by differential equations. Evidently the most interesting case for us is the case when $h > 0$. We shall see further that for this case it is natural to expect the desired property of mixing.

Remark. Let us assume that our cells $C_1, \dots C_n$ are so small that the point ω can be uniquely determined by inclusions (1). In this case the entropy which is computed by the partition $\{C_i\}$ coincides with the entropy of the dynamical system $\{S_t\}$. It is interesting to investigate what is the relation between the diameters of C_i and the minimum sizes where the classical mechanics is still admissible. As far as we know, such an investigation has not been carried out yet.

Consider now examples of systems with positive entropy. It is clear that the above definition of the entropy can be applied to a system with a discrete time scale i.e. we deal with iterations of one transformation T with invariant phase volume. The first two examples refer to this case.

1°. Let M be the space of two-sided sequences $X = \{\chi_i\}$, $-\infty < i < \infty$, where every coordinate χ_i can take only the finite number of values i.... . The phase volume u in M is given by a probability distribution $(P_1, P_2, \ldots P\ )$ and a formula

$$\mu\{X: \chi_{i_1} = t_1, \ldots \chi_{i_n} = t_k\} = P_{t_1} \ldots P_{t_k}$$

For the shift transformation T: $\chi = \{\chi_i\}$ $x' = \{\chi'_i\}$ where $\chi'_i = X_{i+1}$ conserves μ, it can be shown[3] that the entropy h(T) = $-\sum_{i=1}^{2} P_i \log P_i$.

2°. Consider a two-dimensional torus with $d\mu = dx_2\, dx_2$ taken with respect to natural coordinates. Let us consider a transformation T which is given by a matrix

$$\left\|\begin{matrix}\alpha & \beta \\ \gamma & \delta\end{matrix}\right\|, \quad \alpha\delta - \gamma\beta = 1$$

Then its entropy is $h(T) = \log|\lambda|$ where λ is the matrix eigenvalue with largest absolute value (see ref. 11).

3°. Let Q be a unit square from which the circle $(x_1 - \frac{1}{2})^2 + (x_2 - \frac{1}{2})^2 \leqq \frac{1}{4}$ is removed. Let us consider a rectilinear movement of a material point of mass m within Q with reflection from the boundary Q according to the law "The angle of incidence is equal to the angle of reflection". It can be shown that this system is ergodic and has positive entropy (the last assertion is contained in ref. 7).

The notion of K-system is closely related to the notion of entropy. But it is much more difficult to explain its meaning. Roughly speaking K-systems are dynamical systems for which the entropy is the most adequate characterization. A concept similar to that of K-system is widespread in information theory and in the theory of probability. Let us assume that a stationary series of random variables is given as

$$\ldots X_{-n}, \ldots X_{-1}, X_o, X_1 \ldots X_n \ldots$$

It is well known in information theory that this series must have some properties of "regularity" if it is to be used for the transmission of information. More exactly: Let us fix the values X_{-n} $a_{-n}, \ldots X_{-1} = a_{-1}$ i.e. the part of message transmitted until the moment 0; then it is necessary that the conditional probability distribution of the random variable χ_o should be non-degenerate, i.e. not concentrated in one point. This being so χ_o can be used for the transmission of the next symbol of the message because otherwise its value would be already uniquely determined by the previous symbol of the message. Giving some arbitrary values to $a_{-n}, \ldots a_k$, $-\infty < k < \infty$ we shall give for any k a partition of phase space M consisting of realizations of our stationary series up to the moment k. The element of such a partition consists of all messages which have the same past history until the moment k and $\chi_i = a_i$, $-\infty < i \leqq k_o$. It is clear that the partition ξ_{k+1} is a subpartition of ξ_k ; we shall write this as $\xi_{k+1} \geqq \xi_k$; moreover $\xi_k \to \epsilon$ for $k \to \infty$, where ϵ is the partition of M into separate points. Let us demand also that our process $\{\chi\}$ have a property of finite memory: the conditional distribution of $\chi_n = a$ for the fixed a_{-1}, a_{-2} tends to the unconditional distribution of χ_n when $h \to \infty$ (this tendency can take place in measure). The latter condition can be formulated as follows: it is natural to call $\lim_{k \to -\infty} \xi_k$ the finest partition of all partitions which are larger than ξ_k for all k; then the condition of finite memory is: $\lim_{k \to -\infty} \xi_k = \nu$ where ν is the largest partition of M which has a unique element, namely M itself. We come to the conclusion that the system of partitions ξ_k has the following three properties:

1) $\xi_{k+1} = T\xi_k > \xi_k$, 2) $\lim_{k \to \infty} \xi_k = \epsilon$, 3) $\lim_{k \to -\infty} \xi_k = \nu$.

I hope that now the following definition may be clearer.

Definition. The dynamical system $\{S_t\}$ is called a K-system if there exists a measurable partition*) with the following three properties:

---

*) A rigorous definition of measurable partitions has been given by Rohlin[12]. It is clear intuitively what is or piecewise-smooth partition. The concept of measurable partition generalizes it to the same degree as the concept of measurable function generalizes the concept of differential function.

1) $S_t \xi = \xi_t > \xi_o = \xi$ for any $t > 0$

2) $\lim_{t \to \infty} S_t \xi = \epsilon$

3) $\lim_{t \to -\infty} S_t \xi = \nu$

K-systems are always ergodic. They have very good properties of mixing[8,12] - the so-called Lebesgue spectrum of countable multiplicity. For some interesting examples of K-systems the central limit theorem is proved, which asserts that the difference between the time mean $\frac{1}{T} \int_o^T f(S_t \omega)\, dt$ and the phase mean $\int_M f(\omega)\, d\mu$ after multiplication by $\sqrt{T}$ has in the limit $(T \to \infty)$ a gaussian distribution.

In most cases the proof of ergodicity of a classical dynamical system is reduced to the proof that the system is a K-system. So it is for Boltzmann' gas model (see below).

III. K-SYSTEMS AND TRANSVERSAL FOLIATIONS

As we have already mentioned, the term "measurable partition" means a decomposition of the phase space M into nonintersecting parts. We can consider these parts to be smooth submanifolds (surfaces) of our phase space. Now we shall consider the properties of these submanifolds for the K-partition ξ, i.e. the partition ξ which satisfies the conditions 1) - 3) of our previous definition. Let us take a point $\omega \in M$ and a submanifold $C_\xi(\omega)$*), which is an element of the partition ξ containing the point ω. The point ω being fixed, let us take $C_{S_t \xi}(\omega)$ for $t > 0$. It follows from the property 1 on that $C_{S_{-t} \xi} \supset C_\xi(\omega)$. In other words the point ω is contained in an increasing sequence of submanifolds. It is natural to pass over to the limit $t \to \infty$. Then we obtain a submanifold $\Gamma(\omega) = \bigcup_{t=o}^{\infty} C_{S_{-t}\xi}(\omega)$. If the parts $C_{S_{-t}\xi}(\omega)$ were parts of submanifolds of finite sizes, the limit $\Gamma(\omega)$ is a nonbounded submanifold which is situated within M in a rather complicated

*) In concrete examples $C_\xi(\omega)$ is a compact submanifold with the boundary.

manner. From the property 1) we have $\Gamma(S_t\omega) = S_t\Gamma(\omega)$ i.e. the manifolds $\Gamma(\omega)$ transform into each other by the action of shifts along the trajectories.

Let us consider in more detail the character of the transformstion of $\Gamma(\omega)$ into $\Gamma(S_t\omega)$. We shall use now the property 2) of ξ. It follows from this property that the diameter of $C_{S_t\xi}(\omega)$ tends to zero when $t \to \infty$. But $C_{S_t\xi}(\omega) = S_t[C_\xi(S_{-t}\omega)]$. From this formula we can conclude that the transformation of $\Gamma(\omega)$ into $\Gamma(S_t\omega)$ has the character of a contraction. In other words let us take two points $\omega', \omega'' \in \Gamma(\omega)$ and a curve $\{\omega(u)\}$ on $\Gamma(\omega)$ joining ω' and ω''. If our transformation is a contraction then the length of the curve $(S_t\{\omega(u)\})$ must tend to zero when $t \to \infty$. It follows from this condition alone that such a tendency must take place with exponential velocity.

Let us consider the meaning of the last property of $\Gamma(\omega)$. It is easy to see that $\lim_{t\to\infty} \xi_{-t}$ is the partition of submanifolds $\Gamma(\omega)$. The property $\lim_{t\to\infty} \xi_{-t} = \nu$ means that any measurable set which consists of the whole $\Gamma(\omega)$ must have volume 1 or 0 (we assume $\mu(M) = 1$). This condition is equivalent to ergodicity: if it is possible to consider $\Gamma(\omega)$ as trajectories of some dynamical system (perhaps with multidimensional time), then any invariant set composed of these trajectories must have the volume 1 or 0.

We shall call the family of submanifolds $\Gamma(\omega)$ a contracting transversal foliation of our dynamical system if

1) $S_t\,\Gamma(\omega) = \Gamma(S_t\omega)$

2) for any two points $\omega', \omega'' \in \Gamma(\omega)$ the distance between $S_t\omega'$, $S_t\omega''$ tends to zero when $t \to \infty$.

If the last condition is valid when $t \to -\infty$ then we have an expanding transversal foliation.

We shall call the transversal foliation ergodic if any measurable set consisting of submanifolds $\Gamma(\omega)$ has the volume 1 or 0.

Theorem. If the system $\{S_t\}$ has an ergodic contracting transversal foliation then it is a K-system.

This theorem shows us a natural way of proving that our system is a K-system: we must try to construct an ergodic contracting foliation. It may appear that the latter problem is no easier than the initial one. But this is not so. The fact is that if our system $\{S_t\}$ is a K-system then the system $\{S_{-t}\}$ is also a K-system. This assertion is a mathematical theorem for the discrete time case and is valid for all known examples of K-systems with continuous time, although it has not been proved for this case. Therefore it is natural to construct both contracting and expanding transversal foliations. Thus our problem is reduced to the proof of the ergodicity of any of these two foliations. It can be shown by comparatively simple considerations that in natural cases the ergodicity of either of these foliations is equivalent to their common ergodicity. This means that any measurable set which consists of foliates of these two foliations must have volume 1 or 0. This problem is much easier because it has a local character. Now we shall give an example of a system with transversal foliations. In the next paragraph we shall show how to construct transversal foliations for the system with elastic collisions.

An example of a system with transversal foliations.

Let us consider the example 2 of the previous paragraph. The matrix $\left\|\begin{matrix}\alpha & \beta \\ \gamma & \delta\end{matrix}\right\|$ which defines our transformation T has two eigenvalues and two eigenvectors. Let them be substantial. Then any line on the torus parallel to one of the eigenvectors transforms under the action of T into a similar line. The decomposition of the torus into these lines will be a contracting (expanding) transversal foliation if the corresponding eigenvalue is less than 1 (larger than 1).

It is more difficult to describe transversal foliations for the example (3) of the previous paragraph.

IV. TRANSVERSAL FOLIATIONS AND ELASTIC COLLISIONS

Now we shall describe a plan of the proof of the ergodicity of Boltzmann's gas model which is based upon an idea of E. Hopf[13].

The corresponding phase space has 4n - 1 or 6n - 1 dimensions, where n is the number of spheres; the choice of 4 or 6 depends on the dimension of the ball.

Let U be a sufficiently small neighbourhood in M . For the trajectory of a point $\omega \in M$ let us consider the successive moments of collision of balls between themselves and with the walls of the box $..t_o, t_{-1}, ...t_{-1}, t_o, t_1, ...t_n, ..., t_o > 0, t_{-1} < 0$. For any t_i we can fix the character of the collision: either the number of colliding spheres or the number of colliding spheres and the wall. We can consider only such ω for which the number of colliding spheres is not larger than two at any t; in other words at any t only one sphere collides with a wall, other ω having probability 0. Giving to any type of collision a symbol from a finite alphabet E_1, E_2, we can correlate a sequence $E_{i_{-1}}, E_{i_o}, E_{i_n}$, with any point ω , where E_{i_n} is the type of collisions of number n. Let us take also a continuous function $f(\omega)$ and assume that the following properties are fulfilled:

1°. If for two points ω', $\omega'' \in U$ the corresponding sequences $...E'_{i_{-1}}, E'_{i_o}, E'_{i_1}$ and $...E''_{i_{-1}}, E''_{i_o}, E''_{i_1}$ ... coincide then $\omega'' = S_\tau \omega'$ for some τ ;

2°. If for two points ω', ω'' we have $E'_{i_k} = E''_{i_k}$ for each $k \leq k^-$ k^- arbitrary, then the limits

$$\lim_{T \to \infty} \frac{1}{T} \int_0^T f(S_{-t}\omega')\, dt, \qquad \lim_{T \to +\infty} \frac{1}{T} \int_0^T f(S_{-t}\omega'')dt$$

exist or do not exist simultaneously and in the first case are equal; if for two points ω', ω'' we have $E'_{i_k} = E''_{i_k}$ for each $k \geq k^+$, k^+ being arbitrary then analogous properties are valid for limits

$$\lim_{T \to \infty} \frac{1}{T} \int_0^T f(S_t \omega')dt, \qquad \lim_{T \to \infty} \frac{1}{T} \int_0^T f(S_t \omega'')dt$$

3°. For any two points ω', $\omega'' \in M$ there exists a point ω''' such that

$$E'_{i_k} = E'''_{i_k} \quad \text{for each } k \leqq k^-$$

$$E''_{i_k} = E'''_{i_k} \quad \text{for each } k \geqq k^+$$

k^-, k^+ being arbitrary constants. Then the limits

$$\lim_{T \to \infty} \frac{1}{T} \int_0^T f(S_t \omega)\,dt \qquad \text{and} \qquad \lim_{T \to \infty} \frac{1}{T} \int_0^T f(S_{-t} \omega)\,dt$$

are equal and are constant almost everywhere on U. In fact, for any two points ω', ω'' for which

$$\lim_{T \to \infty} \frac{1}{T} \int_0^T f(S_t \omega')\,dt = \lim \frac{1}{T} \int_0^T f(S_{-t} \omega')\,dt = \overline{f}(\omega')$$

$$\lim_{T \to \infty} \frac{1}{T} \int_0^T f(S_t \;'')\,dt = \lim_{T \to \infty} \frac{1}{T} \int_0^T f(S_{-t} \omega'')\,dt = \overline{f}(\omega'')$$

we may take the point ω'' (see 3°). Then from 2° $\overline{f}(\omega') = \overline{f}(\omega'')$ i.e. time averages are constants. U being arbitrary we can conclude the ergodicity of our system. Unfortunately the realization of this plan is difficult as regards certain details and in general is very complicated without the use of transversal foliations. Therefore we shall describe the construction of transversal foliations and the determination of some of their properties which will lead us to the aim.

Let us fix a point ω and construct the foliate $\Gamma(\omega)$ which contains the point ω. Let $S_t\omega = (g_t, v_t)$, where g_t is a projection of S_t on configuration space and v_t is the velocity vector of the whole system. Let us draw from the point g_t segments of trajectories of one and the same length t. Their ends give us a (2n-1)-dimensional piecewise-smooth submanifold $\tilde{R}_t$ in a coordinate space Q. The typical form of $\tilde{R}_t$ is as follows:

The singular points of $\tilde{R}_t$ are the points of recurrence; their appearance is a consequence of the non-differential character of our system.

Let us denote by R_t the set of points $\omega = (q, v)$ where $q \in \tilde{R}_t$ and where v is orthogonal to $\tilde{R}_t$ and is directed in the same way as v_o (i.e. velocity of the initial point ω). Then R_t is a (2n-1)-dimensional piecewise-smooth closed submanifold in the phase space M. The spheres $\tilde{R}_t$ and R_t have rather unexpected properties. For example the area of $\tilde{R}_t$ grows with exponential velocity. More exactly denoting by $\sigma(\tilde{R}_t)$ the area of $\tilde{R}_t$ we can write for almost any q

$$\lim_{t \to \infty} \inf \frac{\ln \sigma(\tilde{R}_t)}{t} > 0$$

The last inequality can be considerably strengthened. To see this, let $d\varphi$ be a small perturbation of the initial point (q_o, v_o) when q_o is immobile and v_o transforms into $v_o + d\varphi = v'$. We shall denote the perturbed point by ω'. For any $t > 0$ let us take $S_t\omega' = (q_t', v_t')$ and construct the line the ends of which are q_t and q_t'. The length of this line is $dl_t = a_t d\varphi$. Then $\lim_{t \to \infty} \frac{\ln a_t}{t} > 0$ for almost any ω and any $d\varphi$. In proving the last relation it is very essential that the elastic collisions have a dispersive character. This relation is decisive for the construction of transversal foliations. If in the process described we had $t \to \infty$ being fixed then it follows that $\tilde{R}_t$ and R_t tend to certain piecewise-smooth submanifolds in Q and correspondingly the limit $\lim_{t \to \infty} R_t$ is the foliate $\Gamma(\omega)$ of our transversal foliation. The main property: $\Gamma(S_t\omega) = S_t\Gamma(\omega)$ is an easy consequence of the process of construction. Besides, from the exponential growth of $\tilde{R}_t$, R_t it follows that the transformation $\Gamma(\omega) \to \Gamma(S_t\omega)$ will be a contraction. Consequently the family of foliates $\Gamma(\omega)$ is the contracting transversal foliation. Substituting -t for t we obtain in an analogous way the expanding transversal foliation.

Let us deduce the ergodicity of our system from the existence of contracting and expanding transversal foliations. Let us assume $f(\omega)$ to be a continuous finite function on M. If ω', ω'' belong to one foliate of the contracting foliation then the distance between $S_t\omega'$, $S_t\omega''$ tends to zero when $t \to \infty$. Therefore the limits

$$\lim_{T \to \infty} \frac{1}{T} \int_0^T f(S_t\omega')\,dt\,, \qquad \lim_{T \to \infty} \frac{1}{T} \int_0^T f(S_t\omega'')\,dt$$

exist or do not exist simultaneously. Just the same is valid for points $\bar{\omega}'$, $\bar{\omega}''$ belonging to one foliate of the expanding transversal foliation with the substitution of -T for T and for points ω', ω'' where $\omega' = S_t \omega''$ for some τ. With probability unity

$$\lim \frac{1}{T} \int_0^T f(S_t \omega) dt = \lim \frac{1}{T} \int_0^T f(S_{-t} \omega)\, dt \tag{3}$$

Our transversal foliations are 2n-1-dimensional. Let us take a compact piece Γ^+ of the contracting foliate. This is a (2n-1)-dimensional submanifold with boundary in M. Let us construct $\Gamma_1^+ = \bigcup_{0 \leq t \leq \tau} S_t \Gamma^+$ for some τ. Then Γ^+ is a 2n-dimensional submanifold. For any point $\omega \in \Gamma_1^+$ the limit

$$\lim \frac{1}{T} \int_0^T f(S_t \omega)\, dt$$

does not depend on ω. For any $\omega \in \Gamma_1^+$ let us now take a compact piece $\Gamma^-(\omega)$ of the expanding foliate. The set $\Gamma_2 = \bigcup_{\omega \in \Gamma_1^+} \Gamma^-(\omega)$ is 4n-1-dimensional. It can be shown that it has a positive volume. If $\omega', \omega'' \in \Gamma_2$ then $\omega' \in \Gamma^-(\bar{\omega}')$, and $\omega'' \in \Gamma^-(\bar{\omega}'')$. For ω', ω'' satisfying (3) we have

$$\bar{f}(\omega') = \lim_{T \to \infty} \frac{1}{T} \int_0^T f(S_t \omega') dt = \lim_{T \to \infty} \frac{1}{T} \int_0^T f(S_{-t} \omega')\, dt$$

$$= \lim_{T \to \infty} \frac{1}{T} \int_0^T f(S_{-t} \bar{\omega}')\, dt = \lim_{T \to \infty} \frac{1}{T} \int_0^T f(S_t \bar{\omega}')\, dt$$

$$= \lim_{T \to \infty} \frac{1}{T} \int_0^T f(S_t \bar{\omega}'')\, dt = \lim_{T \to \infty} \frac{1}{T} \int_0^T f(S_{-t} \bar{\omega}'')\, dt$$

$$= \lim_{T \to \infty} \frac{1}{T} \int_0^T f(S_{-t} \omega'')\, dt = \bar{f}(\omega'') .$$

Consequently the mean $\bar{f}(\omega)$ on Γ_2 is constant almost everywhere. Passing from one set Γ_2 to another, we find that $\bar{f}(\omega)$ is constant almost everywhere.

However, our argument has one gap; for its correctness it is necessary to assume that points $\bar{\omega}'$, $\bar{\omega}''$ satisfy (3). This gap can be filled by using some additional arguments. So $\overline{f}(\omega)$ is constant almost everywhere and the system $\{S_t\}$ is ergodic.

And by these considerations we indeed achieve the realization of our previous plan.

I wish to emphasize that ergodicity takes place if the number of balls is greater than or equal to two.

In conclusion, I wish to express my gratitude to the Arrangements Committee for the invitation to submit this lecture.

REFERENCES

1. N. S. Krylov. Papers about the foundations of statistical physics. Moscow 1950.

2. L. A. Halphin. Doklady AN USSR, 1965, v. 162, No. 6.

3. A. N. Kolmogorov. Doklady AN USSR, v. 119, No. 5, 1958, 861-865.

4. D. V. Anosov. Doklady AN USSR. v. 151, No. 6, 1963, 1250-1253.

5. Ja. G. Sinai. Doklady AN USSR, v. 136, No. 3, 1961, 549-552.

6. Ja. G. Sinai. Doklady AN USSR, v. 131, No. 4, 1960, 752-755.

7. Ja G. Sinai. Vestiik of Moscow State University, ser. Math. and Mech. 1963, No. 5, 6-12.

8. Ja G. Sinai. Isvestya AN USSR ser. math. 25, 6, (1961), 899-924; 30, 1 (1966).

9. Ja G. Sinai. Doklady AN USSR, t. 153, No. 6, 1961-1264.

10. A. G. Kushnirenko. Doklady AN USSR, t. 161, No. 1, 1965, 37-38.

11. Ja G. Sinai. Doklady AN USSR, t. 124, No. 4, 1959, 768-771.

12. V. A. Rohlin. Uspehi Math. Nauk t. XV, b. 4 (1960), 3-26.

13. E. Hopf. Uspehi Math. Nauk, t. IV, 2, 1949, 129-170.

SUMMARIZING REMARKS

G. E. UHLENBECK
The Rockefeller University
New York, U.S.A.

It is, I think, slightly ridiculous to try to summarize the discussions of such a large conference not only because of the great variety of problems, but also because of the great difference in attitudes towards these problems. This is shown for instance by the differences in the mathematical methods which range from the purest, Bourbaki-type of approach to the intuitive quasi-chemical type of treatment. No disparagement is intended by these terms. I find both types equally difficult! They may be needed, although I hope that in the future everything will become more simple.

I hope you will forgive me, therefore, when I don't comment on the many papers we have heard in any detail. Instead I will try to indicate how some of the developments which have been discussed are related to the basic problem of statistical mechanics as I see it.

In my opinion this basic problem is the study of the relation between the macroscopic description of the physical phenomena and the underlying atomic theory. I use on purpose the word "relation" and not the word "explanations." Only rarely can one hope to explain quantitatively the macroscopic properties of matter from the properties of the atoms or molecules. This is partially due to the fact that usually the intermolecular forces are only qualitatively known, and partially to the great complexity of the problem as soon as one leaves the ideal gas phase. Furthermore one is - or perhaps I should say many of us are! - not very much interested in such quantitative explanations. The deep problems are I think of a qualitative nature. Let me mention only the following four questions:

1. How is a closed (and therefore causal) macroscopic description at all possible, and what are its limitations?
2. How can the known macroscopic laws and especially the laws of thermodynamics be explained?
3. What is the explanation of the great qualitative similarity of the macroscopic properties, as for instance the fact that all substances can occur in the solid, liquid or gaseous phase? This indicates, I believe, that these properties depend only on some qualitative features of the interatomic forces, but the precise relation is still far from clear.
4. Is there an essential difference between the classical and the quantum mechanical theory with regard to the relation between the microscopic and macroscopic description of matter?

I believe, that many of our discussions this week can be related to these four problems, so let me try to do this.

A. THE ERGODIC THEORY

This belongs to the second question since the so-called ergodic problem arose and is essential for the explanation of the laws of thermodynamics and especially of the so-called zeroth law, the approach to thermal equilibrium. Let me sketch quickly how it enters.

Representing the system by a point in the phase space (Γ-space), then one knows since Poincaré that the motion of this point on the energy surface is quasi-periodic and shows no trace of an approach to equilibrium. But thermal equilibrium is a macroscopic notion. It is characterized by a small number of macroscopic variables:

$$Y_i = f_i(x_1, x_2 \ldots x_N)$$

which are functions of the phases $x_1 \ldots x_N$ of the molecules and which must have the following properties:

a) Each set of values of the Y_i (≡ given macroscopic state) corresponds to a region on the energy surface.

b) For large N there is one set of values of the Y_i which corresponds to the overwhelmingly largest region.

Now, if the motion of the Γ-points is metrically transitive, then the ergodic theorems show, roughly speaking, that the time a Γ-point spends in a region is proportional to the area of the region. Or if one starts with a probability distribution (≡ ensemble) which at t=0 is different from zero in a region, then in the course of time it deforms into the thinner and thinner ribbon which winds uniformly over the whole energy surface (approach to the microcanonical ensemble), so that the probability of finding the system in any macroscopic state is proportional to its area. Clearly then all the requirements of the zeroth law are fulfilled. But is the motion of a system of molecules metrically transitive? Metrical transitivity means that the energy surface can not be divided in two parts of finite measure, so that if the Γ-point is in one part it stays in that part. It is a mechanical property of the system.

You have heard the great result of Sinai: the motion of N particles ($N \geqq 3$) with short range repulsive forces (for instance hard spheres) is metrically transitive. When this is right (I certainly have not yet digested the proof!), and when it can be generalized to the case when also attractive forces are present, then I think one can say, that the old problem of Boltzmann of explaining thermodynamics from the laws of mechanics, has been finally solved.

The analogous problem in the quantum theory is perhaps simpler, but is less clear to me. Again course-graining is certainly necessary, but whether this is also in the quantum theory equivalent to the notion of macroscopic description or macroscopic measurement is perhaps not so obvious.

B. THE NON-EQUILIBRIUM THEORY FOR DENSE GASES

Here the recent developments have come up with a real surprise, which points out the great difficulty of the first question I mentioned. To appreciate this let me go back to the requirements which the macroscopic variables must fulfill. The two properties of the Y_i which we mentioned already can also be expressed by:

a) A macroscopic description is a <u>contracted</u> description.

b) The macroscopic variables Y_i must be <u>normal</u> variables, which means that

$$\left[\langle Y_i^2 \rangle - \langle Y_i \rangle^2 \right]^{1/2} \ll \langle Y_i \rangle$$

where the averages are over the micro-canonical ensemble. If the system is metrically transitive, this insures the existence of a thermal equilibrium state. One can add:

c) A macroscopic process is necessarily a <u>stochastic process</u>, which means that the Y_i are random variables for which only the successive probability distributions can be defined.

d) A macroscopic process or description must be in some sense a <u>closed</u> description. In <u>which</u> sense is, I think, a very deep problem!

Bogoliubov supposed that for a closed description the macroscopic variables must be on some time scale very slowly varying. They must be <u>secular variables</u>. For a not too dense gas Bogoliubov made plausible that for times of the order of the duration of a collision τ, the first distribution function $F_1(\vec{r}, \vec{p}, t)$ hardly varies, so that on this time scale it could be considered a macroscopic variable for which one expects that there is a closed and causal kinetic equation of the form:

$$\frac{\partial F_1}{\partial t} = A(\vec{r}, \vec{p} \,|\, F_1) \qquad (1)$$

To find the functional A, Bogoliubov used a successive approximation method based on the virial expansion which is in this context an expansion in the ratio of the two times τ and t_o, the time between collisions. This derivation was much clarified by Cohen and co-workers and then came the surprise, first noted by Cohen and Dorfman, that after a certain order the integrals occurring in the successive terms in this expansion diverge!

I think, there is no doubt that this is true and one even understands qualitatively where the divergence comes from. One knows of course that in equilibrium one only has a virial expansion when the forces have a short range. For sufficiently long range forces as for instance in a plasma the virial coefficients diverge so that there is no virial expansion. For non-equilibrium processes, even with short range forces, the dynamics of the interaction of n particles (with $n \geqq 4$) introduces long range correlations (successive collisions with long time intervals) which produce divergences in the virial expansion of the kinetic equation (1).

What one must do now is, I think, less clear. Whether it means that there is no kinetic equation of the form (1), or whether it means that there is such an equation but that it can not be expanded in powers of the density, are questions which are vigorously pursued also for the corresponding Rayleigh-Lorentz problems; and perhaps at the next conference everything will be clarified!

Related is the question of the density dependence of the transport coefficients of gases. Here again, when one starts from the general Kubo-Green expressions for these coefficients and when one then makes a virial expansion one finds the same type of divergences. You have heard that by a re-summation technique one obtains terms which depend on the density logarithmically. This seems quite likely, although I believe that also in this respect much further work is needed.

C. THE EXISTENCE OF THE THERMODYNAMIC LIMIT

The question is under which conditions on the intermolecular forces all the usual assumptions one makes for the thermodynamic functions can be proved rigorously. This clearly belongs to our third problem and it has been almost completely settled.

First one has been able to show under very general assumptions for the intermolecular forces, that for large systems the usual distinction between extensive and intensive variables and the thermodynamic stability conditions follow. For this one has to study the limit $N \to \infty$, $V \to \infty$, $E \to \infty$ with V/N, E/N finite, (which is nowadays called the thermodynamic limit) and one must prove that the entropy (= volume of the energy shell) $S(E, V)$ approaches $Ns(E/N, V/N)$ and that the entropy per particle is a convex function of $\epsilon = E/N$ and $v = V/N$.

Then one must investigate the equivalence of the various statistical ensembles in the thermodynamic limit, which means that one must show that the successive Laplace transforms (with respect to the extensive variables) of the partition function always exist and correspond to the successive Legendre transforms of the characteristic thermodynamic functions.

Finally one must discuss the distribution functions for the various ensembles and show that in the thermodynamic limit they have the expected properties as for instance the product property, the translational and rotational invariance, and so on.

As I said already this has now been accomplished with complete rigour! I don't know whether the minimum conditions on the forces are known, but certainly the usual form of the intermolecular potential of neutral molecules fulfills all the requirements, and also for plasmas there are no difficulties. I think, it is very satisfactory that through these developments a firm foundation is laid for the treatment of the macroscopic equilibrium properties. Of course, a skeptic may say that nothing new has come out, and it is true that it is perhaps more a concern for mathematical hygiene than for a new physical insight. But that is also the case with the ergodic problem, and just as with the work of Sinai, I find it inspiring that through these developments statistical mechanics has become in the last ten years much more mathematically respectable.

Related, although of a different character, are the problems about the convergence of the fugacity and density expansions for thermodynamic functions and for the distribution functions. Quite general results have been obtained, and one has even good estimates for the radius of convergence.

D. THE PROBLEM OF PHASE TRANSITIONS

This also clearly belongs to our third problem. Why do all substances occur in at least three phases, what is the qualitative explanation of the condensation of a vapour or of the melting of a solid? Also with regard to these questions significant advances have been made in the last year, but here one is, I believe, only at the beginning and the problems are far from settled.

The situation is as follows. For long range attractive forces (more precisely for an attractive potential: $\phi(r) = -\gamma^3 F(\gamma r)$ in the limit $\gamma \rightarrow 0$, $\int d\vec{r}\,\phi(r) = -2a$ finite, the so-called van der Waals limit) one can prove rigorously, that one gets a van der Waals-like equation of state which leads to condensation below a certain critical temperature. Also for the corresponding Ising model one obtains strictly the Weiss or Bragg-Williams theory. This is independent of the number of dimensions. Of course one wants to know what happens for finite γ. In this more general case one only knows for sure:

a) In one dimension there is no phase transition.

b) In two and three dimensions there is a transition, but the nature of the transition is still dark. Especially for the Ising model in two dimensions, I believe it is plausible to expect a kind of interpolation between Onsager and van der Waals. Away from the transition point the specific heat would behave van der Waals-like, while close to the critical temperature the specific heat would show the Onsager logarithmic singularity characteristic for short range forces. This is not proved of course but there are some indications. In three dimensions the short range Onsager behavior is still not known.

There is a clear, although perhaps not perfect, analogy between the condensation of a vapour and the ferromagnetic or

Ising transition, which is emphasized by the classical theories. In all these cases one can characterize the phase transition as the onset of long range order. It seems to me that the solid-fluid transition may very well have a quite different character since one of the two phases has already long range order. Very little is known about the theory of the melting process. You have heard about the status of the so-called Kirkwood transition, the phase transition of a fluid of hard spheres near close packing. I am still not sure whether it exists (nothing is really proved!) but even if one believes it (and the empirical arguments are quite convincing!), it is still of course only a caricature of the melting process with perhaps only some physical reality to describe the behavior of the melting line at very high pressures.

The basic difficulty lies perhaps in the fact that one does not really understand the existence of regular solids from the intermolecular forces. Why is it that by taking the minimum of:

$$E = \sum_{i<j}^{N} \phi(|\vec{r}_i - \vec{r}_j|)$$

where $\phi(r)$ has the usual intermolecular form, one obtains for large N (strictly for $N \to \infty$) for the positions $\vec{r}_i$ of the N points a discrete lattice?

This problem (and in fact all the phase transition problems) could perhaps be treated better if somehow one could carry out the limit $N \to \infty$ in the beginning. I hope that the new methods now being developed for infinite systems will throw some light on these problems.

E. IS THERE A MACROSCOPIC QUANTUM THEORY?

This is another way of stating our fourth problem. It was least discussed at this conference. I hope that it will be different when we get together again, because the problem of the macroscopic description of the quantum liquids is certainly one of the most exciting questions of statistical mechanics, which we should not leave to the low temperature physicists! The answer to our fourth problem is clearly yes. There is an essential difference in the macroscopic description of matter between the classical and the quantum theory. But I also believe that the fundamental discussion is still in the beginning stage. Are there new macroscopic variables, which are perhaps complex (like the amplitude and phase of the ground state wave function of a Bose liquid) but which have a well defined relation to the more usual macroscopic variables as for instance the temperature? Is there a theory of quantum phase transitions which is wider and includes the classical theory? Again, I hope that we will hear more about these questions at the next conference!